UNITED NATIONS LIST
OF NATIONAL PARKS AND
EQUIVALENT RESERVES

SECOND EDITION

Prepared and published by the IUCN International Commission
on National Parks pursuant to United Nations Economic and
Social Council Resolution 810 (XXXI).

1971

Publishers HAYEZ
Brussels

UNITED NATIONS
LIST OF NATIONAL PARKS
AND EQUIVALENT RESERVES

established under the responsibility of the International Commission on National Parks of the International Union for Conservation of Nature and Natural Resources by Dr. Jean-Paul Harroy, professor at the University of Brussels, Chairman of the Commission.

The closing date for this Second Edition of the List was 31 May 1967 and the definitive French text was published in August 1967. In the preparation of the present English text, undertaken in consultation with Professor Harroy by Sir Hugh Elliott, Secretary of IUCN's Commission on Ecology, amendments and certain additional material received by the ICNP up to 30 June 1970, have been incorporated.

The financial assistance given by the Department of National Education of the Belgian Government and by the World Wildlife Fund, towards the cost of preparing this edition, is gratefully acknowledged.

ERRATA

MAPS

1. Page 42. *Albania.* No. 4 (Divjaka N.P.) has been omitted. Situated 4 km South of Tirana.

2. Page 93. *Austria.* No. 4 (Karwendelschutzgebiet) replaced by a number 7 on the map.

3. Page 99. *Belgium.* Nos. 3 and 4 (Kalmthout and Genk Reserves) have been reversed.

4. Page 139. *Canada.* No. 13 (Fundy N.P.) is missing. Is situated on the border of New Brunswick and Nova Scotia.

5. Page 165. *Chile.* Nos. 2 and 4 (Nahuelbuta and Tolhuaca N.P.) are situated about 15 mm souther on the map.

6. Page 198. *Falkland.* No. 1 (Kidney Island Nature Reserve) has been omitted. Concerns a small island situated 14,8 km off the coast of Stanley, on the oriental coast of East Falkland.

7. Page 211. *France.* Nos. 4 and 22 (Burrus and Mont Vallier) have been reversed.

8. Page 252. *Hungary.* No. 6 (Lake Velence Reserve) is missing. Situated 55 km NE of No. 1 (Tihany).

9. Page 257. *Iceland.* No. 2 (Eldey Nature Reserve) is missing. Situated on a small island 67 km SW of Reykjavik (near the lighthouse of Reykjanes).

10. Page 359. *Netherlands.* No. 4 (Kobbeduinen) has been omitted. Situated on the fifth island indicated north of the map, in Friesland.

11. Page 372. *Nigeria.* No. 1 (Yankari Game Reserve) is situated 1 cm SE of Bauchi, and not SW of this town.

12. Page 385. *Philippines.* No. 18 in the North of Luzon is in fact No. 16 (Fuyot Spring N.P.).

13. Page 411. *Mozambique.* No. 1 (Gorongosa N.P.) was not printed. Situated approximately 100 km NW of Beira.

14. Page 506. *Togo.* Lome, the capital, was not printed but is indicated south of the country.

15. Page 540. *United Kingdom.* For Birmingham substitute Glasgow — for Glasgow substitute Birmingham.

PHOTOGRAPHS

Page 30. *Argentina.*

The photograph indicated « Los Glaciares N.P. » is in fact Lanin N.P.
The photograph indicated « Lanin N.P. » is in fact Iguazu N.P.
The photograph indicated « Iguazu N.P. » is in fact Los Glaciares N.P.

CONTENTS

CONTENTS

AN ALPHABETICAL INDEX OF COUNTRIES

In addition to the 126 Members of the United Nations, the List covers 14 countries which are not yet Members (although in some cases belonging to the specialised agencies of the U.N.), but which have nevertheless supplied comparable information. In one or two instances, where National Parks administration is closely linked with, and full details have been channelled through, an associated state, the relevant information has for convenience and to avoid repetition, been combined in a single report.

9

Total : 1,204 National Parks and equivalent reserves.

———

10

PREFACE

TO THE SECOND EDITION OF THE LIST

The important role of the United Nations in the field of international conservation of nature and natural resources is becoming more and more fully recognised over the whole surface of the globe. The Resolution adopted by the U.N. General Assembly at its Sixteenth Session in December 1962, on 'Economic Development and Nature Conservation', happily served to endorse the initiative taken in 1959 by the Economic and Social Council when, at the suggestion of the International Union for Conservation of Nature and Natural Resources (IUCN), it undertook the compilation of the first World List of National Parks and Equivalent Reserves.

In this enterprise IUCN was invited to play a leading part by assisting the Secretariat of the United Nations in the preparation of the original List, which was based on replies from 81 countries to a U.N. questionnaire. This was published in two parts in 1961 and 1962, and the two documents provided an excellent basis of discussion for the First World Conference on National Parks. When the participants in this Conference met at Seattle, Washington, in 1962, they agreed unanimously on the need for United Nations sponsorship of successive editions of the List. But they also expressed the view that in the selection of material for future editions certain criteria established by IUCN's International Commission on National Parks should be applied.

It was in the light of these recommendations that the Secretary-General of the United Nations, on 23 April 1963, requested the International Commission on National Parks to prepare a second edition of the List. The achievement of this task required three years of unremitting work and extensive correspondence — often of a very detailed nature — with each one of the member countries of U.N.O., and it was undertaken with tireless efficiency by the Vice-Chairman, now Chairman ([1]), of the Commission, Professor Jean-Paul Harroy. In doing so he had the advantage

---

([1]) *Vice-Chairman 1962-1966, Chairman since July 1966.*

of being simultaneously based at the Commission's Brussels office in the Institut Royal des Sciences Naturelles of Belgium and at the Centre d'Ecologie Humaine de l'Institut de Sociologie de l'Université Libre in the same city.

IUCN entrusted Professor Harroy with the full responsibility for the many different aspects of the preparation of the List. He was most ably assisted in the task by a Belgian geographer, Mlle Paulette Doyen, who was responsible for editing Section IV of each national entry, and by Mlle Jacqueline Henricot, of Brussels, who shouldered the considerable burden of converting the mass of material into typescript. Special thanks are also due to Mr. Fred Packard, of Washington D.C., who had been responsible for the first edition of the List and who now undertook the greater part of the task of revising the report on the National Parks situation in the U.S.A.

I am sure that the publication of this second edition of the List will do much to encourage all member countries of U.N.O. to improve and strengthen what they have already achieved in the way of establishing National Parks. I am equally certain that it will exert a steadily growing influence on each country's conscious appreciation of the extreme importance, from the economic, social, scientific and aesthetic point of view, of this modern method of ensuring the wise and far-sighted use of certain areas of its national soil for the benefit of its people now and in the future.

Washington, 15 January 1967.

HAROLD J. COOLIDGE,
President, International Union for
Conservation of Nature and Natural
Resources.

THE 10th GENERAL ASSEMBLY OF I.U.C.N.
New Delhi, November 1969

RESOLUTION 1

National Park definition.

Considering the importance given by the United Nations to the national Park concept, as a sensible use of natural resources,

and considering the increasing use which has been made during these last few years in some countries of the term « national park » to designate areas with increasingly different status and objectives.

the 10th General Assembly of IUCN meeting in New Delhi in November 1969 recommends that all governments agree to reserve the term « National Park » to areas answering the following characteristics and to ensure that their local authorities and private organizations wishing to set aside nature reserves do the same :

a National Park is a relatively large area 1) where one or several ecosystems are not materially altered by human exploitation and occupation, where plant and animal species, geomorphological sites and habitats are of special scientific, educative and recreative interest or which contains a natural landscape of great beauty and 2) where the highest competent authority of the country has taken steps to prevent or to eliminate as soon as possible exploitation or occupation in the whole area and to enforce effectively the respect of ecological, geomorphological or aesthetic features which have led to its establishment and 3) where visitors are allowed to enter, under special conditions, for inspirational, educative, cultural and recreative purposes.

Governments are accordingly *requested* not to designate as « national park » :

1° a scientific reserve which can be entered only by special permission (strict nature reserve),

13

2° a natural reserve managed by a private institution or a lower authority without some type of recognition and control by the highest competent authority of the country,

3° a « special reserve » as defined in the African Convention of 1968 (fauna or flora reserve, game reserve, bird sanctuary, geological or forest reserve, etc.),

4° an inhabited and exploited area where landscape planning and measures taken for the development of tourism have led to the setting up of « recreations areas » where industrialization and urbanization are controlled and where public outdoor recreation takes priority over the conservation of ecosystems (parc naturel régional, nature park, Naturpark, etc.). Areas of this description which may have been established as « National Parks » should be redesignated in due course.

RESOLUTION 2

Resolution on the United Nations List of National Parks and Equivalent Reserves.

Considering the importance of the work achieved by the International Commission on National Parks at the request of the Economic and Social Council of the United Nations which, in 1959 (Resolution 810, XXXI) asked for the establishment of a United Nations List of National Parks and Equivalent Reserves,

the 10th General Assembly of IUCN meeting in New Delhi in November 1969 *requests* the Economic and Social Council of the U.N. to approve the text of the revised and evaluated edition of the List as prepared and published by the International Commission on National Parks in 1967 in French and in 1969 [1] in English and to certify it as an official document sanctioned by the United Nations.

---

[1] This refers to the Proof copies made available by the publishers for study at the General Assembly : the definitive edition is dated 1970.

EDITOR'S INTRODUCTION

This List has been drawn up at the request of the United Nations and in keeping with Resolution 713 of the twenty-seventh session of the Economic and Social Council held in 1959, which recognised National Parks and equivalent reserves as an important factor in the wise use of natural resources ([1]).

In contrast with the previous edition of the List ([2]), which was published without any modification of the data on nature reserves furnished by governments in response to the U.N. Secretary-General's request, the present Second Edition confines itself to a detailed catalogue only of such protected areas — National Parks and equivalent reserves — as seem to meet the requirements of three criteria laid down by the International Commission on National Parks of the International Union for Conservation of Nature and Natural Resources (hereinafter referred to as the ICNP).

To qualify for inclusion in the List an area must —

 (i) have a statutory basis giving it sufficiently strict protection;
 (ii) be of a certain minimum size;
(iii) be adequately staffed and provided with a big enough annual budget for its maintenance to ensure that statutory protection can be effectively applied.

These three criteria must be taken in conjunction with the definition of equivalent reserves adopted by the Secretary-General in the introduction to his above-mentioned Report E/3436 as follows :

" The term ' equivalent reserves ' would apply to those areas which, although not specifically designated as national parks, qualified for inclu-

---

([1]) See p. 19 for the full text of the Resolution, together with that of the Secretary-General's introduction to the Report, which he submitted, two years later, to the 31st Session of the Economic and Social Council under reference number E/3436.

([2]) The above-mentioned document E/3436, published on 15 February 1961, and the addendum entitled ' Part Two ' submitted to the World Conference on National Parks (Seattle, July 1962) by the International Commission on National Parks.

sion in the International List as significant areas which were given equal protection and which corresponded to the definition given in the London Convention. The list would not include, on the other hand, many reserves such as those set aside for such purposes as the protection of forests, historic monuments or special game species. "

On pages 23 to 33 below, a detailed explanation is given of the basis on which ICNP has established and justifies the three criteria applied to the selection of areas for inclusion in the List. It explains in effect exactly what meaning the Commission attaches to the title 'National Parks and Equivalent Reserves'. It also defines the principles on which numerous exceptions have had to be made if similar general rules for selection are applied to all parts of the world. As a good example of this may be cited the fact that it is almost impossible to find in heavily populated and highly industrialised countries significant natural areas which can be maintained as such simply by prohibiting all human occupation and exploitation. Whereas, therefore, an area situated in a country which has a low level of population and industry is regarded as having adequate statutory protection only when human occupation and exploitation are effectively eliminated, the criterion of 'full protected status' is deemed to be met in industrialised and densely populated countries, even if human exploitation is not wholly suppressed, *provided* it is at least well controlled, delimited and organised in accordance with a scientific management plan and in such a way that the environment is maintained in the balanced condition which can be considered the true aim of conservation.

*
* *

The report on each member country of the United Nations has been prepared in accordance with the foregoing principles. It is set out, as a general rule, under five main headings (¹) :

Section I, except in a few cases where the number of parks and reserves is very large, lists those which are deemed to qualify for inclusion in the List, in the order of their size, and includes in a General Introduction the information on matters not directly relating to the ecology of the listed areas, such as legal, administrative and historical background. Appropriate reference is made to the previous edition of the List, which, as mentioned at the beginning of this Introduction, was initiated by ECOSOC Resolution 713 (XXVII) and published in two parts, by the

---

(¹) In the French text, published in 1967, these were treated as separate Chapters. For reasons explained in a Supplementary Note (see p. 35 below), these have now been appropriately grouped, but the headings are indicated marginally.

United Nations itself in 1961 and by the ICNP in a 1962 addendum. Both parts, which, for convenience, are often referred to in the text by their original reference number or abbreviated title — E/3436 and Part Two, — contain detailed and precise descriptions of some of the protected areas and many of these descriptions are still of course valid.

Under the next three headings all the information of direct or indirect ecological significance is presented for each of the listed areas in turn :

Section II reviews the application of the basic criteria — protected status, size and effective management (as indicated by staff and budget). If, despite some deficiency in respect of one or other of these criteria, it has nevertheless been decided that an area is worthy of inclusion, a brief explanation is given of the reasons for making an exception.

Section III covers such general points as : the date or year in which the park or reserve was established; any noteworthy peculiarities in the administrative or land tenure situation not already described in the General Introduction; the extent to which tourism has been developed and the existing tourist facilities; and what scientific research has been or is being undertaken in the area.

Section IV gives a short description of the ecosystems to which the park or reserve affords protection, comprising :

a) geographical and geological features of the landscape and botanical associations;

b) the characteristic fauna;
and, omitted from the description if inapplicable,

c) particular species, classified in IUCN's " Red Data Books " as in danger of extinction (and therefore, at present, restricted to mammals and birds, pending publication of further volumes), for which the park or reserve acts as a refuge.

Finally, *Section V,* which, for those countries in which no areas can yet be listed, follows directly on Section I, gives details of any parks and reserves which could well have been considered for inclusion in the List if the criteria of adequate protected status, size, staff and budget were more nearly satisfied. It also explains the reasons why no area can be listed or why it has been necessary to exclude a particular area or category of areas, as the case may be. One may certainly express the hope that whenever such exclusion is shown to be due to situations which could easily be rectified by strengthening protected status or increasing staff or financial resources, it need only be regarded as of a temporary nature and will no longer be necessary in a future edition of the List.

* *
*

Finally, it is important to draw attention to the practical benefits which can be expected to accrue from establishing and keeping up to date this United Nations List and, particularly, from its publication.

In the penultimate paragraph of his introductory statement of 15 February 1961 ([1]) to the first edition of the List (E/3436), the Secretary-General of the U.N. emphasised the " widespread interest in the fact that the United Nations is issuing this List ". He goes on to note that " a number of Governments have indicated that new legislative neasures are now under consideration for the establishment and protection of national parks and equivalent reserves ".

A similar reaction, favourable both to the creation of new national parks and to the reinforcing of some of the old ones, has been apparent in many countries as a result of the lengthy correspondence with Governments necessitated by the preparation of a new edition and entered into by the International Commission on National Parks in the name and with the authority (conveyed in his letter of 26 April 1963) of the Secretary-General of the United Nations.

JEAN-PAUL HARROY,
Professor of the Free University of Brussels;
Chairman of IUCN's International Commission
on National Parks.

([1]) See p. 22.

18

INTRODUCTION
BY THE SECRETARY-GENERAL
OF THE UNITED NATIONS

to his report (first edition of the List : document E/3436) submitted to the thirty-first session of the United Nations Economic and Social Council on 15 February 1961

1. The United Nations accorded recognition to the significance of national parks and equivalent reserves as an aspect of the wise use of natural resources, when the Economic and Social Council adopted resolution 713 (XXVII) at its twenty-seventh session in 1959 ([1]), which reads as follows :

" *The Economic and Social Council,*

Noting that national parks and equivalent reserves have been established in most countries which are Members of the United Nations or the specialised agencies, and that they contribute to the inspiration, culture and welfare of mankind,

Believing that these national parks are valuable for economic and scientific reasons and also as areas for the future preservation of fauna and flora and geologic structures in their natural state,

(1) *Requests* the Secretary-General to establish, in co-operation with UNESCO, FAO, and other interested specialised agencies, a list of national parks and equivalent reserves, with a brief description of each, for consideration by the Council at its twenty-ninth session, together with his recommendations for maintaining and developing the list on a current basis and for its distribution ([2]);

([1]) This proposal originated from a resolution concerning national parks and reserves adopted by the Sixth General Assembly of the International Union for the Conservation of Nature and Natural Resources, held at Athens and Delphi, Greece, in 1958, transmitted to the Secretary-General of the United Nations.

([2]) The response to the Secretary-General's invitation to Governments to furnish information for the list was inadequate for the submission of a list at the twenty-ninth session of the Council.

(2) *Invites* State Members of the United Nations and of the specialised agencies to transmit to the Secretary-General a description of the areas they desire to have internationally registered as national parks or equivalent reserves; and

(3) *Furthermore invites* the International Union for Conservation of Nature and Natural Resources and other interested non-governmental organisations in consultative status to assist the Secretary-General, upon his request, in the preparation of the proposed list. "

2. In accordance with the resolution, the International Union was asked to assist in the analysis of the material submitted by Governments and in the preparation of the list. The International Union assigned this responsibility to its International Commission on National Parks, which has been co-operating closely with the Secretariat of the United Nations and collaborating with the United Nations Educational, Scientific and Cultural Organisation and the Food and Agriculture Organisation.

3. Prior to 15 December 1960, fifty-two Governements had responded to the Secretary-General's memorandum of inquiry inviting them to furnish information about their national parks and equivalent reserves for consideration for inclusion in the list. It is proposed to issue the list in two parts : Part One, which has been completed and is submitted for consideration by the Council, represents a preliminary list of national parks and reserves in those countries whose Governments supplied information by 15 December 1960; Part Two will include information from those Governments wishing to add their national parks and reserves to the preliminary list, and appropriate revision and additions to the data that have already been included.

4. It is recommended that the International Union for the Conservation of Nature and Natural Resources be invited to undertake the preparation of Part Two of the list and subsequent additions to it, in consultation with the United Nations, the United Nations Educational, Scientific and Cultural Organisation, the Food and Agriculture Organisation and other interested specialised agencies. In view of the proposed first World Conference on National Parks to be held in Seattle, Washington, United States of America in July 1962, it is hoped that as comprehensive a list as possible will be completed for this Conference.

5. In compiling the material submitted, the definitions set forth in the Secretary-General's memorandum of inquiry were used as guiding principles. They were as follows :

a) The definition in the *Convention Relative to the Preservation of*

Fauna and Flora in their Natural State, done at London, 8 November 1933, reads (Article 2, para. 1) :

" 1. The expression ' national Park ' shall denote an area

a) placed under public control, the boundaries of which shall not be altered or any portion be capable of alienation except by the competent legislative authority; *b*) set aside for the propagation, protection and preservation of objects of aesthetic, geological, prehistoric, historical, archaeological, or other scientific interest for the benefit, advantage or enjoyment of the general public; *c*) in which the hunting, killing or capturing of fauna and the destruction or collection of flora is prohibited except by or under the direction or control of the park authorities. In accordance with the above provisions facilities shall, so far as possible, be given to the general public for observing the fauna and flora in national parks. "

b) The definition in the *Convention on Nature Protection and Wild Life Preservation in the Western Hemisphere,* done at Washington, 12 October 1940, reads :

" 1. The expression ' National Parks ' shall denote : areas established for the protection and preservation of superlative scenery, flora and fauna of national significance which the general public may enjoy and from which it may benefit when placed under public control. (Article 1, para. 1.)

... The Resources of these reserves shall not be subject to exploitation for commercial profit. (Article 3, para. 1.) "

c) The attention of Governments was also drawn to a definition of the term ' equivalent reserves ' suggested during the discussion at the twenty-seventh session of the Council by the representative of the United States of America, which reads :

" The term ' equivalent reserves ' would apply to those areas which, although not specifically designated as national parks, qualified for inclusion in the international list as significant areas which were given equal protection and which corresponded to the definition given in the London Convention. The list would not include, on the other hand, many reserves such as those set aside for such purposes as the protection of forests, historic monuments or special game species. "

6. The material received varied in style, and included comprehensive descriptions of the features and administration of individual national parks and reserves as well as statistical tabulations of various types of reservations. In addition to reserves that clearly came within the scope of

the above definitions, some reserves ranged in size from a few hectares to thousands of square miles; these reserves are afforded varying degrees of protection depending on the particular purposes for which they were established. Accordingly, those national parks and reserves which appeared clearly to come within the definitions have been described briefly in this preliminary compilation, in those instances where such information was made available officially; other reserves have been listed or presented in tabular form; some of the reserves presented in tabular form will probably qualify for inclusion as national parks or equivalent reserves, under the definitions, when further information becomes available.

7. There has been widespread interest in the fact that the United Nations is issuing this list. A number of Governments have indicated that new legislative measures are now under consideration for the establishment and protection of national parks and equivalent reserves. Other Governments have indicated that they intend to submit additional areas for inclusion in the list. Yet other Governments have been so recently established that they have not completed their programmes for national park and reserve systems, and have expressed the hope that they may have an opportunity to add information on their areas for inclusion in the list. It has also been pointed out that the list will be of the greatest interest to the working party on wildlife management established by the Food and Agriculture Organisation's African Forestry Commission.

8. So many valuable data have been received in response to the Secretary-General's request that the Council might wish to request the International Union for Conservation of Nature and Natural Resources to give consideration, on completion of Part Two of the list, to the publication and dissemination of the list for the benefit of all interested countries.

THE CRITERIA FOR SELECTION

established by the International Commission on National Parks

Based on the Memorandum circulated to Governments by IUCN.

After the United Nations Economic and Social Council and IUCN, respectively, issued the first list (in the two sections : ECOSOC : E/3436 of 15.2.61, revised 27.3.62, and Part Two of 31.3.62) enumerating and describing national parks, of very various types, located in 81 ([1]) countries of the world, it seemed very desirable that the work should be continued not only by expanding the existing information, but also by undertaking, for the first time, a selection and classification, which would enable the areas included in the list to be properly comparable with one another.

The purpose of the U.N. and IUCN documents, comprising the first edition of the List, had simply been to present, without alteration, the information obtained from Governments in response to the questionnaire drawn up by the Secretary-General of the U.N. In these circumstances and although the Secretary-General's memorandum (SO.614/2) had of course given as specific guidance as possible, it was only to be expected that, quite apart from the gaps left where no reply was received to the questionnaire, there would be serious inconsistencies in the amount and kind of information supplied under the various headings. Some Governments, for example, listed only their largest or most exceptional areas; others described and enumerated all their reserves both large and small, irrespective of the type of protection accorded and of whether it was total or only partial.

One of the many reasons for these variations was no doubt the difficulty of arriving at a universally acceptable definition of 'national park and equivalent reserve', since the significance of these terms varies from country to country. Nevertheless, the Secretary-General's memorandum SO.614/2 was in fact concerned to circumscribe certain limits, invoking

---

([1]) 52 in the first list and 29 in the second.

for this purpose the definitions adopted by the 1933 London Convention (for Africa) and the 1940 Washington Convention (for the New World). It indicated, for example, that the List should exclude those " reservations set aside purely for the protection of a single species of wildlife or plant, or for limited purposes such as the preservation of an historical object or a forest used for commercial purposes ".

The purpose of the present memorandum, therefore, is to make further progress, on the strength of the experience gained from returns rendered for the first edition of the List and following the lines laid down in the Secretary-General's SO.614/2, in defining what can be properly considered as a national park or equivalent reserve. In short, it seeks to establish, on the basis of the recommendations of the Seattle Conference on National Parks of July 1962, a framework capable of being used for a first selective classification and, at the same time, to take full account of the views of all who are interested in this problem.

THE BASIC PRINCIPLE

To qualify as a national park or equivalent reserve, an area should enjoy general *legal* protection against all human exploitation of its natural resources and against all other derogations of its integrity resulting from human activity. While some departures from this principle may in practice have to be allowed, they should be very exceptional and always treated as exceptions.

EXPLANATORY COMMENTS

1. The fact that the legal status of an area satisfies the basic principle would not necessarily qualify it as a national park or equivalent reserve, if, for example, its size is too small or the status is not adequately enforced, but what would *a priori* rule it out of consideration would be if its status does not also confer *general* protection; exceptions to this condition should only be admitted on very specific grounds.

2. The kind of exploitation of natural resources which should, as a rule, be prohibited in national parks and equivalent reserves would be : agricultural and pastoral activities, hunting, fishing, lumbering and mining and dam construction for the purpose of irrigation or hydro-electric power. The human activities which can be considered as impairing the integrity of an area include residential, commercial or industrial occupation, and the building of roads, railroads, aerodromes, ports, power lines, telephone lines, etc.

3. On the other hand, tourism is not to be included among the economic activities calling for prohibition in national parks and equivalent reserves; quite the reverse, so far as national parks are concerned. 'Equivalent reserves', however, may in some cases be strict natural reserves and, as such, set aside for scientific research, with a more strictly protected status than that of national parks : in these cases tourism is necessarily excluded.

4. Among the exceptions which may therefore be admitted to the rule of *general* protection are those activities which have to be allowed in the promotion of tourism, since the latter is one of the main reasons for the existence of national parks. These include the construction and maintenance of a road network, the setting aside of more or less extensive areas for hotels or other accommodation, with consequential cultivation of vegetables and ornamental plants, and all the other disturbance of the natural environment which economic development for tourist purposes inevitably causes within the area where it is sited (airfields, railways, power lines, telephone lines, pleasure-boat facilities, sports-grounds, golf-links, tennis-courts, etc.).

5. A second broad category of exceptions of a comparable type must also be mentioned, namely the public works necessary for the actual administration of the reserve. They include staff housing, offices, workshops, garages, access roads, gardens, staff recreation facilities and so on.

6. A rather more difficult question is whether an exception may be made of sport fishing, without regarding an area in which it is allowed as debarred from classification as a national park or equivalent reserve. The answer seems to be that it should be treated as a borderline case and only accepted if the sport is authoritatively regulated by fully competent staff.

7. There is no doubt that an area in which the general public is allowed to hunt or shoot should automatically be disqualified as a national park or equivalent reserve, except in extremely rare instances where the hunting zone is very restricted and special reasons can be given to justify an exception.

8. Commercial lumbering is incompatible with the status of a national park or equivalent reserve, except when exploitation is on a very small scale, very occasional and strictly localized.

9. Exceptions may be justified to cover private rights which existed before the reserve was created, such as residential rights or rights to

practise agricultural, pastoral, mining or quarrying activities, always provided that these rights are confined to a small part of the area. They should seldom be permanent and their redemption or termination should be anticipated in the long term.

10. One human activity which may seem but is not, in fact, necessarily incompatible with the status of ' general protection ', is ' management ', that is to say control carried out by those responsible for a reserve with a view to maintaining the natural equilibrium which they consider desirable. This may take place, for instance, when the number of wild animals is considered excessive, when an early burning policy is applied to a national park in the tropics, or when artificial water supplies are provided for animals. It is essential, however, that such measures should be undertaken by authorised staff and that, similarly, where control of wild animal populations becomes necessary, it should never be left to hunters unfamiliar with the area. Special situations may justify exceptions, but only under strict administrative supervision.

11. Practically all the comments made in the preceding paragraphs imply that it may be desirable to sub-divide a protected area into ' zones '. Most national parks and equivalent reserves, through force of circumstances, do in fact naturally fall into a series of distinct subdivisions ([1]). Some are seldom visited and can be kept in an almost pristine state of ' wild nature '; others are greatly influenced by human activities and all the pressure arising from buldings, roads, heavy tourist traffic, even perhaps sport-fishing, which may affect the landscape, the natural vegetation or the behaviour of wild animals (some becoming shy and others abnormally tame). In circumstances such as those described, it is impossible to cover the status of a protected areas by a single definition; it would be necessary to invoke the ' zoning principle ' and to give as full details as possible of the particular situation ([2]).

([1]) The Garamba National Park in the Congo (Kinshasa) could, however, at one time have been quoted as an exception : it was a strict natural reserve of some 491,000 hectares, without a single inhabitant or anyone being allowed within its boundaries except park rangers on patrol; both exploitation and tourism were thus totally excluded.

([2]) Taking the Yellowstone National Park as an example, the data quoted could show that in certain zones a specified percentage of the Park area as a whole corresponds de facto, under the accepted criteria, to that of a strict natural reserve. In other specified zones, if one excludes, as obviously disturbed, a two-mile wide strip on either side of main roads, half a mile each side of the paths, a three-mile radius round the camps and so on, a specified percentage of the park as a whole could be shown to qualify as ' national park ' in the true sense, taking into account the fact that no hunting, cultivation or wood-cutting is allowed, and despite the fact that some people live there and animal photography and sport-fishing are allowed.

THE SUPPLEMENTARY PRINCIPLES

The basic principle of 'general protection, subject to rare exceptions recognised as such', which has been discussed above, could of course be linked with a very large number of complementary considerations capable of being used as methods of determining and assessing the real significance of a protected area. However, for the purposes of this List, it is proposed to take account of only two of the potentially relevant factors, namely (i) the size of the area, and (ii) the extent to which its protected status is enforced. There are unquestionably many other criteria, some of them highly important, but the reasons for discarding them generally stem from the fact that the information needed to apply them is rather inadequate or that their application might tend to confuse the broader issues. Nevertheless, although they will not be used in the present classification of what constitutes a national park and equivalent reserve, four in particular are perhaps deserving of some further comment :

a) **The legal personality or body which actually conferred protected status on an area in question.**

This is a very controversial matter. Some people would assert that only areas whose protected status was conferred by the highest central political body should qualify for inclusion in the United Nations List of National Parks and Equivalent Reserves. Thus, in a country with a federal constitution, any park established by the government of one of the federation's states (a 'state' or 'provincial' park) would be excluded from the List. This argument is supported by the fact that the *permanence* of protected status, reflected by the difficulty which would be experienced by any party wishing " to disavow it, to repeal it or to weaken it ", is at its maximum only in the case of an area protected by an act of the highest central authority.

This view has not been accepted for the purposes of the present List. Indeed, it seems that because of the quality of their organisation and the strictness of their supervision, many state or provincial parks are far more worthy of inclusion on the list than a number of 'national' parks and, further, that the same consideration applies to certain natural reserves owned by private organisations.

In our opinion, the continued existence of a large, well-protected and well-administered state park or reserve such as the 'Veluwezoom' of the Vereeniging tot Behoud van Natuurmonumenten in the Netherlands (3,900 ha), is as well assured as that of a national park established by a central authority. Indeed, such areas are surely typical of what ECOSOC had in mind by the expression 'equivalent reserves'.

b) **The configuration of a protected area.**

The relationship between surface and perimeter is no doubt of some significance, because a circular area is naturally easier to protect than an oblong one. But a criterion based on this fact is of secondary importance and, in practice, difficult to apply. Its value would in any case vary with the particular objective of the protected area, which is discussed in the next paragraph.

c) **The principal aim of protection in any given area.**

As already indicated, the size or shape of a protected area will have a fundamentally different significance according to whether the purpose is, for example, to preserve specially rare and scientifically interesting insect species or, at the other extreme, a remnant population of white rhinoceros. But, once again, it would be a mistake to imagine that this factor is likely to provide a useful criterion for selection. The establishment of a reserve for a single or dominant objective is extremely unusual, although there are a few examples, such as the Udjong-Kulon in Java (*Rhinoceros sondaicus*), the first Albert National Park in 1925 (" to make the world safe for gorillas ") or the Mountain Zebra National Park in the Cape Province.

If rarity and scientific interest of some particular species to which an area affords protection were used in assessing relative importance, the Kaziranga Wildlife Sanctuary in Assam, with its population of Great Indian Rhinoceros, would presumably earn a much higher " award of merit " than the Grand Canyon National Park in the United States. But in fact it is practically impossible to make use of a criterion of this sort except in an entirely subjective manner.

d) **The frequency with which exceptions to the rule of general protection are allowed in a reserve.**

Some authorities have considered that protected areas might be classified according to the quantitative and qualitative importance of exceptions made to the basic status of general protection. Examples of factors which could be taken into account on this principle are :

(i) The percentage of private land remaining in the area;
(ii) the 'zoning' aspect (whether the zones kept free of touristic or other disturbance are few or many);
(iii) the number of residents and/or domestic livestock permitted in the reserve;
(iv) the extent to which sport-fishing is permitted.

28

In practice, however, it seems preferable to treat such factors only as possible criteria for elimination. At one time ([1]), consideration was also given to classification by 'surface area': "large" national parks (over 100,000 ha), "medium" national parks (from 1,000 to 100,000 ha) and "small" national parks (under 1,000 ha) — the last mentioned to be deemed worthy of inclusion in the List only for very special reasons. But again, on reflection, it seemed more sensible to use surface area only as a possible factor for the purpose of exclusion, by ruling, for example, that unless there are particular and properly explained reasons to the contrary, no national park of reserve of under 2,000 ha should be retained in the List. The corollary is that the other factors mentioned above, such as the percentage of private land or the 'zoning' pattern, should be used only in deciding whether an area ought to be excluded from the List, but not for the purpose of placing a reserve in a grade strictly according to the proportion of the well or indifferently protected zones it is estimated to contain.

INCIDENTAL COMMENT

It sometimes happens that protective measures which were not originally intended to safeguard natural species or associations, nevertheless also serve that purpose. This may sometimes justify including in the List of National Parks and Equivalent Reserves areas protected primarily for the sake of historic monuments or archaeological sites. An example of the former is the Angkor National Park in Cambodia, which incidentally protects 7,000 ha of forest, and, in the latter category, one may cite the Bandelier National Monument in New Mexico, U.S.A., in which some 11,000 ha of the xerophytic vegetation enjoy protection because traces of Pueblo Indian troglodytes have been discovered in caves scattered throughout the valleys. The necessary condition for the inclusion of such areas in the List, is, of course, that a biotope of scientific interest benefits from protection given for other reasons.

THE CRITERION OF SIZE

A priori, it seems logical to apply a 'size' criterion to the selection of national parks and equivalent reserves. Otherwise, tiny pieces of land with common species of flora and fauna could claim inclusion in the "roll of honour" merely on the grounds that no stock-farming, hunting, angling, etc. happen to be allowed in them. The following principle can

---

([1]) See memorandum presented at Seattle by Th. Monod and J.-P. Harroy.

therefore be adopted : a national park or equivalent reserve below a certain maximum size which, in other respect, is considered to have a status sufficiently strict to warrant such a title, will not be included in the List unless (and notwithstanding its small size) it is desirable to include it for a particular reason to be briefly explained in the List itself.

What then should be accepted as the minimum size below which reserves would be listed only for exceptional and stated reasons ? Clearly there must be a correlation with the population density of the country concerned, because assured protection for 500 ha in a country as heavily populated as for example, the Netherlands, is of greater significance and more meritorious than the preservation of 5,000 ha in a sparsely inhabited region ([1]).

The criterion finally selected by the ICNP is therefore as follows :

If the population is less than 50 inhabitants to the square kilometre : minimum size 2,000 ha.

If the population is more than 50 inhabitants to the square kilometre : minimum size 500 ha.

N.B. — Another suggestion made during the discussions which led to the above conclusion was that a smaller minimum surface area should be accepted for a natural reserve with a very strict status, than for a national park. For instance, in a sparsely inhabited country, a national park could be listed only if it exceeded 2,000 ha in size, but a strict natural reserve would be acceptable if over 500 ha in size. However, it seemed desirable not to add further complications to the criterion, but instead to recognise the merits of particular strict natural reserves by making use of the possibility of including them, even though their surface area is below the stipulated minimum, so long as the reasons for doing so are specifically mentioned in the citation.

THE CRITERION OF EFFECTIVENESS

Although this must be considered as a very essential criterion, its application requires the greatest tact. It is common knowledge that the natural desire to cut a good figure either at international meetings or in the public opinion of the world as a whole, has sometimes led governments to promulgate impressive legal provisions which imposed very strict regimes of protection on areas where these provisions, if not

---

([1]) Nevertheless, it may sometimes be desirable to vary the interpretation of this view in accordance with zoning principles : thus a national park in the close vicinity of Adelaide is in a different category from a reserve of the same type and size located in the outback of Queensland.

ARGENTINE, Los Glaciares N.P.

ARGENTINE, Lanin N.P.

ARGENTINE, Nahuel Huapi N.P. (photo : I. Costa

ARGENTINE, Iguazu N.P. (photo : I. Costa

STRALIA, Belair N.P.

(photo : Australian Gvt. Tourist Office)

AUSTRALIA, Carnavon N.P.

(photo : H. M. Berney)

AUSTRIA, Seewinkel R.

(photo : F. Vollmar/W

LGIUM, Kalmthout R.

(photo : Fotomarga)

BELGIUM, Kalmthout R.   (photo : K. C. A. Janss

.GIUM, Kalmthout R.

(photo : Fotomarga)

BELGIUM, Furfooz R.   (photo : Ardennes et Ga

quite unknown, were, at least, completely disregarded. It is always much less difficult, expensive, laborious and even sometimes dangerous to draft and enact proclamations prohibiting hunting or the entry of domestic livestock than actually to put a stop to poaching or to pastoral nomadism.

It thus appears necessary to discover one or more *objective* criteria which may help to indicate whether the status which has been promulgated is actually maintained or, at least, whether a sincere and meritorious attempt has been made to maintain it.

The choice of such criteria was not at all easy and their proper application even less so. But, in order to avoid debasing the United Nations List, and thereby undermining its status as a " Roll of Honour " and its effect as an incentive, it has clearly been essential to make the difficult decision not to accept, for example, as qualifying for inclusion in the List, a national park of 200,000 ha, for the administration and supervision of which not even a single full-time man is appointed or for the maintenance of which the annual allocation of funds is ridiculously small.

Nevertheless, as stated, it was most difficult to select objective criteria and it was at the same time necessary to allow those who had the task of actually applying the criteria, (a task always, if possible, to be undertaken in the fullest consultation), very wide latitude in interpretation. To quote a typical example of what is involved, there is no doubt that a forester who has the assistance of several dozen forest guards could perfectly well ensure and maintain supervision of a very large natural reserve, even if none of this staff is on full-time duty. In order to give due weight to this fact when making an assessment, one must be free to arrive at a formula whereby a sufficiently large number of part-time staff can be equated with the number of full-time staff which the strict application of the chosen criterion would demand.

After some hesitation, therefore, the conclusion was reached that the two objective criteria which could be conveniently used in assessing the degree of effort made to enforce the protected status of a particular reserve are, first, the strength of the full-time staff appointed per given area and, secondly, the amount of the annual budget allocated to supervision per given area.

It must again be emphasised that the widest latitude is necessary in the interpretation of the data. For example, if staff of another department gives part-time assistance in supervision, this has to be taken into account not only in evaluating the strength of the normal full-time staff of a particular reserve, but also in estimating the annual expenditure on its management. Conversely, even when a substantial budget appears to be available, it may quite possibly be found that the funds are used only for tourist facilities (roads, picnic areas, camping-grounds, etc.) and none of them to ensure the protection of fauna and flora.

In short, whatever level of staff and budget was proposed as the criterion, it was bound to be somewhat arbitrary, although (as in the case of the size criterion) it was also suggested that the level should be adjusted to the population density and possibly to the economic status of the country concerned. In the event the following scales have finally been adopted :

In countries with a population of less than 50 inhabitants per km^2 :

a minimum of 1 person per 10,000 ha working full-time on management and supervision;

a minimum annual expenditure on management and supervision of U.S. $ 50 per 1,000 ha.

In countries with a population exceeding 50 inhabitants per km^2 :

a minimum of 1 person per 4,000 ha working full-time on management and supervision;

a minimum annual expenditure on management and supervision of U.S. $ 100 per ha.

SUMMARY OF DEFINITIONS

In conclusion, it would seem desirable to summarise in tabular form the definitions of 'national park' and 'equivalent reserve' derived from those established in the relevant international Conventions and developed and adopted for the present edition of the List :

A. — NATIONAL PARK :

An area or part of the national territory which

1) the *central* governmental authority

2) has so ordered that the three basic conditions of our classification are fulfilled :

a) status of general protection,

b) size in excess of a certain minimum,

c) protected status adequately maintained,
and

3) in which that authority permits or actually organizes tourism.

32

B. — EQUIVALENT RESERVE :

Other areas where the three basic conditions of the classification are also fulfilled and which may be either

1) Strict Natural Reserves, when tourism is not permitted, or

2) when their status is not derived from the central governmental authority, State Parks, Provincial, Cantonal or other Local Authority Reserves, or Private Reserves belonging to non-governmental associations.

Provided that it is clearly understood that the above definitions :

1) are valid (until further notice) only for the present purpose, namely the establishment of a List;

2) do not claim to anticipate any regularisation of the nomenclature attaching to protected areas which may eventually be effected by international agreement; and

3) do not imply any question of precedence as between one category of area and another and, in particular, are without prejudice to the evaluation of areas which, while corresponding to the above definitions of 'national park' or 'equivalent reserve', do not officially bear either of those titles.

Brussels, June 1963.

J.-P. HARROY.

SUPPLEMENTARY NOTE ON THE ENGLISH TEXT

In the preparation of the English text of the Second Edition of the United Nations List of National Parks and Equivalent Reserves, of which the French text was published in August 1967, the opportunity has been taken to effect certain re-arrangements. Corrections, new material and other pertinent information received by the International Commission on National Parks since the French text went to press, have also, as far as possible, been incorporated, subject to exigencies of space and to the desirability that major revision or amendment, such as additions to the definitive List, should be deferred to the next or Third Edition.

The main changes in arrangement have already been reflected in the Editor's Introduction (p. 15 above). They involve the inclusion of general introductory material in Section I and the combination of Sections II, III and IV in a single unified description of each park of reserve. The purpose of these changes is to ensure that for every Listed Area all information of ecological significance is brought together in one place and in stereotyped order, thus conforming with and susceptible to the same data-processing procedures as the information now being sought in a major project launched by the Conservation of Terrestrial Communities section of the International Biological Programme (IBP/CT). This project, in which IUCN has the greatest interest and to which the List is already recognized as a most important contribution, aims at a comprehensive inventory and analysis of the habitat-types or ecosystems of the world. The underlying conservation purpose is to discover to what extent these are currently represented in protected areas — hence the relevance and importance of the present List — and what further reservations are required to ensure that examples of all habitat-types remain available for scientific study and, indeed, for the general benefit and interest of mankind.

In pursuit of these objectives and in order to achieve the greatest possible consistency and comparability both within the List itself and with the IBP/CT project, a number of innovations on points of detail have been adopted in the English text. Before dealing with these, however, it may be useful to mention one or two more general matters affecting the use and understanding of the List.

Countries are listed in strict alphabetical order, the names anglicised in accordance with the standard usage of the National Geographic Society's Map of the World (1965), which is also followed for the spelling of place-names referred to in the text. Where the latter can only be found in larger-scale maps, recourse has been had to the " Times " Atlas (1968) or, where possible, to the official national map.

Normally (the few exceptions are clearly indicated in the text), Section I for each country begins with the names of the Listed Areas. They are numbered consecutively and strictly in order of size, either in a single series or, if appropriate, in groups or subdivisions. The names used are those by which the areas are know locally, anglicized as little as possible. In order to obtain information on a particular area the reader has only to turn to the relevant number in the following text, where the details are set out under the sectional heads, II, III, and IV, with their sub-headings *a*), *b*), *c*), etc. Thus, if he is specially interested in tourist facilities he can refer immediately to the information under marginal heading III, or, if seeking details of the fauna, to IV *b*).

Where no endangered species is known to occur in a particular protected area, the sub-heading IV *c*) is omitted from the description. For countries in which no Listed Areas can yet be quoted, only the sectional headings I and V are used, the latter listing the areas, if any, which have been excluded, with such explanations as may be appropriate.

Turning now to points of detail, the aim of maximum consistency and comparability between the data on one country and another has inevitably involved some difficulties due to variations in nomenclature. The arbitrary solution adopted has been to follow certain standard practices which appear to command a reasonably wide measure of support. Thus, for all units of measurement — surface areas, heights, distances — the metric system only is used. Budgetary provisions are quoted in U.S. dollars, generally based on rates of exchange ruling in 1965-1966, unless otherwise indicated.

With regard to scientific nomenclature, it has not been possible in this edition to achieve completely consistent, up to date and systematic usage. The aim has been to cite the common English name (if one exists) and the scientific name the *first* time a species is mentioned in a national report, but on subsequent occasions only the English name. The authority generally followed for botanical nomenclature is " A Dictionary of Flowering Plants and Ferns " by J. C. Willis (6th Edition, 1951), supplemented, particularly for English names in the European context, by Clapham, Tutin and Warburg's " Flora of the British Isles " (1952). For faunal references, the main authorities followed, since by far the greater part of species mentioned in sub-sections IV (*b*) and (*c*) are mammals and birds, are " The Mammals " by Desmond Morris (1965) and

36

" Check-List of Birds of the World " by J. L. Peters *et al.* (1937-1967), supplemented, where necessary, by the well-known series of Field Guides, which now cover a wide geographical and subject range.

Although there was some inconsistency in this respect in the French text, the species now included in sub-section IV (*c*), namely those which are in some danger of extinction and to which the park or reserve gives protection, are now confined to species listed in the standard IUCN series of " Red Data Books " (1966 *et seq.*). As mentioned in the Editor's Introduction, this means that at present only mammals and birds can be quoted, but as work on the plant, reptile, amphibia, fish and other volumes is completed and published, the scope and value of this section can be expected greatly to increase in future editions of the List.

Finally, the opportunity has been taken to revise the sketch-maps which are supplied in the case of all countries having Listed Areas. The aim has been to show not only the location and distribution but also, as far as possible, the shape and size of these areas. Major towns, rivers and lakes are also indicated to the extent necessary for the maps to be used in conjunction with an atlas or large-scale map to verify the position of any particular park in relation to topography and to road, rail, airport or other means of access. The assistance given by Mr. Paul Hubot in the preparation of the maps and, especially, in checking the accuracy of the information on which their value depends, is gratefully acknowledged.

London, November 1968

Hugh F. I. Elliott.

37

AN APPEAL TO THE READER

This book, of which the general content and form have been approved by the United Nations, represents a first attempt at an objective selection of the National Parks and Equivalent Reserves of the world together with a preliminary scientific description of each of them. It has been compiled with the help of many zealous and conscientious contributors, to whom the warmest thanks are due. But sometimes only incomplete replies or even no replies at all have been received to requests for information, so that many errors and gaps inevitably remain to be corrected and filled.

We therefore make an appeal to any reader who consults and uses the List and who finds cause for criticism either in the fact that, in his view, an injustice has been done in the selection or rejection of a particular area or because some detail is incorrect or because some pertinent information is left out. Please do not content yourself with voicing this criticism in your own circle, but be so kind as to take the further step of sending it in writing to the office of the International Commission on National Parks (avenue Jeanne 44, 1050 Brussels). Every such contribution to the next edition of the List will be most gratefully received.

1. AFGHANISTAN

Listed Areas : nil.

Explanation :

No specific information has been received from the Government at Kabul to supplement the reply to an earlier enquiry by IUCN, which stated that " there are no particular areas where nature is under total or partial protection except in the case of some forest regions, and there are no strict nature reserves where human circulation is prohibited ". It is known, however, from contributions made to the IUCN Technical Meeting on Wetland Conservation in S.W. Asia (Ankara, 1967), that considerable interest is now being shown in the reservation of areas in this category, which should in due course qualify for inclusion in the List.

2. ALBANIA

Listed Areas : four.

1. Dajti National Park.
2. Lura National Park.
3. Tomori National Park.
4. Divjaka National Park.

General Introduction :

Legal basis : for all National Parks in Albania, this is the Hunting Law, No. 1351 of 1 November 1951 and the Forest Protection Law, No. 3349 of 3 October 1963.

Administration : responsibility rests with the Ministry of Forests and Water Resources.

Land tenure : the land comprised in the four National Parks is publicly owned.

Tourism : there is free access to all the Parks and no special organisation exists.

Research : nothing has been reported.

All four Parks were listed in E/3436.

Details : application of criteria (II), general information (III) and description (IV) :

1. DAJTI NATIONAL PARK.

a) Status : total protection. There is no human occupancy or exploitation, except for the right held by inhabitants of neighbouring villages to gather dead wood. Hunting is forbidden and ancient grazing rights have been annulled.

b) Area : 3,000 ha.

c) Staff : one forest officer and two full-time forest guards.

d) Budget : special funds are allocated for reafforestation and other forestry work and also for various civil engineering works, such as construction of pioneer camps and villas and installation of electricity, drinking water supplies etc. (February 1966).

41

III.   *Date established :* 1956.

Tourism : a forest lodge has accommodation for 20 persons.   There is a Pioneer camp and a number of villas.   Access is by road from Tirana.

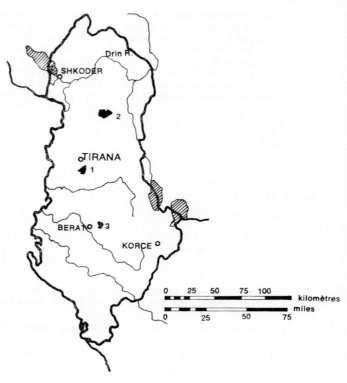

IV.   *Altitude :* 400-1,611 m.

a) A mountain ridge rising like a rampart to the east of Tirana from 400 m to the 1,611 m summit of Dajti; the slopes are partly forested with a mixture of beech *Fagus sylvatica* and pines *Pinus leucodermis* and partly covered by Mediterranean type scrub (*Erica, Arbutus, Quercus ilex*).

b) No information.

2. LURA NATIONAL PARK.

II.   *a)* Status : total protection. No inhabitants (two villages, Cury and Fush-Lura, are near the eastern boundary). No user rights except for wood-gathering.

b) Area : 3,000 ha.

c) Staff : a forester-in-charge and two full-time forest guards.

d) Budget : covers staff salaries only, but more or less fulfils the criterion.

III.   *Date established :* 1956.

42

Tourism : a forest lodge has accommodation for 20 persons. Access is by road from Tirana (130 km) and motorable routes in the Park itself.

IV. *Altitude :* 1,000-2,246 m.

a) Comprises, in principle, two mountain ranges, that of Deja rising from a 1,500 m peneplain to its 2,246 m summit and that of Lura, 1,000 m in altitude at its base, rising to a 2,124 m summit (Kurora Lures); the flanks are covered with heavy pine forest (*Pinus leucodermis, P. peuce, P. sylvestris, P. nigra*), fir (*Abies alba*) and beech *Fagus sylvatica*; there are alpine meadows and numerous mountain lakes.

b) No information.

3. TOMORI NATIONAL PARK.

II. *a)* Status : total protection. No hunting or grazing. Wood-gathering allowed.

b) Area : 3,000 ha.

c) Staff : officer-in-charge, two guards, full-time.

d) Budget : as for Lura National Park.

III. *Date established :* 1956.

Tourism : forest lodge with 20 beds. Access is by road from Berat (35 km), with motorable routes in the Park itself.

IV. *Altitude :* 800-2,400 m.

a) Mountain range rising to the east of the town of Berat; slopes partly forested with beech *Fagus sylvatica* and pine *Pinus leucodermis* and partly consisting of alpine meadows.

b) No information.

4. DIVJAKA NATIONAL PARK.

II. *a)* Status : total protection. No hunting or grazing allowed. The two neighbouring villages (Kulari and Divjaka) exercise a right to gather dead wood.

b) Area : 1,000 ha.

c) Staff : officer-in-charge, two guards, full-time.

d) Budget : special funds available for re-afforestation (300 ha), other forest improvements, opening up of new paths and other civil construction work (forest lodge, rest camp, etc.).

III. *Date established :* 1956.

Tourism : forest lodge with 20 beds. Access from all directions, motorable routes in the Park (closed in winter).

IV. *Altitude :* sea level to 10 m.

a) A long strip of low dunes on the shore of the Adriatic; pine forests (*Pinus halepensis* and *P. pinea*).

b) No information.

V. **Areas excluded :** nil.

3. ALGERIA

I. **Listed Areas :** two.

    1. Chréa National Park.

    2. Ouarsenis National Park.

General Introduction :

The choice of the two areas included is one of the more arbitrary which has had to be made in the present edition of the List. Numerous requests for information made during the course of three years elicited no response. The selection was therefore made on the basis of private information kindly given by a scientist, who during 1965 visited the two Parks listed, in order that at least these two areas should figure as a representative sample and reflect what seems to be a considerable conservation effort on the part of the Algerian authorities.

With regard to the *application of the criteria* generally, the legal status recorded by the original legislation (a Government Decree of 17 February 1921) provides for the " removal of all human interference with vegetation and animal species occurring within the perimeter of a reserve ". According to the information mentioned above, dated August 1965 : " It is in the field of forestry that the new Algeria has made the most remarkable efforts. The control exercised over owners of goats and sheep by the Algerian forest-guards is very much more strict that that of their former French counterparts. When I visited the Ouarsenis Park in June 1965, the condition of the trees and tracks was better than it has been before independence. The same applies to the Chréa Park and it is very likely that the other Parks are looked after equally well ".

The following *general information* is derived from old records :

Administration : Department of Water Resources and Forests of the Ministry of Agriculture.

Land tenure : public ownership.

Research : the fauna and flora of the Algerian National Parks were reviewed in a number of miscellaneous publications prior to 1930.

Details : application of criteria (II), general information (III) and description (IV) :

    1. CHRÉA NATIONAL PARK.

II.   *a*) Status : see introduction.

    b) Area : 1,351 ha.

    c) and *d*) : see introduction.

III.   *Date established :* 3 September 1925.

    Tourism : the summer resort of Chréa, situated at 1,500 m, is the normal objective for visitors. Permission for winter sports is given for a few weeks each year. Access is by the Blida by-road, about three hours drive from Algiers.

IV.   *Altitude :* 1,200-1,629 m.

    a) Comprises the higher part, including the peaks of Coudia Chréa 1,545 m and Pic Sidi Abd-el-Kader 1,629 m, of the wall of mountains forming a section of the Mitidjien Atlas immediately to the south of Blida. Black schistous formation. The main elements of the forest are cedar, with an undercover of holm oak *Quercus ilex*; yew, holly, barberry.

b) Wild boar *Sus scrofa,* jackal *Canis aureus*; many birds, especially insectivorous species, including tits, hoopoes, jays.

2. OUARSENIS NATIONAL PARK.

II.
    a) Status : see introduction.

    b) Area : 1,030 ha.

    c) and *d*) : see introduction.

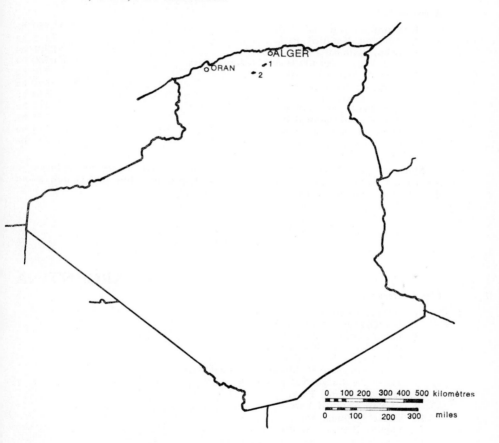

III.
    Date established : 16 April 1924.

    Tourism : access road from Orléansville. Motorable tourist circuit through the mountains via Rond-Point des Cèdres and Aïn Antar.

IV.   *Altitude :* 1,000-1,985 m.

a) Comprises the Ouarsenis massif, a southern ridge of the Tellien Atlas; the high altitude flora is Mediterranean : Atlantic cedar *Cedrus atlantica,* Aleppo pine *Pinus halepensis,* holm oak; *Thuja* sp. (introduced), juniper; Montpellier maple *Acer monspessulanum.*

b) Jackal, hyaena; a few lynx, hares and rabbits; birds of prey find a suitable home in the rocky high-level zones; eagle, falcon, sparrowhawk, buzzard, vulture, short-toed eagle *Circaetus gallicus* and owls.

V.   **Areas excluded :**

1.	Djurdjura National Park	16,550 ha
2.	Akfadou National Park	2,115 ha
3.	Babor National Park	1,701 ha
4.	Cèdres de Teniet-el-Haad National Park	1,500 ha
5.	Edough National Park	770 ha
6.	Planteurs National Park	688 ha
7.	Djebel Gouraya National Park	530 ha
8.	Saint-Ferdinand National Park	412 ha
9.	Aïn N'Sour National Park	279 ha
10.	Mahouna National Park	270 ha
11.	Dar-el-Oued and Taza National Park	230 ha

Many of these Parks, perhaps all of them, might well qualify for inclusion in the United Nations List. It is much to be hoped that full information about them will be obtainable for the next edition.

4. ARGENTINA

I.   **Listed Areas :** twelve.

1. Nahuel Huapi National Park.
2. Los Glaciares National Park.
3. Lanín National Park.
4. Rio Pilcomayo National Park.
5. Los Alerces National Park.
6. Perito Francisco P. Moreno National Park.
7. Tierra del Fuego National Park.
8. Iguazú National Park.
9. El Rey National Park.
10. Chaco National Park.
11. Laguna Blanca National Park.
12. Petrified Forest Natural Monument.

General Introduction :

Administration : Direccion General de Parques Nacionales responsible to the Secretaria de Estado de Agricultura y Ganaderia de la Nacion.

There is a National Parks Council, composed of officials (from the Ministries of Agriculture, Justice and Education) and experts.

Legal basis: a law of 1934, revised in 1958.

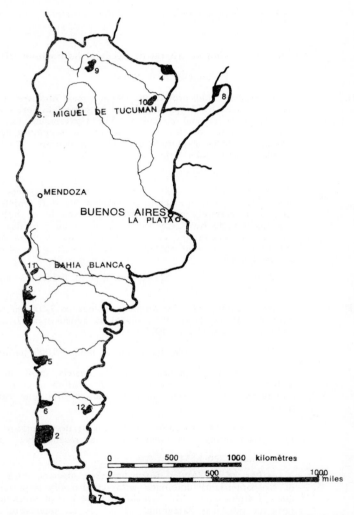

Land tenure: in most cases the land is state-owned. It is probable that the boundaries of Parks will be adjusted to exclude areas from which it has not proved possible to remove human occupants or exploitation. Some sectors of certain National Parks are under heavy economic pressure.

Tourism: entry is unrestricted except for the "Areas intangibles o Regiones virgenes".

47

Research : scientific investigation of the Parks is encouraged and carried out by the scientific staff of the Direccion General de Parques Nacionales. With the latter's approval, many research workers visit the Parks under the sponsorship of the Universities.

All twelve areas were included in Part Two of the previous edition of the List.

Details : application of criteria (II), general information (III) and description (IV) :

1. NAHUEL HUAPI NATIONAL PARK.

II.
a) Status : total protection. Some areas, however, are still in human occupation, grazed by domestic animals or subject to forest exploitation. There are reports of occasional poaching. The Government has announced that it has "every intention of eliminating the human population together with the limited amount of forest exploitation which still persists... ". Sport-fishing is allowed in places, but under strict control.

b) Area : 785,000 ha.

c) Staff : 27 Park guards and a number of labourers. A Government spokesman writes " as to the actual strength of the staff employed to protect the park area, it is certainly rather small, but it should be noted that the number of persons thought by IUCN to be necessary may, in this case, be overestimated, taking into account the vast expanse of empty country, which is totally uninhabited or very seldom visited due to difficulties of access. The same applies to the budget ".

d) Budget : U.S. $ 51,000 per annum (which is higher than required by the criterion).

III.
Date established : the original nucleus of 7,500 ha (a bequest by el Perito Francisco P. Moreno), 1903; 48,000 ha added in 1907, and the present total of 785,000 ha achieved in 1922.

Land tenure : 22,000 ha common land, 95,000 ha owned by villages.

Tourism : well organised. Hotels, hostels; most run by private enterprise, a few State-operated. About 100,000 visitors a year. Educational Museum. Conducted tours. Some ski-runs and ski-lifts, one cable-way. Sport-fishing allowed.

Research : Multiplication of European deer, perhaps rather unwisely introduced, is creating a problem, which has recently been under study.

IV.
Altitude : 720-3,554 m.

a) Part of the Andes, featuring lakes, glaciers, thick forests in which many of *Nothofagus* are dominant, with scientifically important undergrowth species and an alpine zone; Mt. Tronador (3,554 m), of volcanic origin, is the highest peak in northern Patagonia. There is an interesting vegetational transition east to west from pampas, through an intermediate zone, to Valdivia-type forest.

b) Pudu *Pudu* sp., guemal *Hippocamelus bisulcus,* puma *Felis concolor*; condor, many species of duck (Anatidae), cormorant, flamingo, woodpeckers, kinglet *Regulus satrapa,* several species of Rhinocryptidae; introduced : various species of deer, black swan.

48

2. LOS GLACIARES NATIONAL PARK.

a) Status : total protection, but there are a few small villages of pastoralists. Some sectors have been given the status of strict nature reserves and there are " inviolable virgin land " areas with conditional access on special permit.

b) Area : 600,000 ha.

c) Staff : 12 units, but only two Park guards. The authorities explain this by reference to the isolated and empty terrain and the fact that this Park is a typical example of the situation described under Nahuel Huapi above. In addition to the two patrolmen there are a number of labourers and an administrative cadre composed of a superintendent, assistant superintendent, administrative secretary and the heads of various departments.

d) Budget : U.S. $ 7,700. The general observations under ' Staff ' apply also to the budget.

Date established : 1937.

Land tenure : entirely state-ownership.

Tourism : hostel under construction. Access is difficult, but there are about 2,000 visitors a year. Guided tours are arranged. Sport-fishing available.

Altitude : 300-2,441 m.

a) The Andean zone of Santa Cruz province (Fitz Roy being the highest peak) : glaciers, lakes, forests in which *Nothofagus* spp. are dominant; bordered by prairie on the east and snowfields and glaciers on the west.

b) Pudu, guemal, guanaco *Lama guanicoe*; possibly chinchilla *C. laniger*; rhea, condor, eagle.

c) Chinchilla (but reported to be extinct in Argentina — see Red Book).

3. LANÍN NATIONAL PARK.

a) Status : total protection. There are locally a number of old-established holdings for dwellings, stock-raising and forestry, " which it has not been possible to eradicate completely ». But as with Nahuel Huapi the aim is total elimination, etc. Like the Los Glaciares Park the Park contains areas classified as " inviolable virgin lands ".

b) Area : 395,000 ha.

c) Staff : total strength 22 with " a certain number of labourers " (as compared with the 39 required to satisfy the criterion). However, the authorities make the comment that this Park, like the others, contains a number of desolate areas, which justifies a low level of surveillance.

d) Budget : U.S. $ 34,500 (the criterion requirement would be only $ 19,500).

Date established : 1937 (national reserve), 1945 (national park).

Land tenure : 218 ha are common land, 80,000 ha are privately owned and their status is under consideration with a view to possible excision from the Park.

Tourism : several private hotels outside the Park, and one hotel in the Park, built by the State and leased. 20,000 visitors a year, guided tours. Sport-fishing allowed.

Research : the increase of introduced European deer is as much a problem here as in the Nahuel Huapi National Park, No. 1 above.

49

IV.

Altitude : 600-3,776 m.

a) A 'lake district' of 25 lakes dominated by the extinct volcano of Lanín; fine forests of monkey-puzzle trees *Araucaria araucana* and *Nothofagus*, with bracken *Hymenophyllum tortuosum* in the damper prairie.

b) Puma, crab-eating raccoon *Procyon cancrivorus*; condor, egret, duck.

4. RIO PILCOMAYO NATIONAL PARK.

II.

a) Status : total protection. There are some villages of cotton-growers and, in view of the impossibility of removing them, it is expected that the Park boundaries will be withdrawn to exclude them, the rest being kept as far as possible in its pristine state.

b) Area : 285,000 ha.

c) Staff : an officer-in-charge and one guard. This is well below the requisite standard, but the Park has been kept in the List at the request of the Argentine Government, which states that adequate staff is in the course of being recruited. Representations have been made to the authorities to ensure that the criteria under *c)* and *d)* are met.

d) Budget : U.S. $ 2,500.

III.

Date established : 1951.

Land tenure : over 100,000 ha are common land or privately owned. Remainder is state-owned.

Tourism : no accommodation, but the town of Asuncíon and the road which leads to it are nearby.

IV.

Altitude : no information, but doubtless c. 100-200 m.

a) Situated at the confluence of the Pilcomayo and Paraguay rivers, the park consists of a broad plain with prairie and patches of forest; the vegetation is typical of the humid Chaco, the flora including the palm *Copernicia alba, Caesalpinia melanocarpa, Schinopsis balansae, Astronium balansae* and the edible algaroba *Prosopis alba,* also *P. nigra.*

b) Tapir *Tapirus t. terrestris,* puma of the race *Felis concolor osgoodi,* the wild cat *Felis g. geoffroyi;* cayman; the swift *Rhyncotus r. rufescens,* the parrot *Amazona xanthopteryx,* various duck including *Anas versicolor,* stork, egret, wild turkey.

5. LOS ALERCES NATIONAL PARK.

II.

a) Status : total protection. Most of the areas which were formerly open to grazing by domestic stock have now been cleared of this disability. But the estate is still heavily mortgaged. Forest fires are a problem.

b) Area : 263,000 ha.

c) Staff : 15 persons plus "a certain number of labourers" (as compared with a criterion requisite of 26). This is explained in the same way as for Lanín.

d) Budget : U.S. $ 27,750 (criterion requires $ 13,000).

III.

Date established : 1937.

Land tenure : entirely state-owned.

Tourism : two hotels, one private, one leased by the State. 70 km of motorable roads. Sport-fishing. 5,000 visitors a year.

IV.

Altitude : 400-2,280 m.

a) Glacial formation, with numerous lakes and extant glaciers; forests of " larch " or " tamarack " *Fitzroya cupressoides* (hence the name " Los alerces "), *Nothofagus antarctica* and *Maytenus boaria.*

b) An important habitat for guemal and pudu deer, puma, grey fox *Dusicyon griseus*; various monkeys.

6. PERITO FRANCISCO P. MORENO NATIONAL PARK.

II.

a) Status : total protection. Former habitations and estates have been evacuated.

b) Area : 115,000 ha.

c) Staff : regular patrols. This is not up to the standard set by the criterion, but the Park has been kept in the List, at the express wish of the authorities, on the grounds that at present it is subject to no threats which call for strong protection.

d) Budget : U.S. $ 2,500 (about half the criterion requirement).

III.

Date established : 1937.

Land tenure : entirely state-owned.

Tourism : no accommodation. Tourist routes are being planned.

IV.

Altitude : 800-2,770 m.

a) Part of the southern Andean cordillera, comprising a string of lakes (notably L. Aires) and glaciers : Andean-Patagonian type forest, dominated by *Nothofagus pumilio, dombeyei* and *antarctica,* and bush areas of *Berberis laxifolia.*

b) Guanaco, guemal, colpeo fox *Dusicyon culpeu*; condor, black-necked swan *Cygnus melanocoryphus,* long-billed rhea *Pterocnemia pennata.*

7. TIERRA DEL FUEGO NATIONAL PARK.

II.

a) Status : total protection. Uninhabited.

b) Area : 63,000 ha.

c) Staff : 2 units only; the arguments used in the case of Park No. 1 Nahuel Huapi are said to be equally cogent — vast area of desolation etc.

d) Budget : U.S. $ 4,000 (criterion requirement $ 3,250).

III.

Date established : 1960.

Land tenure : state-ownership.

Tourism : one state-owned hotel.

IV.

Altitude : sea level to 1,000 m.

a) Forested region characterised by Andean-Patagonian flora, with very rugged terrain consisting of a chain of steeply-scarped mountains, rivers, lakes and deep valleys; vegetation dominated by *Nothofagus betuloides, pumilio* and *antarctica,* and Winter's bark *Drimys winteri.*

b) Guanaco, hoary fox *Dusicyon vetulus*; parakeet, owl, penguin, albatross, petrel.

8. IGUAZÚ NATIONAL PARK.

II.

a) Status : total protection. This is under threat from a project for harnessing the Iguazú Falls in which the river drops some 80 m.

51

b) Area : 55,000 ha.

c) Staff : 6 units, plus " a certain number of labourers " (compared with a criterion requirement of five).

d) Budget : U.S. $ 13,900.

III.   *Date established :* 1909.

Land tenure : 500 ha common land and 6,000 ha owned by the small town of Puerto Iguazú on the western border of the Park.

Tourism : some modest inns, privately owned, in Puerto Iguazú. Two hotels, one very big, together with an airfield have been built and leased by the State. 58 km of roads. 20,000 visitors a year. Museum.

IV.   *Altitude :* probably 100-700 m (see Brazil No. 1).

a) The laterite soils support sub-tropical forest composed of *Enterolobium contortisiliqua, Cordia trichotoma, Cedrela tubiflora, Aspidosperma polyneuron, Peltophorum dubium* and the Angico gum tree *Piptadenia rigida.*

b) Jaguar *Panthera onca,* ocelot *Felis pardalis,* coati *N. nasua*; water birds such as herons; reptiles.

9. EL REY NATIONAL PARK.

II.   *a*) Status : total protection. Human disturbance which still exists is described as " insignificant ".

b) Area : 44,162 ha.

c) Staff : 2 units, plus " a certain number of labourers " (criterion : 4). Same argument applies as for Lanín National Park, No. 3 above.

d) Budget : U.S. $ 6,000.

III.   *Date established :* 1948.

Land tenure : entirely state-owned.

Tourism : a hotel was under construction by the State in 1963. 13 km of roads. 500 visitors a year.

IV.   *Altitude :* 1,000-1,500 m.

a) More or less sub-tropical vegetation, typical of Tumano-Bolivian woodland : southern butternut *Juglans australis, Cedrela lilloi, Tipuana tipu, Phoebe porphyria.*

b) Sub-tropical fauna of the " Salteno " sub-district : tapir, jaguar, wild cat, giant anteater *Myrmecophaga tridactyla*; birds and reptiles.

10. CHACO NATIONAL PARK.

II.   *a*) Status : total protection. Very few inhabitants in the area, and those remaining are in the process of being evacuated.

b) Area : 15,000 ha.

c) Staff : officer-in-charge and one guard. Also visited from time to time by guard and inspectors from other national parks.

d) Budget : U.S. $ 2,500.

III.   *Date established :* 1954.

Land tenure : State-owned.

Tourism : no accommodation. Far from the normal tourist routes.

V.   *Altitude :* no information, but probably c. 200 m.

a) A broad plateau of which about half is taken up by great marshes in the region of the humid forests of the eastern Chaco; the characteristic tree is *Schinopsis balansae* and also to be found are : *Astronium balansae, Caesalpinia melanocarpa, Prosopis alba* and *nigra, Copernicia alba, Patagonula americana.*

b) Tapir, mouse opossum *Marmosa agilis chacoensis,* Azara's fox *Dusicyon gymnocercus antiquus,* Geoffroy's cat *Felis g. geoffroyi,* otter; many species of duck.

11. LACUNA BLANCA NATIONAL PARK.

II.   *a*) Status : total protection.

b) Area : 11,250 ha.

c) Staff : one unit.

d) Budget : U.S. $ 2,200 (criterion requirement $ 550).

III.   *Date established :* 1949.

Land tenure : state-ownership.

Tourism : no accommodation; a road runs along the lake from south-west to north-east through the Park, which is about 200 km west of Neuquén.

IV.   *Altitude :* not reported, but the lake lies between the 1,000 and 2,000 m contours.

a) Forest vegetation of no special interest surrounds the lake, the whole reserve being 15×7.5 km or considerably larger than the actual lake.

b) Black-necked swan *Cygnus melanocoryphus,* Andean flamingo *Phoenicoparrus andinus,* the cariama *Chunga burmeisteri,* heron, owl.

12. PETRIFIED FOREST NATURAL MONUMENT.

II.   *a*) Status : total protection. No human occupancy.

b) Area : 10,000 ha.

c) Staff : an officer-in-charge.

d) Budget : U.S. $ 1,500.

III.   *Date established :* 1954.

Land tenure : state-ownership.

Tourism : no accommodation. Far from normal tourist routes, in central Patagonia.

IV.   *Altitude :* no information, but probably c. 600 m.

a) A rocky terrain clothed in thin xerophile vegetation (Patagonian steppe); the monument comprises a petrified forest of *Araucaria mirabilis,* individual trees attaining a height of 100 m and a diameter of 3.5 m.

b) Rhea, guanaco.

V.   **Areas excluded :** nil.

53

5. AUSTRALIA

I. **Listed Areas :** seventy-two.

Most of these areas were included and described, sometimes in considerable detail, in E/3436. They are regionally distributed and dealt with in the present List, State by State, as follows :

A. — New South Wales	11
B. — Victoria	14
C. — South Australia	10
D. — Western Australia	5
E. — Northern Territory	4
F. — Queensland	25
G. — Tasmania	3
H. — Papua and New Guinea	—

Section V, giving some detail of areas at present excluded from the List, is similarly subdivided and placed at the end of the Australian report.

A. — NEW SOUTH WALES.

I. **Listed Areas :** eleven.

1. Kosciusko State Park.
2. Blue Mountains National Park.
3. New England National Park.
4. Morton National Park.
5. Ku Ring Gai Chase.
6. The Royal National Park.
7. Gibraltar Range National Park.
8. Mt. Kaputar National Park.
9. Brisbane Water National Park.
10. Warrumbungle National Park.
11. Dorrigo National Park.

General Introduction :

Legislation : the Kosciusko State Park was established by a special Act of Parliament; the other protected areas were officially declared as such by the Minister for Lands by virtue of the powers accorded to him by various Acts : the Public Trusts Acts (1894-1944), the Public Parks Act (1912), Crown Lands Consolidation Act (1913), Fauna Protection Act (1948). In 1964 a National Parks and Public Reserves Bill was introduced and was finally enacted on 1 October 1967, which has the effect of providing a more secure planning basis, eliminating the remaining forestry exploitation from reserved areas and for the first time giving the N.S.W. Parks and Reserves the full protection of the law.

Administration : Department of Lands. Each park is administered by a specific body (Trust) composed of local officials and residents. Voluntary organisations often collaborate. This arrangement which has the effect of appealing to the devoted support of disinterested persons while leaving the door open for specialist intervention, has an originality which is deserving of attention. In 1961 a post of Administrator of Parks and Reserves was created in the Department of Lands at Sydney, with the responsibility of assisting the Trusts in their work of organising and protecting the Parks, and under the 1967 legislation this was incorporated in a National Parks and Wildlife Service, in which Parks and Reserves may be vested (as had been done by the end of 1968 for Nos. 1, 5 and 6 in the List).

Land tenure: with some exceptions, which are mentioned in the detailed data, all areas are state-owned.

Tourism: Already well-provided for and in course of considerable further development (see below). The interpretative services are however still scarcely developed. Two museums are planned. Sport-fishing is allowed in certain places.

Research: no centralised organisation. The Australian Academy of Sciences is much concerned with the threat of hydro-electric development hanging over the Kosciusko State Park. A New South Wales National Parks Association runs a campaign in support of National Parks.

Details : application of criteria (II), general information (III) and description (IV) :

1. KOSCIUSKO STATE PARK.

a) Status : total protection. The " Snowy Mountains Hydro-Electric Scheme " occupies one sector of the Park, which confers both the advantages (such as the strict protection of the catchment area) and usual disadvantages (conflict over the siting of electric power-lines) of such a situation. Still some grazing rights and forest exploitation. The Park includes a " primitive area " gazetted in January 1963.

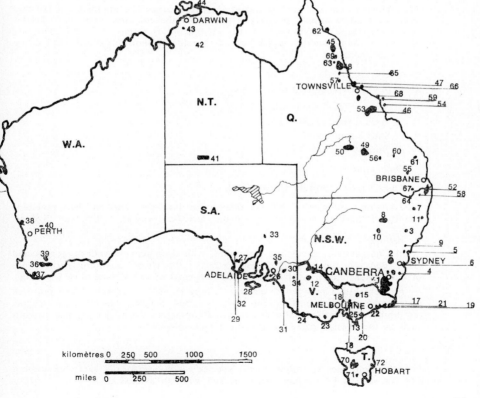

b) Area : 601,008 ha, of which the " primitive area " accounts for 18,130 ha.

c) Staff : 26 in the Park, 9 at Sydney, augmented during the height of the tourist season.

d) Budget : Averaging U.S. $ 269,000 (£A 120,000).

Date established : 1944 (Kosciusko State Park Act).

III. *Administration :* ten Trustees, empowered to promulgate " primitive areas " closed to tourists.

Land tenure : still includes a few pieces of private property.

Tourism : accommodation (over 1,000 beds) includes Thredbo Lodge and village and five modern hotels; ski-lodges (private clubs); ski-lifts. Organised excursions. The Snowy Mountains Hydro-Electric Authority exercises a major role in these developments. 46 km from Canberra, 576 km from Sydney.

IV. *Altitude :* 450-2,200 m.

a) The only extensive alpine region in Australia; typical glacial formation (moraines, corries, ice-smoothed rock faces, clay-varves, glacial lakes); alpine and sub-alpine zone flora, high altitude eucalypt zone.

b) Duck-billed platypus *Ornithorhyncus anatinus* *, echidna or spiny-anteater *Tachyglossus sitosus* *, grey kangaroo *Macropus canguru,* marsupial and pouched mice, wild cat, wombats, phalangers (especially the common " possum " *Trichosurus vulpecula*), broad-toothed cat *Mastacomys fuscus* *; emu, lyre-bird *Menura novae-hollandiae,* black-backed magpie *Gymnorhina tibicen* and currawongs *Strepera* spp.

2. BLUE MOUNTAINS NATIONAL PARK.

II. *a*) Status : total protection.

b) Area : about 68,000 ha.

c) Staff : four units.

d) Budget : U.S. $ 40,000 (1964).

III. *Date established :* 1959.

Land tenure : entirely Crown land.

Tourism : intensive. Accommodation in built-up areas in the immediate vicinity of the Park, which is on a main electrified railway 96 km from Sydney.

III. *Altitude :* 50-1,300 m.

a) Characteristic sandstone formation, with deep narrow valleys, gorges and cliffs; dense humid tropical forest bordering the rivers, including many kinds of eucalyptus; the flora of the plateaux is typical of the Hawkesbury sandstone.

b) Duck-billed platypus *, echidna *, grey kangaroo, marsupial and pouched mice, wild cat; lyre-bird *, currawong or bell magpie, black-backed magpie (or piping crow-shrike), satin bower-bird *Ptilonorhynchus violaceus,* and pigeons such as the Wonga pigeon *Leucosarcia melanoleuca.*

---

* Throughout the Australian report species which are *locally* rare, but do not qualify for section IV *c*), have been marked with an asterisk.

3. NEW ENGLAND NATIONAL PARK.

I.

a) Status : total protection, except for limited forestry exploitation.

b) Area : 22,460 ha.

c) Staff : two.

d) Budget : U.S. $ 5,600 (1964).

II.

Date established : 1935 (16,600 ha); extended to 22,460 ha in 1940 and 1942.

Land tenure : Crown land.

Tourism : little in the way of facilities; a few paths and camping places, one mountain chalet for hikers and one " tourist cabin ". The headquarters of the Park Ranger, recently built, incorporates a " visitors' centre " and a small shop. Other developments are planned.

V.

Altitude : 300-1,560 m.

a) Mountainous area on the eastern flank of the Great Dividing Range; humid tropical primeval forest in which noteworthy species are red cedar, hoop pine *Araucaria cunninghamii* and butter-tree *Bassia* sp.

b) Duck-billed platypus *; pigeons, satin bower-bird, brush turkey *Alectura lathami* *, lyrebird and many other species characteristic of humid forest.

4. MORTON NATIONAL PARK.

I.

a) Status : total protection.

b) Area : 18,000 ha.

c) Staff : one.

d) Budget : U.S. $ 5,600.

III.

Date established : 1938 (when named the " Morton Primitive Area "). Became a National Park in 1964.

Land tenure : includes some pieces of privately-owned land.

Tourism : undeveloped. Access by motor-road to the boundary, thence by motorable tracks. Some refuge-shelters. 160 km along the coast from Sydney.

IV.

Altitude : 150-750 m.

a) A hilly area with sandstone peaks and fairly good vegetation cover including *Eucalyptus coriacea,* mixed with other eucalypt species and in places resembling heathland. Dense humid forest in the valley bottoms and broad-leaved forest on the slopes.

b) Platypus *, echidna *, grey kangaroo, marsupial and pouched mice, wild cat; bower-bird, pigeons including the Wonga *, lyre-bird *, magpie and currawong.

5. KU RING GAI CHASE.

II.

a) Status : total protection, but excessive tourist pressure locally and sport-fishing permitted.

b) Area : 15,200 ha.

c) Staff : 22, including 12 rangers.

d) Budget : of the order of U.S. $ 112,000.

III.

Date established : 1894, with later extensions.

Land tenure : Crown land.

Tourism : intensive, being in the near neighbourhood of Sydney. Elaborate network of roads in the reserves, which borders on two others (No. 6 " Royal " and No. 9 " Brisbane Water "). A Centre for recreation at Bobbin Head. Water sports, camping, picnic sites, " game park " (for koala). A new visitors' centre and headquarters office were completed in 1965.

IV.

Altitude : sea level to 230 m.

a) A very hilly sandstone area close to Sydney; steep slopes lead down to the sea; scrub with humid tropical forest along the valleys and inlets; a very rich flora.

b) Duck-billed platypus *, echidna *, grey kangaroo, marsupial and pouched mice; bower-bird, pigeons including the Wonga * and lyre-bird *.

6. THE ROYAL NATIONAL PARK.

II.

a) Status : total protection.

b) Area : 14,620 ha.

c) Staff : 30, including a Superintendent and 2 rangers.

d) Budget : of the order of U.S. $ 89,600.

III.

Date established : 1886, when named " The National Park "; designated " The Royal National Park " in 1955.

Land tenure : Crown land.

Tourism : active, with Sydney only 32 km away. A small amount of accommodation (100 beds). Recreations include canoeing, swimming, picnicking etc.

IV.

Altitude : sea level to 220 m.

a) Situated on the Pacific coast, with rocky headlands and sandy beaches; a coastal eucalypt forest and humid tropical forest along the streams.

b) Duck-billed platypus *, echidna *, grey kangaroo, marsupial and pouched mice, wild cat; bower-bird, Wonga pigeon *, lyre-bird *, magpie, currawong, gull, heron, ibis, egret.

7. GIBRALTAR RANGE NATIONAL PARK.

II.

a) Status : total protection.

b) Area : 13,800 ha.

c) Staff : one ranger.

d) Budget : U.S. $ 11,200 (1964).

III.

Date established : 1963.

Land tenure : Crown land.

Tourism : not yet organised, but a house for the Ranger and Park head-quarters were under construction in January 1966.

Altitude : 200-1,200 m.

a) Mainly granite area, with traces of tertiary basalt outflows; the vegetation on the granitic soils is in sharp contrast with the humid forest which covers the rich basaltic soils.

b) Echidna *, grey kangaroo, wombat; lyre-bird *, magpie, currawong.

8. MOUNT KAPUTAR NATIONAL PARK.

a) Status : total protection.

b) Area : 6,200 ha, which will probably be extended to 14,080 ha, but there have been disputes over the exact siting of the boundaries.

c) Staff : one unit.

d) Budget : U.S. $ 20,250.

Date established : 1925 (768 ha), 1955 (increased to 1,060 ha), brought up to its present area in 1964.

Land tenure : Crown land.

Tourism : little organisation, even the staff accommodation is quite recently built. Three "tourist cabins" were completed in 1965. The Park can be reached by tarred road, but is nevertheless some distance from the main flow of tourists.

Altitude : 220-1,500 m.

a) A hilly section of the Nandewar Range, with steep slopes, deep gorges and cliffs.

b) Grey kangaroo, wallaroo *Macropus robustus,* koala *Phascolarctos cinereus* *, possum, wild cat, pouched mice; brush turkey *, cockatoo, parrot.

9. BRISBANE WATER NATIONAL PARK.

a) Status : total protection.

b) Area : 6,077 ha.

c) Staff : 3 full-time rangers, plus several persons who act in an honorary capacity.

d) Budget : U.S. $ 14,800 (1964).

Date established : 1959.

Land tenure : Crown land.

Tourism : the Park is classified as a "natural area" where visitors can enter, but iti is not planned to provide much in the way of local tourist facilities. Accommodation is available outside the park and it should be remembered that Sydney is only 85 km away by the Pacific Highway.

Altitude : sea level to 240 m.

a) Consists of a number of parallel sandstone ridges, with steep faces on the sea side; the crests are characterised by Hawkesbury sandstone flora and in the narrow valleys are remnants of humid tropical forest.

b) Echidna *, platypus *, grey kangaroo, marsupial and pouched mice, wild cat; bower-bird, Wonga pigeon *, lyre-bird *, magpie, currawong, gull, heron, ibis, egret.

II.

10. WARRUMBUNGLE NATIONAL PARK.

a) Status : total protection.

b) Area : 3,320 ha in 1967; extended to 9,541 ha in 1969.

c) Staff : 3 units.

d) Budget : U.S. $ 15,120 (1964).

III.

Date established : 1953.

Land tenure : Crown land.

Tourism : few facilities as yet, but an active Board of Trustees is planning for progressive development, while bearing in mind the needs of conservation (e.g. it " does not intend to criss-cross the area with roads but make trails "). Some camping facilities are available and simple overnight accommodation.

IV.

Altitude : 500-1,200 m.

a) Mountain ridge dominating the neighbouring plain; a volcanic area (no longer active) with among other features the cylindrical form of an old volcano (Crater Bluff); a varied flora.

b) Echidna *, kangaroo, wallaroo, koala, possum, pouched mice, wallabies including the rock wallaby Petrogale sp. *; wedge-tailed eagle Uroaetus audax, parrot, falcon.

II.

11. DORRIGO NATIONAL PARK.

a) Status : total protection.

b) Area : 1,549 ha.

c) Staff : one.

d) Budget : U.S. $ 10,800.

III.

Date established : 1927, extended in 1936.

Land tenure : Crown land.

Tourism : few facilities. Treated as " unspoiled natural forest, dedicated for the preservation of the natural flora ". Shelters, picnic-places with tables, paths.

IV.

Altitude : 150-1,100 m.

a) Comprises the Dorrigo plateau, with very steep sides, of a mountainous character near the sea, covered with thick bush, climbing plants, dense undergrowth and broad-leaved forest; remarkable waterfalls.

b) Pigeons, lyre-bird, brush turkey *, satin bower-bird and other bird species typical of humid forest.

B. — VICTORIA.

I.

Listed Areas : fourteen.

1. (12) Wyperfeld National Park.
2. (13) Wilson's Promontory National Park.
3. (14) Hattah Lakes National Park.
4. (15) Mount Buffalo National Park.
5. (16) King Lake National Park.
6. (17) Mallacoota Inlet National Park.

60

7. (18)   Fraser National Park.
8. (19)   Alfred National Park.
9. (20)   Lakes National Park.
10. (21)   Wingan Inlet National Park.
11. (22)   Lind National Park.
12. (23)   Port Campbell National Park.
13. (24)   Mount Richmond National Park.
14. (25)   Fern Tree Gully National Park.

N.B. — Numbers in brackets refer to the List number in the overall Australian series; the Parks are listed in order of size.

General Introduction :

Legislation : National Parks Act 1956 (No. 6023) supplemented by a National Parks Act 1958 (No. 6326).

Administration : a National Parks Authority, established under the provisions of the above-mentioned legislation and of which the Director is the Executive Officer. It has eleven members and extensive powers, with numerous local committees. Surveillance of the Parks is strengthened by personnel of other governmental departments, viz. the Fisheries and Wildlife Department, Forests Commission, Police Department and Lands Department.

Land tenure : most of the Parks are Crown land.

Tourism : being developed under the direction of the National Parks Authority. The latter is empowered by a law enacted in 1960 to lease plots to private firms for hotels, sport grounds, etc. In some places sport-fishing is allowed under control.

Research : the National Parks Association of Victoria, a non-governmental organisation, has launched a programme of exploration and inventory. Many lists (of the flora, birds, etc.) and studies (geological, etc.) have already been published, referring to individual Parks. Mention should also be made of « Victoria's Resources », the journal of the Natural Resources Conservation League of Victoria, which carries many articles on the National Parks.

Details : application of criteria (II), general information (III) and description (IV) :

1. (12)   WYPERFELD NATIONAL PARK.

a) Status : total protection. The Park is inaccessible and its south-west sector semi-desert.

b) Area : 56,000 ha.

c) Staff : a single, mobile, Ranger. This is somewhat inadequate but see (*a*) above (inaccessibility).

d) Budget : U.S. $ 20,600 (1965/6).

Date established : original steps taken in 1909, full status conferred in 1921; extension 1933.

Land tenure : public ownership and surrounded by unoccupied publicly owned land.

61

Tourism : difficult, due to remoteness (450 km from Melbourne) and semi-desert character of the Park. Accommodation available in the nearest town-ships. " Camp-fires " are organised for some hundreds of participants. Only one road of access.

Research : the Park is popular and well-supported by the people of the neighbourhood, especially as regards assistance for research workers. J. N. Rowan and R. G. Downes have published a study of the area and there are various lists and inventories.

IV.

Altitude : 75-120 m.

a) A sample of the semi-desert landscape of the arid Mallee scrub, with dried up beds of ancient lakes. The western part is mainly composed of sandhills, covered with heath and thicket, while the east is dominated by the Mallee. A rich xerophytic flora.

b) Echidna, black-faced variety of grey kangaroo *Macropus canguru melanops,* Mitchell's hopping mouse *Notomys mitchelli* *; parrots (including the Regent Parrot *Polytelis anthopeplus*), emu, cockatoos (including Major Mitchell's or pink cockatoo *Kakatoe leadbeateri*), Mallee-fowl *Leipoa ocellata* *. Over 100 species of birds.

2. (13) WILSON'S PROMONTORY NATIONAL PARK.

II.

a) Status : total protection. Endangered by grass and bush fires.

b) Area : 48,340 ha.

c) Staff : about 20 units, full-time throughout the year.

d) Budget : U.S. $ 100,000 (1965-1966).

III.

Date established : original steps taken in 1898, full status conferred in 1905, revised in 1912.

Land tenure : Crown land.

Tourism : much activity, upwards of 100,000 visitors a year. Motel blocks. Very comfortable. Camping area with full facilities. Access by rail and road, 240 km from Melbourne. The main excursion is to the lighthouse at the South-East Cape (Australia's " Land's End ").

Research : numerous scientific publications.

IV.

Altitude : sea level to 770 m.

a) A mountainous region on the sea-coast, with 130 km of bays, creeks and beaches. The vegetation has been badly affected by fires; it includes eucalyptus, acacias, tea trees *Melaleuca* sp., heaths and ferns.

b) Echidna, kangaroo, wallaby, koala, possum, little pouched mouse *Antechinus* sp. *, bandicoot; parrot (including ground parrot *Pezoporus wallicus* *); altogether there are more than 140 species of birds.

c) Ground parrot.

3. (14) HATTAH LAKES NATIONAL PARK.

II.

a) Status : total protection. Considerable difficulty has been experienced in eliminating commercial fishing.

b) Area : about 20,000 ha.

c) Staff : two.

d) Budget : U.S. $ 15,000 (1965-1966).

II.

Date established : 1960.

Land tenure : Crown land.

Tourism : only just beginning to be developed.

V.

Altitude : 50-70 m.

a) Part of the Mallee scrub region; there are five lakes fringed with *Eucalyptus camaldulensis; Callitris* pines; riverine vegetation and Mallee scrub.

b) Mitchell's hopping mouse; provides a refuge for pelican, duck, egret, cormorant, grebe, red-necked avocet *Recurvirostra novae-hollandii* and other waterfowl, mallee-fowl or " lowan " *.

4. (15) MOUNT BUFFALO NATIONAL PARK.

I.

a) Status : total protection.

b) Area : 10,912 ha.

c) Staff : 3 full-time and some part-time assistants.

d) Budget : U.S. $ 30,240 (1965-1966).

III.

Date established : 1898.

Land tenure : public ownership.

Tourism : the origins of this Park go back to the activities of an Alpine Club founded in 1888. Its organisation is slanted towards mountaineering and winter-sports; a ski-lift, 2 chalets (270 beds), etc. Access by road, 330 km from Melbourne. The Catani Lake, regularly stocked with exotic species, is open to sport-fishing. Water-skiing is not allowed, but canoes and yachts (not motorboats) are permitted and the lake is freely used for skating in winter.

Research : being composed of a vast granitic plateau, the Park has lent itself especially to geological study.

IV.

Altitude : 275-1,680 m.

a) A mountainous area of the north-east of the State of Victoria, dominating the surrounding terrain. The granite of which it is composed is at all stages of evolution and cut by a deep gorge to a depth of 250 m. *Eucalyptus coriacea* forest at the higher levels with some *Eucalyptus gigantea*; *gigantea* is, however, dominant on the level rock-free ground between the hills, but does not form forests; alpine vegetation at higher altitudes.

b) Echidna, wombat, wallaby, kangaroo and many species of birds including lyre-bird *.

5. (16) KING LAKE NATIONAL PARK.

II.

a) Status : total protection.

b) Area : 5,632 ha in three sections.

c) Staff : two full-time, one half-time.

d) Budget : U.S. $ 31,360 (1965-1966).

III.

Date established : 1928.

Land tenure : publicly owned.

Tourism : a good network of roads in the Park; landscape of great beauty featuring the Mason's Falls. No hotels in the Park and camping not permitted. Numerous day excursionists come by car and bus the 70 km from Melbourne, which lies to the south-west. Three areas are open to visitors : Jehorophat Gully, Dame Melba's Lookout and Mason's Falls.

IV.

Altitude : 150-600 m.

a) A wooded area, falling into three sections, one to the north-west in which Mason's Falls are situated, one to the south-east comprising the Jehorophat Valley, and a third surrounding the Wombelano Falls; dominant vegetation includes several species of eucalyptus and acacia; ferns and orchids.

b) Platypus, wombat, black-tailed wallaby *Protemnodon bicolor,* possum, koala; over 100 species of birds including lyre-bird, golden whistler *Pachycephala pectoralis,* redthroat *Pyrrholaemus brunneus,* honeyeaters and king parrot *Aprosmictus scapularis.*

6. (17) MALLACOOTA INLET NATIONAL PARK.

II.

a) Status : total protection.

b) Area : 4,490 ha.

c) Staff : one full-time Ranger is shared between this Park and the three neighbouring Parks, Alfred, Lind and Wingan.

d) Budget : U.S. $ 9,180 (1965-1966).

III.

Date established : 1932.

Land tenure : public ownership, but with about a hundred hectares privately owned in various blocks, which has led to a number of boundary and other disputes; many problems have arisen about the use of the land — for holiday housing, etc.

Tourism : difficult of access, by rail, road and sea 530 km from Melbourne. Movement within the Park is also difficult, especially during the rains. Accommodation at Mallacoota, not in the Park itself. Camping is inhibited by the lack of drinkable water. Coastal waters where sport-fishing is available are not included in the Park. Canoeing.

IV.

Altitude : sea level to 50 m.

a) Comprises the shores of the Mallacoota Inlet. Cliffs dating from the Lower Palaeozoic along the coast. Sandy beaches.

b) A rich avifauna (cormorant, pelican, curlew, heron, cockatoo, parrot) — a total of 240 species.

7. (18) FRASER NATIONAL PARK.

II.

a) Status : total protection.

b) Area : 3,100 ha.

c) Staff : 2 units.

d) Budget : U.S. $ 58,250 (1965-1966).

III.

Date established : 1957.

Land tenure : public ownership.

Tourism : the Park is adjacent to the unprotected Eildon Reservoir, which attracts many tourists for fishing, water-sports, etc. No accommodation in the Park. Camping, picnic sites. On the Eildon lake there is, however, a reservation of 480 ha known as the Eildon Water Reserve, which extends from high water level to one chain (about 20 m) above high water level and is administered by a special Committee of Management, working closely with the Park authorities.

64

IV.

Altitude : 300-500 m.

a) Situated near the artificial lake of the Eildon Reservoir not far from Melbourne. Many eucalyptus species, including *Eucalyptus hemiphloia, E. poly-anthemos, E. rubida*; open savannah with fairly steep hills.

b) Kangaroo, wombat; birds characteristic of tall timber, waterfowl.

8. (19) ALFRED NATIONAL PARK.

II.

a) Status : total protection.

b) Area : 2,162 ha.

c) Staff : see under Mallacoota (No. 6 above).

d) Budget : U.S. $ 900 plus salary element (1965-1966).

III.

Date established : 1925 (linked with Lind Park, No. 11 below, which dates from a year later).

Land tenure : public ownership.

Tourism : infrequent. A very primitive biotope, remote and difficult of access in the interior, even though a trunk road (National Highway No. 1) crosses it.

IV.

Altitude : 120-560 m.

a) Geologically recent, mountainous; contains a good sample of the sub-tropical humid forest of Victoria : *Cissus hypoglaucus, Tristania laurina, Acacia melanoxylon;* many ferns and some tree orchids in the narrow valleys.

b) Wallaby, bandicoot, possum; cormorant, heron, cockatoo, forest birds.

9. (20) LAKES NATIONAL PARK.

II.

a) Status : total protection.

b) Area : 2,115 ha.

c) Staff : 2 units, part-time.

d) Budget : U.S. $ 5,350 (1965-1966).

III.

Date established : 1927-1928, under the name of " Sperm Whale Head National Park ".

Land tenure : public ownership.

Tourism : difficult. No accommodation. There is one motorable track into the Park, but easier access by water than land.

IV.

Altitude : sea level to 30 m.

a) Part of the series of Gippsland Lakes; enormous stands of *Thryptomene miqueliana*; western limit of *Eucalyptus botryoides,* fringes of *Banksia* and tea-tree *Melaleuca*; sand-dunes.

b) Possum, koala, kangaroo; rich avifauna, including the ground parrot *Pezoporus wallicus* *; waterfowl and seabirds.

c) Ground parrot.

10. (21) WINGAN INLET NATIONAL PARK.

II.

a) Status : total protection.

b) Area : 1,897 ha.

c) Staff : see under Mallacoota (No. 6 above).

d) Budget : U.S. $ 960 plus salary element (1965-1966).

III.   *Date established :* 1909.

Land tenure : public ownership. Surrounded by publicly owned forest and also some Crown land.

Tourism : being developed. Like Mallacoota, which is supervised by the same Ranger, it attracts fishermen, since the coastal waters are open for fishing. However, unlike Mallacoota, these waters constitute a bird sanctuary. No accommodation in the Park. The roads of access are difficult. Still a comparatively undisturbed area, of some historical interest (landing-place of George Bass in 1797).

IV.   *Altitude :* sea level to 250 m.

a) Part of the land bordering the estuary of the Wingan river; contains some very beautiful beaches bounded by an ancient raised marine terrace.

b) Rich coastal fauna, particularly birds.

11. (22) Lind National Park.

II.   *a)* Status : total protection.

b) Area : 1,153 ha.

c) Staff : see under Mallacoota (No. 6 above); the Ranger has, however, only taken over this area as recently as 1966.

d) Budget : U.S. $ 900 plus salary element (1965-1966).

III.   *Date established :* 1926.

Land tenure : public ownership.

Tourism : limited. A few tracks run into the Park, but no picnic sites have yet been developed, nor is there any accommodation in the Park or even much to speak of in the neighbouring little townships.

IV.   *Altitude :* 30-300 m.

a) Situated in the Bemm watershed and distinguished by very steep-sided valleys; a very rich flora (including, notably, *Telopea oreades*); semi-tropical forest with *Acacia melanoxylon, Tristania laurina, Bedfordia salicina, Olearia argophylla, Pittosporum undulatum, Pomaderris apetala* and many species of eucalyptus (*E. oblepia, E. botryoides, E. sieberiana, E. sideroxylon*).

b) Forest fauna.

12. (23) Port Campbell National Park.

II.   *a)* Status : total protection.

b) Area : between 700 and 800 ha.

c) Staff : 1 unit, with seasonal assistance.

d) Budget : U.S. $ 24,200 (1965-1966).

III.   *Date established :* 1960.

Land tenure : public ownership.

Tourism : important and likely to increase, in this picturesque coastal region visited by thousands of holidaymakers. Controlled camping areas. Sea fishing (the waters are not included in the Park).

66

V.   *Altitude :* sea level to 5 m.

    a) A coastal belt in the south-west of Victoria.

    b) Little or fairy penguin *Eudyptula minor,* mutton-bird or short-tailed shearwater *Puffinus tenuirostris* and other seabirds.

13. (24) MOUNT RICHMOND NATIONAL PARK.

I.   *a)* Status : total protection.

    b) Area : 600 ha (an extension is likely).

    c) Staff : 1 unit, part-time.

    d) Budget : U.S. $ 3,000 (1965-1966).

II.   *Date established :* 1960.

    Land tenure : public ownership.

    Tourism : no plans as yet for development. This is mainly a botanical reserve, with a very active management Committee.

    Research : A Flora has been published.

V.   *Altitude :* 100-230 m.

    a) 450 species of plants including 50 orchids; eucalyptus, lobelia, acacia.

    b) The potoroo or long-nosed rat-kangaroo *Potorous tridactylus* * may still survive; over 90 species of birds listed.

    c) Potoroo.

14. (25) FERN TREE GULLY NATIONAL PARK.

I.   *a)* Status : total protection.

    b) Area : 371 ha.

    c) Staff : 3 units.

    d) Budget : U.S. $ 15,680 (1965-1966).

II.   *Date established :* dates back to 1887, but made a National Park in 1928.

    Land tenure : public ownership.

    Tourism : in the near vicinity of Melbourne, the Park receives a large number of visitors, approaching 100,000 a year. Access by rail and numerous roads; picnic sites. The Park was devastated by a deplorable fire in 1962, but is being steadily rehabilitated.

V.   *Altitude :* 150-490 m.

    a) Situated 35 km from Melbourne in the hilly Dandenong range; many species of ferns and orchids; the slopes of the hills are clothed in thick forest of tall mountain eucalypts, especially *E. regnans,* spotted eucalyptus, " messmates " and long-leaved box-trees.

    b) Echidna, possum, wombat, wallaby; a rich avifauna.

AUSTRALIA

C. — SOUTH AUSTRALIA.

I.   **Listed Areas :** ten.

     1. (26) Belair National Park.
     2. (27) Hincks, Murlong and Nicholls Wild Life Reserve.
     3. (28) Flinders Chase Reserve.
     4. (29) Hambidge Wild Life Reserve.
     5. (30) Billiatt Wild Life Reserve.
     6. (31) Archibald Makin Wild Life Reserve.
     7. (32) Lincoln Wild Life Reserve.
     8. (33) Wilpena Pound.
     9. (34) Peebinga Wild Life Reserve.
   10. (35) Chaunceys Line (Ferries and McDonald Reserves).

N.B. — Figures in brackets refer to the List number in the overall Australian series.

General Introduction :

All the areas except the first are included on the express recommendation of the South Australian Government. Most of them are Wild Life Reserves and all except two are administered by the same authority as the Belair National Park. Together they total a little more than 200,000 ha and the over-all budget provided for the Commissioners who run them, considerably exceeds the U.S. $ 10,000 which would be required by the criterion. However, the staff employed consists of only a few full-time and a large number of part-time employees, whose value is not easy to assess. On the whole the International Commission on National Parks criteria can be considered to be satisfied, but the situation outlined above makes it impossible to supply precise staff and budget details for each reserve.

Legislation : Fauna and Flora Reserve Act, 1919 and 1935. National Park and Wild Life Reserves Act, 1891 and 1955.

Administration : the responsible body, set up in 1891 to administer the Belair National Park, is the " Commissioners of the National Park ", later renamed " Commissioners of the National Park and Wild Life Reserves ". This body has a membership of 13 under the chairmanship of the Minister of Lands. In addition to the National Park it is responsible for 19 Wild Life Reserves. The Fauna and Flora Board of South Australia has a consultative scientific role, and also temporary responsibility for administering certain reserves (at the moment only one — Flinders Chase No. 3 (28) below). There is also a Committee on Agriculture, which is consulted, and the Tourist Bureau has some say in the matter.

Land tenure : most of the land is in public ownership. But there is considerable uncertainty in such cases as those of Belair and Flinders Chase, where the reserves have been declared under executive rather than legislative powers.

Tourism : active and in some areas undergoing rapid development, though elsewhere still at an early stage.

Research : increasing interest on the part of the Royal Society, the Field Naturalists' Society and the University of Adelaide.

68

Details : application of criteria (II), general information (III) and description (IV) :

1. (26) BELAIR NATIONAL PARK.

I.

a) Status : total protection, but about a third of the Park is used intensively for touristic purposes and some sectors have been degraded by former stock-grazing and slaughter of game.

b) Area : only 897 ha, which is very small, but the proximity of Adelaide (13 km away) is cited as justification for retention.

c) Staff : 3 units for conservation and another dozen for the purposes of tourism, sports and recreation.

d) Budget : over U.S. $ 89,600 (£A 40,000) a year.

II.

Date established : 1891.

Land tenure : State ownership.

Tourism : eight " Park-keepers " look after some 60 tennis courts, sports grounds, golf-links, etc. No accommodation. Unrestricted entry for day visitors only. On some holidays as many as 30,000 visitors. Panoramic observation point. No guided tours. Dense network of roads.

V.

Altitude : 250-480 m.

a) Situated in the Mount Lofty range, the western part which is fairly level separated from the east by the Eden-Moana fault; the eastern sector of the plateau is dissected by rather deep valleys; wooded savannah (*Eucalyptus odorata, E. leucoxylon, E. viminalis, E. camaldulensis*) is well-developed on the podsols of the prairie, while sclerophyllous forest (*E. obliqua, E. cosmophylla, E. fasciculosa*) dominates the eluviated podsols, and there is also a dry variety of sclerophyllous forest (*E. leucoxylon* and *odorata* with *Casuarina muelleriana* and *Xanthorrhoea simiplana*) on lateritic podsols.

b) Forest fauna.

2. (27) HINCKS, MURLONG AND NICHOLLS WILD LIFE RESERVE.

I.

a) Status : total protection; an uninhabited area.

b) Area : 65,326 ha including a separated section of 2,409 ha.

II.

Date established : 1957. The Park is named after the three " Hundreds " (administrative Divisions) in which it is situated.

Land tenure : public ownership.

Tourism : little developed. No accommodation. The one road and three motorable tracks are unfortunately as much used by poachers and people stealing wood for fuel etc. as by visitors.

V.

Altitude : no information.

a) Parallel lines of sandy hills on a S.E./N.W. axis and about 6 to 12 m high occupy the northern part of the Park; the hills are covered with Mallee scrub and genista bushes; similar vegetation in the hollows but thicker; some heath, " oak " and thorn scrub and tea-tree on the hills. The south of the Park has some limestone areas, with small patches of *terra rossa* and a few sandy hills; the genista/Mallee association (Mallee-broom bush) is characteristic of the whole area; 102 plant species have been listed in the reserve.

b) Black-faced race of grey kangaroo *Macropus canguru melanops,* wallaroo *M. robustus,* probably the fat-tailed marsupial mouse *Sminthopsis crassicaudata,* the pygmy phalanger *Cercartetus concinnus* and the hopping mouse *Notomys mitchelli.*

3. (28) FLINDERS CHASE RESERVE.

II.
a) Status : total protection.

b) Area : 54,272 ha.

c) Staff : a resident ranger and an assistant are housed in the Chase.

III.
Date established : 1919 (after 26 years of effort).

Administration : the only Park under the management of the Flora and Fauna Board of South Australia.

Land tenure : entirely Crown land.

Tourism : A road of medium quality brings visitors (nearly 10,000 a year) the 96 km from Kingscote. There are tracks in the Reserve, but at present (1966) no accommodation, pending the conversion of some old buildings, including those of the redundant Cape de Coudie lighthouse reserve, recently acquired for the purpose.

Research : This reserve on Kangaroo Island is regarded by local scientists as the best natural sanctuary in the State. It was devastated by fire in 1958, and it will be some time before the effects have worn off.

IV.
Altitude : at sea level.

a) The western end of Kangaroo Island, comprising a plateau dissected by numerous watercourses and ending in a line of cliffs on the north and west coast, with many caves; there are old and new dune systems; the dominant vegetation of the lateritic soils is composed of *Eucalyptus baxteri* and *E. cosmophylla,* and the eucalyptus associations vary with the variations of the soil; the flora of the Reserve includes species typical of Western Australia and Tasmania.

b) Echidna *Tachyglossus aculeatus,* platypus *Ornithorhynchus anatinus *,* a race of grey kangaroo *Macropus canguru fuliginosa,* dama wallaby *Protemnodon eugenii,* " possum " *Trichosurus vulpecula* and the pygmy phalanger or mouse possum *Cercartetus concinnus.* Introduced species : koala *Phascolarctos cinereus,* rat kangaroo *Bettongia leseuri *,* Queensland ring-tailed phalanger *Pseudocheirus peregrinus.* A rich avifauna of 120 species, including emu *Dromaius novae-hollandiae diemenensis,* black cockatoos *Calyptorhynchus* spp. and the brush-turkey *Alectura lathami.*

c) Leseur's rat kangaroo.

4. (29) HAMBIDGE WILD LIFE RESERVE.

II.
a) Status : total protection.

b) Area : 37,546 ha in two adjoining sections.

III.
Date established : 1957. This and the following Reserves were placed in the charge of the Commissioners in 1962.

Land tenure : public ownership.

Tourism : not specially organised.

70

V.

Altitude : no information.

a) A sandy expanse, with soils of consolidated *solonetz,* and some water-worn sandy hills, with brownish-red earth, Mallee soils and some *terra rossa*; the dominant vegetation is Mallee-broom bush with *Eucalyptus incrassata, E. leptophylla, E. flocktoniae* and tea tree *Melaleuca uncinata.*

b) The mouse sminthopsis *Sminthopsis murina,* black-faced grey kangaroo, brush-tailed rat kangaroo *Bettongia penicillata* *, the pygmy phalanger *Cercartetus nanus*; various bats; many reptiles including the goanna *Varanus* sp.; many birds, including mallee-fowl *Leipoa ocellata* and bronze-wing dove *Phaps chalcoptera.*

c) Brush-tailed rat kangaroo.

5. (30) BILLIATT WILD LIFE RESERVE.

II.

a) Status : total protection. An inaccessible area.

b) Area : 22,400 ha.

c) Staff : no details : surveillance is only possible in 4-wheel drive vehicles.

III.

Date established : 1940.

Tourism : very little and not organised. Access is difficult, by a track and then on foot only.

IV.

Altitude : no information.

a) A zone of sandy hills with some lateritic intrusions; the dominant vegetation is Mallee scrub comprising five species of eucalyptus, mixed to a great or lesser extent with cypress pines *Callitris* spp. and tea-tree *Melaleuca pubescens.*

b) Kangaroo; mallee-fowl, western whipbird *Psophodes nigrogularis leucogaster* *.

c) Western whipbird (a relict species of great interest).

6. (31) ARCHIBALD MAKIN WILD LIFE RESERVE.

II.

a) Status : total protection.

b) Area : 17,420 ha.

III.

Date established : 1953.

Tourism : little activity. The nearest town, 16 km away, is Keith on the Adelaide to Melbourne road.

IV.

Altitude : no information, presumably near sea level.

a) An area of sand dunes overlying the clay formation of the ancient Pleistocene delta of the Murray River; on the windward side of the dunes *Eucalyptus baxteri* scrub; on the thicker sand a scrub of *Banksia ornata, Xanthorrhoea australis* and *Casuarina pusilla*; where the sand deposit is of medium thickness *Eucalyptus leptophylla,* and where it is rather thin Mallee broom bush (*E. incrassata, E. leptophylla, Melaleuca uncinata*); elsewhere, in pockets of richer soil, *Eucalyptus fasciculosa.*

b) Kangaroo; emu, many thornbills *Acanthiza* spp., shy heath wren *Hylacola cauta,* striated field wren *Calamanthus fuliginosus.*

71

7. (32) Lincoln Wild Life Reserve.

II.   *a*) Status : total protection.

         b) Area : 14,208 ha.

III.   *Date established :* 1957. Formerly named the " Flinders District Reserve ".

Tourism : developments are planned for this picturesque coastal area, 24 km from Port Lincoln.

IV.   *Altitude :* sea level.

a) The plateau of the Eyre peninsula, mainly calcareous, bounded by sea on north, west and east; soils and vegetation, like those of the small unlisted " Hundred of Lake Wangary Reserve ", composed of skeletal limestone, *terra rossa* and *rendzina*; predominant plant association is *Casuarina stricta* — *Melaleuca pubescens*; on the red calcareous soils an *Eucalyptus diversifolia* association occurs.

b) Rich avifauna includes osprey *Pandion haliaetus,* white breasted sea-eagle *Haliaetus leucogaster,* Port Lincoln parrot *Barnardius zonarius,* rock parrot *Neophema petrophila,* honeyeaters of many genera and species.

8. (33) Wilpena Pound.

II.   *a*) Status : total protection.

         b) Area : 7,936 ha.

         c) Staff : " the appointment of a government Ranger is warranted ".

III.   *Date established :* 1945.

Tourism : since its inception this Reserve has been a great success. On some weekends more than 10,000 campers are present. The main season is March to October. A well-equipped chalet can accommodate 60 persons. Additional accommodation is being built. Access is by a road which is in need of improvement. The network of roads within the Reserve itself also needs to be brought up to standard so as to be usable at all seasons.

IV.   *Altitude :* highest point 1,170 m.

a) An excellent example of a synclinal valley, 16 km long and 6.5 km wide, situated in the Flinders range. The flat or slightly undulating valley bottom is walled in with red sandstone cliffs; along the watercourses and in damp depressions are *Eucalyptus camaldulensis* associations; grassy expanses in the basin which was formerly covered with *Callitris glauca*; the slopes are clothed in dense vegetation, *Eucalyptus morrisii* extending to the top of the hills and *E. intertaxta* and *Casuarina stricta* likewise covering some areas from the depression up to the higher elevations.

b) No information.

9. (34) Peebinga Wild Life Reserve.

II.   *a*) Status : total protection. The two farms formerly in the area have been evacuated.

         b) Area : 1,610 ha.

III.   *Date established :* 1940, when 2,435 ha in extent. Reduced to 1,610 ha when handed over to the Commissioners in 1962.

Tourism : undeveloped.

72

V.

Altitude : no information.

a) Part of the Mallee country, very similar to the Billiatt Reserve, No. 5 (30); the " red Mallee " *Eucalyptus oleosa* is common. There is a risk of shifting sand due to deforestation.

b) Kangaroo; mallee-fowl, western whipbird, mallee emu-wren *Stipiturus mallee,* shy heath wren, crested bell-bird *Oreoica gutturalis,* many raptors including Nankeen kestrel *Falco cenchroides,* little falcon *F. longipennis,* goshawk *Accipiter fasciatus,* spotted harrier *Circus assimilis,* wedge-tailed eagle *Uroaetus audax* and little eagle *Hieraetus morphnoides.*

c) Western whipbird.

10. (35) CHAUNCEYS LINE.

II.

a) Status : total protection but " some destruction of kangaroos has occurred ".

b) Area : 800 ha in two blocks, 240 (Ferries) and 560 (McDonald). Size reduced but " the last place in South Australia where *Leipoa,* the mallee-fowl, occurs in its native state ".

c) Staff : " local residents and police effectively combine to protect ". Supervised from Belair — " the roving W.R. officer pays regular visits ".

III.

Date established : 1956; this applies to the two linked Reserves, Ferries and McDonald, which were set up simultaneously and taken over by the Commissioners. There had previously been a small part of the area with the status of a Fauna Reserve since 1938.

Tourism : not extensive. No accommodation or facilities. Still no staff quarters.

IV.

Altitude : no information.

a) Comprises two adjacent Reserves, Ferries and McDonald, situated on the eastern flank of the Lofty Ranges; a sample of undulating and sandy countryside of the Mallee-broom bush *Eucalyptus incrassata* — *Melaleuca uncinata* association.

b) Kangaroo; mallee-fowl and other rare species of mallee country, wood swallows *Artamus* spp., white-winged triller *Lalage tricolor,* parrots, nightjars.

D. — WESTERN AUSTRALIA.

I.

Listed Areas : five.

1. (36) Stirling Ranges National Park.
2. (37) Nornalup National Park.
3. (38) Yanchep Park.
4. (39) Porongorups National Park.
5. (40) John Forrest National Park.

N.B. — Figures in brackets refer to the List number in the over-all Australian series.

AUSTRALIA

General Introduction :

Legislation : the Land Act, 1933-1958, is the actual instrument for the setting up of Natural Reserves. The latter are placed in three categories, A, B and C, National Parks being in category A. The Parks and Reserves Act of 1895, provided for the management of Reserves formerly promulgated by the Governor and, in particular, for the constitution of Committee or Boards of Management responsible locally for managing the Reserves.

Administration : a National Parks Board, responsible to the Ministry of Agriculture. Note also the " Fauna Protection Advisory Committee " of the same Government department. The Board is in fact responsible for the management of only a small fraction of the reserved areas established under the Land Act (which total 20 million hectares). The Board is assisted by local Committees.

Land tenure : Crown land.

Tourism : well-developed in some areas.

Research : there is no central organisation for the scientific investigation of the National Parks.

Details : application of criteria (II), general information (III) and description (IV) :

II.   1. (36) STIRLING RANGES NATIONAL PARK.

a) Status : total protection. Undisturbed except for " clearing of tracks and sign-posting ".

b) Area : 108,000 ha.

c) Staff : one " Ranger, provided with a 4-wheel drive vehicle and caravan, who constantly patrols... ". This is well below the criterion standard, but has been accepted at the suggestion of the local authorities, on the grounds of the high mobility of the Ranger and the uninhabited character of the area.

d) Budget : unspecified, but the minimum of $ 5,000, which would satisfy the criterion, is covered by the Ranger's salary, transport and travelling.

III.   *Date established :* 1913.

Tourism : a build-up is expected, but so far not very apparent. Access is by road (56 km from Albany) and there is a good network within the Park; also tourist footpaths. No accommodation on the spot.

IV.   *Altitude :* sea level to 1,090 m.

a) A region of high relief, with some peaks of over 1,000 m. Most of the reserve has been denuded of trees, but here and there on the lower slopes stands of Wandoo, Jarrah and Marri, *Eucalyptus redunca* var. *elata, E. marginata* and *E. calophylla,* are to be found.

b) The frog *Metacrinia nichollsi,* trapdoor spiders *Eucyrtops riparia* and *Aganippe occidentalis,* land snails *Bothriembryon indutus* and *B. kingii.*

2. (37) NORNALUP NATIONAL PARK.

II.   *a*) Status : theoretically total protection, but great difficulty has been experienced in preventing clandestine and illegal erection of holiday chalets in the remoter areas of the Park.

74

b) Area : 13,200 ha, some sections separated from the main block.

c) Staff : " a resident Ranger; further supervision provided by Forest Department personnel ".

d) Budget : as required for the support of the staff.

III.   *Date established :* not known.

Tourism : there is a good potential, witness the illegal incursion of persons building " more or less permanent holiday cottages on Crown land ". Steps are being taken by the Department of Lands and the Town Planning Board to regularise these occupancies and to replace haphazard incursions by planned and controlled development. The first Plan is being launched at Coalmine Beach (a yachting centre).

IV.   *Altitude :* sea level.

a) Varied landscape of beaches, dunes and hills. The hills which command the inlets of the southern coast are clothed in forest of giant eucalyptus — the chief species being *Eucalyptus diversicolor, E. jacksoni* and *E. guilfoylei,* with a thick undergrowth of acacia, banksia and casuarina; the coastal dunes have an especially rich flora.

b) Grey kangaroo *Macropus canguru,* short-nosed bandicoot *Thylacis obesulus;* the frog *Crinia laevis* (occurring nowhere else in Western Australia).

3. (38) YANCHEP PARK.

II.   *a)* Status : most of the area is totally protected, the remainder being " developed for the cultivation of native plants and the display of native animals ". also sports facilities.

b) Area : 2,664 ha.

c) Staff : « a dozen resident staff ».

d) Budget : to cover staff.

III.   *Date established :* 1905; also called the " Yanchep Park and Beach Reserve ".

Tourism : very active, Perth being only 48 km away. Main facilities are sports grounds, picnic sites and swimming baths. Animals reared in semi-captive conditions include koala, emu, kangaroo and many birds. There is a modern hotel and guest-houses, with an influx of up to 200,000 visitors a year. Celebrated caves.

IV.   *Altitude :* sea level.

a) A characteristic sample of this part of the coast, sandy deposit on calcareous base; dominant tree is *Eucalyptus gomphocephala,* with an undergrowth of banksia, casuarina, acacia and other species; caves.

b) Grey kangaroo, possum, *Trichosurus vulpecula,* koala *Phascolarctos cinereus;* emu *Dromaius novae-hollandiae;* cave fauna.

4. (39) PORONGORUPS NATIONAL PARK.

II.   *a)* Status : total protection.

b) Area : 2,154 ha.

c) Staff : patrols carried out by a Ranger from the Stirling Ranges National Park.

d) Budget : covers element of ranger's expenses.

III.   *Date established :* not known.

Tourism : the situation is the same as that for the adjoining Stirling Ranges National Park, No. 1 (36) above. There are some fine view points.

IV.   *Altitude :* maximum 634 m.

a) A region of rather high relief. The Karri forest (*Eucalyptus diversicolor*) grows up to 60 m tall; here and there are forests of Jarrah *E. marginata* mixed with Marri *E. calophylla* and *E. cornuta* (which grows to about 10-15 m in height).

b) Fauna typical of the south-west; remarkable as the only area where the geographical range of the two tree frogs *Hyla moorei* and *H. cyclorhynchus* overlap.

5. (40) JOHN FORREST NATIONAL PARK.

II.   *a*) Status : similar to that of Yanchep Park.

b) Area : 1,565 ha (the proximity of Perth taken into account to justify retention).

c) Staff : 12 units, mainly employed on tourist and recreational organisation.

d) Budget : stated to exceed considerably the level required under the criterion.

III.   *Date established :* 1900.

Tourism : similar to that of the Yanchep Park; about half the distance of that Park from Perth, namely 24 km. Sundry facilities, such as lawns, sports grounds, swimming-baths, picnic sites, large car-parks. A huge influx of visitors at holiday times.

IV.   *Altitude :* near sea level.

a) Occupies the coastal plain bordering the Indian Ocean; a wooded region, which constitutes the northern extremity of the Jarrah zone of the Darling Ranges; in addition to *Eucalyptus marginata,* the other dominant species are *E. calophylla, E. redunca* var. *elata* and, in the inundation zones along the watercourses, *E. rudis*; the undergrowth is composed of banksias, casuarinas and acacias.

b) No information.

E. — NORTHERN TERRITORY.

I.   **Listed Areas :** four.

1. (41) Ayers Rock and Mount Olga National Park.
2. (42) Katherine Gorge National Park.
3. (43) Howard Springs Recreation Reserve.
4. (44) Cobourg Peninsula Sanctuary.

N.B. — Figures in brackets refer to the List number in the over-all Australian series.

General Introduction :

Legislation : reserves were established by Proclamation of the Governor-General of the Commonwealth of Australia, made under the Crown Lands Ordinance (1924, 1931, 1939 and 1952). A National Parks and Gardens Ordinance was enacted in 1955.

Administration : the first three of the listed areas are under the management of a Northern Territory Reserves Board, established by the above-mentioned National Parks and Gardens Ordinance of 1955. The fourth area, classified as a " Sanctuary ", is the responsibility of the Chief Inspector of Wildlife of the Directorate of Annual Industry at Darwin.

Land tenure : all land is in public ownership.

Tourism : beginning to be developed.

Research : no central organisation.

Details : application of criteria (II), general information (III) and description (IV) :

1. (41) AYERS ROCK AND MOUNT OLGA NATIONAL PARK.

II.
    a) Status : total protection. Uninhabited, arid area.

    b) Area : 124,672 ha.

    c) Staff : full-time curator and assistant curator, part-time clerk; " this staff is adequate for our purposes " (Sept. 1965).

    d) Budget : U.S. $ 28,000 (1964-1965).

III.
    Date established : 1958.

    Tourism : 445 km from Alice Springs by the land route, which is now possible for ordinary vehicles; can be reached by air by a daily service during 9 months of the year and a thrice weekly service during the remaining 3 months. Camping facilities available (shower-baths). Due to its aridity, only a very small part of the Park is usually frequented by visitors, who tend to concentrate at the two points which give their name to the Park. Visitors must travel by car, not on foot.

IV.
    Altitude : 500-850 m.

    a) Ayers Rock and Mount Olga are two contrasting features, the former an enormous monolith rising nearly vertically to over 330 m from a plinth of sandy desert, its base measuring about 3.6×2.4 km. The " Olga " group is about 32 km to the west and comprises a number of great monoliths occupying an area 7.2×4.8 km. Rock paintings have been discovered. The vegetation is composed of mallee, acacia, spinifex and the eucalypts known as desert oak, bloodwood and ironwood.

    b) Kangaroo, dingo *Canis dingo*, bandicoot; emu.

2. (42) KATHERINE GORGE NATIONAL PARK.

II.
    a) Status : total protection. A deeply entrenched canyon; uninhabited.

    b) Area : 22,424 ha.

    c) Staff : " full-time staff planned for 1966-1967 financial year ".

    d) Budget : U.S. $ 6,720.

III.   *Date established :* not known.

Tourism : very restricted.

IV.   *Altitude :* 120 m.

a) The gorge cuts through red and brown quartzites, which form a wall nearly 60 m high; the gorge is 90 m broad and extends for 24 km; some vegetation in the fissures of the cliffs.

b) Wallaby; *Crocodilus johnstonii*; parrots, finches.

3. (43) HOWARD SPRINGS RECREATION RESERVE.

II.   *a*) Status : total protection is accorded to this " rare jungle patch ", which is in the vicinity of an area visited by large numbers of tourists.

b) Area : 280 ha, well below the criterion standard, but accepted because of the proximity of Darwin, the interest of the biotope and the fact that it is properly looked after and conserved.

c) Staff : 3 units, a Curator and two full-time assistants.

d) Budget : U.S. $ 34,850 (1965-1966).

III.   *Date established :* 1952.

Tourism : facilities for visitors, mostly from nearby Darwin, include a dam which is used for bathing and picnic sites.

IV.   *Altitude :* 15-30 m.

a) Subtropical vegetation (eucalypts and jungle); watercourses and springs.

b) Wallaby; finches, parrots.

4. (44) COBOURG PENINSULA SANCTUARY.

II.   *a*) Status : stricter than that of other Northern Territory reserves; total protection, uninhabited; entry by permit only.

b) Area : 192,660 ha.

c) Staff : " one ranger full-time and periodical visits of other *ex officio* rangers ". Barely satisfies the criterion, but the uninhabited character of the area may be taken into account.

d) Budget : U.S. $ 16,100 in 1965 (as compared with the $ 9,600 required by the criterion) : " anticipated that budgetory expenditure will increase in 1966 and 1967 ".

III.   *Date established :* 1924, when it was much smaller in size and classified as a " Native Flora and Fauna Reserve ". Became a Wildlife Sanctuary embracing the whole peninsula in 1964, under the Northern Territory Wildlife Ordinance 1963.

Tourism : 190 km from Darwin and accessible only by sea (no road), which presents a considerable obstacle to tourists. The particular interest of this area, apart from the local (marsupial) fauna, is that it supports the wild descendants of animals introduced from Asia in 1830. At the moment no tourist developments are contemplated; visits may only be made on the authority of the Chief Inspector of Wildlife and in 1965 there were less than 30 visitors altogether, 8 of them being members of a scientific expedition.

V.   *Altitude :* 6-75 m.

a) A very large peninsula, 6 to 15 metres above the surface of the sea, but with two small hills 75 m high; eucalyptus forest, and a tropical type of forest which is in effect a continuation of the mangroves along the coast to the south.

b) Kangaroo, various small marsupials; asiatic buffalo *Bubalus bubalis* introduced; rich avifauna (grebe, heron, ibis, swan, duck, falcon, pigeon and the scrub fowl *Megapodius reinwardt tumulus*).

F. — QUEENSLAND.

Listed Areas : twenty-five.

1. (45) Daintree Gorge (or Windsor Table) National Park.
2. (46) Eungella National Park.
3. (47) Hinchinbrook Island National Park.
4. (48) Bellenden Ker National Park.
5. (49) Carnavon National Park.
6. (50) Salvator Rosa National Park.
7. (51) Mount Elliott National Park.
8. (52) Lamington National Park.
9. (53) Conway Range National Park.
10. (54) Whitsunday Island National Park.
11. (55) Bunya Mountains National Park.
12. (56) Robinson Gorge National Park.
13. (57) Crystal Creek National Park.
14. (58) Mount Barney National Park.
15. (59) Hook Island National Park.
16. (60) Isla Gorge National Park.
17. (61) Mount Walsh National Park.
18. (62) Flinders Island Group (or Maclear) National Park.
19. (63) Barron Falls National Park.
20. (64) Castle Rock National Park.
21. (65) Palmerston National Park.
22. (66) Magnetic Island National Park.
23. (67) Bald Rock National Park.
24. (68) Gloucester Island National Park.
25. (69) Thornton National Park.

N.B. — Figures in brackets refer to the List number in the over-all Australian series.

General Introduction :

Queensland has no less than 74 national parks of over 400 ha or 1,000 acres in size, all of them well supervised, and, in addition, several hundred " scenic areas " (of less than 1,000 acres), which are also under strict supervision. The 25 listed areas are those which exceed 2,000 ha and thus satisfy the ICNP criterion. The application of this criterion has in a few instances seemed rather arbitrary, since some areas which have thereby been excluded might well deserve a place on the List if " worthiness were judged on quality and not necessarily on extent ", as one of our Brisbane informants remarked. It should also be noted that out of some twenty areas in the wet tropical lowlands of north Queensland recently recommended for reservation as samples of a habitat type unique in Australia, four totalling nearly 8,500 ha were reported in a letter of December 1968 to be now established as full National Parks.

With regard to staff and budget, it has not been possible to give details park by park, since in many cases units or items are concerned with several parks and scenic areas. But taken as a whole the criteria seem fairly well satisfied. Thus the total protected area is of the order of 470,000 ha, which to meet the criteria would require 47 staff units and the budgetary equivalent of U.S. $ 23,500; in fact, the total staff numbers nearly 60 and the total budget exceeds $AU 170,000 or about U.S. $ 190,000, of which, according to information dated January, 1966, about half could be attributed to the 25 Parks included in the List.

Since the status of all Parks is that of total protection, this is not quoted individually and only the area of each park and, in some instances, information on the quality of supervision are quoted.

Legislation : the Forestry Act 1959, which includes in its sub-title the phrase : " ... to make provision for the Management of National Parks and Scenic Areas ". Also relevant is the Fauna Conservation Act 1952, which invests all National Parks automatically with the status of faunal sanctuaries.

Administration : Department of Forestry.

Land tenure : all the land is under government control, but is not specifically rated as Crown Land, but more as " vacant land ".

Tourism : this has been well developed under the initiative of the Forestry Department, which is responsible for building roads (carefully sited), making foot-paths and improving the facilities generally. In view of the large number of parks and scenic areas, development has to proceed in gradual stages and of the 25 listed Parks only a dozen could yet be said to be fully equipped (details are given under each Park). Taking the parks and scenic areas as a whole, the annual incursion of visitors approaches the million mark. The general policy of the Department is to keep motor-traffic off the Park roads and limit movement to footpaths, which are often well signposted and the subject of descriptive commentaries in the pamphlets on sale to visitors. It is worth noting that the main flow of tourism tends to concentrate in some of the 48 small national parks not included in the List, most of which, as one would expect, are situated in populous areas and near the larger towns. A beginning has been made with interpretative services.

Research : a good deal of work is being done, but not yet on a planned system which would be apppropriate to the network of national parks in this State. On 6 January 1966, a zoologist was appointed to strengthen the Parks staff. Research is also encouraged by the National Parks Association, a private organisation.

Details : application of criteria (II), general information (III) and description (IV) :

1. (45) DAINTREE GORGE (OR WINDSOR TABLE) NATIONAL PARK.

II. *b*) Area : 58,823 ha.

c) and *d*) Staff and budget : no provision; area is protected by inaccessibility.

II.   *Date established :* 1962; modified in 1965.

Tourism : just beginning. Very difficult of access. No accommodation or other facilities.

V.   *Altitude :* 320-1,290 m.

a) A plateau with a ruling altitude of 1,050 m, situated on the eastern side of the Great Dividing Range; many gorges and waterfalls, of which the most remarkable are the Adeline Falls, a series of six falls dropping some 300 m; tropical Queensland forest.

b) No information.

2. (46) EUNGELLA NATIONAL PARK

I.   *b)* Area : 49,040 ha.

c) and *d)* Staff and budget : quite adequate; three full-time employees, plus outside assistance for part-time.

II.   *Date established :* 1941; modified in 1962.

Tourism : 37 km of footpaths; good tourist potential.

V.   *Altitude :* 320-1,244 m.

a) A mountainous area dominating the coast in central Queensland; streams, falls and cascades; tree-fern jungle, palms and vines on eastern slopes and in the gorges; eucalyptus forest on the western scarp of the Clarke Range; fine panoramas.

b) Many bird species; one cave provides one of the few known nesting-places in Queensland of the grey swiftlet *Collocalia francica.*

3. (47) HINCHINBROOK ISLAND NATIONAL PARK.

I.   *b)* Area : 39,348 ha.

c) and *d)* Staff and budget : no resident staff (a totally uninhabited island).

II.   *Date established :* 1932; modifications 1960.

Tourism : no developments yet, except for " some facilities at main landing points ".

V.   *Altitude :* sea level to 1,095 m.

a) Regarded as the second largest uninhabited island in the world (after Isle Royale in Lake Superior in the State of Michigan); beaches, slopes covered with bush and humid forest, many small waterfalls and peaks, forming a wonderful backdrop to the famous Hinchinbrook Channel.

b) No information.

4. (48) BELLENDEN KER NATIONAL PARK.

I.   *b)* Area : 32,431 ha.

c) and *d)* Staff and budget : no resident staff.

II.   *Date established :* 1921; modified in 1960.

Tourism : no facilities as yet.

81

IV.   *Altitude :* 30-1,608 m.

a) The mountainous region of the Bellenden Ker Range, very precipitous and comprising the highest summits in Queensland; humid tropical forest; rich vegetation including ferns and orchids. Traces of ancient aboriginal tribes.

b) Tree kangaroos *Dendrolagus* spp., bats, rodents, marsupials; a rich avifauna (200 species) of which the most interesting are the golden bower-bird *Prionodura newtoniana*, tooth-billed bower-bird *Scenopoeetes dentirostris*, red boobook owl *Ninox lurida*, chowchilla *Orthonyx spaldingi*, brush turkey *Alectura lathami*, scrub fowl *Megapodius reinwardt yorki*, spotted cat-bird *Ailuroedus melanotus* and cassowary *Casuarius australis*.

5. (49) CARNAVON NATIONAL PARK.

II.   *b)* Area : 26,930 ha.

c) and *d)* Staff and budget : quite adequate.

III.   *Date established :* 1938; modified in 1954.

Tourism : a good potential. Facilities exist, including well-equipped camp-sites.

IV.   Altitude : 320-970 m.

a) Part of the eastern side of the Great Dividing Range, with sandstone cliffs and deep gorges; the gorge cut by the Carnavon Creek is a cleft 32 km long and 45 to 300 m wide, enclosed by sandstone walls some 180 m high; there are many secondary gorges, narrow and deep, radiating from the main gorges; numerous caves; the vegetation is principally composed of an open forest of spotted eucalyptus; cabbage-palms are common; tree ferns are also to be found and, in the shadier places, various orchids.

b) Platypus *Ornithorhynchus anatinus* *, several species of wallaby (including the brush-tailed rock wallaby *Petrogale penicillata* * and pretty-face wallaby *Protemnodon elegans*), grey kangaroo, " possum " *Trichosurus vulpecula*, koala *Phascolarctos cinereus*, little northern dasyure *Satanellus halucatus*.

c) Brush-tailed rock wallaby.

6. (50) SALVATOR ROSA NATIONAL PARK.

II.   *b)* Area : 26,272 ha.

c) and *d)* Staff and budget : no resident staff as yet, but this is a remote Park in an uninhabited area.

III.   *Date established :* 1957; modified in 1963.

Tourism : no facilities yet.

IV.   *Altitude :* 320-700 m.

a) In the eastern part of the Great Dividing Range, around the source of the Nogoa river; many waterfalls (Major Mitchell, Belinda, etc.); the thin overlay of sandstone has eroded into interesting configurations; the discharge from the springs is more than 500,000 litres a day.

b) No information.

7. (51) MOUNT ELLIOTT NATIONAL PARK.

II.   *b)* Area : 24,301 ha.

c) and *d)* Staff and budget : no resident staff; patrols.

II.   *Date established :* 1940; modified in 1961.

    Tourism : no facilities yet, but a good potential.

V.   *Altitude :* 170-1,213 m.

    a) Rocky and fairly steep slopes of a granitic character; the forest is principally eucalyptus, but there are a few islands of humid forest in sheltered folds.

    b) No information.

8. (52) LAMINGTON NATIONAL PARK.

I.   *b)* Area : 19,631 ha.

    c) and *d)* Staff and budget : very adequate; 8 full-time units, allocated between the two main stations.

II.   *Date established :* 1915; modified in 1963.

    Tourism : 130 km of marked footpaths. Various equipment and ancillary facilities. A good potential.

V.   *Altitude :* 250-1,190 m.

    a) A mountainous area, with many peaks, gorges and waterfalls (over 500 of them); the greater part of the Park is covered in rich humid forest, with tree ferns and orchids; at higher levels there is forest of antarctic beech *Nothofagus moorei* and eucalyptus, and at the summit heaths and stunted eucalypts.

    b) A rich avifauna, including Prince Albert's lyre-bird *Menura alberti* *, brush turkey, regent bower-bird *Sericulus chrysocephalus,* satin bower-bird *Ptilonorhynchus violaceus,* paradise rifle-bird *Ptiloris paradiseus,* green cat-bird *Ailuroedus crassirostris,* eastern bristle-bird *Dasyornis brachypterus,* rufous scrubbird *Atrichornis rufescens,* seven species of pigeon, six species of parrot, many cockatoos, kinglets and honey-eaters.

9. (53) CONWAY RANGE NATIONAL PARK.

I.   *b)* Area : 19,449 ha.

    c) and *d)* Staff and budget : patrols only.

II.   *Date established :* 1962.

    Tourism : good potential, but no facilities as yet.

V.   *Altitude :* sea level to 561 m.

    a) Mountainous area, with slopes which are steep in places going up from sea level through humid forest to drier forest country of eucalyptus and hoop pine *Araucaria*; these forested hills form the main background of Whitsunday Passage and the Whitsunday Islands archipelago.

    b) No information.

10. (54) WHITSUNDAY ISLAND NATIONAL PARK.

I.   *b)* Area : 10,926 ha.

    c) and *d)* Staff and budget : no resident staff in this uninhabited island; it is visited by patrols from the neighbouring Long, Linderman and South Molle islands.

II.   *Date established :* 1936; modified in 1944.

    Tourism : except for a few " facilities ", not yet developed.

IV.   *Altitude :* sea level to 438 m.

a) One of the Whitsunday group of islands; a wild area, with steep hills covered with hoop pines and jungle; there is a beach of fine sand on the eastern coast. At higher elevations there is a little humid forest interspersed with stands of *Araucaria*.

b) No information.

11. (55) BUNYA MOUNTAINS NATIONAL PARK.

II.   *b*) Area : 9,806 ha, subdivided into adjacent blocks belonging to two different Forest divisions, recently (1969) enlarged to 12,092 ha.

c) and *d*) Staff and budget : quite adequate; two full-time employees.

III.   *Date established :* 1908; modified in 1960.

Tourism : good potential, some facilities including 24 km of signposted foot-paths and picnic sites.

IV.   *Altitude :* 630-1,135 m.

a) A mountain chain forming part of the Great Dividing Range, splendid " bunya " (*Araucaria bidwillii*) forest, also broadleafed forest of red gum and " yellow stringybark ", humid tropical forest, with some conifers, and a drier type of tropical forest; in the hills at the western foot of the range *Backhousia* scrub is found, from which there is a transition to an association of bottle-trees *Brachychiton rupestris* and cypress on Mount Kangaroo and the higher western slopes.

b) No information.

12. (56) ROBINSON GORGE NATIONAL PARK.

II.   *b*) Area : 8,903 ha.

c) and *d*) Staff and budget : no information.

III.   *Date established :* 1953; modified in 1963.

Tourism : access is difficult and the neighbouring region practically uninhabited. There are very few visitors and no facilities as yet.

IV.   Altitude : 320-600 m.

a) Part of the Expedition Range in the watershed of Robinson Creek; the Robinson Gorge itself is walled in by sandstone cliffs 180 m high; the Stackvale Creek Gorge which branches from the latter is similar; the forests are a mixture of eucalyptus, *Angophora, Callitris, Casuarina, Acacia, Livistona, Brachychiton, Xylomelum, Petalostigma, Exocarpus, Capparis, Owenia* and *Lysicarpus*.

b) No information.

13. (57) CRYSTAL CREEK NATIONAL PARK.

II.   *b*) Area : 7,060 ha (formerly slightly larger).

c) and *d*) Staff and budget : visited by patrols and the people who live nearby, being favourably disposed towards the Park, also assist in its supervision.

III.   *Date established :* 1952.

Tourism : not much developed, except for minor facilities, but with a good potential. Along the Park border a very picturesque motor-road leads to Mount Spec.

V.   *Altitude :* 50-960 m.

a) Covers the watershed of Crystal Creek, which is a permanent stream in a granitic massif; many waterfalls and cascades; forest is mainly eucalyptus, but downstream at lower elevations there are some scraps of humid forest; on the summit ridge high forest with a closed canopy (the only example of this type which remains in the area and is accessible to visitors); the characteristic plant is an epiphytic orchid *Phalaenopsis* sp.

b) No information.

14. (58) MOUNT BARNEY NATIONAL PARK.

I.   *b)* Area : 5,253 ha.

c) and *d)* Staff and budget : no permanent staff. The neighbourhood is fairly well populated, but access to the Park is not easy, and supervision and control by local volunteer effort is practicable.

II.   *Date established :* 1947.

Tourism : no facilities as yet.

V.   *Altitude :* 200-1,353 m.

a) A very hilly area with closed eucalyptus forest; Mount Barney is the second highest point in southern Queensland; the flora at higher elevations presents an interesting transition between coastal vegetation and that of the granitic belt situated on the other side of the watershed.

b) No information.

15. (59) HOOK ISLAND NATIONAL PARK.

I.   *b)* Area : 5,180 ha.

c) and *d)* Staff and budget : no permanent staff. Uninhabited. Looked after in the same way as Whitsunday National Park, No. 10 (54) above.

II.   *Date established :* 1936.

Tourism : no facilities as yet.

V.   *Altitude :* sea level to 453 m.

a) Mainly eucalyptus forest, with some large stands of *Araucaria* and some remnants of closed forest; precipitous slopes with rocky-sided hills; a part of the coast which recalls the Scandinavian fjordland.

b) No information.

16. (60) ISLA GORGE NATIONAL PARK.

I.   *b)* Area : 4,654 ha.

c) and *d)* Staff and budget : no staff. Uninhabited and fairly inaccessible area.

I.   *Date established :* 1964.

Tourism : no facilities as yet.

IV.
      Altitude : about 300 m.

      a) Mainly eucalyptus forest.

      b) No information.

17. (61) MOUNT WALSH NATIONAL PARK.

II.
      b) Area : 2,987 ha.

      c) and *d*) Staff and budget : no staff has been appointed.

III.
      Date established : 1947.

      Tourism : an area used by climbers, but no facilities.

IV.
      Altitude : 220-645 m.

      a) Very precipitous slopes and cliffs, with opportunities for mountaineering; dominant forest is eucalyptus, but there is a little humid forest and some *Araucaria*.

      b) No information.

18. (62) FLINDERS ISLAND GROUP NATIONAL PARK.

II.
      b) Area : 2,962 ha.

      c) and *d*) Staff and budget : no staff has been appointed.

III.
      Date established : 1939. The name of this Park, situated in the Maclear Parish in the extreme north of Queensland, has not been settled : Flinders, Stanley, Maclear, Blackwood, Denham Island are all used.

      Tourism : still no facilities in this totally uninhabited area.

IV.
      Altitude : sea level to 320 m.

      a) Group of small islands.

      b) No information.

19. (63) BARRON FALLS NATIONAL PARK.

II.
      b) Area : 2,833 ha.

      c) and *d*) Staff and budget : no staff has been appointed.

III.
      Date established : 1940.

      Tourism : good potential, but not yet developed. The Cairns-Kuranda railway traverses the Park and there is a motor-road into it, leading to a hydro-electric dam.

IV.
      Altitude : 30-678 m.

      a) A remarkable gorge, some 240 m deep, along which the Cairns-Kuranda railway passes; the gorge itself was formerly covered by dense closed forest, which is now rather degraded; the Barron Falls in the gorge are very picturesque but dry up in the dry season when the whole flow of water is diverted through the hydro-electric installation.

      b) No information.

20. (64) CASTLE ROCK NATIONAL PARK.

II.
      b) Area : 2,755 ha.

c) and *d*) Staff and budget : very adequate. The Park is near No. 23 (67) Bald Rock National Park and, with the purchase of a small 53 ha block, now adjoins it, so that both Parks can be looked after by one full-time ranger.

II.   *Date established :* 1932; modified in 1964.

Tourism : good potential, but no facilities as yet.

V.   *Altitude :* 930-1,267 m.

a) Granitic formation in a mountainous landscape, culminating in the Castle Rock; vegetation not very dense eucalyptus, banksia and acacia; an abundant flush of flowers in September-November.

b) Common wombat *Vombatus ursinus* * (specialised mainland form regarded by some as a distinct species from *Vombatus hirsutus*), " possum "; rich avifauna including the lyre-bird *Menura novae-hollandiae* *.

21. (65) PALMERSTON NATIONAL PARK.

I.   *b*) Area : 2,667 ha.

c) and *d*) Staff and budget : quite adequate; there is a resident ranger.

II.   *Date established :* 1941; modified in 1955.

Tourism : good potential; some facilities.

V.   *Altitude :* 750-1,090 m.

a) A sample of typical north Queensland jungle (humid tropical forest); many waterfalls.

b) A rich avifauna includes the noisy pitta *Pitta versicolor,* cassowary, rifle-bird, brush turkey and scrub-fowl.

22. (66) MAGNETIC ISLAND NATIONAL PARK.

II.   *b*) Area : 2,533 ha (about half the island).

c) and *d*) Staff and budget : quite adequate; includes a warden who also looks after a park on the mainland.

III.   *Date established :* 1954.

Tourism : good potential. A start has been made in providing facilities.

IV.   *Altitude :* sea level to 496 m.

a) Very hilly relief, with shingle promontories and bays with sandy beaches; there are coral reefs in some of the bays; dense vegetation.

b) No information.

23. (67) BALD ROCK NATIONAL PARK.

II.   *b*) Area : 2,489 ha.

c) and *d*) Staff and budget : quite adequate; see Castle Rock National Park, No. 20 (64) above.

III.   *Date established :* 1932; modified in 1964.

Tourism : good potential like No. 20 (64), but no facilities as yet.

IV.   *Altitude :* 750-1,090 m.

a) Mountainous landscape dominated by the Bald Rock; scattered eucalyptus, banksia and acacia vegetation; good flush of flowers September-November.

b) Wombat *Vombatus hirsutus* (=*ursinus*), " possum "; rich avifauna, including the lyre-bird *Menura novae-hollandiae* *.

24. (68) GLOUCESTER ISLAND NATIONAL PARK.

II.   *b*) Area : 2,460 ha.

c) and *d*) Staff and budget : no permanent staff. Uninhabited area.

III.   *Date established :* 1938.

Tourism : no facilities as yet.

IV.   *Altitude :* sea level to 580 m.

a) Rocky and mountainous island, with cliffs along the coast, except on the west, near Bona Bay, where landing is facilitated by a beach; there are some smaller beaches on the south-west; thin eucalyptus forest, with some scraps of more humid-type forest, and a little *Araucaria* in sheltered valleys.

b) No information.

25. (69) THORNTON NATIONAL PARK.

II.   *b*) Area : 2,331 ha.

c) and *d*) Staff and budget : no staff attached to this Park which is completely inaccessible.

III.   *Date established :* 1962.

Tourism : no facilities yet.

IV.   Altitude : 190-1,372 m.

a) The summit of Thornton mountain has no proper peak, but is a rather flat area of about 100 ha, which is always wet and is covered with heaths and bush; on the slopes there is dense humid forest, where some new species have recently been discovered and described, but the whole area needs much more investigation, since it certainly constitutes one of the most biologically interesting in Queensland.

b) No information.

G. — TASMANIA.

I.   **Listed Areas :** three.

1. (70) Cradle Mount and Lake St. Clair National Park.
2. (71) Mount Field National Park.
3. (72) Freycinet Peninsula National Park.

N.B. — Numbers in brackets refer to the List number in the over-all Australian series.

General Introduction :

Legislation : Scenery Preservation Act 1915.

Administration : Scenery Preservation Board of the Lands and Surveys Department with seven members. The executive authority is the Superintendent of Scenic Reserves and four " constituted subsidiary boards ", which share the work of assisting the central Board at Hobart on a geographical basis.

Tourism : the Board is responsible for tourist development, for which certain sums are allocated from its official budget, additional amounts being raised by loans.

Research : no central organisation.

Details : application of criteria (II), general information (III) and description (IV) :

1. (70) CRADLE MOUNT AND LAKE ST. CLAIR NATIONAL PARK.

I.

a) Status : total protection : " unspoiled scenic area, important watershed, hydro-electric power system ". A section of the forest land is still privately owned.

b) Area 133,250 ha.

c) Staff : 7 full-time units, plus additional labour.

d) Budget : U.S. $ 22,400, exclusive of salaries.

II.

Date established : 1922.

Land tenure : public land, except for the privately-owned forest enclosure.

Tourism : active. Access by road, with road and footpath network in the Park itself. A " Waldheim Self-Service Chalet ". Other accommodation on Lake St. Clair and a mountain hut on Mt. Cradle. Picnic sites. Other development in hand. About 15,000 visitors a year.

V.

Altitude : 600-1,600 m.

a) Part of the mountainous region of north-west Tasmania, culminating in Mt. Ossa (the highest peak in Tasmania); streams and lakes, Lake St. Clair being used as a reservoir; pine forest, eucalyptus, humid tropical forest, savannah and open plains vegetation; glacial landscape around Cradle Mount.

b) Platypus *Ornithorhynchus,* Tasmanian echidna *Tachyglossus setosus,* wild cat, Tasmanian devil *Sarcophilus harrisi,* bandicoot, four species of phalanger or " possum ", wombat *Vombatus ursinus,* wallaby, kangaroo; three species of snake.

c) The thylacine or Tasmanian tiger *Thylacinus cynocephalus,* of which there is a chance that some survive in the west of the Park, though there has been no definite record for 15 years (up to 1965).

2. (71) MOUNT FIELD NATIONAL PARK.

I.

a) Status : total protection; wood-cutting rights still exist in the western margin of the park; sport-fishing is permitted; there is a reservoir lake.

b) Area : 16,808 ha.

c) Staff : 6 units.

d) Budget : U.S. $ 15,600.

III.   *Date established :* 1916.

Tourism : due to proximity to Hobart (80 km), there is a large influx of visitors at weekends, for picnics, winter sports, skiing; numbers estimated at " dozens of thousands " in summer, " thousands " in winter.

IV.   *Altitude :* 150-1,400 m.

a) Mountainous zone, gashed by narrow valleys; lakes, waterfalls; many traces of ancient glaciation (moraines, valley bottom deposits especially of boulder clay); varied vegetation, including, notably, humid tropical forest, high level moorland bogs, and the following unusual species : *Biglandulosum anodopetalum, Nothofagus gunnii* and *Richea pandanifolia* (the latter endemic).

b) Platypus, echidna and all the other species listed above for No. 1 (70) Cradle Mount and Lake St. Clair National Park.

c) Thylacine could conceivably still exist in this Park also, but it is extremely unlikely.

3. (72) FREYCINET PENINSULA NATIONAL PARK.

II.   *a*) Legal status : total protection.

b) Area : 6,420 ha.

c) Staff : 3 units.

d) Budget : U.S. $ 4,300.

III.   *Date established :* 1916.

Tourism : being developed.

IV.   *Altitude :* sea level to 400 m.

a) Situated on the east coast of Tasmania; granite hills.

b) All the species mentioned for the other two Tasmanian Parks.

c) Thylacine : said to have been once sighted in the last 15 years.

H. — PAPUA AND NEW GUINEA.

I.   **Listed Areas :** nil.

* *
*

V.   **Areas excluded :**

A. — NEW SOUTH WALES.

1.	Bouddi National Park	512 ha
2.	Burrinjuck National Park	42 ha
3.	Fraser Park	861 ha
4.	Garrawarma Park	586 ha
5.	Glenbawn National Park	138 ha
6.	Heathcote Primitive Area	705 ha
7.	Keepit National Park	18 ha
8.	Lane Cove National Park	332 ha
9.	Mount Canobolas National Park	1,644 ha
10.	Wyangala National Park	427 ha
11.	The Barren Grounds Faunal Reserve	1,472 ha
12.	Nadgee Faunal Reserve	11,200 ha
13.	Kinchega National Park	42,400 ha

90

Of the above areas Nos. 1-10 have been omitted from the List, often regretfully and probably wrongly, because of failure to come up to the criterion standard of size. Nos. 11 and 12 are ruled out because their legal status is not strict enough. These 12 areas were included in E/3436. No. 13, situated in the dry area of western N.S.W. and particularly suited to kangaroo management, is excluded because full details are not yet available.

In addition four important new National Parks were established in 1969 :

14. Kanangra-Boyd National Park	39,272 ha
15. Cocopara National Park	8,232 ha
16. Barrington Tops National Park	13,671 ha
17. Morton (incorporating Barangary and Bundanoon)	20,705 ha

B. — VICTORIA.

1. Churchill National Park	191 ha
2. Yarra Valley National Park	240 ha
3. Bulga National Park	80 ha
4. Glenaladale National Park	150 ha

All these four areas are ruled out by size criterion. The first three areas were included in E/3436, as also was " Tower Hill National Park " (544 ha), which latter was reclassified as a Wild Life Reserve. In addition, mention must be made of Mount Eccles National Park, recently enlarged to 390 ha and also of three National Parks established in 1968/1969, but failing to satisfy the staff and budget criteria : Little Desert (34,748 ha), Lower Glenelg (8,960 ha) and Captain James Cook (2,680 ha).

C. — SOUTH AUSTRALIA.

Three large National Parks recently established (according to a 1970 report) details of which are still missing : Yumbarra (104,960 ha), Gammon Wilderness (11,264 ha), and Innes (6,020 ha).

Several smaller National Parks and a score of Wild Life Reserves are also excluded because their standard of supervision or because their size does not meet the criteria.

D. — WESTERN AUSTRALIA.

Some forty areas, most of which were listed as " national parks " in E/3436, but all of which have had to be eliminated for failing to satisfy one or other of the criteria. This is in agreement with the local Authorities, who mention that they " are gazetted as reserves but are not in any way controlled... ".

E. — NORTHERN TERRITORY.

1. Simpson's Gap National Park, included in E/3436 and now excluded because it is less than a square mile (260 ha) in extent and " staff is unlikely to be warranted for many years... ".

2. Devil's Marbles National Park, 1,808 ha; no supervision (" development limited to providing roadside fireplaces ").

3. Alice Springs Telegraph Station National Park, 440 ha. Although having the title of a National Park and well supervised (the headquarters of the Northern Territory Parks Service is in fact situated here), the area is excluded because it serves only to protect a site of historical interest.

4. Berry Spring Public Park and Recreation Reserve, 128 ha, and a number of other " natural monuments " of small dimensions or of little interest from the point of view of the conservation of natural environments.

5. Tanami Sanctuary, 14,490 square miles (3.8 million ha); excluded because " no staff stationed full-time in the area for the purpose of supervision ".

F. — QUEENSLAND.

1. In addition to the 25 listed areas and the 49 other National Parks referred to below several National Parks have been established since 1967, of which full details are not yet to hand: Simpson Desert (518,000 ha), on the border with South Australia and the Northern Territory, 3rd Brigalow Belt (10,568 ha), Southwood Brigalow Belt (6,992 ha), Cape Upstart (5,400 ha), Girraween (5,042 ha) and Herbert River Falls (2,400 ha).

2. Forty-nine National Parks ranging in size from 400 to 2,000 ha are excluded. As previously stated this omission is arbitrary and, in several particular cases, to be regretted. Reference should also be made to the General Introduction to the report on Queensland, where the recent establishment of four more National Parks in the humid tropical lowland zone is briefly recorded, bringing the total number of National Parks in the State to the very large total of 79.

3. 179 Scenic Areas, which, by definition, must be less than 400 ha in extent. Even in this category there are quite a number of areas thus excluded, which would have found a place in the List if they had been situated in certain other countries of the world.

G. — TASMANIA.

1. Four National Parks of over 2,000 ha, but excluded because the local Authorities reported (November 1965) that " they are unstaffed and therefore not effectively policed " :

Lake Pedder National Park	23,600 ha
Ben Lomond National Park	15,800 ha
Frenchman's Cap National Park	10,151 ha
Hartz Mountains National Park	8,920 ha

2. One National Park, Mount Barrow, 453 ha, excluded because it does not meet the size criterion.

3. Mount Strzelecki Mountain Reserve, 3,400 ha, excluded because there is no information about supervisory staff.

4. Twelve " Coastal Reserves " varying in size between one and 640 ha.

5. Four " Waterfall Reserves " of between 20 and 310 ha.

6. Four " River Reserves ".

7. Four " Cave Reserves ".

8. Four " Scenic Roads ".

9. Seven " Fern Gullies and Forests " of between a half and 79 ha.

All the above areas were listed in E/3436, but do not meet the conditions which have to be satisfied to earn them a place in the present list.

H. — PAPUA AND NEW GUINEA.

1. One National Park, Wariarata, 6,562 ha, established 1967 under the National Parks and Gardens Ordinance 1966; not yet meeting the criteria of effective management.

6. AUSTRIA

Listed Areas : six.

A. — STRICT NATURAL RESERVES.
   1. Rothwald.

B. — RESERVES (NATURSCHUTZPARKE).
   2. Tauern.

C. — INTERMEDIATE.
   3. The reserves of the Neusiedlersee and Seewinkel.

D. — PARTIAL RESERVES (NATURSCHUTZGEBIETE).
   4. Karwendelschutzgebiet.
   5. Grossglockner and Pasterze mit Gamsgrube.
   6. Lainzer Tiergarten im Wienerwald.

General Introduction :

The preparation of the report on Austria and the choice of a fair sample of areas which could properly be included in the United Nations List have proved to be very difficult. If the criteria adopted for selection were strictly applied, the results would inadequately reflect the considerable national effort to preserve natural species, associations and landscape in the face of the rapid economic development of a country in which the population averages some 100 inhabitants to the km². Account has also to be taken of the fact that the physical geography of Austria is unsuited to the establishment of strict nature reserves because of the inherent characteristics of the two zones into which it is divided — on the one hand, the habitable areas, which are densely populated and where there is no room for such reserves, and on the other hand, the mountains, where conservation of natural associations which merit protection can best be achieved not by stopping agricultural exploitation, grazing, etc., but, on the contrary, by taking steps to see that such human activities continue on the same basis as in the past.

93

Furthermore, when the long list of areas included in E/3436 was studied, it became clear that protective measures adopted in Austria are of very variable quality; it was not easy to find areas where a sufficiently strict legal status has been duly enforced by the authorities and supported by the requisite staff and funds.

The same procedure has, therefore, been followed as in the case of the German Federal Republic and a somewhat arbitrary choice (which can no doubt be improved upon in future) has had to be made with the help of the competent Austrian authorities. In the absence of complete information, however, it has not been possible to indicate how the criteria of effective operation (staff and budget) apply to each of the six areas included in the List.

For the purposes of selection these fall into four groups :

A. — One reserve which meets all the ICNP criteria : legal status, area and effective operation. Some other reserves of a similar standard exist, but they are too small in size.

B. — A complex of mountain country which — like the Lüneburger Heide in Germany — has been designated a " Naturschutzpark ". It qualifies in size, but is not kept under surveillance although human exploitation is inhibited by the nature of the terrain. Consequently it cannot truly be regarded as " protected ".

C. — A group of areas, usually referred to by the very well-known name of the lake region in which they are situated : some of the reservations satisfy the criterion of status and effectiveness, but they do not meet requirements in respect of size.

D. — Three " Naturschutzgebiete ", which do not in fact satisfy the criterion of adequate legal status, but are included *pro forma* so that their main features can be described. There are a number of other areas of the same type, which could equally well have been chosen in place of the three examples selected.

Legislative Status : under the Austrian constitution each Province has autonomous powers in regard to conservation measures. Central Government legislation only applies in Provinces which have not passed their own legislation, which in some cases has only been done quite recently. In Burgenland, for example, Central Government legislation was only abolished and replaced by a new nature preservation law in 1961. It is by virtue of this 1961 legislation that an ordinance of 1962 placed the protection of the Neusiedlersee upon a new basis.

Administration : the areas are all administered by the Provincial Forest Departments, unless otherwise noted.

A. — STRICT NATURAL RESERVES.

Details : application of criteria (II), general information (III) and description (IV) :

1. ROTHWALD (Lower Austria).

II.   *a*) Status : strict nature reserve. Uninhabited forest; no exploitation. Movement through the area is controlled. Is situated within the Landschaftschutzgebiet Oetscher und Dürrenstein (36,000 ha), a sparsely inhabited mountain area.

b) Area : 600 ha.

c) and *d*) Staff and budget : the reserve is privately owned and under the supervision of the owners.

GIUM, Genk R.   (photo : Van Houtte)

BELGIUM, Genk R.   (photo : Studio N

AH, Kinabalu N.P.

(photo : B. Harrison)

CAMBODGE, Angkor N.P.   (photo : Ou-Ki

...ADA, Banff N.P.   (photo : M. Leiska)

...ADA, Riding Mountain N.P.   (photo : National and Historic Parks Branch)

CANADA, Mt. Revelstoke N.P.

(photo : National and Historic Parks Br

NADA, Waterton Lakes N.P.

NADA, Cape Breton Highlands N.P.

CANADA, Prince Albert N.P.   (photo : National and Historic Parks B

I.   *Date established :* 1942, as a part of the Landschaftschutzgebiet Oetscher und Dürrenstein created in 1940.

Land tenure and tourism : privately owned forests. The owners take great interest in the management of the reserve, but are prepared to authorise visits.

V.   *Altitude :* 1,000-1,500 m.

a) Largest virgin forest in Central Europe; beech, fir, spruce.

b) Forest fauna.

B. — RESERVES (NATURSCHUTZPARKE).

2. TAUERN NATURSCHUTZPARK (Salzburg).

a) Legal status : zone protected *de facto* against exploitation by its inaccessible character and lack of economic value. Comprises a number of noncontiguous pieces of land, acquired by private organisations and by the Federal Forest Service.

b) Area :

(i) The Tauern Naturschutzpark proper, owned by the Verein Naturschutzpark of Stuttgart — about 5,000 ha;

(ii) an as yet unnamed sector, owned by the Federal Forest Service (Österreichischen Bundesforte) — about 9,000 ha;

(iii) also unnamed, owned by the Österreichischen Alpenverein — a little over 20,000 ha.

c) and *d)* Staff and Budget : none; the area may, however, be given the status of an National Park or " Naturpark " of the German pattern.

Date established : the original 1,200 ha of the Stuttgart Verein Naturschutzpark sector was bought in 1913; the Alpenverein sector in 1938-1939. However, there has long been a proposal that a 130,000 ha protected area should be established with status varying from sector to sector, and this was reported (1965) to be again under active consideration.

Tourism : alpine facilities; no special organisation.

Altitude : 1,000-3,674 m.

a) High mountains of Tauern, the highest point being the summit of the Gross-Venediger; glacial formations; forests mainly coniferous; spruce, silver fir *Abies alba,* pine, larch.

b) Alpine fauna, including red deer *Cervus elaphus,* chamois *R. rupicapra,* marmot *M. marmota,* varying hare *Lepus timidus*; ptarmigan *Lagopus mutus,* Bonelli's warbler *Phylloscopus bonelli,* alpine pipit *Anthus spinoletta* and snow finch *Fringilla nivalis.*

C. — INTERMEDIATE.

3. NEUSIEDLERSEE AND SEEWINKEL RESERVES (Burgenland).

a) Status : region of great scientific and ecological value, threatened for several reasons — level of the lake depends on the outflow located in Hungary; invasion by water plants, especially *Phragmites,* and the modification of " puszta " by agricultural development; reed cutting with heavy tractors; prospecting for oil; tourist and vacation development (roads, hotels, cottages).

95

4

Since 1935, some measure of protection has been given. A Landschaftschutz-gebiet (landscape protection zone) status applies to a wide geographical area, but is of limited practical significance. On the other hand, the Austrian Federation for Nature Conservation (Österrechischer Naturschutzbund), by the purchase of certain small areas, mainly consisting of the water surface of the Lacken or alkaline ponds, had established by 1966 about a dozen reserves which fully satisfy the ICNP criteria. Various intermediate measures have included the setting aside of an area west of Seewinkel in 1936, as a separate "Naturbanngebiet", while, since 1966, conservation planning has been greatly stimulated by the activities of the World Wildlife Fund (Austrian National Appeal) which have led to the leasing or securing of hunting rights over additional key areas, which it is hoped ultimately to purchase and make into full reserves.

b) Area : the Austrian sector of the Neusiedlersee extends over 35,000 ha (open water 17,000 ha). The Landscape Protection Zone covers practically the whole area. The reserves owned by the Nature Conservation Federation amount to c. 1,000 ha, the rented area is 440 ha and the area over which control of hunting has been obtained c. 1,500 ha.

c) Staff : four professional guards appointed by the government of Burgenland. Also biological station staff.

d) Budget : covers staff salaries and postings.

III.   *Date established :*

(i) Five legal enactments, dated 20 August 1936, set aside certain zones as "Banngebiet", but ceased to have effect on 31 December 1945;

(ii) the dozen reserves owned by the Austrian Nature Conservation Federation were declared under Ordinances of 1 August 1952 (five) and 7 March 1957 (seven), under the title of "Pachtgebiete" (leased-territory);

(iii) an Ordinance by the Governor of Lower Danube, dated 30 May 1940, placed the lake area and Seewinkel under the status of Landschaftsschutzgebiet. This was confirmed on 15 June 1962 by new legislation.

Administration : the Government of Burgenland has set up a joint planning board for the Neusiedlersee and also a Nature Conservation Commission.

Research : in 1950 the Neusiedlersee biological station was founded, but destroyed by fire in 1960. It was not reconstructed, but has in effect been replaced by new station at Rust (on the west bank) which is a branch of the Wilhelminerberg Biological Station of Vienna. Effective protection has been given by the Federal Government to one of the west bank heronries. Lake museum and ornithological observatory at Neusiedel. Numerous scientific studies have been made of the remarkable biotopes of this area and there has been a great effort, at both the national and international level, to make its conservation more effective.

IV.   *Altitude :* 180 m.

a) The drainage system of the Neusiedlersee constitutes the only "lake-steppe" in Central Europe, and includes a variety of saline associations : the wetland vegetation has affinities with that of the Black Sea; some survivals from the glacial period, such as the langwort or white false helleborine *Veratrum album* (Liliaceae). These species still occur in less saline places, despite post-glacial reafforestation. The hydrochemical diversity of the alkaline ponds of Seewinkel creates unique conditions for both flora and fauna.

b) Big colonies of breeding birds, the most spectacular of which are purple heron *Ardea purpurea*, great white heron *Egretta alba*, and spoonbill *Platalea leucorodia*. Around the lake and especially in the Seewinkel, important breeding grounds of Anatidae, Rallidae, Laridae and waders, great numbers of which also pass through on migration, while the grassy flats are one of the main wintering grounds of grey geese *Anser* spp. and other wildfowl. The area is also one of the best in Central Europe for seeing raptors, including white-tailed eagle *Haliaetus albicilla,* the imperial eagle *Aquila heliaca* and lesser spotted eagle *Aquila pomarina,* and altogether some 300 species of birds have been recorded; reptiles include the field adder *Vipera ursinii.*

D. — PARTIAL RESERVES (NATURSCHUTZGEBIETE).

4. KARWENDELSCHUTZGEBIET (Tyrol).

a) Status : the ancient form of land use of this sparsely inhabited country has been maintained in order to preserve the existing biological balance. Cattle grazing and controlled hunting (to keep the numbers of wild animals in check) are permitted.

b) Area : 72,000 ha.

c) and *d*) Staff and budget : supervision undertaken by the forest guards of Tyrol.

Date established : 1933 and 1943.

Altitude : 1,100-2,756 m.

a) Part of the calcareous mountain ranges of the Alps extending north from Innsbruck.

b) No information.

5. GROSSGLOCKNER AND PASTERZE MIT GAMSGRUBE (Carinthia).

a) Status : the policy applied to this high montaine area is identical with that described for the Karwendelschutzgebiet above.

b) Area : 3,698 ha.

c) and *d*) Staff and budget : forest guards.

Date established : 1935.

Altitude : 2,200-3,797 m.

a) Mountain area in Hohe Tauern, including the glacial landscape of the Grossglockner; alpine fauna and flora, with glacial epoch relics.

b) Alpine fauna.

6. LAINZER TIERGARTEN IM WIENERWALD (Vienna).

a) Status : former imperial hunting area, with the same status as the Natur-schutzgebiet, namely, controlled hunting, forest exploitation under strict limits, intensive tourism (Sunday outings for the Viennese) within the wider zone of the Wienerwald which is a Landschafteschutzgebiet (landscape protected zone).

b) Area : 2,300 ha.

c) and *d*) Staff and budget : forest service supervision.

Date established : 1941.

Tourism : see under II, *a*) above.

97

IV.   *Altitude :* 250-514 m.
        a) Part of Wienerwald.
        b) A small forest fauna.

V.   Areas excluded :

A very long list of areas or zones accorded some sort of protection in Austria was included in E/3436 of the previous edition of the List and should be consulted by those requiring information about the exclusions from the present List.

One of the Natural Monuments mentioned on page 43 of E/3436, namely the Krimmler Waterfalls, has been awarded (1969) the Council of Europe's diploma.

7. BARBADOS

I.   Listed Areas : nil.

V.   Explanation :

No information received, but it seems doubtful whether any reserve meriting consideration for inclusion in the List has yet been established in this densely populated island. Only some 18 ha are rated as forest land out of a total surface area of 43,027 ha and at least 27,900 ha are under cultivation.

8. BELGIUM

I.   Listed Areas : nine.

A. — NATIONAL NATURE RESERVES.
    1. Hautes Fagnes National Nature Reserve.
    2. Westhoek National Nature Reserve.

B. — THE AREAS PROTECTED BY THE ASSOCIATION FOR " RÉSERVES NATURELLES ET ORNITHOLOGIQUES DE BELGIQUE ", of which the four most important are :
    3. Kalmthout.
    4. Genk.
    5. Zwin.
    6. Blankaart.

C. — THE AREAS PROTECTED BY THE " ARDENNE ET GAUME " ASSOCIATION, of which the three most important are :
    7. Furfooz.
    8. Vague des Gomhets.
    9. Lesse et Lomme.

General Introduction :

Administration : the National Reserves are the responsibility of the " Conseil Supérieur des Réserves Naturelles Domaniales et de la Protection de la Nature " and are under the supervision of State Forestry Service personnel. The areas belonging to the two private Associations are administered by those Associations. Both the National Reserves were listed and briefly described in Part Two of the previous edition of the List.

Tourism : the National Nature Reserves are divided into strict reserves, where tourists are not allowed to enter, and national park areas where no limitations are imposed on entry and movement of visitors. Entry is controlled in the case of some of the private Reserves.

Research : actively sponsored in all areas. Examples are given below.

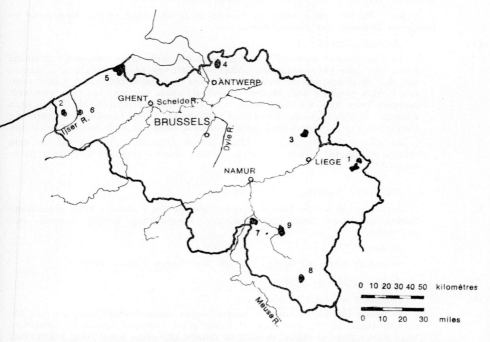

Details : application of criteria (II), general information (III) and description (IV) :

A. — NATIONAL NATURE RESERVES.

1. HAUTES FAGNES NATIONAL NATURE RESERVE.

a) Status : total protection. Human inhabitants have been excluded and no cultivation or grazing by domestic stock is permitted. No cutting of wood allowed, the greater part of the rare botanical associations of the Fagnes (upland mosses) having been left undisturbed. The decision not to allow the development of plantations in extensions of the Reserve comprising certain enclaves of State Forest, has been approved by Royal Decree. Fishing is forbidden, and

99

moreover practically non-existent, and hunting and trapping rights have been terminated. Locally, steps have been taken to rehabilitate certain biotopes (by restoring the natural drainage of parts of the forest which have become degraded, etc.).

b) Area : 2,013 ha in the main block, plus several isolated forest patches amounting to 1,404 ha, but the total has more recently been quoted as 3,651 ha.

c) and *d*) Staff and budget : supervision and maintenance are undertaken by the Administration des Eaux et Forêts. Official assurance has been given that the criteria are fully satisfied.

Date established : 1957, with an extension from 1,439 to 3,417 ha in 1964.

Research : The Scientific Station of the Hautes Fagnes, attached to the University of Liege, was set up in 1924.

N.B. — In 1966 the Council of Europe made an award to this Reserve of its European Diploma for Nature Protection.

IV.   *Altitude :* 500-675 m.

a) The general form of this high plateau, with tarns and stony drainage lines, and also the vegetation, reflect the imprint of its periglacial climate : the two chief features of the " fagnes " are *Sphagnum*-dominated raised peat-bog (which, together with Molinia grassland, where the peat has been removed, occupies over half the total area) and *Calluna*-dominated heath. The flora includes : *Arnica montana,* chickweed wintergreen *Trientalis europaea,* cranberry *Vaccinium oxycoccus* and *Andromeda polifolia*; there are some spruce plantations.

b) Wild cat *Felis silvestris*; black grouse *Lyrurus tetrix*; one of the rare species of clouded yellow butterflies, *Colias palaeno* (perhaps no longer to be found ?).

2. WESTHOEK NATIONAL NATURE RESERVE.

II.   *a*) Status : as for the Hautes Fagnes Reserve, No. 1 above. Total protection : human habitation, cultivation, pasturage, wood-cutting, fishing, hunting, etc., prohibited.

b) Area : 337 ha.

c) and *d*) Staff and budget : as for the Hautes Fagnes Reserve.

III.   *Date established :* 1957.

IV.   *Altitude :* sea level to 15 m.

a) Sandy beach and rows of coastal dunes, separated by pans, showing the various stages in the evolution of these sandy biotopes (dunes in formation, fixed dunes, moving dunes, decalcified dunes); the usual dune-fixing vegetation : marram, creeping willow and sand sedge; several species of orchid; yellow-wort *Blackstonia perfoliata* occurs, its only station in Belgium.

b) There is a rich coastal fauna and avifauna.

B. — AREAS MAINTAINED BY THE ASSOCIATION FOR RESERVES NATURELLES ET ORNITHOLOGIQUES DE BELGIQUE.

3. KALMTHOUT.

II.   *a*) Status : in this and the next three areas, one or two of which are surrounded by special protective zones, no human habitation, cultivation, pasturage, wood-cutting, hunting, trapping or fishing are, in general, allowed and this applies equally to the two privately-owned sections, except for limited forest exploitation and some very restricted hunting activity. Rabbits are controlled.

b) Area : 727 ha, held on lease by the Association from the Commune which owns the land, to which must be added two neighbouring private properties, totalling 645 ha in all.

c) and *d*) Staff and budget : a full-time warden is employed and a part-time conservator, plus game-keepers in the private properties.

Date established : 1964 (in its present form).

Research : schemes for research work in the Association's Reserves are now well established and educational centres are being set up.

Altitude : 20-25 m.

a) A fine cross-section of the Campine landscape, with heath, marshland, dunes and woods, in the vicinity of the delta formed by the Escaut, Meuse and Rhine; marram-grass *Ammophila arenaria,* creeping willow and various heaths such as bog heather *Erica tetralix* and ling *Calluna.*

b) A good area for birds, both breeding species and migrants; nesting colonies of black-headed gulls *Larus ridibundus* and black terns *Chlidonias niger*; shelduck *T. tadorna,* pochard *Aythya ferina,* curlew *Numenius arquata,* black-tailed godwit *L. limosa,* black-necked grebe *Podiceps nigricollis.*

4. GENK.

a) Status : as for No. 3 (i) Kalmthout. The protected biotopes mostly originate in human activities : for example the upkeep of fish-ponds involves management practices (annual draining at the beginning of winter, which disturbs the waterfowl), if the biotope itself is to be maintained. Otherwise total protection is given except for the use of small meadows for pasture and the control of rabbits.

b) Area : a total of 220 ha, fenced, of which 70 ha are strict nature reserve.

c) and *d*) Staff and budget : full-time warden and part-time conservator.

Date established : 1956.

Research : see No. 3 (i) Kalmthout.

Altitude : about 50 m.

a) A marshland area in the Stiemerbeek valley, on the edge of the Campine plateau, with ponds, peaty bogs, reed-beds, dunes and heaths; a varied flora with glacial relics : rare plants include quill-worts *Isoetes lacustris* and *echinospora,* water lobelia *Lobelia dortmanna* and *Andromeda polifolia.*

b) A rich avifauna : black tern, bittern *Botaurus stellaris,* little bittern *Ixobrychus minutus,* marsh harrier *Circus aeruginosus,* nightjar *Caprimulgus europaeus.*

5. ZWIN.

a) Status : as for No. 3 (i) Kalmthout.

b) Area : 125 ha with a further 25 ha across the frontier in Holland, and a surrounding protected zone of 1,500 ha. Total protection is given to the

101

125 hectares. In the protected 1,500 ha zone, some fields and meadows are grazed, there is restricted shooting and the capture of birds for ringing is permitted.

c) and *d*) Staff and budget : a full-time warden and part-time conservator.

III. *Date established :* 1952.

Research : see No. 3 (i) Kalmthout. The Zwin Reserve is particularly important in this respect.

IV. *Altitude :* sea level to 5 m.

a) Salt marsh or meadow of the ancient mouth of the river Zwin, regularly inundated by sea water and with halophilous vegetation (glasswort *Salicornia herbacea,* seablite *Suaeda maritima,* sea purslane *Halimione portulacoides* and *pedunculata,* sea lavender *Limonium vulgare*); lines of dunes. A region of great interest for the study of the evolution of the North Sea coast.

b) A rich avifauna : shelduck, ringed plover *Charadrius hiaticula,* avocet *Recurvirostra avosetta,* little tern *Sterna albifrons,* hoopoe *Upupa epops.*

6. BLANKAART.

II. *a*) Status : as for 3 (i), Kalmthout.

b) Area : 100 ha plus an adjacent private property of 300 ha. Fenced in. In the 100 hectare block the greater part (70 ha) is occupied by a lake and its reed-beds, and total protection is accorded. In the 300 ha of private ground, controlled shooting and fishing takes place.

c) and *d*) Staff and budget : a full-time warden and part-time conservator, with game-keepers in the privately-owned sector.

III. *Date established :* 1959.

Research : see No. 3 (i) Kalmthout.

IV. *Altitude :* about 5 m.

a) Part of the marshy ground on the right bank of the river Yser, the lake occupying the more low-lying area; the partial silting of the lake has resulted in the formation of reed-beds (*Phragmites,* with marsh vetches *Lathyrus* spp., sea milkwort *Glaux maritima* and marsh marigold *Caltha palustris*).

b) Bittern, marsh harrier, Montagu's harrier *Circus pygargus.*

C. — AREAS MAINTAINED BY THE « ARDENNE ET GAUME » ASSOCIATION.

7. FURFOOZ.

II. *a*) Status : no human habitation, cultivation, domestic stock, hunting or fishing permitted; only a certain amount of forest exploitation under strict control and limits.

b) Area : 65 ha, of which 50 are completely protected.

c) and *d*) Staff and budget : the area is supervised by three wardens and a conservator. The annual budget of the Association approaches U.S. $ 22,000 and its entirely devoted to the maintenance of its reserves.

III. *Date established :* 1952.

Research : the scientific investigation of the " Ardenne et Gaume " Reserves is very systematic and has resulted in a number of publications.

V.   *Altitude :* 105-215 m.

a) A site of considerable geological interest in the carboniferous limestone along the river Lesse, with many examples of typical Karstic phenomena (caverns, upthrows etc.); prehistoric (flint implements) and historic sites; deciduous woodland, some meadowland, rocky cliff-walls overlooking the Lesse.

b) Flora and fauna typical of calcareous terrain (similar to that of the Lesse et Lomme Reserve, No. 4 (iii) below).

8. VAGUE DES GOMHETS.

I.   *a*) Status : identical with that of No. 4 (i) Furfooz.

b) Area : 47 ha.

c) and *d*) Staff and budget : three wardens and a conservator. Maintained from the Association's annual budget of upwards of U.S. $ 22,000.

II.   *Date established :* 1963.

Research : see under No. 4 (i) above, Furfooz.

V.   *Altitude :* about 320 m.

a) Boggy depressions in an open area in the beech and conifer forest of Suxy; *sphagnum*-filled boggy hollows; gorse and heath in the drier sectors; typical flora of the bog and heath of the Ardennes (including *Arnica montana*).

b) Roe deer *C. capreolus* and red deer *Cervus elaphus,* wild boar *Sus scrofa,* wild cat *Felis silvestris.*

9. LESSE ET LOMME.

I.   *a*) Status : designated by the Association as the "National Park of Lesse and Lomme", this reserve comprises a mixture of woods and wilderness, in which grazing-rights still exist to the extent deemed necessary to maintain the balance of the biotope, and forest exploitation and hunting still take place, but in which nevertheless, in keeping with the 'zoning' principle, certain sectors are such that the whole area deserves to be included in the List.

b) Area : 975 ha in all, though only a part of this could claim to satisfy the criterion of fully protected status (see *a*) above).

c) and *d*) Staff and budget : three wardens and a conservator and share of the Association's total annual budget of about U.S. $ 22,000.

II.   *Date established :* 1958.

Research : see under No. 4 (i) above, Furfooz.

V.   *Altitude :* 153-314 m.

a) Part of the calcareous cushion of La Famenne, situated on the confluence of the rivers Lesse and Lomme, and of the greatest interest to all branches of natural science; exhibits examples of important Karstic formations, of which the best known are the Han and Rochefort caverns; coral reefs; both the microclimate and vegetation of the calcareous formations are very peculiar — dry short-grass sward with a rich calcicole and thermophilous flora (orchids, anemones including the pasque flower *A. pulsatilla*, gentians, etc.); characteristic woodland of broad-leaved species and Austrian pine *Pinus nigra.*

b) Salamander *Salamandra maculosa.*

103

V.   **Areas excluded :**

A. — Fourteen Reserves belonging to the Association for " Réserves Naturelles et Ornithologiques ", ranging in size from 5 to 300 ha. The most remarkable of these is the Snepkensvijver Reserve, a mere 20 ha, which provides a sanctuary for nearly 15,000 pairs of nesting birds, mainly black-headed gulls (it is supervised by a full-time warden and a conservator).

B. — Twelve Reserves belonging to the " Ardenne et Gaume " Association, ranging from one to 206 ha. The chief ones include the Bohan-Membre (169 ha, of which 30 are protected from all forestry exploitation), and the Nismes-Olloy of 303 ha.

C. — The Tikke Groeken Reserve of 50 ha, belonging to the De Wielewaal (" Golden Oriole ") Ornithological Society.

D. — Five newly created State Nature Reserves, of which the first two should certainly be included in the next edition of the List : Bruyères de Kalmthout (800 ha), Bruyères de Mechelen-aan-de-Maas (400 ha), Rochers de Champalle et Poilvache (48 ha), Fagne de Montleban (22 ha) and Lande de Bihin (15 ha).

9. BOLIVIA

I.   **Listed Areas :** nil.

V.   a) **Explanation :**

Although there are various relevant legal provisions, they do not yet appear to have been implemented. Bolivia was not included in either E/3436 or Part Two of the previous edition of the List.

b) **Areas excluded :**

1. Mount Sajama National Park.

This Park has been the subject of frequent negotiations, being of special interest because it contains the Kenua Forest, which, at 4,900 m., is situated at the highest elevation of any forest in the world : the dominant species of the forest is the rosaceous *Polylepis tarapacana* PHIL., related to burnet.
The forest was first described by the Swedish botanist Eric Asplunden in 1921. Despite the number of representations made to the authorities designed to assure its conservation, which led in 1939 to the promulgation of the National Park, the demand for charcoal to satisfy the needs of the city of La Paz has resulted in the handing over of this remarkable forest to the charcoal-burners, who by 1946 had left only a few isolated trees. At the same time in the absence of any supervision, poachers succeeeded in exterminating the typical fauna of the Sajama massif (which reaches 6,000 m in altitude) and notably, the last remaining population of the true chinchilla *C. laniger*. In 1954, however, measures for the re-afforestation or rehabilitation of some 75,000 ha were announced by the then newly established Forest Service.

2. The Miriquiri National Park.

On the 5 November 1945, two National Parks were promulgated under a new law, one of them being the above-mentioned Sajama National Park, which seems to indicate that the earlier decree of 1939 had by then become overlooked. The Miriquiri was the second of the National Parks thus established. The law provided for the setting up of a Committee charged with the task of fixing the boundaries and investigating the area, with a view to the preparation of suitable regulations for its supervision. No news of the completion of this task is yet to hand.

3. The National Parks of Huayana Potosi, Chacaltaya and Milluri Peaks.

Situated in the Andean *cordillera.* Set up by a law enacted on 4 July 1942. Hunting prohibited in the Parks, but supervision and management made the responsibility of a special section of a Sports Association.

4. Maliaza National Park.

Near La Paz. Set up by Supreme Decree No. 4309 of November 1956, which provided for the publication of Regulations. These had not yet been issued in 1965. The Park appears however to be only 74 ha in area.

5. Two other Parks of small size :

La Barranca, 1966 ... ... 247 ha
Cerro Comanche, 1963 ... ... 50 ha

6. Three projects for important new Parks which were under consideration in May 1967 :

Yapacani-Ichilo National Park ... ... 836,000 ha
Rio Negro-San Martin National Park . ... 736,000 ha
Guanay Norte National Park . ... 403,750 ha

10. BOTSWANA

Listed Areas : one.

1. Area adjoining Gemsbok National Park (Kgalagadi District).

General Introduction :

This single area was also included in the previous edition of the List, E/3436.

Details : application of criteria (II), general information (III) and description (IV) :

1. AREA ADJOINING GEMSBOK NATIONAL PARK (Kgalagadi District).

   a) Status : all hunting forbidden in what is mainly a desert and uninhabited region, though occasionally entered by nomadic Bushmen.

   b) Area : 960,000 ha.

   c) and *d)* Staff and budget : the Government of the former Bechuanaland Protectorate officially requested the South African National Parks Board of Trustees to authorise the staff of the neighbouring Kalahari Gemsbok National Park also to undertake the supervision of this area. Supervision of the periphery (see relevant entry under South Africa) is deemed adequate.

105

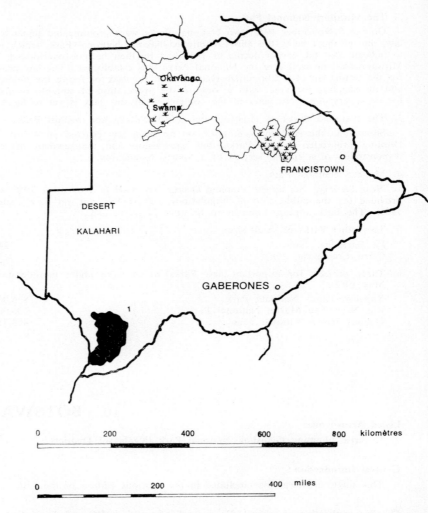

III. *Date established :* as a game reserve by High Commissioner's Notice No. 107 of 1940; declared a sanctuary under the Fauna Conservation Proclamation of 1961.

Administration : responsibility of the Ministry of Mines, Commerce and Industry.

Tenure : public land.

Tourism : there is no accommodation, but Game Rangers willingly escort visitors into the Reserve.

Research : no special organisation has been set up.

106

V.

Altitude : about 1,200 m.

a) Part of the Kgalagadi District in the south-west of Botswana, with an arid climate; in the ancient channels of the Nosob drainage line there is some park-like country with small trees.

b) Eland *Taurotragus oryx*, gemsbok *Oryx gazella*, hartebeest *Alcelaphus* sp., springbok *Antidorcas marsupialis*, wildebeest *Connochaetes taurinus* and lion *Panthera leo*.

Areas excluded :

Chobe Game Reserve.
Mogobane Bird Sanctuary.
Bathoen Dam Bird Sanctuary.
Central Kalahari Game Reserve.
Moremi Wildlife Reserve.

These five areas were declared reserves under the Fauna Conservation Proclamation of 1961. There is a good prospect of official action in the near future to establish full legal protection for the Moremi Wildlife Reserve (about 5,300 km²), which has been described as " an invaluable entity " in a paper by K. L. Tinley, issued in 1966 by the Okavango Wildlife Society under the title of " An ecological reconnaissance of the Moremi Wildlife Reserve ". The Chobe Reserve, now understood to have full national park status, is generally regarded as the best area in the country and F.A.O. is giving substantial technical assistance in its development.

11. BRAZIL

Listed Areas : eleven.

1. Iguaçu National Park.
2. Monte Pascoal National Park.
3. Brasília National Park.
4. Aparados de Serra National Park.
5. Itatiaia National Park.
6. Soòretama Biological Reserve.
7. Serra dos Orgãos National Park.
8. Caparaó National Park.
9. Sete Cidades National Park.
10. Tijuca National Park.
11. Jacarepaguá Biological Reserve.

General Introduction :

The entire structure of the Brazilian National Parks is undergoing a thorough reorganisation at the present time (1967). A " Brazilian Commission on National Parks " has been given extensive powers to study the existing situation and make appropriate recommendations. Its members during 1966 travelled over 30,000 kilometres and visited all the National Parks listed below, including those relegated to Section V, with the exception of Xingu

There are fifteen effective and legally constituted National Parks in Brazil, but according to a member of the above-mentioned Commission only nine of these at present satisfy the criteria laid down by the ICNP, although six more could well qualify in the near future to be included in the U.N. List.

Legislative basis : Federal Decrees.

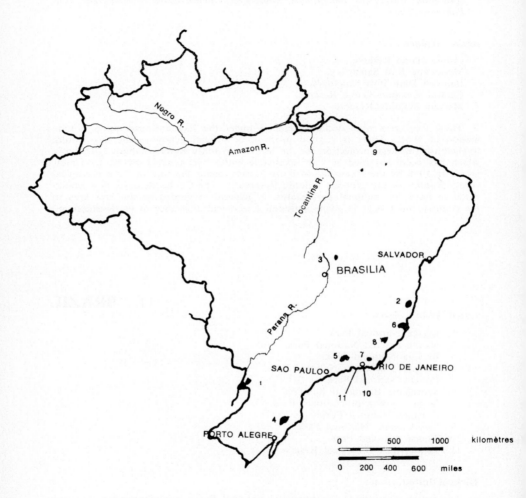

Administration : responsibility lies with the Ministry of Agriculture's Division of Research and Nature Conservation, a section of the Instituto Brasileiro de Desenvolvimento Florestal — based at Rio de Janeiro. The Park Regulations have to have the approval of the Ministry of Agriculture. There are special provisions for the Biological Reserves (see below).

Land tenure : in some cases the land is only partly owned by the State, because delimitation of the Parks is not yet complete and several private estates still survive within the boundaries, which may take some time to eliminate completely.

No information on Brazil was published in E/3436 or Part Two of the previous edition of the List.

Details : application of criteria (II), general information (III) and description (IV) :

1. IGUAÇU NATIONAL PARK (Parana State).

I.
   a) Status : total protection.

   b) Area : about 180,000 ha in two blocks.

   c) Staff : an administrator and his assistant, 11 guards and 10 handymen.

   d) Budget : U.S. $ 43,500 (this and the figures quoted below under this head are based on the 1966 Budget).

II.
   Date established : 10 January 1939 (Federal Decree No. 1035).

   Tourism : a modern hotel is situated near the Falls. More simple hotel accommodation is also available there and at Foz (a short distance away by a good road). An airport of international standard.

   Research : facilities for research workers include accommodation and supplies.

V.
   Altitude : 120-730 m.

   a) The National Park comprises two blocks, of which the smaller is at a lower altitude (220 m. a.s.l.) and contains the Park headquarters and, of course, the famous Iguaçu Falls (dropping some 85 m). There is subtropical forest with *Ilex, Podocarpus, Aspidosperma, Cedrela, Cariniana, Philodendron*, tree-ferns (*Alsophila, Hemitelia, Cyathea*), lianas, orchids, mosses, begonias, etc. The more extensive block and also the higher in altitude is covered in subtropical deciduous forest in which the handsome Assai palm *Euterpe edulis* is abundant. It is also the western habitat limit of the Brasilian conifer *Araucaria angustifolia*.

   b) Mammals : capybara *Hydrochoerus hydrochaeris*, black howler *Alouatta caraya* and puma *Felis concolor;* birds : the chimango caracara or carrion-hawk *Milvago chimango*, rufous oven-bird *Furnarius rufus*, white-tailed trogon *Trogon strigilatus* (=*viridis*) and crested caracara or caranco carrion-hawk *Polyborus plancus brasiliensis*; reptiles : broad-snouted cayman *Caiman latirostris*, dwarf cayman *Paleosuchus palpebrosus*, the urutú viper *Bothrops alternata*.

2. MONTE PASCOAL NATIONAL PARK (Bahia State).

II.
   a) Status : total protection.

   b) Area : 37,000 ha.

   c) Staff : 16 units (not counting administrative personnel).

   d) Budget : U.S. $ 9,400.

III.
   Date established : 29 November 1961 (Federal Decree No. 242).

   Land tenure : entirely state-owned land.

   Tourism : six people can be accommodated and there is a landing-ground for small planes at the Park headquarters.

   Research : nothing organised.

109

IV.   *Altitude :* sea level to 580 m.

a) Evergreen rain forest adjacent to the beach; sand bars (" restinga "). On the higher slopes of Mt. Pascoal the forest is not so tall. This natural reserve, which is encircled by deforestation, will soon be the last refuge of the rosewood *Dalbergia nigra,* the Peroba tree *Paratecoma peroba* and several other species the wood of which is particularly valued for cabinet-making.

b) Mammals : jaguar *Panthera onca,* tapir *Tapirus terrestris,* otter *Lutra platensis,* brown howler *Alouatta guariba,* collared peccary *Tayassu tajacu*; birds : bare-faced curassow *Crax fasciolata,* black-fronted piping guan *Pipile jacutinga,* rusty-margined guan *Penelope superciliaris,* channel-billed toucan *Rhamphastos vitellinus ariel* and spot-winged wood-quail *Odontophorus capueira.*

3. BRASÍLIA NATIONAL PARK (Federal District).

II.   *a)* Status : total protection.

b) Area : 13,000 ha.

c) Staff : an administrator, 15 guards, 20 handymen and some administrative personnel.

d) Budget : U.S. $ 54,500.

III.   *Date established :* 29 November 1961 (Federal Decree No. 241).

Land tenure : entirely state-owned land.

Tourism : within easy reach of the Federal capital. Many roads and footpaths through the Park.

Research : work in progress, mainly under the auspices of the University of Brasília.

IV.   *Altitude :* 1,200 m.

a) A sample of the " cerrado " (thicket or wooded savannah), typical of the central Brazilian plateau, with gnarled and twisted trees and numerous termite-mounds. Around the water-points, which are associated with outcrops of the phreatic substratum, concentrations of " cerradão " or denser thicket occur, with stands of " buriti "-palm *Mauritia vinefera* in the damp hollows and of Velloziaceae, where rock nears the surface.

b) Mammals : black howler, the newly-described rodent *Juscelinomys candangus,* hoary fox *Dusicyon vetulus,* six-banded armadillo *Euphractus sexcinctus,* cavy *Galea spixii,* forest rabbit *Sylvilagus brasiliensis*; birds : lesser yellow-headed vulture *Cathartes burrovianus urubutinga,* burrowing owl *Speotyto cunicularia grallaria,* spotted tinamou *Nothura maculosa,* toco toucan *Ramphastos toco,* curl-crested jay *Cyanocorax cristatellus*; reptiles : the fer-de-lance or jararaca viper *Bothrops jararaca,* the musurana *Pseudoboa cloelia* and the great teju lizard *Tupinambis teguixin.*

4. APARADOS DA SERRA NATIONAL PARK (Rio Grande do Sul State).

II.   *a)* Status : total protection.

b) Area : 13,000 ha.

c) Staff : 8 units (excluding administrative personnel).

d) Budget : U.S. $ 36,600.

II.

Date established : 17 December 1959 (Federal Decree No. 47446).

Land tenure : most of the land is still in the process of being taken over by the State, but effective supervision is already exercised over the greater part of it.

Tourism : tarmac road of access, a modern restaurant, visitors' chalets (the first of which were put into service in February 1967).

Research : sporadic (various unconnected studies have been made of the fauna and flora).

V.

Altitude : 20-800 m approximately.

a) A coastal area with precipitous cliffs (« aparados ») on the border of the State of Rio Grande do Sul and the State of Santa Catarina, forming part of the Serra Geral. The escarpments are cleft by a series of spectacular canyons (" taimbés "), of which the most remarkable, the " Taimbèsinho ", has vertical walls some 400 m high; some of their vegetation is reminiscent of that of the Patagonian mountains, including such species as *Gunnera*. The gently undulating plateaux support scattered forest patches, some of them mainly *Araucaria angustifolia*, others rich in species of Myrtaceae, in several cases growing up to the lip of the canyons or " taimbés ". There are many small lakes at various stages of evolution towards the end-product of peat-bogs.

b) Mammals : pampas cat *Felis colocolo pajeros,* seven-banded armadillo *Dasypus septemcinctus*, opossum *Didelphis aurita*; birds : azure jay *Cyanocorax caeruleus,* rufous oven-bird and chimango caracara; reptiles : the urutú viper and snake-eating snake *Rachidelus* (=*Clelia*) *brazili*.

5. ITATIAIA NATIONAL PARK (Rio de Janeiro and Minas Gerais States).

I.

a) Status : total protection. Still includes a number of private properties in the lower-lying sectors of the Park.

b) Area : 12,000 ha.

c) Staff : an administrator, 8 administrative agents, 10 guards and 20 handymen.

d) Budget : U.S. $ 28,900.

II.

Date established : 14 June 1937 (Federal Decree No. 1713).

Land tenure : state-owned land, except for the fairly numerous private properties at lower altitudes.

Tourism : three private hotels, seven huts near the Park headquarters (alt. 800 m) and on the plateau (2,350 m). The plateau can be reached by vehicles. Regional Museum. Mountaineering opportunities.

Research : work carried out goes back to Saint-Hilaire (1822), Sellow (1830), Glaziou (1872), Wawra von Fernsee (1879), Ule (1894), Dusen (1902), and there is a large bibliography. Eight Bulletins have been published by the Park. Laboratory. *N.B.* — This Park was established around the old Itatiaia biological station belonging to the Botanical Garden of Rio.

V.

Altitude : 750-2,787 m.

a) Situated in the Mantiqueira range one of the major volcanic massifs in Brazil. Up to 1,600 m there is humid tropical forest with lianas, lichens, ferns, orchids and begonias. Then from 1,600 to 2,000 m, at the cloud level, the forest is not so tall but equally rich in species. Finally at the highest altitude,

111

up to the summit of the Agulhas Negras, 2,787 m, there is a beautiful high level flora with more than a hundred endemic species, including the genus *Itatiaia cleistopetala* ULE, which has only one species.

b) Mammals : jaguar, crab-eating fox *Cerdocyon thous,* the lesser-anteater *Tamandua tetradactyla,* crab-eating raccoon *Procyon cancrivorus,* coati *Nasua nasua,* ocelot *Felis pardalis brasiliensis*; birds : king vulture *Sarcoramphus papa,* turkey vulture *Cathartes aura rupicollis,* brown tinamou *Crypturellus obsoletus,* magpie tanager *Cissopis leveriana major,* toco toucan, short-tailed ant-thrush *Chamaeza brevicauda*; reptiles : jararaca viper, coral snake *Micrurus corallinus,* iguanid lizard *Tropidurus torquatus* and snake-necked tortoise *Hydromedusa maximiliani*; amphibia : blacksmith tree-frog *Hyla faber.*

6. SOÒRETAMA BIOLOGICAL RESERVE (Espirito Santo State).

II.
a) Status : total protection, no tourism.

b) Area : 12,000 ha.

c) Staff : an administrator, with 2 assistants, 6 guards and 6 handymen.

d) Budget : U.S. $ 7,700.

III.
Date established : 21 September 1943, when the area was made over to the Federal Government by Espirito Santo State Decree No. 14977, to form the only Federal Biological Reserve.

Land tenure : entirely state-ownership.

Tourism : not permitted.

Research : hitherto mainly zoological, but current interest has switched to the flora and especially problems of plant recolonisation.

IV.
Altitude : sea level to about 500 m

a) Forested slopes along the coast which constitute the meeting place of two floras, that of the Amazon basin and that of the Atlantic littoral. The example usually quoted is the fact that both the Amazonian *Euterpe oleracea* and the coastal Assai palm *E. edulis* are found. The forest is of a semi-deciduous tropical type, success in preventing fires over a considerable number of years having allowed the re-habilitation of blocks of this forest, which, in addition to *Paratecoma peroba,* features the rosewood *Dalbergia nigra,* cedar *Cedrela fissilis,* the Brazilian milk-tree or masseranduba *Mimusops elata,* etc.

b) Mammals : tapir, red brocket deer *Mazama americana,* collared peccary, brown howler and yapok *Chironectes minimus*; birds : harpy eagle *Harpia harpyja,* solitary tinamou *Tinamus solitarius,* yellow-legged tinamou *Crypturellus noctivagus,* red-breasted toucan *Ramphastos dicolorus,* bare-faced curas-sow, black-fronted piping guan and a large number of humming-birds (Trochilidae). According to A. Ruski the greatest concentration of the latter in the world is to be found in Espirito Santo State, including 90 % of all Brazilian species (information supplied in February 1967 by H. E. Strang, to whom the greater part of the present account of Brazilian nature reserves is owed); reptiles : bushmaster *Lachesis muta,* wood tortoise *Testudo denticulata.*

7. SERRA DOS ORGÃOS NATIONAL PARK (Rio de Janeiro State).

II.
a) Status : total protection.

b) Area : 10,500 ha.

c) Staff : an administrator with an assistant, 6 guards and 35 handymen.

d) Budget : U.S. $ 43,600.

III.

Date established : 30 November 1939 (Federal Decree No. 1822).

Land tenure : entirely state-ownership.

Tourism : the town of Teresopolis, which is much frequented by and has good facilities for tourists is nearby. There is an excellent road of access, footpaths, a cabin which can take 30 people, with a restaurant, near the Park headquarters, mountain huts, each with 18 beds, at 1,600 and 1,920 m and remarkably good mountaineering.

Research : work carried out originated with Sellow (1815), Langsdorff (1816), Martius (1817), Raddi (1818), Beyrich (1823), etc. and there is a considerable bibliography.

IV.

Altitude : 600-2,270 m.

a) The Orgãos range in which the Park is situated is chiefly composed of gneiss and granite, and famous for the Dedo de Deus (Finger of God) pinnacle. The plant-life is luxuriant and varied, due to the wide range of altitude from humid tropical forest, full of lianas, ferns, epiphytes (orchids, bromelias, etc.) to high shrubby prairie, culminating in the peak of Pedra do Sino (2,270 m) which is notable for an endemic species *Prepusa hookeriana.*

b) Mammals : common opossum *Didelphis marsupialis,* the philander opossum *Caluromys philander,* masked titi *Callicebus personatus,* paca *Cuniculus paca,* agouti *Dasyprocta aguti*; birds : spot-winged wood-quail, mantled hawk *Leucopternis polionota,* solitary and brown tinamous; reptiles : black- and -yellow rat snake *Spilotes pullatus,* colubrid snake *Dryadophis bifossatus,* iguanid lizard *Urostrophus vautieri*; amphibia : the horned frog *Ceratophrys dorsata.*

c) Woolly spider-monkey *Brachyteles arachnoides.*

8. CAPARAÓ NATIONAL PARK (Espirito Santo and Minas Gerais States).

a) Status : total protection.

b) Area : 10,400 ha.

c) Staff : 12 units (excluding administrative personnel).

d) Budget : U.S. $ 14,000.

III.

Date established : 24 May 1961 (Federal Decree No. 50646).

Land tenure : only half is state-owned, but protection and supervision extends to the whole area.

Tourism : accommodation is obtainable at Presidente Soares not far from the Park. There is a mountain hut at fairly high level on the Pico da Bandeira, Brazil's third highest mountain (2,890 m).

Research : casual.

IV.

Altitude : 100-2,890 m.

a) A mountain massif of which the side situated in the State of Espirito Santo is facing the sea, the moisture-laden winds from which account for the presence of rain-forest. In the Minas Gerais State sector, there are three successive vegetation belts : up to 1,800 m rain-forest, similar to that on the other side but without the oceanic influence; from 1,800 to 2,400 m a mixture of bushy associations (in sheltered hollows) and high level prairie; and finally, above 2,400 m only open prairie and rocky shelves with various species of Ericaceae, Melastomataceae, Myrtaceae, etc.

b) Mammals : margay cat *Felis wiedi*, capuchin monkey *Cebus libidinosus*, black-pencilled marmoset *Callithrix penicillata*, nine-banded armadillo *Dasypus novemcinctus* and red brocket; birds : saffron toucanet *Andigena bailloni*, small-billed tinamou *Crypturellus parvirostris*, red-ruffed fruit crow *Pyroderus scutatus*; reptiles : bushmaster.

c) Woolly spider-monkey *Brachyteles arachnoides*.

9. SETE CIDADES NATIONAL PARK (Piauí State).

II.
a) Status : total protection.

b) Area : 7,770 ha.

c) Staff : 6 units (excluding administrative personnel).

d) Budget : U.S. $ 11,600.

III.
Date established : 8 June 1961 (Federal Decree No. 50744).

Land tenure : nearly all state-owned.

Tourism : accommodation for 12 people available and supplies obtainable. The special attraction is the weird landscape resulting from sculpture by erosion of the sandy formations which compose it. June to August, the early months of the dry season, is the best period for a visit.

Research : casual.

IV.
Altitude : averages 200 m.

a) Woody savannah (" campos cerrados ") with gallery forest; stands of " buriti "-palm and carnauba-palm *Copernicia cerifera* in the more humid pans. The Park's characteristic landscape is due to the erosion of the cretaceous sandstone of the Serra Negra into monumental blocks of peculiar shape and form.

b) Mammals : jaguarondi *Felis yaguaroundi*, rock cavy *Kerodon rupestris*, punare *Cercomys cunicularis*, ashy opossum *Marmosa cinerea*, lesser anteater and brocket *Mazama simplicicornis*; birds : greater rhea *Rhea americana*, flaming or sun parrakeet *Aratinga jandaya* (=*solstitialis*), red-legged seriema *Cariama cristata*, the pigeon *Columba picazuro*; reptiles : great teju lizard.

10. TIJUCA NATIONAL PARK (Guanabara State).

II.
a) Status : total protection (although the Park still includes some private property, which is gradually being taken over).

b) Area : 3,200 ha.

c) Staff : an administrator, with 10 administrative agents, 35 guards and 3 drivers.

d) Budget : U.S. $ 27,800.

III.
Date established : 6 July 1961 (Federal Decree No. 50923) : the Park now includes the forest reserves belonging to the Federal Forest Service which, since 1870, has struggled to protect the vegetational cover of the hydrological catchment overlooking and supplying Rio de Janeiro. The area has been a public park for recreational purposes since 1944, and was first named the Rio de Janeiro National Park, but has recently been renamed to avoid confusion with other Parks in the area.

Land tenure : now mostly under state-ownership.

Tourism : in the immediate vicinity of Rio de Janeiro. An excellent road system and established circuits for visitors.

Research : plans for development are now being made.

Altitude : 100-1,021 m.

a) Lying to the west of Rio de Janeiro, the Park comprises rain forest and rehabilitated forest on the slopes of Mt. Tijuca, of very considerable interest. In 1862, the State began to buy back and reafforest old coffee plantations; the process of recolonization, in the course of a century, has been so complete that the uninformed observer would be unable to distinguish between original virgin forest and the rehabilitated forest areas.

b) Mammals : the weeper capuchin *Cebus nigritus,* black-pencilled marmoset, the tayra *Eira barbara,* Allamand's grison *Galictis vittata,* three-toed sloth *Bradypus tridactylus,* Ingram's tree squirrel *Sciurus ingrami*; birds : swallow-tailed manakin *Chiroxiphia caudata,* channel-billed toucan and naked-throated bellbird *Procnias nudicollis*; reptiles : jararaca viper, colubrid snake *Chironius carinatus,* ground boa *Tropidophis paucisquamis*; amphibia : horned frog *Ceratophrys boiei,* Girard's frog *Zachaenus parvulus* and the Dendrobatid frog *Dendrophryniscus brevipollicatus.*

11. JACAREPAGUÁ BIOLOGICAL RESERVE (Guanabara State).

a) Status : partly (about 1,000 ha) under total protection, the rest being open to visitors and less strictly controlled.

b) Area : 2,800 ha in three blocks. Two of these, Sernambetiba and Marapendi, are strictly protected and account for 700 ha. The main block of 2,100 ha is named Jacarepaguá-Camorim-Tijuca.

c) Staff : 12 units.

d) Budget : on the basis of *c)* the criterion would be met.

Date established : 1960 (the year in which the protected area was decreed to be " for public use ").

Administration : this is not a Federal Government reserve; it is administered by a " Chefe " responsible to the Natural Resources Department of Guanabara State.

Land tenure : a small part is state-owned, but most is still in private ownership.

Tourism : an elaborate organisation and still being developed. There are plans for creating a large zoological and botanical garden and a site to to be reserved for campers and Scouts, though the rest of the reserve will still be given a strict conservation status. Guided visits and handbooks available.

Research : kept under strict scientific control (" on an ecological basis "), with regular attention to ecological observations " following the most modern scientific practices ". Some popular treatises have been published.

Altitude : sea level.

a) This group of three reserves, as described above in Section II (*b*), comprises land above and below water in the lagoon area extending west of the Barra da Tijuca. It contains the last surviving sample of the original " restinga " or sand bar in Guanabara State, with the fauna and flora associated with lagoons and the coast.

b) A rich avifauna.

V.   **Areas excluded :**

1. Paulo Afonso National Park (16,890 ha), established on 24 November 1948; organised and provided with supervisory staff. However, its principal feature of interest, the Rio São Francisco Falls, is also the reason for its omission from the List. A hydroelectric installation and the building of a town has resulted in the recent (1969) extinction of this Park. The Falls are now under the direct administration of the electricity company.

2. Ubajara National Park (5,600 ha), situated in Ceará State and established in 1959; the Park includes thick forest on the slopes of a narrow valley and the " Ubajara Caves " in the limestone massif. It is of considerable geological interest. Various human activities and habitations persist. State purchase of the land is planned. Budget : U.S. $ 25,400, covering a staff of 6.

3. Araguáia National Park (2 million ha), situated in Goiás State and established on 31 December 1960; the Park comprises the whole of the island of Bananal, the largest island in any river of the world. The situation regarding ownership of the land is not clear. It seems difficult in practice to get more than about half the island effectively reserved. The fauna is a rich one, especially in respect of birds and fish. However, hunting and fishing are rampant and do much damage, and are not at all easy to bring under control. Tourism is already flourishing. There is an aerodrome. Budget : U.S. $ 11,600, covering a staff of 6.

4. Emas National Park (88,750 ha), situated in the States of Goias and Mato Grosso and established on 11 January 1961. Most of the land has still to be bought back or expropriated from private ownership. Markedly undulating region of prairies, with termite-hills, savannah woodland and gallery forest and an abundant and varied fauna. Budget : U.S. $ 9,400, covering a staff of 8.

5. Tocantins National Park (625,000 ha), situated in Goiás State and established on 11 January 1961. Only a very small fraction of the land is state-owned. Could become one of the most important national parks in the country, with its fine waterfalls and plant associations typical of the Amazonian Hylea and of the great central plateau of Brazil. Budget : U.S. $ 9,400, covering a staff of 6.

6. Xingu National Park (2,200,000 ha), situated in the Mato Grosso State and established on 14 April 1961; this Park, unlike the others, is not the responsibility of the Ministry of Agriculture but of the Ministry of the Interior. It is administered as an " Indian Park " and a constituent part of the Indian reservation. In a report presented to the First World Conference on National Parks at Seattle in 1962, the Brazilian Forest Service stated that the " Xingu National Park could within the next ten years become one of the most important in the world ". Much scientific works is now being carried out in the area.

7. Sete Quedas National Park (10,000 ha), situated in Paraná State and established on 30 May 1961. This Park has been very largely invaded by cultivation and is to be sacrified to a hydroelectric installation. Possibly a nucleus of some 230 ha could be saved as a natural monument. There are spectacular waterfalls. The staff numbers two.

8. São Joaquim National Park (49,300 ha), situated in Santa Catarina State and established on 6 July 1961. State-ownership of the land has still to be achieved. Could become a national park of great value, with its high level plant associations and its *Araucaria* forests. Brazil's coldest area. The staff numbers two.

9. In July 1968, the establishment of the " Parque Nacional Indigena " of Tumucumaque on the frontier with Surinam and French Guyana, was approved. The park extends over 2,500,000 ha, but its status as an Indian reservation would

116

appear to be the same as No. 6 above, Xingu, and make it unlikely to qualify for the List; the criterion calling for effective supervision would, in particular, raise difficulties, which have not yet been resolved.

It should be emphasised that at any time in the future (i.e. after February 1967) some of the nine areas listed above might justifiably be admitted to the U.N. List, but up to that date the staff allocated on a full-time basis to the management of this group of natural reserves, which totals about seven million hectares, was reported to have been reduced and very inadequate.

It should also be noted that there may well be some Parks belonging to individual States of the Brazilian Confederation or to municipalities which, on examination of their status and degree of supervision, could quite properly be admitted to the List. Such an examination is now being undertaken.

12. BRITISH HONDURAS

Listed Areas : nil.

a) **Explanation :**

A letter from the Principal Secretary of the Ministry of Natural Resources, Commerce and Industry, Belize, dated 24 August 1964, stated : " There are no National Parks or reserves in this country falling within the scope of the definition mentioned in the Memorandum (*sc.* of the ICNP) ".

b) **Areas excluded :**

1. Hummingbird Highway Nature Reserve.

This Reserve was established some long time ago but is reported to have been " so thoroughly devastated by the hurricane (of 1961) that it seemed unreasonable at the time to proscribe salvage logging in the area ".

2. Sixteen forest reserves.

These also constitute game reserves and the most important of them, Chiquibul, comprises 96,000 ha of forest which are under rational exploitation, and 85,000 ha of protected watersheds. The latter also serve to protect such species as tapir, jaguar and puma. The total extent of these sixteen Reserves is about half a million hectares, of which some two-thirds are under exploitation.

13. BRUNEI

I.   **Listed Areas :** nil.

V.   **Explanation :**

According to a statement by the Brunei delegation at IUCN's South-east Asia Conservation Conference at Bangkok in December 1965, no areas meet the conditions laid down by ICNP. However, a paper prepared for the UNESCO Regional Working Group which met immediately before the Conference, in November 1965, stated that " under the Brunei Five-year National Development Plan for 1962-1966, provisions are made for the creation of a State Park ".

14. BULGARIA

I.   **Listed areas :** thirty.

A. — RESERVES :

1. Ousoun Bodjak (Lopouchna) Reserve.
2. Djendema Reserve.
3. Parangalitza Reserve.
4. Maritza Lakes (Maritchini Esera) Reserve.
5. Doupkata Reserve.
6. Boatine Reserve.
7. Baevi Doupki Reserve.
8. Koupena Reserve.
9. Bistrichko Branichte Reserve.
10. Srebarna Reserve.
11. Dolna Toptchia Reserve.
12. Alibotouche Reserve.
13. Vassil Kolarov Reserve.
14. Silkossia Reserve.
15. Tchervenata Stena Reserve.
16. Gorna Toptchia Reserve.
17. Gabra Reserve.
18. Ostritza Reserve.
19. Malka Djindjiritza Reserve.
20. Skochnik Reserve.
21. Kaliakra Reserve.
22. Kamtchia Reserve.
23. Tissova Bartchina Reserve.
24. Dervicha Reserve.
25. Patleyna Monastery Reserve.

B. — PEOPLE'S PARKS :

26. Vitocha Park.
27. Vikhren Park.
28. Zlatni Piassatzi Park.
29. Steneto Park.
30. Ropotamo Park.

118

General Introduction :

In the case of the majority of the areas listed no specific details are given of " staff " and " budget ". This is because supervision in fact devolves on the Forests administration and it frequently happens that it is carried out on a part-time basis by Forest rangers during the course of their other duties. Assurances have, however, been given that strict supervision is everywhere maintained and that in every case it can be assumed that the criterion of effectiveness is being substantially met. Similar considerations apply to the Budget. The information received from Sofia gives no details but states specifically in the case of each area that " the funds required to maintain and protect this reserve are annually provided in the National Budget ".

Legislation : based on a Nature Protection decree dated 27 August 1960, brought into force by Rules published on 5 June 1961. This legislation applies equally to Reserves and National Parks (Article 7 of the Rules), the latter being after-wards given the title of People's Parks.

Administration : as previously stated, the responsibility of the Forest department.

Land tenure : state-ownership throughout. Boundaries are everywhere marked by the same symbol — the silhouette of a lammergeyer. The boundaries of several reserves in certain parts of the country have also been fenced.

Tourism : concentrated on the People's Parks and much effort is being put into its development, especially by the State enterprise " Balkantourist ". No charge for entry.

Scientific research : there are several biological stations, and the Universities are very active. The Academy of Sciences has a Nature Protection Commission.

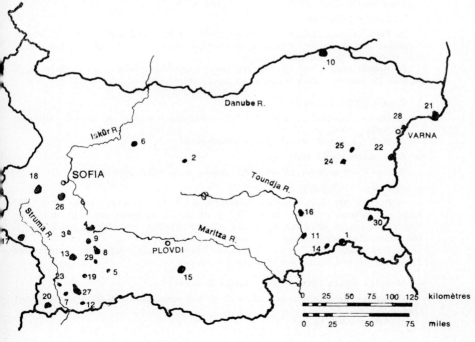

BULGARIA

No information on Bulgaria was included in the previous edition of the List, E/3436 and Part Two.

Details : application of criteria (II), general information (III) and description (IV) :

A. — RESERVES.

1. OUSOUN BODJAK (LOPOUCHNA) RESERVE.

II.
a) Status : no exploitation allowed in this uninhabited high altitude forest area.
b) Area : 2,836 ha.

III.
Date established : 1956.
Tourism and research : no noteworthy developments.

IV.
Altitude : 100-150 m.
a) Part of the hilly Strandja region. Centuries-old forest, in which the dominant species is oak, with an admixture of beech Fagus sylvatica, Quercus hartwissiana, Rhododendron ponticum, Daphne pontica and holly Ilex aquifolium.
b) Red deer Cervus elaphus, wild boar Sus scrofa, marten M. martes; eagle-owl B. bubo.

2. DJENDEMA RESERVE.

II.
a) Status : general protection. No inhabitants.
b) Area : 1,775 ha (of which some 470 ha of rock and deep gorges have never been disturbed by human exploitation).

III.
Date established : 1953.

IV.
Altitude : 1,500-2,000 m.
a) Part of the Balkan mountain chain; beech and oak forest, firwoods, meadows and rocks — forming a spectacular landscape. A 100 m high waterfall is one of the notable features.
b) Brown bear Ursus arctos, red deer, chamois R. rupicapra; golden eagle Aquila chrysaetos, black vulture Aegypius monachus.

3. PARANGALITZA RESERVE.

II.
a) Status : general protection. No commercial traffic or activity allowed.
b) Area : 1,580 ha.
c) Staff : a forest officer and a forest-guard.

III.
Date established : 1933.
Research : a number of scientific studies have been published.

IV.
Altitude : 1,400-2,050 m.
a) Part of Mt. Rila. Spruce forest Picea excelsa occupies about 70 % and Scots pine Pinus sylvestris about 20 % of the area; there are also stands or isolated examples of silver fir Abies alba, Rumelian pine Pinus peuce, beech and aspen Populus tremula.
b) Red deer, roe deer C. capreolus, brown bear; eagle-owl, capercaillie Tetrao urogallus, hazel hen Tetrastes bonasia.

4. MARITZA LAKES (MARITCHINI ESERA) RESERVE.

II.
a) Status : no exploitation allowed in this uninhabited high altitude forest area.
b) Area : 1,509 ha.

120

Date established : 1951; various modifications in 1956, 1960 and 1961.

Tourism : some tourist routes go through this Reserve.

Altitude : 1,900-2,925 m.

a) A high level sector of Mt. Rila, culminating in the Monssala peak. Forests of silver fir, Rumelian pine and mountain pine *Pinus mugo*; high mountain meadows, rocky stretches; specially protected plants are *Primula deorum, Anemone narcissiflora, Aquilegia aurea* and globe flower *Trollius europaeus*.

b) Chamois, brown bear.

5. DOUPKATA RESERVE.

a) Status : general protection.

b) Area : 1,232 ha.

c) Staff : two guards, responsible to two different Conservators, since this Reserve is split between two different Forest sections.

Date established : 1961.

Altitude : 1,100-1,200 m.

a) Part of the Rhodope mountains and falling within the influence of the Mediterranean climate; forests of Scots pine and spruce, some of the trees over 200 years old.

b) No information.

6. BOATINE RESERVE.

a) Status : general protection.

b) Area : 1,226 ha.

c) Staff : one special warden.

Date established : 1948.

Tourism : not permitted.

Altitude : 900-1,500 m.

a) Part of the great Balkan beech forest, with 200 year old trees.

b) No information.

7. BAEVI DOUPKI RESERVE.

a) Status : total protection. Some parts of the reserve have suffered from disturbance, but there are still some good untouched primitive areas.

b) Area : 848 ha.

c) Staff : a special warden.

Date established : 1934.

Tourism : confined to fixed paths.

Altitude : 1,300-2,100 m.

a) A mountainous region which gives an excellent opportunity for studying vegetational succession at different altitudes; larch *Larix decidua,* fir, spruce, fir and spruce mixed, Norway spruce *Picea excelsa,* white pine; alpine meadow, rocks and permanent snow-fields; edelweiss *Leontopodium alpinum,* limestone features such as numerous chasms.

b) Chamois, brown bear; capercaillie.

121

BULGARIA

8. KOUPENA RESERVE.

II.   *a*) Status : general protection.

b) Area : 819 ha.

III.   *Date established :* 1961.

IV.   *Altitude :* 500-800 m.

a) Landscape of the western Rhodope range.

b) No information.

9. BISTRICHKO BRANICHTE RESERVE.

II.   *a*) Status : general protection; one of the two reserves established within the Vitocha Park (No. 26 below).

b) Area : no information.

III.   *Date established :* 1935.

IV.   *Altitude :* 1,430-2,282 m.

a) North-east face of Mt. Vitocha; Norway spruce forest, with other typical montane species, great sallow *Salix caprea,* silver birch *Betula verrucosa,* Scots pine, some silver fir and, at 1,650 m, Rumelian pine; particularly interesting flora with species representative of western Europe, the Arctic and southern Europe, and several endemics.

b) Wild boar, fox *V. vulpes,* rabbit *Oryctolagus cuniculus* and red squirrel *Sciurus vulgaris.*

10. SREBARNA RESERVE.

II.   *a*) Status : this Reserve comprises a lake on which all economic exploitation has been stopped, except for cutting of rushes (by the State enterprise " Kamachit ") and fishing, both restricted to the season after the departure of migratory birds.

b) Area : 600 ha.

c) Staff : one special Forest Guard.

III.   *Date established :* 1948.

Tourism : closed to visitors between March and November except on a special pass.   A film has been made of this Reserve.

Research : there is a biological station in the Reserve, with a full-time naturalist in charge, administered by the Zoological Institute for the Bulgarian Academy of Sciences.

IV.   *Altitude :* 10-11 m.

a) A lake area largerly covered with rushes; many floating islands 1 to 3 metres thick.

b) A rich avifauna : over 100 species have been recorded including Dalmatian Pelican *Pelecanus crispus,* gulls, swans, several herons.   An important nesting area.

122

11. DOLNA TOPTCHIA RESERVE.

I.
 a) Status : total protection; an up-to-date establishment for breeding and rearing pheasants is situated nearby.
 b) Area : 538 ha. Formerly more extensive but reduced in size in 1961.

II.
 Date established : 1960.

V.
 Altitude : 117 m.
 a) Along the bank of the Toundja river; undisturbed forest, in which various creeping plants, notably silk-vine *Periploca graeca* (Asclepiadaceae) and the climbing lily *Smilax excelsa,* are to be found.
 b) Pheasant *Phasianus colchicus.*

12. ALIBOTOUCHE RESERVE.

I.
 a) Status : general protection.
 b) Area : 524 ha.

II.
 Date established : 1951.

V.
 Altitude : 1,140-2,212 m.
 a) The north flank of Slavianka or Alibotouche mountain; limestone formations; redcone pine *Pinus leucodermis* plantations; among the protected species of the natural vegetation are : maidenhair fern *Adiantum capillus-veneris, Fritillaria drenovskyi* and *Viola delphinantha.*
 b) No information.

13. VASSIL KILAROV RESERVE.

I.
 a) Status : general protection.
 b) Area : 420 ha, a little less than the criterion.
 c) Staff : a special warden.

II.
 Date established : 1960.
 Tourism : kept strictly to defined routes.

V.
 Altitude : 1,600-1,850 m.
 a) Situated in the western part of the Rhodope mountains; spruce forest, with trees 100 to 160 years old, and Scots pine; a particularly rich and interesting flora due to the calcareous soil.
 b) Red deer, roe deer, brown bear.

14. SILKOSSIA RESERVE.

I.
 a) Status : general protection.
 b) Area : 390 ha, rather less than the criterion.

II.
 Date established : 1931 (the first Reserve created in Bulgaria).

V.
 Altitude : 100-150 m.
 a) Centuries-old oak forest, typical of Mt. Strandja.
 b) Red deer, wild boar, jackal *Canis aureus.*

123

15. TCHERVENATA STENA RESERVE.

II.   *a*) Status : general protection.

b) Area : 230 ha, well below the criterion, but retention in the List requested because of the rare flora (only station in Bulgaria of the lady's-slipper orchid).

III.   *Date established :* 1962.

IV.   *Altitude :* 800-1,500 m.

a) Part of the central Rhodope mountains; specially protected plants include lady's-slipper orchid *Cypripedium calceolus,* yew *Taxus baccata,* holly, spurge laurel *Daphne laureola,* Haller's pasque-flower *Anemone halleri rhodopea* and the false-whorled teasel *Morina persica*; a number of endemic Balkan species such as *Saxifraga stribrnyi,* the umbellifer *Seseli rhodopeum, Scabiosa rhodopensis, Salvia rhodopea, Hypericum degenii* and the milkwort *Polygala rhodopea;* Mediterranean and sub-mediterranean elements also occur.

b) No information.

16. GORNA TOPTCHIA RESERVE.

II.   *a*) Status : general protection.

b) Area : 100 ha only, but retention in the List requested because this is the only place inland where a sample still exists of forest typical of the shores of the Black Sea and the Kamtchia.

III.   *Date established :* 1951.

IV.   *Altitude :* 118 m.

a) In the river Toundja basin; forest identical to that of the Black Sea coast and of the Kamtchia, and the only place where it can be found inland.

b) No information.

17. GABRA RESERVE.

II.   *a*) Status : general protection. Formerly exploited.

b) Area : 90 ha, but retention in the List requested because of the unique occurrence and undisturbed state of the larch forest in the area.

c) Staff : in view of the interest of this Reserve, a special forest guard is provided.

III.   *Date established :* 1949.

IV.   *Altitude :* 950-1,150 m.

a) Contains the only larch forest in the Mt. Ossogovo area, also oak and beech; a rather dry climatic region.

b) No information.

18. OSTRITZA RESERVE.

II.   *a*) Status : general protection.

b) Area : 78 ha, but retention in the List requested because this Reserve is a " Mediterranean oasis ", with an extraordinarily rich flora.

c) Staff : a forest guard has been appointed to maintain and protect the Reserve.

II.   *Date established :* 1936, as a " National Park ", but later placed in the " Reserves " category.

Tourism : entry by special permit only, the movement of visitors in the Reserve being strictly controlled and confined to fixed routes.

Research : some thirty publications on the flora.

V.   *Altitude :* 750-1,149 m.

a) The Reserve encircles Mt. Ostritza; a Mediterranean flora associated with calcareous soil, rich in rock-plants and plants of alpine meadows; 300 species recorded, including many endemics and several new to science; broad-leaved forest on the northern slopes.

b) No information.

19. MALKA DJINDJIRITZA RESERVE.

I.   *a*) Status : general protection.

b) Area : 68 ha, but retention in the List requested because of the ancient natural stands of Rumelian pine.

II.   *Date established :* 1952.

V.   *Altitude :* 1,900-2,000 m.

a) Northern slopes of Mt. Pirine; *Pinus peuce* over 600 years old.

b) No information.

20. SKOCHNIK RESERVE.

I.   *a*) Status : general protection.

b) Area : 67 ha, but retention in the List requested because of the very old chestnut forest.

II.   *Date established :* 1954.

V.   *Altitude :* 700 m.

a) On the northern slopes of Mt. Belassitza; centuries-old sweet chestnut *Castanea sativa* forest.

b) No information.

21. KALIAKRA RESERVE.

I.   *a*) Status : general protection.

b) Area : 53 ha, but retention in the List requested because of the special interest of the flora and fauna.

II.   *Date established :* 1941.

V.   *Altitude :* sea level to 30 m.

a) A Black Sea headland, with rare limestone-loving plants.

b) The rocks are frequented by Mediterranean monk seals *M. monachus* and shags *Phalacrocorax aristotelis*; the rare mollusc *Zebrina varnensis* occurs.

c) Mediterranean monk seal.

125

22. KAMTCHIA RESERVE.

II.
a) Status : general protection.

b) Area : 52.4 ha, but retention in the List requested because of its special interest (see below) and need for protection.

III.
Date established : 1951.

IV.
Altitude : near sea-level.

a) Part of the ancient virgin forest of the Black Sea coast; centuries-old ash Fraxinus sp. and elm; numerous creeping plants make it difficult to penetrate the forest (Smilax excelsa, Periploca graeca, ivy Hedera helix, traveller's joy Clematis vitalba and the wild grape vine Vitis sylvestris); in the Lessinski and Mazni lagoons the white and yellow waterlilies Nymphaea alba and Nuphar luteum are found.

b) Red deer, roe deer, wild boar, fox, marten, squirrel; rich avifauna (black stork Ciconia nigra, several woodpecker species etc.).

23. TISSOVA BARTCHINA RESERVE.

II.
a) Status : general protection.

b) Area : 19 ha, but retention in the List requested because of its junipers (see below).

III.
Date established : 1949.

IV.
Altitude : 450-650 m.

a) A small Reserve near the Kresna gorge; contains the largest sample of Juniperus excelsa forest in the country.

b) No information.

24. DERVICHA RESERVE.

II.
a) Status : general protection.

b) Area : 11 ha, but retained in the List because the Reserve comprises the only Bulgarian forest in which the horse chestnut is found.

III.
Date established : 1948.

IV.
Altitude : 180 m.

a) Part of the Balkan range; only station of horse chestnut Aesculus hippocastanum in Bulgaria.

b) No information.

25. PATLEYNA MONASTERY RESERVE.

II.
a) Status : general protection.

b) Area : 3 ha only, but retained in the List as the sole Bulgarian station of the Judas-tree, for the protection of which the Reserve was created.

III.
Date established : 1948.

IV.
Altitude : 150 m.

a) On the north flank of the eastern Kodzha Balkan range, near the small town of Preslav, south of Kolarovgrad; Judas-tree Cercis siliquastrum.

b) No information.

126

B. — PEOPLE'S PARKS.

26. VITOCHA PARK.

a) Status : although very much frequented by tourists, this Park has :
(i) general protection throughout; no habitation or exploitation allowed; hunting, fishing and even the picking of flowers forbidden;
(ii) a water-catchment zone completely closed to visitors;
(iii) two Reserves within its boundaries : Bistrichko Branichte (for spruce forest; listed above as No. 9) and Torpheno Branichte (for high montane peat-bog).

b) Area : 22,800 ha.

c) Staff : well supervised, by both the Central Governement and Municipal authorities in Sofia.

Date established : 1934.

Tourism : near Sofia, with which it is connected by a panoramic road, this Park has a network of roads, tourist chalets and resthouses, two restaurants maintained by the State enterprise " Balkantourist ", two cableways and fixed " camp-fire " sites.

Research : systematic scientific studies are carried out; the Academy of Sciences maintains a scientific station in the Yourouchki Grob area; there is a meteorological observatory on the top of the highest peak, Tcherni Vrakh.

Altitude : 700-2,260 m.

a) A mountainous region culminating in the Tcherni Vrakh, with its observatory; broad-leaved forest of oak, beech, birch, hornbeam *Carpinus betulus* and maple *Acer* sp., also coniferous forest of spruce and pine; the open areas are grassy or stony; specially protected plants include globe flower, *Lilium jankae, Clematis alpina, Anemone narcissiflora* and *Aquilegia aurea.*

b) Brown bear; many deer, chamois (reintroduced); varied birdlife.

27. VIKHREN PARK.

a) Status : the Park has three zones :

(i) an important scientific zone, where no exploitation is allowed and visitors have to keep to fixed paths;
(ii) a tourist zone, sprinkled with chalets, roads, etc., where tree-felling, to keep the forest in a healthy state, and reafforestation are practised;
(iii) a zone in which the forest is fully exploited.

b) Area : 6,736 ha.

c) Staff : the Park is strictly supervised.

Date established : 1962.

Tourism : very active in the zone allotted to it. The Park is adjacent to Baevi Doupki Reserve (No. 7 in the List).

Altitude : 1,100-2,915 m.

a) The higher levels of Mt. Pirine, together with some of the surrounding country; forests mainly of Norway spruce, Rumelian pine and redcone pine; alpine meadows, rocky zone, lakes, stretches of permanent snow.

b) Chamois, brown bear.

5

BULGARIA

28. ZLATNI PIASSATZI PARK.

II. a) Status : no habitation or exploitation is permitted.

b) Area : 2,031 ha.

III. *Date established :* 1943.

Tourism : from the point of view of visitors, this Park is more akin to a city park.

IV. *Altitude :* 20-250 m.

a) A woody belt of nearly virgin forest surrounding the holiday homes area (" Golden Sands ") of Varna, which is 17 km away.

b) No information.

29. STENETO PARK.

II. a) Status : no habitation or exploitation (other than touristic is permitted).

b) Area : 1,666 ha.

III. *Date established :* 1963.

Tourism : the Park forms the centre of what is in general an area well developed for tourists. One of its tourist attractions is a giant tree.

IV. *Altitude :* 1,000-1,550 m.

a) Situated in the gorge of the river Tcherni Ossam; ancient coniferous and broad-leaved forest, the latter mainly beech; precipitous valley walls and waterfalls.

b) Red deer, roe deer, chamois, brown bear; golden eagle.

30. ROPOTAMO PARK.

II. a) Status : forest protected from exploitation. Reserves within the Park boundaries include — Arkoutino (97 ha), Morski Peline (14 ha), Zmiiski Ostrov (14 ha) and Vodnite Lilii.

b) Area : 847 ha.

III. *Date established :* 1940, modifications in 1956, and declared a People's Park in 1962, when its size was enlarged.

Tourism : numerous hotels, motels, restaurants and camping sites in the vicinity of the Park. A tarmac road to the Park from Bourgas, and it can also be reached by water.

IV. *Altitude :* sea level.

a) Situated where the Ropotamo river enters the Black Sea; sand dunes and halophytic vegetation; typical coastal forest (*Smilax excelsa, Periploca graeca,* traveller's joy, ivy and wild grapevine, ash and centuries-old elms *Ulmus* sp.); the four Reserves included in the area (see II(a) above) were established respectively to protect — aquatic vegetation and birds (Arkoutino); *Artemisia maritima* (Morski Peline=sea wormwood); *Nymphaea alba* (Vodnite Lilii=water lily); the river-mouth, with its cactus-covered banks and waterfowl (Zmiiski Ostrov=Snake Island).

b) Red deer, roe deer, fallow deer *D. dama,* wild boar; rich avifauna includes white-tailed sea-eagle *Haliaetus albicilla,* wild geese, the black woodpecker *Dryocopus martius* and other woodpecker species.

128

Areas excluded :

A. — Twenty-six Reserves of small size, which have no special reason to justify their inclusion in the List.

B. — 366 " Natural Monuments ".

C. — Two " Protected Sites ".

15. BURMA

Listed Areas : one.

1. Pidaung Game Sanctuary.

General Introduction :

The information given below is based on a private communication received some time ago. The Burmese authorities themselves have not yet found it possible to respond to official requests for further details.

The legislative basis of reserves or game sanctuaries was originally provided by the " Burma Game Rules " of 1927. Responsibility for their administration now lies with the Forest Department of the Ministry of Agriculture.

The previous edition of the List, E/3436, included 12 " hunting reserves ", of which the Pidaung reserve was one.

Details : application of criteria (II), general information (III) and description (IV) :

1. PIDAUNG GAME SANCTUARY.

a) Status : control is more strict than in the case of the ordinary " hunting reserve ", but certain user rights have locally been given official recognition, notably in the vicinity of six villages — e.g. entry and free movement, fuel-cutting and gathering (of fruit and flowers, etc.). There are three tea plantations inside the reserve toward the south. Fishing is permitted everywhere.

b) Area : 72,500 ha (comprising the main block of 51,000 ha, a " southern extension " of some 20,000 ha and two small extensions on the east and west).

c) Staff : 12 units (a Game Ranger, 4 Game Keepers and 7 armed guards).

d) Budget : the salaries paid to the staff would satisfy the criterion.

Date established : a " Pidaung Reserve " has existed since 1913. The " Pidaung Game Sanctuary " was created by a Notice published on 8 April 1938. A proposal has been made to convert it into " the Kachin State Park ".

Land tenure : public ownership.

Tourism : the Sanctuary is near the city of Myitkyina and the railway. There are 72 km of motorable road, including a closed-circuit of 32 km, and 78 km of footpaths. Salt licks, observation posts (machan), a Forest Resthouse (the hotel planned in 1940 has not yet been built) and a two-roomed mountain-hut at Kasung Hka are provided, but there are few visitors.

BURMA

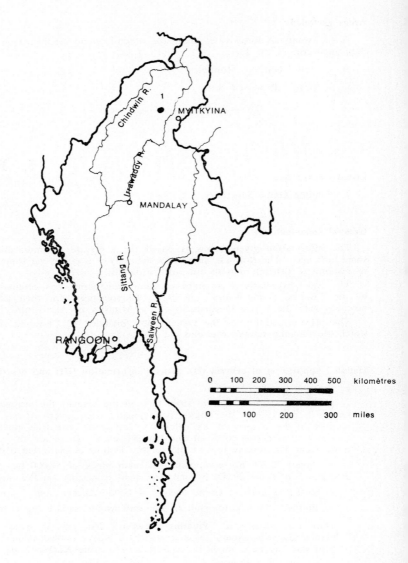

Research : no specific organisation. A report was prepared for IUCN by the American Committee for International Wildlife Protection in 1963.

IV.   Altitude : 800-2,200 m.
       a) Comprises grassy plains or " lwins " typical of the Irrawaddy river valley, and hills covered with thick evergreen jungle; clumps of giant Ficus spp.

130

b) Elephant, buffalo *Bubalus bubalis,* banteng *Bos banteng burmanicus,* sambar *Cervus unicolor,* leopard, sun bear *Helarctos malayanus,* hog-deer *Axis porcinus,* tiger, muntjac *Muntiacus* sp.; many gallinaceous birds such as pea-cocks, pheasants and jungle-fowl.

Areas excluded :

The legal status of other "hunting reserves" is theoretically the same as that of the Pidaung Sanctuary, being based on the 1927 Game Rules, but the standard of supervision is markedly lower and many sectors, much more so than in the case of Pidaung, have seriously deteriorated since protection was first accorded. This has been due, first, to the War, during which the Japanese encouraged or carried out much felling of the forests and killing of animals, and, later, to poaching and illegal cutting of wood.

The eleven other "hunting reserves" listed in the previous edition of the List are :

1.	Schwezet-taw	55,134 ha
2.	Kyatthin	26,920 ha
3.	Shwe-u-daung	20,967 ha
4.	Kahilu	16,049 ha
5.	Mulayit	13,719 ha
6.	Maymyo	12,684 ha
7.	Mongmit (adjacent to No. 3)	11,648 ha
8.	Tavoy	4,918 ha
9.	Kadoe	2,330 ha
10.	Taunggyi	1,553 ha
11.	Wetthigan	518 ha

16. BURUNDI

Listed Areas : nil.

Areas excluded :

The partial hunting reserve of Lake Rwihinda. This lake, with its numerous floating islands, is an important breeding place of migratory and resident birds, some fifty species of which have been listed. The lake covers an area of about 600 ha. The Reserve, in which all birds have been strictly protected since 1956, takes in a belt one kilometre wide round the margin of the lake.

It should also be noted that in 1963 a mission of the joint FAO/IUCN "African Special Project" drew attention to the possibility of establishing at least one National Park, to be situated on the wooded watershed of the Congo-Nile, and a full Reserve for fauna and flora in the savannah country of the Ruzizi Plain. The actual delta of the Ruzizi river was also recommended for the setting up of a bird sanctuary.

17. BYELORUSSIAN SSR

See under No. 130 Union of Soviet Socialist Republics.

18. CAMBODIA

Listed Areas : one.

I.
    1. Angkor National Park.

General Introduction :

There is as yet no specific law covering national parks and natural reserves in Cambodia (the Angkor National Park having been set up by what amounted to an *ad hoc* procedure). Attention is however being given to the drafting of a law which would provide for a more regular procedure for establishing natural reserves by decree (" Kret ") made on the initiative of the Minister of Agriculture.

Responsibility for the maintenance and running of protected natural sites (supervision and protection from poaching and illegal cutting of wood, reafforestation) lies with the Service des Eaux et Forêts.

The Angkor National Park was included in Part Two of the previous edition of the List.

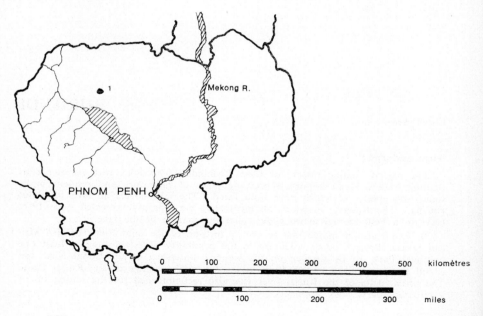

Details : application of criteria (II), general information (III) and description (IV) :

1. ANGKOR NATIONAL PARK.

a) Status : there is complete protection in the uninhabited perimeter zone. During the troubled period between 1945 and 1954, some clearing was carried out in the areas included in the National Park, since the protective measures decreed were directed chiefly to preserving the ruins of the famous temples. In the process villagers destroyed not only many hectares of high forest but also practically all the existing game. But in 1963, the Royal Government removed most of the trespassers and decided to undertake the reafforestation of the clearings. The " Conservation of Angkor " organisation is collaborating in this task with the Service des Eaux et Forêts, which has taken up the work of reafforestation with great enthusiasm and vigour and also plans to reintroduce animals, such as sambar, muntjac, monkeys and peafowl. A start has been made in the 48 ha (800×600 m) surrounds of the little Banteay Kdey temple, where of the various introduced species the sambar *Cervus unicolor* has been the most successful.

b) Area : 10,717 ha, but an alteration is planned whereby a sector of the Western Baray would be cut out of the Park, apparently because it has too many inhabitants to make it possible ever to give it proper protection; this would be compensated by adding some sectors on the east. It is to be hoped that this sacrifice of the Western Baray can somehow be avoided.

c) Staff : 45 wardens, of whom the majority needless to say are employed more for the supervision of the temples than of the forest.

d) Budget : U.S. $ 4,200 a year for fauna protection and about $ 5,000 for reafforestation, in addition to the very large budget devoted to the " Monuments and Sites " — U.S. $ 400,000 by the Cambodian Treasury and U.S. $ 450,000 deriving from French sources.

Date established : 1925.

Administration : in addition to the responsibilities of the Service des Eaux et Forêts (described in the General Introduction), the Temples themselves are administered by the " Conservation of Angkor " organisation, which is responsible to the Ministry of Education and the Fine Arts, and has very extensive powers within the perimeter. Further, the Ministry of Tourism is responsible for information and interpretative services. A Management Committee combines representatives of these three departments, to ensure necessary coordination and, by a decree No. 464-CE of 20 July 1967, the Government has appointed a serving officer of the Army as a special delegate, with responsibilities for the artistic treasures, forests and reafforestation of the Park.

Land tenure : public ownership.

Tourism : naturally most of the visitors are attracted by the archaeological features of the Park. SOKHAR (the Société Khmère des Auberges Royales), which is responsible to the Ministry of Tourism, runs the huge " Auberge Royale des Temples " in the National Park near Angkor-Wat and several other hotels nearby at Siem Reap.

Altitude : 120 m.

a) The landscape comprises the remnants, such as escaped clearing, of the thick forest which had swallowed up the temples.

b) Mention has already been made of the plan to reintroduce into the forest certain mammals such as monkeys and deer, as well as birds (peafowl). One feature of the fauna, which is however of great interest and well worth protec-

133

tion, is the fish population which has established itself in the reservoir lake built by the Khmers, the famous Western Baray, and the canals which lead out of it. This population has no connection with that of the surrounding hydrographic system, and its endemism certainly makes its study and, hence, its protection a matter of importance. Unfortunately it is precisely the areas bordering the Western Baray which contain most inhabitants and the proposal, previously mentioned, to change the Park boundaries contemplates excluding this zone from the Park, though it is one in which protection should be strengthened rather than removed.

V. **Areas excluded :**

A number of proposals are being worked out, by which, briefly, existing faunal reserves would be regraded and classified as National Parks, strict Nature Reserves and protected zones under the " Kram " (the law being drafted to regulate hunting and nature conservation). The list of these reserves is as follows and the position reached as at January 1966 is indicated :

1. Phnom-Priech : The latest information indicates that this large faunal Reserve, of 195,120 ha, now qualifies for inclusion in the List and should find a place in the next Edition. The forest is free from exploitation, no agriculture or industrial activities are allowed and wild animals, which include the unique bovine, the kouprey (a Red Data Book species), are strictly protected. Considerable funds have been made available over the last ten years and management practices have included bush-fire prevention etc. The staff comprises an officer of the Service des Eaux et Forêts and 10 guards (four of them in charge of wildlife).

2. Kirikom : 81,720 ha; 3 guard-houses, 4 guards.
3. Phom Kravahn : 280,640 ha; 3 guard-houses, 5 guards.
4. Koulen Promtep : 1,460,000 ha; 2 guard-houses, 5 game-keepers.
5. Lomphat : 197,480 ha; no guard-houses as yet, but 5 game-keepers.

Reference should also be made to :

Forest Reserves, of which there are altogether more than 200, covering 4 million hectares, but in which only the forest itself is protected;
The Tonle Sap Reserve established for pisciculture.

19. CAMEROON

I. **Listed Areas :** three.

1. Boubandjidah National Park.
2. Benue National Park.
3. Waza National Park.

General Introduction :

Responsibility for administering the Parks is vested in the Direction des Eaux et Forêts of the Secrétariat d'Etat de la Production Rurale.

No mention was made of Cameroon in either E/3436 or Part Two of the previous edition of the List.

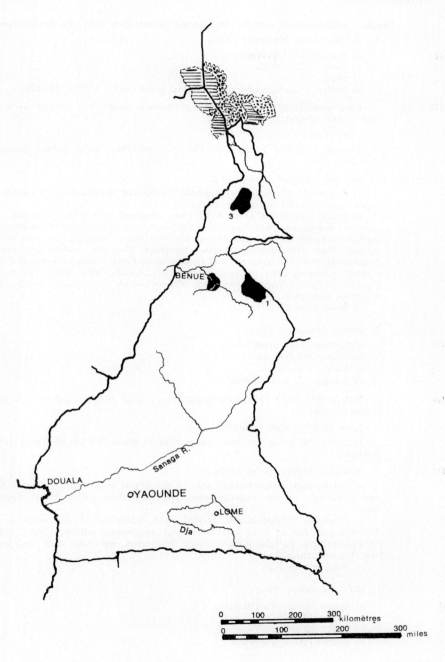

BENUE

Sanaga R.

DOUALA

oYAOUNDE

oLOME

Dja

0   100   200   300 kilomètres

0   100   200   300 miles

135

Details : application of criteria (II), general information (III) and description (IV) :

1. BOUBANDJIDAH NATIONAL PARK.

II.

a) Status : total protection.
b) Area : 220,000 ha.
c) Staff : 12 units.
d) Budget : maintenance and running (1964-1965) : U.S. $ 140,000.

III.

Date established : 1964, having previously since 1947 ranked as a forest and faunal reserve.

Land tenure : state ownership.

Tourism : 32-bed hotel; 240 km of motorable track; landing-ground for aircraft.

IV.

Altitude : highest point 600 m.

a) A peneplain covered with woody Soudanian savannah (of a hygrophilous type), gallery-forest along the rivers.

b) Black rhinoceros *Diceros bicornis,* elephant *Loxodonta africana,* Derby eland of the eastern race *Taurotragus derbianus congolanus,* oribi *Ourebia oribi,* buffalo *Syncerus caffer,* topi *Damaliscus korrigum,* hartebeest *Alcelaphus buselaphus,* roan *Hippotragus equinus,* reedbuck *Redunca arundinum,* bushbuck *Tragelaphus scriptus,* grey and red-flanked duiker *Sylvicapra grimmia* and *Cephalophus rufilatus,* lion, leopard, hyaena *C. crocuta,* wild dog *Lycaon pictus,* cheetah *Acinonyx jubatus,* wart-hog *Phacochoerus aethiopicus,* giraffe, hippopotamus, crocodile.

c) Black rhinoceros.

2. BENUE NATIONAL PARK.

II.

a) Status : total protection.
b) Area : 180,000 ha.
c) Staff : 9 units.
d) Budget : U.S. $ 15,000.

III.

Date established : 1964, having previously since 1932 ranked as a forest and faunal reserve.

Land tenure : state ownership.

Tourism : no hotel, but four camps with 26 beds; 200 km of tracks; landing-ground.

IV.

Altitude : highest point 1,100 m.

a) Forms part of the western side of the Benue river valley; wooded Soudanian savannah of the hygrophilous type, with fine gallery-forest along the rivers.

b) Elephant, hippopotamus, Derby eland, waterbuck *Kobus ellipsiprymnus,* Buffon's kob *Kobus kob,* hartebeest, topi, reedbuck, bushbuck, grey and red-flanked duikers, buffalo, giraffe, black rhinoceros, wart-hog, wild dog, leopard, lion, hyaena, cheetah.

c) Black rhinoceros.

3. WAZA NATIONAL PARK.

II.

a) Status : total protection.
b) Area : 170,000 ha.
c) Staff : 22 units.
d) Budget : U.S. $ 20,000.

II.   *Date established :* 1962, having previously since 1934 ranked as a forest and faunal reserve.

Land tenure : state ownership.

Tourism : 60-bed hotel; 420 km of tracks; landing-ground.

V.   *Altitude :* 320 m.

a) Part of the Chad basin, the landscape on the west being forested with a Soudano-Sahelian flora (dominated by acacias), and to the east great grassy plains, which are flooded during the rainy season.

b) Giraffe, Buffon's kob, bushbuck, reedbuck, grey duiker, topi, roan, Korin gazelle *Gazella rufifrons,* wart-hog, elephant, lion, cheetah, leopard, hyaena; large numbers of birds near the swamps (pelicans, crowned crane *Balearica pavonina,* ducks, geese, egrets, marabou *Leptoptilus crumeniferus,* hornbills, secretary-bird *Sagittarius serpentarius,* bateleur eagle *Terathopius ecaudatus,* fish-eagle *Cuncuma vocifer,* jabiru *Ephippiorhynchus senegalensis*).

V.   **Areas excluded :**

A. — The Faro Forest and Faunal Reserve : 330,000 ha. This will perhaps eventually merit consideration for inclusion in the List. At present its legal status is not sufficiently secure and its staff (7 units) and budget (U.S. $ 4,000) fail to meet the criteria.

B. — The following Faunal Reserves :

The Dja	526,000 ha, only 1 guard.
Campo	330,000 ha, 1 guard.
Douala-Edéa	160,000 ha, no supervision.
Bafia	42,000 ha, 1 guard.
Nanga-Eboko	16,000 ha, 1 guard.
Kala Maloué	4,000 ha, 1 guard.

All these Reserves give protection to game animals only.

C. — Mention may also be made of :

The Sanaga Hippopotamus Reserve : a 200 km stretch of the Sanaga river; no special supervision;

The Ossa and Meria Lakes Bird Reserve; also without any particular supervision;

The Upper Faro Hippopotamus Reserve : over 10 km of the Faro river.

D. — Finally, two game reserves in West Cameroon should perhaps be included in the List, when adequate information can be obtained to supplement the few details received at the end of 1966 :

1. Kimbi River Game Reserve : 4,960 ha, 2 guards, budget $ 4,800.
2. Mbi Crater Game Reserve : 366 ha, 1 guard, budget $ 4,800.

137

I.   Listed **Areas** : forty-seven.

A. — NATIONAL PARKS :

1. Wood Buffalo National Park.
2. Jasper National Park.
3. Banff National Park.
4. Prince Albert National Park.
5. Riding Mountain National Park.
6. Kootenay National Park.
7. Glacier National Park.
8. Yoho National Park.
9. Cape Breton Highlands National Park.
10. Waterton Lakes National Park.

11. Terra Nova National Park.
12. Mount Revelstoke National Park.
13. Fundy National Park.
14. Elk Island National Park.
15. Prince Edward Island National Park.
16. Point Pelee National Park.
17. Georgian Bay Island National Park.
18. St. Lawrence Islands National Park.

B. — PROVINCIAL PARKS :

a) Alberta :
19. Cypress Hills.
20. Dinosaur.
21. Crimson Lake.
22. Entrance.

b) Ontario :
23. Algonquin.
24. Quetico.
25. Lake Superior.
26. Mississagi.
27. Killarney.
28. Sibley.
29. Obatanga.
30. Bon Echo.
31. Nagagamisis.
32. Greenwater.
33. Neys.

34. Esker Lakes.
35. Grundy Lake.
36. Ojibway.
37. Rondeau.

c) Quebec :
38. La Vérendrye.
39. Les Laurentides.
40. Mont Tremblant.
41. Gaspesie.
42. Mont Orford.

d) Newfoundland :
43. Serpentine.
44. Pitts Pond.
45. Barachois Ponds.
46. Butter Pot.
47. Sir Richard Squires Memorial Park.

General Introduction :

In order to avoid repetition, it seems desirable to summarise here the information which applies to all or most of the listed areas. Beginning with the criteria :

II.   *a) Status :* all the 47 areas strictly conform to the criterion of total protection laid down by the International Commission on National Parks. On this basis it has been possible to include all the Federal National Parks, but in the case of the Provincial Parks " the result of applying higher standards of protection and management is that some of the areas previously listed (in E/3436) are not now (4 August 1964) advanced by the Provinces as satisfying the criteria ".

138

CANADA

CANADA

b) Area : as will be seen from the detailed information on each Park, the criterion of size is largely satisfied, although certain exceptions advocated by the Canadian authorities have been allowed, e.g. : " where our national parks are small, there are, of course, special reasons for establishing these areas as national parks. Georgian Bay Islands National Park was established to preserve examples of the islands that form the archipelago in Georgian Bay. Point Pelee National Park is an unique area containing the " Carolinian " type of vegetation; in addition it is a key point on the migration routes of waterfowl and other birds and an important bird sanctuary. St. Lawrence Island National Park was established to preserve for public enjoyment examples of the unique and well-known Thousand Islands area of the St. Lawrence River. Prince Edward Island National Park is an elongated shoreline park established to preserve an outstanding example of dunes, beaches, cliffs and backshore and the associated biotic communities ".

c) Staff :

(i) The total area of Federal National Parks is of the order of 7,494,400 ha (29,275 sq. m.), of which the huge " Wood Buffalo " on the borders of northern Alberta and the Northwest Territories accounts for no less than 4,428,000 ha (17,300 sq. m.). If one excludes the latter rather exceptional case — it is an uninhabited area —, the remaining 3 million hectares would on the basis of the International Commission on National Parks criterion demand in principle some 300 full-time supervisory personnel. The actual strength of the Parks staff, including the headquarters office at Ottawa, is quoted by the National Parks Branch as follows :

15 Park superintendents; 222 administrative, technical and scientific officers (including the Director, Assistant-Director, Regional Directors and Divisional Chiefs); 128 members of the Park Warden Service; 654 labour and maintenance men; 1,495 seasonal staff.

(ii) According to the information received, the Provincial Parks staff satisfies the criterion laid down by the ICNP. To take Quebec as an example, the relevant section of the report reads : " In the two largest Parks, Les Laurentides and La Vérendrye, we have not at first sight the warden strength required by the size of these Parks. It must be emphasised, however, that the respective totals of 43 and 30 wardens and patrolmen refer solely to staff specifically employed on surveillance. We have not taken into account the Lands and Forests department fire-fighters, who live in the parks and also have responsibilities as water-bailiffs and game-keepers. In addition one could well include the camp staff who, although mainly occupied in administrative duties, are also responsible for seeing that fishing regulations are observed. In short, although the figures quoted for these two parks work out at only .39 and .25 wardens per 10,000 ha, this does not really represent the true situation. We can therefore claim that for the five Parks listed the criteria laid down by the International Commission are in fact fully satisfied ".

d) Budget : since budgetary provisions are closely linked with the size of staff, it can be accepted without further elaboration that for Canada as a whole the ICNP criterion is largely satisfied.

Under the heading of general information, the following points may be noted :

III.   *Administration :* the National Parks Act of 1930, as revised in 1952, vests the administration of the Canadian National Parks in the Ministry of Indian Affairs and Northern Development (National and Historic Parks Branch). It is subdivided into three regional sections : West, Central and Atlantic. Administration of Provincial Parks is also the responsibility of the public service.

140

Land tenure : public ownership throughout, both at the Federal and Provincial level.

Tourism : a considerable effort has been made to organise facilities for tourism and public information, through the Information and Interpretative (Park Naturalist) Sections of the Federal Department. Similar efforts are being made at the Provincial level.

Research : naturalists attached to the Parks Department at Ottawa and Field Biologists of the Canadian Wildlife Service conduct research mainly in connection with problems arising from the scientific management of the protected areas, notably the control of hunting. Collecting for scientific purposes is subject to special licence. A special effort is made to support the two Sections which, as noted above, are responsible for tourist organisation and public information.

All the National Parks and most of the Provincial Parks now listed were also included and described in the previous edition of the List, E/3436.

Details : application of criteria (II), general information (III) and description (IV) :

N.B. — Information under sections II *a*), *c*) and *d*) is only included when it amplifies or differs from that given in the General Introduction.

A. — NATIONAL PARKS.

1. Wood Buffalo National Park (Alberta).

I.
   a) Status : the exercise of certain traditional Indian rights is still permitted.
   b) Area : 4,428,000 ha.

II. *Date established :* 1922.

Tourism : no accommodation, except for a medium-sized chalet used by summer vacationers.

V. *Altitude :* 212-732 m.
   a) Created specifically for the protection of the remaining bison herds; a sample of the vast stretches of the central Canadian plain.
   b) Wood buffalo *Bison bison athabascae* and plains buffalo *Bison b. bison*; also a population of hybrid bison; migrating birds : geese, duck, swans; the whooping crane *Grus americana* nests in the Park.
   c) Whooping crane; wood bison.

2. Jasper National Park (Alberta).

I.
   a) Status : the town of Jasper is situated within the Park.
   b) Area : 1,075,000 ha.

II. *Date established :* 1907.

Tourism : several hotels at Jasper; 960 km of road; 470,000 visitors a year.

V. *Altitude :* 1,058-3,747 m (the summit of Mt. Columbia).
   a) Part of the Rocky Mountains in which numerous peaks and ridges are separated by deep valleys; lakes and the famous glaciers of the Columbia Icefield; hot springs; coniferous forests (pine and Douglas fir *Pseudotsuga*) cover the lower slopes (up to 1,800 or 2,000 m), above which there is a typically alpine landscape.

141

b) Grizzly bear *Ursus arctos,* mule deer *Odocoileus hemionus,* bighorn sheep *Ovis canadensis,* Rocky Mountain goat *Oreamnus americanus,* caribou *Rangifer tarandus,* wapiti *Cervus canadensis,* moose *A. alces*; many fur-bearing animals; eagles.

3. Banff National Park (Alberta).

II. *b*) Area : 656,000 ha, adjoining No. 2 Jasper National Park.

III. *Date established :* 1887.

Tourism : the town of Banff with 3,000 inhabitants is situated within the Park, and has lavish hotel facilities. There is also a famous group of hotels at Lake Louise : 1,650,000 visitors a year; two museums; the Banff area is a popular centre for winter sports and summer activities.

IV. *Altitude :* 1,383-3,628 m (summit of Mt. Forbes).

a) Typical of the central part of the Canadian Rockies, with many peaks and lakes and excellent examples of tectonic features such as faulted and anticlinal blocks, etc.; hot springs; forests of pine, spruce *Picea,* fir, aspen *Populus tremuloides* and (above 1,350 m) birch *Betula* sp.

b) Varied and abundant fauna : Rocky Mountain goat, bighorn sheep, mule deer, moose, wapiti, grizzly and black bear *Ursus americanus*; birds include golden eagle *Aquila chrysaetos,* ptarmigan *Lagopus* sp., the grosbeak *Pheucticus melanocephalus,* waterfowl.

4. Prince Albert National Park (Saskatchewan).

II. *b*) Area : 383,000 ha.

III. *Date established :* 1927.

Tourism : 135,000 visitors a year; hotels at Waskesiu.

IV. *Altitude :* 532-900 m.

a) Numerous lakes and rivers among coniferous and broad-leaved forests (pine, fir, birch, aspen); geologically a transitional strata zone.

b) Mule deer, wapiti, black bear; wolf *Canis lupus,* coyote *Canis latrans,* lynx *Felis lynx*; muskrat *Ondatra* sp., beaver *Castor fiber*; abundant waterfowl.

5. Riding Mountain National Park (Manitoba).

II. *b*) Area : 294,000 ha.

III. *Date established :* 1929.

Tourism : hotels; 700,000 visitors a year; a museum at Wasagaming, the headquarters of the Park.

IV. *Altitude :* highest point 600 m.

a) A wooded plateau of which the 300-350 m high escarpment dominates the neighbouring plain; many glacial tarns, some several kilometres in length; among the commoner trees are white and black spruce, maple *Acer* sp. and birch; the landscape ranges from prairie and parkland to typical eastern forest.

b) Interesting fauna and avifauna, including grizzly and black bears, deer, wapiti, moose; coyote, wolf, beaver, several species of squirrel; swans, cormorant, pelican, bittern *Botaurus lentiginosus.*

142

6. KOOTENAY NATIONAL PARK (British Columbia).

I.

II.
b) Area : 139,000 ha.

Date established : 1920.

V.
Tourism : motels with the Park boundaries; 570,000 visitors a year; the Radium Hot Springs have swimming baths with natural hot water.

Altitude : highest point 3,440 m (summit of Mt. Deltaform).

a) Part of the Canadian Rockies, of special geological interest (hot mineral springs, canyons); forest in the valleys, alpine meadows at higher levels.

b) The fauna is typical of this part of the Rockies, with black bear, wapiti, mule deer and Rocky Mountain goat.

7. GLACIER NATIONAL PARK (British Columbia).

I.
b) Area : 135,250 ha.

II.
Date established : 1886.

Tourism : one motel in the Park; 750,000 visitors a year.

V.
Altitude : highest point 3,423 m (summit of Mt. Dawson).

a) In the mountains of British Columbia, with snow peaks, glaciers and lakes; contains the largest caverns known in Canada; thick coniferous forest; alpine tundra.

b) Black and grizzly bears, caribou, moose, wapiti, mule deer and Rocky Mountain goat.

8. YOHO NATIONAL PARK (British Columbia).

I.
b) Area : 129,750 ha.

II.
Date established : 1920.

Tourism : this Park, which adjoins the Banff National Park in Alberta (No. 3 above), has the town of Field within its borders : 675,000 visitors a year.

V.
Altitude : 1,440-3,492 m (summit of Mt. Hungabee).

a) A mountainous region with peaks, snow and ice fields, and waterfalls of which the best known is the Takakaw Falls, 540 m high; thick forest on lower slopes and in the canyons; lakes set in alpine meadows, which are certainly among the most beautiful mountain lakes in North America.

b) Fauna typical of the Canadian Rockies.

9. CAPE BRETON HIGHLANDS NATIONAL PARK (Nova Scotia).

I.
b) Area : 93,950 ha.

II.
Date established : 1956.

Tourism : there is a lodge-cum-motel in the Park and other accommodation just outside it in the fishing villages on the borders of the Park; 600,000 visitors a year.

V.
Altitude : highest point 524 m.

a) A region of hills and mountains extending from the Atlantic Ocean to the Gulf of St. Lawrence; the lower slopes are covered with broad-leaved and coniferous forest (fir, maple, beech, birch), while the higher plateau has thickets of everlastings and mosses.

143

  b) Mule deer, wapiti, moose, lynx, beaver, muskrat, otter *Lutra canadensis*; many species of birds including black guillemot *Cepphus grylle* and puffin *Fratercula arctica*.

10. WATERTON LAKES NATIONAL PARK (Alberta).

II. *b*) Area : 51,950 ha.

III. *Date established :* 1895, forming part of an "International national park" with the Glacier National Park of the U.S.A. and officially known as the Waterton-Glacier International Peace Park.

  Tourism : a small group of hotels and motels within the Park provides accommodation, and there are 440,000 visitors a year.

IV. *Altitude :* 1,278-2,692 m (summit of Mt. Alderson).

  a) A very wild montane area of glacial formations (cirques, trough valleys, lakes); the dense coniferous forests are dominated by abrupt scarps, especially in the red clays and yellow shales areas; the flora of the alpine meadows is the best to be found in any national park of Canada.

  b) Mule deer, bighorn sheep and Rocky Mountain goat, grizzly and black bears, wapiti, moose; some paddocked bison.

11. TERRA NOVA NATIONAL PARK (Newfoundland).

II. *b*) Area : 39,250 ha.

III. *Date established :* 1957.

  Tourism : there is a motel in the Park; 55,000 visitors a year.

IV. *Altitude :* sea level to 320 m.

  a) Forest with bare ground and rocky hills, associated with the shaded gullies leading down to the sea; in fact a typical sample of the coastal landscape of this region, with bays, promontories and inlets.

  b) Moose, woodland variety of caribou, black bear, lynx, muskrat, beaver, many species of birds.

12. MOUNT REVELSTOKE NATIONAL PARK (British Columbia).

II. *b*) Area : 25,600 ha.

III. *Date established :* 1914.

  Tourism : accommodation is available in the town of Revelstoke, outside the Park; 750,000 visitors a year.

IV. *Altitude :* 456-2,774 m (summit of Mt. Coursier).

  a) Alpine ridges and plateau, with snowfields, glaciers, lakes, alpine meadows and a very rich flora.

  b) Grizzly and black bears, caribou, mule deer.

13. FUNDY NATIONAL PARK (New Brunswick).

II. *b*) Area : 20,350 ha.

III. *Date established :* 1948.

  Tourism : a motel in the Park and other accommodation just outside it. 500,000 visitors a year.

V.   *Altitude :* sea level to 380 m.

a) A hilly plateau of which the steep wooded flanks overlook the Bay of Fundy; spruce and balsam-fir *Abies balsama* mixed with maple.

b) Moose, deer, black bear; many species of fur-bearing animals and of birds; also fauna and flora of the intertidal zone.

14. ELK ISLAND NATIONAL PARK (Alberta).

I.   *b)* Area : 19,250 ha.

II.   *Date established :* 1913.

Tourism : accommodation outside the Park; 200,000 visitors a year.

V.   *Altitude :* highest point 755 m.

a) An area of hills, meadows, lakes and forests of aspen and spruce.

b) The plains race of bison, deer, wapiti, moose.

15. PRINCE EDWARD ISLAND NATIONAL PARK.

I.   *b)* Area : 1,790 ha.

II.   *Date established :* 1937.

Tourism : the only accommodation in the Park itself is provided by one Lodge, but there are numerous other chalets in the neighbourhood.

V.   *Altitude :* highest point 8 m.

a) Part of the north coast of Prince Edward Island in the Gulf of St. Lawrence; sandy beaches, dunes, low sandstone cliffs; forests of red and other species of maple, white spruce; lakes.

b) Fur-bearing mammals, such as muskrat, squirrel, fox *Vulpes* sp., mink *Mustela vison* and American marten *Martes americana*; a good avifauna.

16. POINT PELEE NATIONAL PARK (Ontario).

I.   *b)* Area : 1,535 ha.

II.   *Date established :* 1918.

Tourism : no accommodation, but 780,000 day visitors a year.

V.   *Altitude :* highest point 175 m.

a) A section of a peninsula in Lake Erie; the southern part is very wooded while on the north there are lagoons and marshes; the common trees are red oak *Quercus* sp., red cedar *Juniperus* sp., maple, hackberry *Celtis* sp., cactus, prickly pear *Opuntia* and many southern species found nowhere else in Canada.

b) Deer, red fox *V. vulpes,* muskrat, raccoon *Procyon lotor,* coyote; many species of birds, both breeding and migrants (the Park is an important stopping-place for migrants).

17. GEORGIAN BAY ISLAND NATIONAL PARK (Ontario).

I.   *b)* Area : 1,380 ha.

II.   *Date established :* 1929.

Tourism : a campsite on Beausoleil Island; 18,000 visitors a year.

145

IV.   *Altitude :* highest point 229 m.

a) Comprises 42 islands in Georgian Bay of Lake Huron, only one of which is of any size; the islands are separated by narrow channels and the larger ones are covered with broad-leaved or mixed broad-leaved and conifer forests.

b) White-tailed deer *Oidocoileus virginianus,* raccoon, red fox, porcupine *Erethizon dorsatum,* striped skink *M. mephitis,* red and grey squirrels; many birds especially warblers and thrushes.

18. St. Lawrence Islands National Park (Ontario).

II.   *b*) Area : 69 ha.

III.   *Date established :* 1914.

Tourism : no accommodation, but camping-sites; 75,000 visitors a year.

IV.   *Altitude :* highest point 99 m.

a) Situated on the St. Lawrence river, the Park includes 12 islands of the Thousand Islands group; pine, oak, maple and birch on the top of the low granite cliffs. One limestone island.

b) No information.

B. — PROVINCIAL PARKS.

a) **Alberta.**

19. Cypress Hills Provincial Park.

II.   *b*) Area : 19,500 ha.

III.   *Date established :* 1951.

Tourism : accommodation, chalets and a small Holiday Camp in the Park.

IV.   *Altitude :* 1,219-1,432 m.

a) Bordering the Elkwater Lake; the higher hills have been moulded by non-glacial erosion and there is a relict pre-glacial flora (pine, spruce and aspen).

b) Moose, wapiti, whitetail deer, pronghorn antelope *Antilocapra americana,* bobcat *Felis rufa,* lynx; a rich avifauna includes partridge *Perdix* (introduced), ruffed grouse *Bonasa umbellus,* sharptailed grouse *Pedioecetes phasianellus,* ring-necked pheasant *Phasianus colchicus* (introduced) and Merriam's turkey *Meleagris gallopavo* subsp. (introduced).

20. Dinosaur Provincial Park.

II.   *b*) Area : 8,828 ha.

III.   *Date established :* 1955.

IV.   *Altitude :* 720 m.

a) Section of the " badlands " of Alberta; topography is the result of climate and erosion working on flat soft mesozoic sedimentary rock, leaving mounds and turrets of resistant sandstone (also many vertebrate fossils); vegetation of the semi-arid prairie (cactus, sagebrush *Artemisia tridentata*), with poplars and willows along the Red Deer River.

b) Whitetail and mule deer, pronghorn antelope, coyote, bobcat, muskrat, beaver; ring-necked pheasant and partridge (introduced); sharptailed grouse.

21. CRIMSON LAKE PROVINCIAL PARK.

   b) Area : 3,136 ha.

   Date established : 1949.

   Altitude : 1,000 m.

   a) Rolling hills of glacial origin bordering the Lake; dense forest of lodge-pole pine, spruce and fir with some poplars and willows.

   b) Wapiti, moose, mule and whitetail deer, black bear, red squirrel, mink, marten, beaver, weasel, muskrat, lynx, coyote, wolf; spruce grouse *Canachites canadensis,* sharptailed and ruffed grouse.

22. ENTRANCE PROVINCIAL PARK.

   b) Area : 2,560 ha.

   Date established : 1958.

   Altitude : 1,275 m.

   a) Landscape bearing the signs of former glaciation; lakes surrounded by coniferous forest, lodgepole pine *Pinus contorta,* spruce and also such broad-leaved species as poplar, birch and willows.

   b) Mule deer, moose, wapiti, black bear, red squirrel, mink, marten, otter, beaver, muskrat, lynx, coyote, wolf; bird species include sharptailed, ruffed and spruce grouse.

b) **Ontario.**

23. ALGONQUIN PROVINCIAL PARK.

   a) Status : limited hunting and trapping, as well as forest exploitation, are allowed in some sectors of the Park. Sport-fishing is also authorised except in a 7,700 ha " Research Area ".

   b) Area : 753,599 ha.

   Date established : 1893.

   Tourism : great recreational value as canoe country; lodges and many camping-sites.

   Altitude : 180-480 m.

   a) Part of the pre-Cambrian shield, with rivers, lakes, prairie and forest; on the east the forest is secondary and composed of poplar, white birch, white pine, black and white spruce and balsam fir; on the west a mixed forest of sugar maple *Acer saccharum* and yellow birch, with some beech, white pine, black and white spruce, balsam fir, black cherry *Prunus serotina* and " hop " hornbeam *Carpinus caroliana.*

   b) Wolf, black bear, muskrat, marten, beaver, whitetail deer, moose, mink, otter; raven *Corvus corax,* ruffed grouse, scarlet tanager *Piranga olivacea,* pileated woodpecker *Dryocopus pileatus,* grey jay *Perisoreus canadensis.*

24. QUETICO PROVINCIAL PARK.

   a) Status : forest exploitation is allowed in a quarter of the Park, and trapping locally, but no hunting. Sport-fishing is authorised.

   b) Area : 464,913 ha, adjacent to the Boundary Waters Canoe Area in the U.S.A.

III.   *Date established :* 1913.

Tourism : camping-sites on the periphery.

IV.   *Altitude :* 396 m.

a) Pre-Cambrian shield, largely covered by boreal forests of spruce, poplars, white birch, jack pine *Pinus banksiana* and balsam-fir, as well as white and red pine and basswood *Tilia* on southern aspects.

b) Black bear, wolf, mink, marten, otter, lynx, whitetail deer, moose; raven, grey jay, spruce grouse, goldeneye *Bucephala clangula,* loon *Gavia* sp., osprey *Pandion haliaetus,* bald eagle *Haliaetus leucocephalus,* parula warbler *Parula americana,* white-throated sparrow *Zonotrichia albicollis.*

25. LAKE SUPERIOR PROVINCIAL PARK.

II.   *a)* Status : limited forest exploitation and trapping allowed.   Moose-hunting is forbidden only in two areas, totalling 10,815 ha.   Sport-fishing permitted.

b) Area : 136,216 ha.

III.   *Date established :* 1944.

Tourism : camping places are mainly situated along a road which borders the Park.

IV.   *Altitude :* 180-480 m.

a) Landscape of the Lake Superior shoreline, offering excellent examples of post-glacial beaches; mixed forest of poplar, birch, elm, ironwood and basswood, maple, oak, cedar, pines and firs, with conifers dominant in the north. The cool, moist climate of the lake shores supports an arctic-alpine flora.

b) Beaver, wolf, lynx, moose, marten, otter; loon, grey jay, raven, white-throated sparrow.

26. MISSISSAGI PROVINCIAL PARK RESERVE.

II.   *a)* Status : controlled hunting, trapping and felling to be allowed.   Also sport-fishing.

b) Area : 38,593 ha.

III.   *Date established :* 1965 (when still not completed)

Tourism : a camp on the boundary.

IV.   No information.

27. KILLARNEY PROVINCIAL PARK.

II.   *a)* Status : no hunting or trapping, but lumbering operations allowed under control, and sport-fishing.

b) Area : 36,423 ha.

III.   *Date established :* 1964.

IV.   *Altitude :* 300-500 m.

a) Part of the pre-Cambrian shield with a very bold relief and predominantly granite formations; steep narrow river valleys and lakes; mixed forest of sugar maple and birch, with conifers on the higher shallow soils.

b) Whitetail deer, moose, black bear, wolf, beaver, otter; birds include hermit thrush *Hylocichla guttata,* indigo bunting *Passerina cyanea*; rivers and lakes full of fish.

28. SIBLEY PROVINCIAL PARK.

a) Status : trapping and hunting forbidden but some controlled forestry exploitation; sport-fishing.

b) Area : 21,350 ha.

Date established : 1963.

Tourism : several camping places.

Altitude : 240-300 m.

a) A peninsula jutting into Lake Superior; pre-Cambrian shield covered with shales and with conglomerates, limestones and sandstones, sills, dykes and faults; the forest, which has suffered a good deal of degradation from fire and parasitic disease, is mainly balsam fir and white spruce in the centre, poplar, birch and pine in the north and south.

b) Whitetail deer, moose, wolf, lynx, mink, beaver; osprey, bald eagle, raven, loon, goldeneye.

29. OBATANGA PROVINCIAL PARK RESERVE.

a) Status : hunting and trapping forbidden but controlled lumbering in certain places; sport-fishing.

b) Area : 13,500 ha.

Date established : 1944, enlarged in 1963.

Tourism : some sites set aside for camping

Altitude : 360-540 m.

a) A fairly level stretch of country between Lake Superior and Hudson Bay; outcrops of sandy granite, poorly drained, covered with black spruce *Picea mariana*; pre-Cambrian; many lakes and rivers; also big stands of white spruce, balsam fir, birch, aspen and black poplar *Populus nigra*.

b) Moose, black bear, timber wolf, beaver, mink, marten, otters, abundant fish (northern pike, walleye).

30. BON ECHO PROVINCIAL PARK.

a) Status : sport-fishing, lumbering, hunting and trapping are all permitted locally, but strictly controlled.

b) Area : 6,161 ha.

Date established : 1965 (when still not completed).

Tourism : one main camping place, accessible by road.

Altitude : 260 m.

a) Part of the pre-Cambrian granitic shield with a sharp relief; rivers deeply trenched, hills and lakes; the primary pine forest on the east has been replaced by secondary forest of poplar, red and sugar maple, balsam fir and some pine; mixed forest on the western side.

b) Black bear, wolf, moose, beaver, mink, black squirrel, muskrat, eastern chipmunk *Tamias* sp.

31. NAGAGAMISIS PROVINCIAL PARK.

a) Status : hunting forbidden, but trapping and lumbering allowed under control; sport-fishing.

b) Area : 4,807 ha.

149

III.   *Date established :* 1963.

        Tourism : camping-grounds provided.

IV.   *Altitude :* 274 m.

        a) Many small lakes (including Lake Nagagamisis) and terraces of a fluvio-glacial origin; mixed forest of pines, firs, birch and poplar.

        b) Black bear, moose, wolf, beaver, mink, marten, otters; a few woodland caribou may survive.

32. GREENWATER PROVINCIAL PARK.

II.   *a*) Status : similar to that of No. 31 Nagagamisis.

        b) Area : 4,274 ha.

III.   *Date established :* 1963.

IV.   *Altitude :* 290 m.

        a) On the northern edge of the Great Clay Belt; an esker or post-glacial gravel ridge 60 m high in the centre of the Park; secondary forest of poplar, birch, spruces and balsam fir.

        b) Black bear, mink, marten, moose, muskrat, woodchuck (marmot) *Marmota monax,* beaver, snowshoe hare *Lepus americanus,* red fox; ruffed and spruce grouse.

33. NEYS PROVINCIAL PARK.

II.   *a*) Status : identical to that of No. 30 Bon Echo.

        b) Area : 3,298 ha.

III.   *Date established :* 1965 (when still not completed).

IV.   *Altitude :* 180-450 m.

        a) Part of the pre-Cambrian shield on the north shore of Lake Superior; glacial deposits; boreal forest of spruces, balsam fir, birch, poplar and jack pine.

        b) Woodland caribou, beaver, mink, muskrat, flying-squirrel *Glaucomys* sp., woodchuck, porcupine, varying hare, red fox; great blue heron *Ardea herodias,* grey jay, raven, olive-sided flycatcher *Nuttalornis borealis,* loon.

34. ESKER LAKES PROVINCIAL PARK.

II.   *a*) Status : similar to that of No. 31 Nagagamisis.

        b) Area : 3,109 ha.

III.   *Date established :* 1957.

IV.   *Altitude :* 330-350 m.

        a) Vast sand and gravel deposits of glacial origin; the main esker or gravel ridge is flanked by 27 lakes; pine forest with birch and poplar, tamarack *Larix americana* and black spruce in the marshy areas.

        b) Moose, black bear, beaver, mink, lynx.

35. GRUNDY LAKE PROVINCIAL PARK.

II.   *a*) Status : hunting, trapping and wood-cutting are forbidden, but sport-fishing allowed.

        b) Area : 2,481 ha.

Date established : 1959.

Tourism : camping places.

Altitude : 180-210 m.

a) A fairly level section of the pre-Cambrian shield; outcrops of granite, many lakes; forest of sugar maple and birch (especially in the east) and, in the west, of poplar, birch, pines, spruce and balsam fir.

b) Black bear, wolf, whitetail deer, moose, beaver, marten, otter, muskrat, mink.

36. OJIBWAY PROVINCIAL PARK RESERVE.

a) Status : hunting, trapping and lumbering allowed in places. Sport-fishing.

b) Area : 2,481 ha.

Date established : 1965 (when not yet completed).

Tourism : camping facilities.

Altitude : 360 m.

a) Part of the pre-Cambrian shield, in which the granite outcrops are interspersed with clay and sand deposits; many rivers; forest of birch, spruce, pines and poplar.

b) Black bear, whitetail deer, moose, wolf, beaver, mink, muskrat, otter, marten; the rivers are full of fish.

37. RONDEAU PROVINCIAL PARK.

a) Status : wood-cutting and trapping are not permitted, but limited shooting of waterfowl is allowed in places. Sport-fishing.

b) Area : 2,227 ha.

Date established : 1894.

Tourism : camp-grounds.

Altitude : 170 m.

a) A low peninsula with a beach along the lake shore, marsh and forests, mainly of oak and pine, but also some birch, maples, American elm and other species typical of more southern hardwood forest and Carolinian flora, of which this is the last remnant in public ownership in Ontario.

b) Whitetail deer, opossum *Didelphis marsupialis,* grey squirrel, muskrat, raccoon; fox snake *Elaphe vulpina,* soft-shelled turtle *Amyda ferox*; Acadian flycatcher *Empidonax vivescens,* mockingbird *Mimus polyglottos,* blue-grey gnatcatcher *Polioptila caerulea,* prothonotary and cerulean warblers *Protonotaria citrea* and *Dendroica cerulea,* orchard oriole *Icterus spurius,* cardinal *Richmondera cardinalis* and mourning dove *Zenaidura macroura.*

c) **Quebec.**

38. LA VÉRENDRYE PROVINCIAL PARK.

a) Status : limited hunting of moose; sport-fishing; forest exploitation; but no human habitation or domestic stock.

b) Area : 1,142,000 ha.

151

III.   *Date established :* 1939.

IV.   *Altitude :* averaging 350 m.

   a) An area of hills, lakes and rivers, with forests of evergreen species such as balsam fir, black spruce, grey, red and white pine; to the south, stands of silver birch, black cherry, maple, aspen; many peat bogs.

   b) Moose, bear, wolf.

39. LES LAURENTIDES PROVINCIAL PARK.

II.   *a*) Status : generally similar to No. 38 La Vérendrye; the number of moose which may be hunted is based on a quota which is scientifically laid down.

   b) Area : 927,500 ha.

III.   *Date established :* 1895.

   Tourism : facilities very well developed.

IV.   *Altitude :* 200-250 m.

   a) Many lakes and rivers; tree cover of many resinous evergreens — balsam fir, black and white spruces, red and grey pines; also some stands of tamarack.

   b) Moose, bear, wolf.

40. MONT TREMBLANT PROVINCIAL PARK.

II.   *a*) Status : no hunting; wood-cutting under supervision; fishing; but no habitation or agriculture.

   b) Area : 278,750 ha.

III.   *Date established :* 1895.

IV.   *Altitude :* 930 m.

   a) A mountainous region, with the rivers deeply trenched; lakes of glacial origin; coniferous and broad-leaved forest (balsam fir, black spruce, white spruce, sugar maple, birch, poplar, aspen).

   b) Roe deer, moose, wolf, bear.

41. GASPESIE PROVINCIAL PARK.

II.   *a*) Status : similar to that of No. 40 Mt. Tremblant.

   b) Area : 127,500 ha.

III.   *Date established :* 1937.

IV.   *Altitude :* 1,250 m.

   a) A region of hills and low mountains; characteristic resinous forest of the boreal zone — balsam fir, black spruce; an alpine flora in the Chic-Choc mountains.

   b) Caribou, moose, pronghorn, bear.

42. MONT ORFORD PROVINCIAL PARK.

II.   *a*) Status : the same as for No. 40 Mt. Tremblant.

   b) Area : 3,750 ha.

III.   *Date established :* 1938.

V.   *Altitude :* not reported.

a) A sample of composite forest in a temperate climate; main species are sugar and red maples, beech, yellow birch *Betula lutea,* fir and spruce.

b) Pronghorn.

d) **Newfoundland.**

43. SERPENTINE PROVINCIAL PARK.

a) Status : sport-fishing for trout and Atlantic salmon is allowed under strict regulations; otherwise there is no hunting, habitation or other form of economic exploitation.

b) Area : 9,200 ha.

Date established : 1939.

Altitude : 45 m (the level of Lake Serpentine)-600 m.

a) Landscape of the extreme northern end of the Appalachians; thick coniferous forest up to 300 m, then bare rock.

b) Moose, lynx, otter, beaver, black bear; willow grouse *L. lagopus,* bald eagle, wildfowl.

44. PITTS POND PROVINCIAL PARK.

a) Status : as in No. 43 Serpentine Park, no economic development is allowed; negotiations are afoot to transfer these areas from Provincial to Federal National Park Service jurisdiction, with a view to incorporating them in the Terra Nova National Park (No. 11), which they adjoin.

b) Area : 4,096 ha.

Date established : 1959.

Altitude : highest point 200 m.

a) Comprises a lake lying in a depression in the Devonian granite; on the east there is an abrupt transition from granite to pre-Cambrian sedimentary rocks.

b) Moose, lynx, caribou, beaver, black bear; bald eagle, wildfowl.

45. BARACHOIS PONDS PROVINCIAL PARK.

a) Status : no hunting; trout and Atlantic salmon fishing allowed.

b) Area : 2,800 ha.

Date established : 1961.

Tourism : encouraged, but the paths and roads which may be used, camping and picknicking are regulated; there are some bathing places. No plans have, however, been made for providing hotels, motels or huts.

Altitude : 22-360 m.

a) The western Flank of the Long Range Mountains which belong to the same geological system as the Appalachians in the U.S.A. The high level rocks of the upland are pre-Cambrian anorthosites.

b) Moose, lynx, beaver, otter, fox, black bear; waterfowl, ptarmigan, bald eagle.

46. BUTTER POT NATIONAL PARK.

II.
   a) Status : hunting prohibited, fishing allowed.

   b) Area : 1,730 ha.

III.
   Date established : 1958.

   Tourism : situation similar to that of No. 45 Barachois Ponds.

IV.
   Altitude : 105-300 m.

   a) Pre-Cambrian volcanics and granite underlie the rolling terrain of this section of the Appalachian system, covered with glacial deposits (many erratic blocks).

   b) Moose, lynx, beaver, otter, fox; waterfowl, ptarmigan, bald eagle.

47. SIR RICHARD SQUIRES MEMORIAL PARK.

II.
   a) Status : a mainly undisturbed area with no exploitation, except for very intensive sport-fishing.

   b) Area : 1,556 ha.

III.
   Date established : 1954.

   Tourism : celebrated for its salmon catches (no less than 3,000 were hooked in 1964 in the pool known as Big Falls).

IV.
   Altitude : 45-90 m.

   a) Carboniferous formation, transected by the Hunter river, with its very winding course and its spectacular falls which are situated on the eastern boundary of the Park.

   b) Moose, lynx, black bear, snowshoe hare; a few caribou.

V.   **Areas excluded :**

There are in the first place a large number of Provincial Parks, several of which were mentioned in E/3436, which the Canadian authorities themselves do not consider as satisfying the criteria laid down by the ICNP. These include all the Provincial Parks of British Columbia, Manitoba, New Brunswick, Nova Scotia, Prince Edward Island and Saskatchewan, and, in addition, many of the smaller Parks in Alberta, Ontario, Quebec and Newfoundland. For example, the total number of Alberta and Ontario Provincial Parks is 37 and 115 respectively, of which only 4 and 15, respectively, have been included in the List. In the last-named Province one Park which should no doubt be included in the next edition of the List is the first Park for the specific protection of the polar bear *Thalarctos maritimus,* which the Ontario Government reported that it had set up in April 1968, over an area of some 1,813,000 ha.

The case of the Provincial Parks of Saskatchewan is worth quoting in some detail, since it explains how the selection for the present List has been made. When the authorities in Ottawa first considered the criteria for selection established by ICNP, they wrote (August 1964) : " None of the Provincial Parks of Saskatchewan could be classed as completely protected areas. However, Saskatchewan has suggested that the Parks listed below (four names were given) may qualify, in that hunting is permitted only when a harvest of a certain species is required. "

This proposal was accepted and the text was prepared accordingly, but when it was checked by the authorities at Regina, they wrote of their own accord :

154

" After examining with great care the criteria... we are forced to the conclusion that none of our Provincial Parks would qualify in the world list. We say this because Saskatchewan Parks, although managed with the aims of public outdoor recreation in mind, are also managed on a ' multi-use ' basis as far as other purposes are concerned. For example : *a*) grazing is permitted on the basis of the agricultural carrying capacity of the park terrain; *b*) hunting is permitted on exactly the same licence basis and game management policies as elsewhere in the province; *c*) timber cutting and sawmill operations are permitted; *d*) angling and commercial fishing... are permitted on a licence basis; *e*) there are some permanent residents and a good deal of summer cottage occupancy; and *f*) oil exploration and well-development are permitted, and mining operations would not be excluded ".

As a result of these observations the four Parks, which had provisionally been listed pending a final check by the Provincial authorities, had after all to be excluded.

Quite a number of other protected areas have had to be omitted from the List because it was not considered that the degree of protection accorded in them was sufficient to meet the fundamental criterion. They include Game Preserves, Bird Sanctuaries, Game Sanctuaries and Wilderness Areas and were enumerated in the previous edition, E/3436, to which reference may be made.

21. CENTRAL AFRICAN REPUBLIC

Listed Areas : four.

1. Vassako-Bolo Strict Natural Reserve.
2. Bamingui-Bangoran National Park.
3. Saint-Floris National Park.
4. André Felix National Park.

General Introduction :

Administration : the Service des Eaux, Forêts et Chasses, at Bangui, is responsible.

Legal status : founded on the Nature Protection Law enacted on 19 August 1960. On 10 December 1960 an Order was signed providing for the internal regulation of the various National Parks and Faunal Reserves (no separate mention of the Vassako-Bolo Reserve).

Land tenure : public ownership throughout.

Tourism : plans are under consideration for " opening up increasing numbers of motorable tracks and establishing rest-camps for tourists ".

Research : there is no central organisation as yet nor have there been any special publications of note.

The listed areas Nos. 2-4, together with two of those (Nos. 5 and 6) now relegated to Section V, were described in Part Two of the previous edition of the List.

CENTRAL AFRICAN REPUBLIC

Details : application of criteria (II), general information (III) and description (IV) :

1. VASSAKO-BOLO STRICT NATURAL RESERVE.

II.

a) Status : originally this Reserve was separate from the Bamingui-Bangoran National Park, with which it has now been incorporated. It enjoys total protection and even entry and movement within it have to be specially authorised.

b) Area : 150,000 ha.

c) Staff : a large proportion of the 37 persons assigned to the parks and reserves of the North Central province of the Republic operate in the Vassoko-Bolo region.

d) Budget : no information, but *c)* gives some indication.

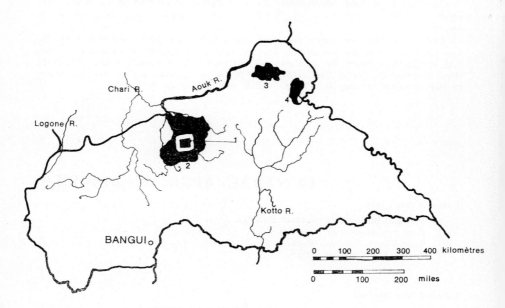

III.

Date established : 1940, by Order of the then Governor-General of French Equatorial Africa in terms of the London Convention of 1933.

IV.

Altitude : 400-600 m.

a) Part of a huge plateau-like peneplain ranging from 400-500 m and dominated by a number of granito-gneissic Kopjes rising a further 100 m; more or less wooded savannah interspersed with open savannah which becomes marshy during the rains; dry forest of *Isoberlinia*; gallery forest.

b) Soudano-guinean fauna; black rhinoceros *Diceros bicornis,* elephant *Loxodonta africana,* hippopotamus *H. amphibius,* buffalo *Syncerus caffer,* eland *Taurotragus oryx,* roan *Hippotragus equinus,* oribi *Ourebia ourebi,* hartebeest *Alcelaphus buselaphus,* warthog *Phacochoerus aethiopicus,* bush pig *Potamochoerus porcus,* lion and leopard *Panthera leo* and *pardus,* hyena *H. hyaena,* jackal *Canis mesomelas,* small carnivores.

c) Black rhinoceros.

156

2. BAMINGUI-BANGORAN NATIONAL PARK.

   a) Status : total protection.

   b) Area : 1,000,000 ha.

   c) Staff : somewhat inadequate. The 37 units referred to under No. 1 above (an Inspector of Hunting, stationed at Ndele, 18 guards and 18 guides) are responsible for these million hectares, but also for three adjacent Reserves — Gribingui-Bamingui (500,000 ha), Koukourou-Bamingui (150,000 ha) and Mia-méré-Miadiki (250,000 ha). Nevertheless the virtually uninhabited character of the whole region provides sufficient grounds for accepting the staff situation, although with some misgivings.

   d) Budget : no information.

   Date established : a hunting reserve was created here in 1916, which was upgraded to a National Park by decree in 1936, its status being confirmed by the law of 1960.

   Altitude : 400-600 m.

   a) The general description of the Vassako-Bolo Reserve, No. 1 above, applies equally to this Park.

   b) In addition to species mentioned above for the Vassako-Bolo, Buffon's kob *Kobus kob,* reedbuck *Redunca arundinum* and waterbuck *Kobus ellipsiprymnus* are found.

   c) Black rhinoceros.

3. SAINT-FLORIS NATIONAL PARK.

   a) Status : total protection.

   b) Area : 100,700 ha.

   c) Staff : in the North-east province like the North Central the total strength is 37, made up of an Inspector of Hunting, stationed at Ouadda, 18 guards and 18 guides. Of these some half-dozen of the guards and guides are responsible for the Saint-Floris National Park.

   d) Budget : in addition to provision for staff salaries, the sum of U.S. $ 4,000 was allocated (1959) to Parks and Reserves of the North-east province.

   Date established : a hunting reserve was proclaimed in 1916 and confirmed in 1925; elevated to National Park status in 1933 (when it was named " La Matoumara "), which was confirmed in the 1960 Law, when the area was enlarged from 40,000 to the present 100,700 ha.

   Altitude : 400 m.

   a) Part of the upper basin of the Chari river, characterised by wooded Soudanian savannah interspersed with marshy areas of savannah which are seasonally flooded during the rains (a few permanent swamps which last through the dry season, including that of Saint-Floris itself).

   b) During the dry season great concentrations of elephant, buffalo, large antelopes, giraffe, lion, hyaena, cheetah *Acinonyx jubatus*; a rich avifauna of tens of thousands of birds, especially egrets.

4. ANDRE FELIX NATIONAL PARK.

   a) Status : total protection.

   b) Area : 170,100 ha.

c) Staff : the same situation as for the Saint-Floris Park, No. 3 above, sharing the total North-east Province strength of 37 effectives.

d) Budget as for the Saint-Floris Park.

III.   *Date established :* 1960, under the special law — considerably later than the other Parks.

IV.   *Altitude :* 400 m.

a) The general description of the Saint-Floris National Park, No. 3 above, applies equally to Andre Felix.

b) The fauna is virtually identical with that of Saint-Floris.

V.   **Areas excluded :**

A. — Two very important Reserves, which the Government of the Republic announced on 8 February 1966, were, in respect of part of the area, due very shortly to be brought under stricter control, while the remaining sections had just been or soon would be set aside as Hunting Reserves for the purpose of being sub-let as such :

1. Ouandjia-Vakaga : 965.000 ha. This is transected by a new track leading from Ndele to Birao. A tourist company has in fact invested some U.S. $ 240,000 in the area on sundry facilities and equipment during a period of three years.

2. Yata-N'Gaya : 509,500 ha. Some U.S. $ 360,000 are currently being invested in this area.

From the point of view of tourism, these two areas seem to hold out promise of a great future. As soon as areas devoted to hunting-tourism have been properly demarcated from those which satisfy the ICNP criteria, there is every prospect that it will be possible to include some sectors in the United Nations List.

B. — Also excluded are those Faunal Reserves which provide only for the protection of the larger game animals :

a) North Central Province :

1. Gribingui-Bamingui	500,000 ha
2. Koukourou-Bamingui	150,000 ha
3. Miaméré-Miadiki	250,000 ha

b) North-east Province :

4. Aouk-Aoukalé	319,000 ha

c) Obo District (on the Sudan border):

5. Zemongo	950,000 ha

d) Bossangoa and Batangafo District :

6. Nana Barya	220,000 ha

This Faunal Reserve perhaps deserves to be specially noted, despite being limited to game protection only. In 1959 a small allocation of U.S. $ 800 was made to cover equipment and a supervisory staff of 4 guards and 4 guides.

GO DEMOCRATIC REPUBLIC, Albert N.P.

(photo : G. F. de Witte)

GERMANY, Lüneburgerheide   (photo : K. Bi

CE, Samarias N.P.

(photo : Dr. Schultze-Westrum)

FRANCE, Camargue R.

(photo : Weber and Hafner/WWF)

CE, Vanoise N.P.   (photo : F. Vollmar/WWF)

ECUADOR, Galapagos N.P.   (photo : Dr. I. Eibl-Eibl

GUATEMALA, Atitlan N.P.   (photo : R. Reyes

NA, Kaieteur N.P.   (photo : R. H. Mc Connell)

ITALIA, Gran Paradiso N.P.   (photo : F. Vollmar)

ITALIA, Abruzzi N.P.   (photo : F. Vollmar)

Listed Areas : seven.

A. — NATIONAL PARKS :

    1. Wilpattu National Park.
    2. Ruhunu National Park.

B. — STRICT NATURAL RESERVES :

    3. Wasgomuwa Strict Natural Reserve.
    4. Yala Strict Natural Reserve.
    5. Ritigala Strict Natural Reserve.
    6. Hakgala Strict Natural Reserve.

C. 7. Gal Oya National Park.

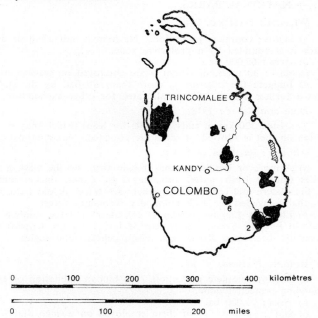

General Introduction :

Administration : vested in the Minister of Lands Irrigation and Power, respon-sible to whom are the Warden of the Department of Wildlife and an Advisory Committee, under the chairmanship of the Warden, with eleven members. The total staff for the two National Parks in category A plus the four Strict Natural Reserves plus an ancillary system of " sanctuaries " and " intermediate zones " amounts to 218 units.

Gal Oya National Park is administered by what in effect is an autonomous body, the Gal Oya Development Board, set up under an Act of Parliament of Ceylon for the development of the River Valley — hence its classification in the separate category C.

Land tenure : all the areas, including the Gal Oya, are under public ownership.

Tourism : the National Parks are open to visitors but not the Strict Natural Reserves.

Scientific research : the ban on visitors to Strict Natural Reserves is in effect waived for naturalists engaged in research; ecological observations are also maintained by the staff.

A description of the three National Parks was included in the previous edition of the List, E/3436, and the four Strict Natural Reserves were mentioned but not described.

Details : application of criteria (II), general information (III) and description (IV) :

A. — NATIONAL PARKS.

1. Wilpattu National Park.

II.   *a*) Status : complete protection. No human habitation or exploitation. The Park is surrounded by a protective zone.

b) Area : 65,000 ha.

c) Staff : 30 units, of whom 9 are employed on warden duties.

d) Budget : the criterion is more than satisfied by the staff salaries above and a further U.S. $ 3,500 is allocated for other expenditure.

III.   *Date established :* 1938.

Tourism : 320 km of track suitable for jeeps (which may be hired); no circulation on foot is allowed. Guides are provided. Accommodation for 12 visitors.

IV.   *Altitude :* sea level to 180 m.

a) A more or less level sandy region with, on the west, a string of natural lakes (mostly fresh water) surrounded by dunes, thicket and forest patches; in the eastern and central sectors there are traces of old fields which have been gradually invaded by thicket and dry secondary forest.

b) Elephant *Elephas maximus,* axis deer *A. axis,* sambar *Cervus unicolor,* buffalo *Bubalus bubalis,* sloth bear *Melursus ursinus,* leopard *Panthera pardus;* hornbills, bee-eaters, flycatchers, ibises, pelicans and eagles.

2. Ruhunu National Park.

II.   *a*) Status : complete protection. No human habitation or exploitation. Surrounding protective zone.

b) Area : 23,000 ha.

c) Staff : 30 units, 16 of them employed on warden duties.

d) Budget : criterion very fully satisfied by staff salaries above, with a further U.S. $ 7,000 allocated for other expenditure.

III.   *Date established :* 1958 (13,000 ha only, the other 10,000 being added in 1964).

Tourism : travelling in the Park only allowed by car, 48 km of jeep track. Lodging for 16 visitors.

IV.   *Altitude :* sea level to 160 m.

a) A coastal zone, with lagoons and dunes, rocks, scrub and thorn jungle; traces of ancient cultivation, dating from the second century B.C., are to be found on the plains, with remains of Buddhist monasteries of the same era perched on the rocky pinnacles.

b) Elephant, sambar and other deer, leopard, crocodile *Crocodilus porosus*; a rich avifauna (including peafowl *Pavo cristatus,* cormorants, plovers, grey heron *Ardea cinerea,* imperial pigeon *Muscadivora aenea).*

B. — STRICT NATURAL RESERVES.

3. WASGOMUWA STRICT NATURAL RESERVE.

a) Status : absolute protection, not even open to visitors. But the area is threatened by the " Minipe Scheme " which could result in the loss of the greater part of the Reserve, leaving only the steep slopes above the 150 m contour which do not sustain wild life.

b) Area : 28,000 ha.

c) Staff : 4 units.

d) Budget : staff salaries meet the criterion and, in addition, an annual allocation of U.S. $ 2,000.

Date established : 1937.

Altitude : 100-650 m.

a) Access is difficult. Soil very fertile, the central part of the Reserve consisting of a narrow valley between two steep ridges of the Sudukanda hills; the vegetation varies from thick forest at lower levels and along the Mahaweli Ganga river, to open forest and scrub.

b) Elephant, sambar, buffalo, axis deer, sloth bear, leopard.

4. YALA STRICT NATURAL RESERVE.

a) Status : absolute protection.

b) Area : 27,500 ha.

c) Staff : 5 units.

d) Budget : criterion met by staff salaries, plus annual allocation of U.S. $ 11,000.

Date established : 1937.

Tourism : visitors restricted, but there is a " main park bungalow ".

Altitude : sea level to 30 m.

a) A flat sandy area, especially near the shore, except that some of the the sand dunes rises to 30 m; the jungle is low and bushy but thicker further inland, where there are rocky outcrops with caves.

b) Sloth bear, buffalo, deer, sambar, elephant, monkeys, leopard. Birdlife is plentiful.

5. RITIGALA STRICT NATURAL RESERVE.

a) Statut : absolute protection.

b) Area : 1,450 ha (Ceylon's population density is 151 persons to the square kilometre).

c) Staff : 3 units.

d) Budget : criterion met by expenditure on staff salaries; additional allocation of U.S. $ 2,000.

Date established : 1937.

IV.   *Altitude :* 750 m.

a) An isolated mountain in the middle of a plain, with its climate dominated by the south-west monsoon resulting in six rainless months; the amount of precipitation rises, however, with altitude and supports a humid upland flora of more than 100 species, a number of them endemics.

b) No information.

6. HAKGALA STRICT NATURAL RESERVE.

II.   *a)* Status : absolute protection.

b) Area : 1,100 ha.

c) Staff : 3 units.

d) Budget : criterion met by expenditure on staff salaries; additional allocation of U.S. $ 2,000.

III.   *Date established :* 1937.

IV.   *Altitude :* about 1,000 m.

a) Upland flora.

b) No information.

C. — 7. GAL OYA NATIONAL PARK.

II.   *a)* Status : general protection, no habitation or exploitation. Three adjacent reserves or sanctuaries serve as buffer zones for the Park.

b) Area : 25,000 ha.

c) Staff : at least 7 units.

d) Budget : U.S. $ 3,000.

III.   *Date established :* 1954.

Tourism : since the Park consists essentially of a reservoir lake surrounded by thick hygrophilous forest, visits to it for the most part take the form of trips on the lake in hired launches; there are some jeep tracks and walking is also allowed. Accommodation is provided by two well-equipped bungalows. There is a plan to open a museum. Tourists are accompanied by guides.

IV.   *Altitude :* 78-720 m.

a) A reservoir lake situated in rather flat country, but dominated by some gneissic hills 150 m high and, on the border of the Park, by a considerably higher range of hills; dry evergreen forest occupies about a quarter of the area and the remainder is scattered tree grassland savannah.

b) Elephant, buffalo, muntjac *Muntiacus* sp., axis deer, leopard, jackal *Canis aureus*; python *P. molurus,* cobra *N. naja*; plentiful birdlife.

V.   **Areas excluded :**

32 " sanctuaries ", totalling 160,000 ha (areas in which hunting is forbidden but there is no other control); the largest of these sanctuaries is 37,000 ha and the smallest only a single hectare.

6 " intermediate zones ", totalling slightly more than 14,000 ha, where exploitation is under control, but hunting, although subject to regulations, is permitted.

The Government of Ceylon advises that " Intermediate Zones and Sanctuaries should not figure in the List ".

162

Listed Areas : two.

1. Zakouma National Park.
2. Manda National Park.

General Introduction :

The Parks are administered by the Ministère des Eaux, Forêts, Pêches et Chasses. The land included in them is under State ownership.

The Zakouma National Park was cited in Part Two of the previous edition of the List, as was the Siniaka-Minia Reserve, which has now been excluded for reasons explained in Section V below.

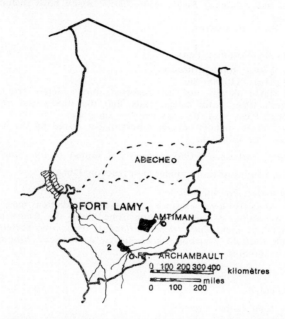

Details : application of criteria (II), general information (III) and description (IV) :

1. ZAKOUMA NATIONAL PARK.

a) Status : total protection; several villages were evacuated in 1963, leaving only the village of Bône, which is also scheduled for evacuation. At the same time customary rights have been completely abolished.

b) Area : 297,200 ha; the Park forms the centre of a faunal reserve of 2,060,000 ha.

c) Staff : 17 units.

d) Budget : U.S. $ 28,000, excluding allocations for capital equipment.

Date established : 1963 (formerly a faunal reserve since 1958).

Tourism : there is a rest-camp on the banks of the Bahr Tinga; 200 km of motorable tracks.

IV.   *Altitude :* 300 m.

a) Fairly level country, but on the west the pinnacles of Bône and Ibir overlook the plain from heights of 300 and 150 m respectively; in this western area there is a mixture of open forest and densely wooded savannah, dominated by *Combretum* spp. and Leguminaceae; to the east there are grassy depressions, flooded during the rains and with some marshes remaining during the dry season, interspersed with *Acacia* (*seyal, sieberiana,* etc.) woodland.

b) Elephant, *Loxodonta africana,* black rhinoceros *Diceros bicornis,* buffalo *Syncerus caffer,* all the antelopes of central Chad except eland *Taurotragus* (e.g. roan *Hippotragus equinus,* topi *Damaliscus korrigum,* kobs *Kobus* spp., blue duiker *Cephalophus monticola,* also a few greater kudu *Tragelaphus strepsiceros*); giraffe *Giraffa camelopardalis;* lion and leopard *Panthera leo* and *pardus,* possibly cheetah *Acinonyx jubatus;* hyaena *Crocuta crocuta;* baboon *Papio papio;* patas monkey *Erythrocebus patas;* many birds including ostrich *Struthio camelus.*

c) Black rhinoceros.

2. MANDA NATIONAL PARK.

II.   a) Status : total protection.

b) Area : 110,000 ha.

c) Staff : details not yet reported, but a letter from Fort Lamy dated 3 March 1966, states categorically that the supervision of this newly created National Park may be regarded as adequate.

d) Budget : details not yet reported, but stated by the letter under reference to meet the criterion.

III.   *Date established :* 1965 (formerly a faunal reserve since 1951).

Tourism : rest-camp under construction (1966).

IV.   *Altitude :* No information.

a) A fairly level expanse of typical Soudanian bush savannah, together with a section of the inundation zone along the Chari River.

b) Giant eland *Taurotragus derbianus,* roan, topi, hartebeest, various species of kob, buffalo, warthog *Phacochoerus aethiopicus,* hippopotamus *H. amphibius;* carnivores.

V.   **Areas excluded :**

Three total faunal reserves :

1. Bahr Salamat ...   .   2,060,000 ha
This reserve encloses the Zakouma National Park (No. 1 in the List).

2. Siniaka-Minia .   ...   426,000 ha
It had been intended to retain this reserve (which was included in the previous edition of the List) in view of its staff of six wardens and the budget of U.S. $ 140,000 allocated for its equipment in 1964-1965, and particularly as a plan had been announced to give it National Park Status. However the letter of 3 March 1966, stated that the plan for a National Park was on the point of being abandoned and made it necessary to cancel the intention.

3. Douguia ...   .   59,400 ha
On partial reserve (established for the protection of kudu only) :

4. Abou-Telfane .   ...   110,000 ha

164

24. CHILE

Listed Areas : four.
1. Cape Horn National Park.
2. Nahuelbuta National Park.
3. Fray Jorge National Park.
4. Tolhuaca National Park.

General Introduction :

Legislation : the Chilean National Parks were established under *Articles* 10 and 11 of the Forest Law of 30 June 1931. It must be noted that these Articles do not in fact in themselves provide the assurance of that complete protection for the natural environment of the Parks, which is considered necessary under the " legal status criterion " for areas to be included in the present United Nations List. The preamble to Article 10, indeed, actually begins with the phrase : " With

165

the object of regulating the timber trade... ". Moreover, the title "Tourist National Park (parques nacionales de turismo)" used in Chile, leaves no room for doubt that recreation has priority over conservation.

However, it was reported in July 1968 that, following IUCN's Latin-American Conference on the Conservation of Renewable Natural Resources held at Bariloche, Argentina, in March/April of that year, an entirely new Conservation and National Parks Law was being enacted in Chile and had already been passed by the Chamber of Deputies.

Administration : vested in the Servicio Agricola y Ganadero of the Ministry of Agriculture.

Land tenure : state-ownership, with some enclaves of private land; the main difficulty is illegal settlement, the Chilean Government having indeed a considerable job to prevent "colonos" establishing themselves, without permission, on lands that it has set aside for national parks.

Tourism : every effort is being made to welcome visitors and facilitate their stay in the Parks.

Scientific research : no specific organisation has been set up.

The previous edition of the List, E/3436, contained descriptions of the four Parks now listed as well as of all those relegated to Section V.

Details : application of criteria (II), general information (III) and description (IV) :

1. CAPE HORN NATIONAL PARK.

II.   *a)* Status : total protection. In fact, this amounts to giving a legal sanction for *de facto* protection, since the island which constitutes the Park is uninhabited and the lighthouse maintained by the Chilean navy is an automatic one.

b) Area : 63,093 ha.

c) Staff : nil.

d) Budget : nil.

III.   *Date established :* 1945.

Tourism : the sole means of access is by boat.

IV.   *Altitude :* sea level to 50 m.

a) The most southerly island of the coastal archipelago; autochthonous flora characteristic of southern Chile : southern beech *Nothofagus dombeyi, N. betuloides* etc.

b) Typical south Chilean fauna.

2. NAHUELBUTA NATIONAL PARK.

II.   *a)* Status : general protection. The Park is uninhabited and forest exploitation and hunting are forbidden.

b) Area : 5,415 ha.

c) Staff : a conservator with a small labour force.

d) Budget : the staff salaries are sufficient to satisfy the criterion.

166

Date established : 1939.

Tourism : access by road.

Altitude : 1,000-1,500 m.

a) Forest with pure stands of "monkey-puzzle" pines *Araucaria araucana* and stands mixed with other species; on the eastern side of the Nahuelbuta ridge *Nothofagus* forest occurs.

b) Montane fauna.

3. FRAY JORGE NATIONAL PARK.

a) Status : general protection.

b) Area : 6,845 ha.

c) Staff : a conservator with a small labour force.

d) Budget : staff salaries are sufficient to satisfy the criterion.

Date established : 1941.

Tourism : situated 20 km from the Pan-American Highway, with a motorable road of access into the Park built in 1955.

Altitude : sea level to 760 m.

a) A mountainous area containing remnants of the sub-tropical forest which formerly covered northern Chile; notable species include the tique *Aextoxicon punctatum,* the myrtle or "petrillo" *Myrceugenia correaefolia, Azara borealis* and Winter's bark *Drimys winteri*; the shrubby associations are composed chiefly of *Baccharis, Fuchsia* and barberry *Berberis.*

b) Argentine skunk *Conepatus chinga,* pampas and mountain cats *Felis colocolo* and *jacobita* and the rat chinchilla *Abrocoma murrayi.*

4. TOLHUACA NATIONAL PARK.

a) Status : general protection, although sport-fishing is allowed in the Malleco lake.

b) Area : 3,500 ha.

c) Staff : a conservator with a small labour force.

d) Budget : covers the salaries of staff.

Date established : 1935.

Tourism : access by rail to Curacautin and thence by 35 km of unmetalled road; the Park is situated near the Tolhuaca Thermal Baths; winter sports facilities.

Altitude : 1,500-2,000 m.

a) Forests, mainly composed of *Araucaria araucana* and *Nothofagus* species : *obliqua, pumilio, procera* and *dombeyi.*

b) No information.

Areas excluded :

Altogether, about forty Parks have had to be omitted from the List, although it has not been possible to do this with the formal approval of the Chilean authorities due to lack of reply to requests for the relevant information.

The exclusion has not been applied without hesitation, but is based on information from various sources and, in particular, on an analysis of the Report presented by the Chilean Forests Department to the Seattle Conference in 1962. In this Report in which the serious problem of illegal settlement, referred to above in the Introduction, is treated with great frankness, the following very significant sentence occurs: "According to an investigation carried out in 1961 of State-owned National Parks and Reserves, several of them were found to be completely occupied by colonists".

This explains and justifies the selection of only four Parks and the removal for the time being from the United Nations List of the following areas:

1. San Rafael Lake National Park.
    590,000 ha; 1945; inhabited; grazed by domestic stock.

2. Vicente Pérez Rosales National Park.
    135,175 ha; 1926; tourists are attracted to this Park "not only by the fine scenery but especially by the abundant fishing and shooting"; it would seem therefore that even hunting is permitted.

3. Puyehue National Park.
    75,000 ha; 1941; as above, "abundant fishing and hunting".

4. Juan Fernandez Island National Park.
    18,300 ha; 1935; the Park consists of three small islands inhabited by fishermen who cultivate the soil and hunt without restriction, have introduced domestic animals and have as their principal occupation the capture and sale of crayfish. One of these islands is "Robinson Crusoe's island".

5. Los Paraguas National Park.
    18,000 ha; 1940; human habitations; winter sports centre.

6. Easter Island National Park.
    17,000 ha; 1935; mainly of anthropological interest — the Moais; the inhabitants, also fishermen, are of Polynesian ancestry.

7. Pirihueico National Park.
    13,950 ha; 1945; "great abundance of sites suitable for fishing and shooting".

8. Villarica National Park.
    13,780 ha; 1940; this Park is perhaps on the borderline for inclusion in the List, as it is inaccessible and has few inhabitants; but it still has no supervision.

9. Lago Penuelas National Park.
    9,055 ha; 1959; unlike the previous Park, this enjoys some supervision, but the natural features do not receive any specific protection. The Park in fact comprises plantations of cypressus, eucalyptus, pines, acacias, etc., designed to protect the catchment of the Valparaiso water supplies, and scraps of original forest (the boldo *Peumus boldus,* the meiten *Maytenus boaria,* the soap-tree *Quillaja saponaria,* the broad-leaf pepper-tree *Schinus latifolius* etc.) are unfortunately exceptional. Crowds of visitors.

10. Lago Grey National Park.
    4,332 ha (elsewhere quoted as 24,532 ha); 1959; the whole Park is used for sheep pasture and the forests are methodically burned to create or maintain new grazing; there is no supervision.

In addition to the above the following small National Parks have had to be excluded because they also fail to satisfy the criterion of size:

11. La Barra del Rio Bueno.
    424 ha; 1949; " ... a place much frequented by tourists and lovers of *fishing and shooting...* ".

12. Bosque Santiago.
    174 ha; 1957; again mainly plantations of exotic species on the outskirts of Santiago.

13. Talinay.
    114 ha; 1945; no supervision. The sheep and goats which devastate this Park should be strictly outlawed, not to mention the gatherers of firewood, because it contains extremely interesting botanical associations of thorny species of southern origin, similar to those of the Fray Jorge (No. 3 on the List).

14. Contulmo.
    82 ha; 1941; " ... for abundant fishing and shooting... ".

15. Leo-Lleo.
    80 ha; 1959; contains some very interesting dunes.

16. Cerro Nielol.
    76 ha; 1939; the public park of the town of Temuco; a puma *Felis concolor* was recorded here in 1968.

17. Gabriel Coll.
    31 ha; 1951; public park of the town of La Serena; mostly introduced species.

18. Isla la Pinta.
    3.5 ha; 1955.

Finally, the Pedro de Valdivia National Park, established in 1952, has also been excluded; its area is unknown and it is situated in the heart of the town of La Serena.

25. CHINA (TAIWAN) ([1])

Listed Areas : nil.

a) **Explanation :**

Although there are signs of a keen interest in the establishment and organisation of national parks and equivalent reserves, it is clear that nothing has yet happened in Taiwan beyond the stage of initial preparations and the point has not yet been reached where any areas satisfy the criteria laid down for the present List. It is to be hoped that the necessary steps will soon be achieved. A specialist form the United States National Parks Service has submitted a report which sets out comprehensive and detailed proposals.

([1]) No information has been obtainable concerning the situation in the Chinese People's Republic.

b) **Excluded areas :**

The following are the three principal National Parks projects :

1. Mount Yangming National Park.

28,400 ha; near Taipeh; a section of the coast, rising to wooded mountains, with a peninsula (Ya-lieu) containing some extraordinary geological curiosities. The area is already visited by numerous tourists (a million in 1963).

This region was partly put under reserve as early as 1936, when the Japanese were administering the island, under the name of Mount Tatun Group, a chain of extinct volcanoes. The reserve was then 8,265 ha in area, of which 2,625 ha were under public ownership and the rest private land. However, the war prevented this theoretical status from being translated into fact and after the war the area suffered a good deal of deterioration. It now seems that it will be difficult to establish a reserve at Mt. Yangming, which will really answer up to the conditions laid down by the ICNP.

2. The Taroko Gorge.

This is a deep, narrow and picturesque gorge in the east of the island, with much geological interest. Here also a national park was declared by the Japanese, but in contrast to Yangming, where the current project envisages a reserve three times the size of that of 1936, the Chinese plans for Taroko Gorge today are much less ambitious than those embodied in the Japanese decision. Now, in effect, it has become only a question of protecting the gorge itself, whereas in 1937 the plan was for a 272,590 ha Park, taking in not only the Gorge but also several national forests covering Mt. Sylvia and many other peaks over 3,000 m high. As with Mt. Yangming, the Japanese initiative had no practical result. The region has acquired some historical interest as the site of fierce battles. It still contains some relatively untouched sectors where interesting plants such as *Taiwania cryptomeroides* and *Abies kawakamii* are to be found and a sample of the local fauna survives : clouded leopard *Neofelis nebulosa*, Pallas's cat *Felis manul*, yellow-throated marten *Martes flavigula*, Swinhoe's pheasant *Lophura swinhoii*, etc.

3. Mount Ali and Mount Morrisson.

This again is a revival of an old Japanese project, which during the same period (1936) incorporated these two peaks in a 185,980 ha national park, named Yushan-Alishan. Yushan, which is the other name for Mt. Morrisson, means Jade Mountain and its peak is the highest in Taiwan. Unfortunately, the Japanese exploited the forest to the point where it was virtually worked out.

The population of Taiwan has more than doubled during the last twenty years, from 6 to over 12 millions. The accompanying development — new settlement, road building, exploitation of forests and minerals etc. — has resulted in many of the areas which the Japanese planned to protect being now greatly degraded and ceasing to justify action to establish them as sanctuaries. But although the Taroko-Sylvia and Mt. Morrisson projects cannot be revived in the form in which they were first designed some thirty years ago, the Government of Taiwan could nevertheless still include in reservations some ten to twenty thousand hectares of superb country near Morrisson and Sylvia mountains, while the Taroko Gorge is still capable of being made into a reserve of the greatest interest.

26. COLOMBIA

Listed Areas : nil.

a) **Explanation :**

Developments in Colombia, which would no doubt have justified the inclusion of several areas in the List, unfortunately came a little too late for consideration to be given in this Second Edition. For example, up till May 1967, Las Farallones de Cali N.P. and Puracé N.P., although established by a departmental decision, had not yet been confirmed by Central Government Decree. Similarly, of the several parks administered by the Corporación autonoma de los Valles del Magdalena y Sinú (CVM), an organisation somewhat similar to the Tennessee Valley Authority, the Sierra de la Macarena Reserve was still in the process of organisation and equipment (a budget of 1 million pesos having been made available for wardens, scientific research etc.), while the Isla de Salamanca N.P., of which two-thirds was classified as a " primitive undisturbed area ", had only just received an allocation for wardens and equipment.

Since the middle of 1967, however, great progress has been made as shown by the details set out below. For three of the Parks sufficient details had been received by the time the present Edition went to press to enable a short description to be given.

No information on Colombia was included in the previous edition, E/3436 and Part Two, of the List.

b) **Areas excluded :**

1. Sierra de la Macarena Reserve.
   (See *c*) below for details.)

2. Farallones de Cali National Park.
   (See *c*) below for details.)

3. Tayrona National Park.
   Officially established in 1967 by a Resolution of the Colombian Institute for Agrarian Reform; plans are being prepared for its development.

4. Cuenca de la Laguna de la Cocha y Patascoy National Park.
   Established 1968 : 58,564 ha.

5. Sumapaz National Park.
   Established 1968 : 30,000 ha.

6. Uraba National Park.
   Established 1963 and now being developed : 29,000 ha.

7. Isla de Salamanca National Park.
   Reorganised in 1967 : 20,912 ha. Situated in the north of the country, this park as already noted includes a specially protected area (13,742 ha). The administrative headquarters, where the 6 wardens are based, includes a laboratory.

8. Chinganza National Park.
   Established 1968 : 20,000 ha.

9. Puracé National Park.
   (See *c*) below for details.)

171

10. Sierra Nevada de Santa Marta National Park.
Officially established in 1967 by a Resolution of the Colombian Institute of Agrarian Reform; plans are being prepared for its development : 12,000 ha.

11. Guasca National Park.
Established 1968 : 3,000 ha.

12. Cueva de los Guacharos ("Cavern of the Oil-Birds") National Park.
A small park, established 1963, and now being developed : 700 ha.

13. Yotoco National Park.
Another small park dating from 1963 and now being developed : 559 ha.

c) **Descriptions of Parks for which information is available :**

No. 1. SIERRA DE LA MACARENA RESERVE.

Status : there is a tropical diseases research station in the Reserve.

Staff : 15 guards, armed and vested with full powers, distributed among five guard-posts.

Area : 1,131,000 ha.

Altitude : 50-2,500 m.

a) A zone in which the flora of the Andes and the flora of the Guyanas meet.

b) A rich fauna; three species of deer, spectacled bear *Tremarctos ornatus,* common tapir *Tapirus terrestris*; endemic species of fish.

c) Spectacled bear.

No. 2. LAS FARALLONES DE CALI NATIONAL PARK.

Area : 120,000 ha.

Altitude : 100-4,100 m.

a) Reported to have a specially luxuriant flora.

b) Pudu deer *P. pudu,* mountain tapir *Tapirus pinchaque,* spectacled bear; birds include toucans and eagles.

c) Spectacled bear, mountain tapir, pudu. (Resolution No. 25 of the First World Conference on National Parks, Seattle 1962, calls for special protective measures for theses three "Red Book" species.)

No. 9. PURACÉ NATIONAL PARK.

Area : 12,000 ha.

Altitude : 2,000-4,640 m.

a) An active volcano of which the summit is permanently under snow; humid sub-tropical forest and *páramos* on the slopes.

b) Spectacled bear, mountain tapir, pudu deer.

c) All three of the mammals mentioned.

27. CONGO DEMOCRATIC REPUBLIC
(Kinshasa)

Listed Areas : three.

1. The Upemba National Park.
2. Albert National Park.
3. The Garamba National Park.

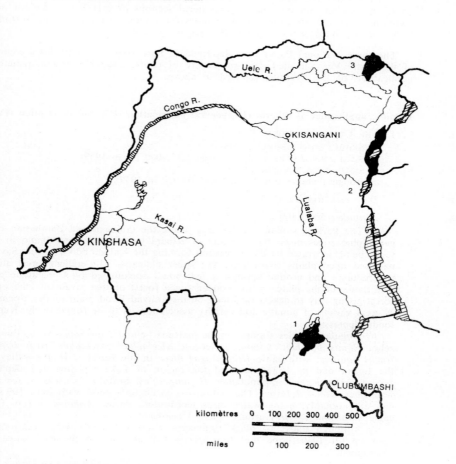

General Introduction :

Administration : at present undertaken by the Ministry of Agriculture of the Republic, although theoretically under Statutory provisions (loi Fondamentale); the maintenance of the Parks is still vested in the " Institut des Parcs Nationaux du Congo " formerly based on Brussels but, with effect from January 1967, replaced by a new Institute or Service with headquarters at Kinshasa.

CONGO DEMOCRATIC REPUBLIC (Kinshasa)

Land tenure : the territory of the Parks is under public ownership.

Scientific research : undertaken since 1933, on a systematic basis, by the Institut des Parcs Nationaux du Congo Belge which in a series entitled "Exploration scientifique des parcs nationaux du Congo" has published some 300 volumes, containing 500 papers, 33,000 pages and descriptions of 4,500 new species.

Tourism : this has been organised mainly for the Parc National Albert, based on Rwindi Camp, but only in very restricted sections of that Park. Up till now there has been little development of facilities for visitors to the two other National Parks. Entry is by permit for which a fee is charged.

The three National Parks were described in Part Two of the previous editions of the List. Very detailed descriptions are of course available in the numerous publications of the Institute, referred to above.

Details : application of criteria (II), general information (III) and description (IV) :

II.
    1. THE UPEMBA NATIONAL PARK.
       a) Status : strict natural reserve.
       b) Area : 950,000 ha (reduced from 1,173,000 ha in 1959).
       c) Staff : total strength 130.
       d) Budget : about U.S. $ 30,000 ($ 64,000 in 1959).

III.
    Date established : 1939.

IV.
    Altitude : 500-1,800 m.

    a) The Park is situated in the area where the Guinean and Zambesian biogeographic zones meet, the plateaux of Kibara to the north and Biano in the south being separated by the depression forming the Kalomondo Trench. Savannah and open plains characterise the upper plateaux, with gallery-forest along watercourses and around springs; a few ponds surrounded by Cyperaceae spp The flanks of the plateaux are wooded (open forest or tree savannah), the open forest giving way to acacia savannah on the alluvial flood plain of the Upemba. A great variety of aquatic and marshy associations is to be found in the Kamolondo depression.

    b) Ungulate species abound on the plateaux : eland *Taurotragus oryx,* Böhm's zebra *Equus burchelli böhmi,* hartebeest *Alcelaphus buselaphus,* roan *Hippotragus equinus*; with sable *Hippotragus niger* in the forests. In the valley of the Lufira and its tributaries and the region of Lake Upemba are elephant *Loxodonta africana,* hippopotamus *H. amphibius,* buffalo *Syncerus caffer* and waterbuck *Kobus defassa.* The avifauna is particularly good, with some 500 species and, notably, many water birds (cormorant, darter *Anhinga,* heron, fish-eagle *Cuncuma vocifer*) around Lake Upemba.

    c) Although tracks of black rhinoceros *Diceros bicornis* were occasionally seen up till 1940, hope that this species still survives in the Park must be abandoned.

    2. ALBERT NATIONAL PARK.

II.
    a) Status : strict natural reserve, except for the fisheries permitted in Lake Edward.
    b) Area : 800,000 ha.
    c) Staff : total strength 420.
    d) Budget : about U.S. $ 50,000 ($ 120,000 in 1959).

1. *Date established :* 1925, with modifications in 1935.

V. *Altitude :* 900-5,119 m.

a) As might be expected from its considerable size and varied topography, the Parc National Albert comprises a remarkable range of different habitats, from north to south :

1. Transitional closed-canopy forest linking up with the montane forest of the middle Semliki;

2. The mountain massif of the Ruwenzori with its vegetation belts ranging from equatorial forest to afro-alpine associations, surmounted by glaciers and permanent snow;

3. The grasslands of the upper Semliki;

4. Lake Edward with its breeding colonies of birds, such as cormorant *Phalacrocorax* spp. and marabou *Leptoptilos crumeniferus*;

5. The extinct volcano of Tshiaberimu, inhabited by a remnant of mountain gorilla *Gorilla g. beringei*;

6. The Rwindi-Rutshuru plain, with savannah and abundant game;

7. The block of active volcanoes (Nyiragongo, Nyamuragira), with lava flows and hot springs;

8. The Virunga group of extinct volcanoes, their *Hagenia* forests also harbouring the mountain gorilla.

b) The fauna includes many large mammals : mountain gorilla, chimpanzee *Pan troglodytes,* elephant, hippopotamus, the black and red forms of buffalo, several antelopes, lion and leopard *Panthera leo* and *pardus,* wild dog *Lycaon pictus,* okapi *Okapia johnstoni,* aardvark *Orycteropus afer.*

c) Mountain gorilla.

3. THE GARAMBA NATIONAL PARK.

a) Status : strict natural reserve.

b) Area : 492,000 ha.

c) Staff : total strength 70.

d) Budget : about U.S. $ 20,000 ($ 40,000 in 1959).

I. *Date established :* 1938.

V. *Altitude :* 900-1,060 m.

a) A gently undulating peneplain, covered with rather poor woody savannah. Towards the Sudan frontier on the north-east some dry forest. Some good gallery-forests, notably along the Aka, Dungu and Garamba watercourses. Numerous valleys with extensive papyrus *Cyperus* sp.

b) White rhinoceros *Ceratotherium sinum cottoni,* giraffe *Giraffa camelopardalis,* elephant, buffalo, hippopotamus, a dozen kinds of antelope including eland; lion, leopard, wild dog; chimpanzee, black-and-white colobus *Colobus polykomos,* aardvark, pangolin *Manis* sp. and many species of migratory birds.

c) White (or square-lipped) rhinoceros of the northern race *cottoni.*

V.   Areas excluded :

Apart from the Game Reserves, which do not meet the criteria laid down for National Parks and Equivalent Reserves, the Kivu Province of the Congo has had since 1937 the Mount Kahuzi zoological and forest Reserve, which would certainly have merited eventual inclusion in the List if its hitherto inadequate supervision had been brought up to standard.

In 1964 and 1965 this Reserve unfortunately suffered from serious depredations; woods were cut down and cleared for cultivation and above all there was heavy hunting pressure, which was particularly deplorable as the mountain gorilla was among its chief victims. In 1966, action was taken locally to put a stop to this poaching and set up effective supervision, but by 1968 the situation had again badly deteriorated. However, the Central Government at Kinshasa is known to be well-disposed, in principle, to a National Park, thus giving effect to the Resolution (No. 15) adopted by the 9th General Assembly of IUCN (Lucerne 1966). One can, therefore, still hope that a fourth National Park will eventually be added to the List. Meanwhile it is encouraging to note that the Minister of Agriculture on two occasions in 1966-1967 personally inspected the three existing National Parks and, in doing so, requested the assistance of a representative of the ICNP (Dr. K. Curry Lindahl of Sweden).

28. CONGO REPUBLIC (Brazzaville)

I.   Listed Areas : one.

1. Odzala National Park.

General Introduction :

Administration : Ministry of Agriculture.

Land tenure : public ownership.

Tourism, etc. : there is no special organisation, the one Park listed being practically inaccessible, and for the same reason nothing has been done in the way of scientific research.

The Odzala Park was mentioned in Part Two of the previous edition of the List.

Details : application of criteria (II), general information (III) and description (IV) :

II.   1. Odzala National Park.

a) Status : established in 1935, with the status of a strict natural reserve in terms of the London Convention of 1933, and elevated in 1940 to that of a National Park under the same Convention.

b) Area : 110,000 ha (according to the latest information obtained from Brazzaville in 1962).

c) Staff : one warden only. The Park has however been judged to qualify for the List on the grounds (i) that the Congo Republic is still faced with considerable political difficulties and (ii) that the Park is situated in a largely uninhabited region, so that it does not suffer from poaching or other threats, the few groups of Pygmies to be found in it being in symbiosis with the fauna.

d) Budget : provision (of which the exact amount is unknown) is made in the annual budget of the Republic.

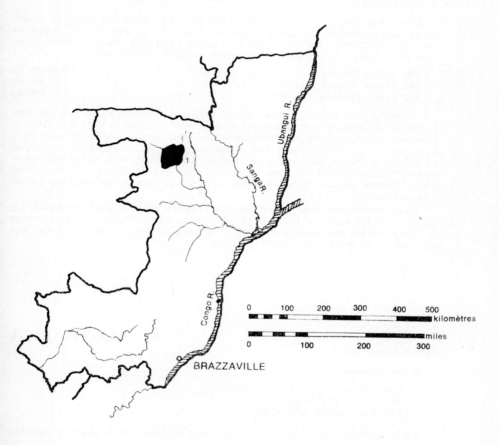

I.   *Date established :* 1935, with modifications in 1940.

Tourism : difficult of access throughout the year; small airstrip at Kelle, 85 km away and 500 km from Brazzaville.

Altitude : 400 m.

a) A plateau covered by humid tropical forest, mostly of secondary origin; on the southern edge this passes into savannah.

b) Elephant *Loxodonta africana,* buffalo *Syncerus caffer,* including the pigmy variety, bongo *Taurotragus eurycerus*; anthropoid apes including the lowland or typical race of gorilla; bushpig *Potamochoerus porcus*; leopard *Panthera pardus* and golden cat *Felis aurata* — in short the typical fauna of the great Congo tropical forest.

V.   **Areas excluded :**

Three Reserves, formerly well-supervised and from which all rights of exploitation have been legally excluded by law, so that in theory and perhaps in practice they are uninhabited and the fauna has enjoyed real and total protection, have only been omitted from the List with some hesitation.   They are :

The Léfini Reserve ...   .   450,000 ha
The Mount Fouari Reserve ...   .   18,000 ha
The Lekoli-Pandaka Reserve ...   .   50,000 ha

According to a report presented at the Bukavu Conference in 1953, a part-time Game Officer and four full-time Game Guards were allocated to the Léfini Reserve. However, recent requests for information addressed to the Brazzaville authorities have received no official reply, and it has therefore not been considered suitable to include thse three Reserves in the United Nations List, even though the Inter-State Office of African Tourism indicated at the end of March 1965 that " the Mount Fouari and the Léfini Reserves continue to receive the attention of the technical services ".

Three other faunal reserves and two partial faunal reserves, totalling 608,000 ha, are listed in the report of the IUCN/FAO African Special Project, a representative of which visited the country in 1963, when one of them, North Nyanga, was reported to be quite undisturbed.

29. COSTA RICA

I.   **Listed Areas :** nil.

V.   a) **Areas excluded :**

1. Cabo Blanco Strict Natural Reserve.
2. Montanas del Zurqui.
3. Las Tres Marias y la Concordia.

There is also a strip along the Pan-American Highway which has been declared a protected zone.

b) **Explanation :**

No specific measures to provide for the supervision and maintenance of the above areas have yet been officially confirmed nor have details as to status, size, research and other facilities, geology, flora and fauna been supplied.   However, in the case of the Cabo Blanco Reserve, World Wildlife Fund initiative and the interest and generosity of Philadelphia Conservationists Inc. led to considerable progress being reported by August 1965. Actually established on 26 October 1963 by Presidential Decree, this 1,172 ha reserve (of which 751 ha are forest) was demarcated and a warden posted to it by the end of that year, the Institute of Lands and Settlement (ITCO) being vested with authority to regulate entry and to administer the reserve. Some 16 families lived in and owned the land and had to be expropriated, but this was due to be completed by the end of 1965, a firm undertaking having been entered into by the Government for effective maintenance and management. When implementation of these undertakings is confirmed, the Reserve may well qualify for the List.

The areas numbered 2 and 3 above are ones which were excluded from alienation as long as 1888.

Negotiations were also reported (August 1965) to be on foot for the establishment of an " international boundary park " on the frontier with Panama.

Costa Rica was not included in E/3436 or Part Two of the previous edition of the List.

30. CUBA

Listed Areas : four.

1. Cupeyal Natural Reserve.
2. El Cabo Natural Reserve.
3. Jaguani Natural Reserve.
4. Cabo Corrientes Natural Reserve.

General Introduction :

The legal basis for the four reserves is provided by Resolution 412, 3, 1963 of the President, Dr. Carlos Rafael Rodrigues, drafted by the Instituto Nacional de Reforma Agraria. The Comisión Nacional de la Academia de Ciencias, which is responsible for running the reserves, is also in charge of research. No provision for tourists has been made.

Cuba was not included in E/3436 or Part Two of the previous edition of the List.

Details : application of criteria (II), general information (III) and description (IV) :

1. CUPEYAL NATURAL RESERVE.

a) Status : total protection, no hunting, fishing, no agriculture of any sort. Entry completely prohibited.

b) Area : 10,260 ha.

c) and *d*) Staff and budget : « these areas were transferred to the National Commission of the Academy of Sciences... in order that it should undertake their supervision and conservation, solely for the purposes of scientific research ". It has not been possible to obtain details of the financial and staffing resources available to the Commission for maintaining and supervising the Reserves.

179

III.   *Date established :* 1963.

IV.   *Altitude :* 400-800 m.

a) A mountainous lateritic area, with mixed conifer and broad-leaved forest. The forest in the southern part of the reserve was formerly exploited.

b) Mammals : long-tailed hutia *Capromys p. pilorides*; birds : Cuban solitaire *Myadestes elisabeth*, Gundlach's and sharp-shinned hawks *Accipiter gundlachi* and *striatus*, red-tailed hawk *Buteo jamaicensis solitudinis*, Cuban parrot and parakeet *Amazona l. leucophala* and *Aratinga euops*.

c) *Campephilus principalis bairdii*, the Cuban race of the ivory-billed woodpecker; Gundlach's hawk; the Isle of Pines race of the Cuban solitaire, *Myadestes elisabeth retrusus*.

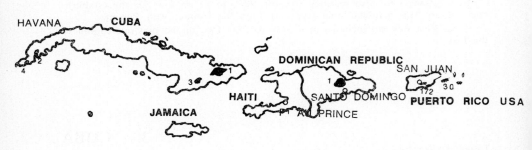

2. El Cabo Natural Reserve.

II.   *a*) Status : as for No. 1.

           b) Area : 7,535 ha.

           c) and *d*) Staff and budget : as for No. 1.

III.   *Date established :* 1963.

IV.   *Altitude :* sea level to 10 m.

a) Flat, rocky terrain; tropical forest, somewhat degraded by exploitation.

b) Mammals : whitetail deer *Odocoileus virginianus*, two races of long-tailed hutia *pilorides* and *prehensili*; birds : Cuban bullfinch *Melopyrrha n. nigra*, Key West, ruddy and grey-headed quail-doves *Oreopeleia chrysia, montana* and *caniceps*, red-necked pigeon *Columba squamosa*, Cuban trogon *Priotelus t. temnurus* and Cuban tody *Todus multicolor*.

3. Jaguani Natural Reserve.

II.   *a*) Status : as for No. 1.

           b) Area : 4,932 ha.

           c) and *d*) Staff and budget : as for No. 1.

III.   *Date established :* 1963.

180

Altitude : no information.

a) and *b)* No information.

c) Cuban ivory-billed woodpecker.

4. CABO CORRIENTES NATURAL RESERVE.

a) Status : as for No. 1.

b) Area : 1,578 ha.

c) and *d)* Staff and budget : as for No. 1.

Date established : 1963.

Altitude : sea level to 10 m.

a) Tropical forest, still unexplored in 1944; flat stony soil; traces of former exploitation in the forest margin.

b) Fauna identical to that of No. 2 above.

Areas excluded :

1. Sierra del Cristal National Park.

    Established 1930 : 26,305 ha. Invaded by cultivators and herdsmen and cut by motor roads. Although hunting is still prohibited, the area is not maintained and was classified by the Cuban authorities on 1 July 1965 as " non-existent ".

2. National Hunting and Fishing Reserve of the Cienaga de Zapata.

    Established 1936 : 179,450 ha. Degraded, unsupervised and also classified on 1 July 1965 as " non-existent ".

3. Cienaga de Zapata National Park.

    A 50,000 ha National Park was demarcated within the Cienaga de Zapata Reserve in 1959, and put under an independent authority, mainly for the development of tourism. However it has not been included in the List because " there are areas of agricultural livestock and forestry exploitation within this tourist zone ".

4. La Guira National Park.

    1959 : 1,000 ha. Restaurant, chalets, cafeterias, sport grounds.

5. La Gran Piedra National Park.

    1959 : 1,000 ha. Developed as No. 4 for recreational purposes; museum.

These last two " national parks " are run by the National Institute for the Tourist industry.

I. **Listed Areas :** nil.

V. **Areas excluded :**

One protected forest, known as the Athalassa, near Nicosia, which is 774 ha in area. However, its status does not give it complete protection and no information has been obtained as to the standard of supervision or the budget provided for its maintenance.

32. **CZECHOSLOVAKIA**

I. **Listed Areas :** three.

    1. High Tatra National Park.
    2. Mountains of the Giants (Krkonose) National Park.
    3. Pieniny National Park.

General Introduction :

Legislation : the legal basis of the Parks is provided by Laws of 1955 (Slovakia) and 1956 (Bohemia-Moravia). Each National Park is established under these Laws by decree of the Governement or the Slovak National Council.

Administration : responsibility of the Ministry of Culture (Prague) and Ministry of Culture (Bratislava), supported by the State Institute for the Protection of Historic Monuments and Conservation of Nature. Also eleven Regional or County Centres at each of which the department responsible for Nature Protection is represented.

Land tenure : the land in most cases is publicly owned, but where private property is included in a National Park, the owner is indemnified for being obliged to conform to the legal requirements.

Tourism : is regarded as one of the main objects of the National Parks — " these ' islands '... intended for the relaxation and well-being of the people... ".

Research : actively pursued, chiefly under the Institute referred to above, which publishes the well-known journal " *Ochrana Prírody* ".

Czechoslovakia was not represented either in E/3436 or Part Two of the previous edition of the List.

Details : application of criteria (II), general information (III) and description (IV) :

1. HIGH TATRA NATIONAL PARK.

a) Status : complete protection, except for some forest exploitation under control. There are a few small strict nature reserves in the Park, which is otherwise fully open to visitors.

b) Area : 50,000 ha, plus a controlled area of 70,000 ha.

c) Staff : a Director supported by some 130 full-time or part-time supervisory personnel.

d) Budget : 15 m crowns (=about U.S. $ 1,500,000).

Date established : 1948, with further development in 1954. This Park is situated on the border with Poland and, being immediately adjacent to a Polish National Park, constitutes a classic example of international co-operation in the establishment of National Parks in a national frontier zone. There is effective collaboration at both the scientific and tourist level, and in fact joint scientific effort dates back to 1924, well before full protected status was applied to the areas concerned.

Tourism : well developed, accommodation being provided in the supporting " controlled area ", with its village, holiday homes, sanitoria, camping sites, etc. Some 325 km of footpaths or trails. There is a very active Research Station and a Museum.

Altitude : highest point 2,663 m.

a) A part of the Carpathians of eastern Slovakia; crystalline and calcareous rocks and Mesozoic dolomites; sharp alpine relief with the usual glacial features of lakes, moraines, etc.

b) Chamois *R. rupicapra,* bear *Ursus arctos,* wolf *Canis lupus,* wild cat *Felis silvestris,* lynx *Felis lynx,* marmot *M. marmota.*

2. KRKNOSE OR MOUNTAINS OF THE GIANTS NATIONAL PARK.

a) Status : complete protection except for wood-cutting and limited human habitations; small sections are classed as strict natural reserves.

b) Area : 38,000 ha.

c) Staff : a Director, with 5 assistant-officers, and park wardens.

d) Budget : 600,000 crowns (=about U.S. $ 60,000).

183

CZECHOSLOVAKIA

III. *Date established :* 1963.

Tourism : intensively developed; the ski-runs are renowned and much frequented; there are holiday chalets and sanitoria in the Park, under strict control. The Park is also on the Polish frontier and international collaboration is being developed.

Research : is carried on in the Park, especially in the strict reserves, which are called " National Nature Reserves ".

IV. *Altitude :* highest point 1,603 m.

a) Part of the mountains of Bohemia with their typical rounded formations of Caledonian and Hercynian folding, smoothed by former glaciation; alpine meadows, peat-bog, vast forests; some volcanic features such as basalt outcrops. The plants include some endemic species (e.g. *Sorbus sudetica*) and glacial relicts (cloudberry *Rubus chamaemorus,* alpine saxifrage *Saxifraga nivalis,* etc.).

b) Boreo-arctic relict species include the Alpine shrew *Sorex alpinus,* the ring ousel *Turdus torquatus* and nutcracker *Nucifraga caryocatactes.*

3. PIENINY NATIONAL PARK.

II. *a*) Status : complete protection.
b) Area : 2,150 ha.
c) Staff : a Director, wardens.
d) Budget : covers staff salaries.

III. *Date established :* 1967.

Tourism : also situated on the Polish frontier, the small size of this Park restricts the possibilities of tourist development. Although in view of its recent creation no research station has yet been established, a good deal of scientific investigation has already been carried out in the area.

IV. *Altitude :* highest point 982 m.

a) This is a limestone region with typical flora, cut by the deep valley of the Dunajec river.
b) The fauna is characteristically calcophile and thermophile.

V. **Areas excluded :**

A. — The " Protected Landscapes ", which are protected zones of typical countryside, with a status rather similar to that of National Parks and a staff averaging about 3 officers supported by wardens :

1. Sumava Forest : 163,000 ha, established in its present form since 1963, but in fact the oldest natural reserve in the country and possibly to be made a new National Park; altitude 1,000 m; the most wooded area in the country.

2. Ceský ráj or " Bohemian Paradise " : 12,000 ha, established in 1955; altitude 400 m; sandstone with isolated volcanic hills.

3. Moravský Kras (" Moravian Karst ") : same area and date as No. 2; altitude 500 m; karstic Devonian limestone, caves and grottoes.

4. Slovenský ráj (" Slovakian Paradise ") : 14,478 ha, 1964; altitude 800 m; karstic landscape, waterfalls, famous ice cave.

5. Malá Fatra : altitude 1,600 m; plateau of granites, limestones and dolomites; spruce and beech forest, rich flora.

6. Jizerské hory : 35,000 ha; altitude 900 m; mountain forest and peat bogs.

184

B. — The National Nature Reserves. Several of these should no doubt be included in the List, because they are strictly protected areas of great scientific and research importance, but the full details and precise standard of supervision are not yet known. These Reserves number no less than 407, 40 of which are rated as of special interest. The following is only a provisional sample, which it is hoped to replace by an authoritative selection in the next edition of the List :

1. Zlatna na Ostrove : 9,000 ha, 1955; cultivated steppe, the habitat of the the great bustard *Otis tarda.*

2. Karlštejn and Koda Reserves : 1,547 and 464 ha, 1952 and 1955; limestone; thermophile steppe and woodland steppe flora.

3. Ardršpašsko-teplické skály : 1,772 ha, 1933; cretaceous sandstone, canyons.

4. Velký a Maly Tisý : 608 ha, 1956; two lakes; marsh birds, including bittern *Botaurus stellaris.*

5. Súlovské skály : 600 ha, 1933, famous for its geomorphological formations of conglomerate limestones.

6. Lednické rybníky : 553 ha, 1953; lakes formed by the ancient course of the river Dyje; a stopping-place for migrant birds, nesting colonies of herons.

7. Šúr : 500 ha, 1952; a relict scrap of virgin forest in a lowlying basin.

8. Demänovská dolina : 400 ha, 1933; limestone; caves.

9. Novozámecký rybník : 350 ha, 1933; lake; aquatic birds.

10. Pavlovské kopce : 300 ha, 1946-1953; calcareous hills, thermophile flora.

11. Rejvíz : 260 ha, 1955; mountain peatland.

12. Velka kotlina : 224 ha, 1955; glacial valley with conifer and broadleaf forest and good montane flora.

13. Soos : 221 ha, 1964; shallow depression with peatbog and a shield of diatomaceous shales; mineral springs, with carbon dioxide emissions; a good number of rare halophile plants.

14. Harmanecká dolina : 50 ha, 1949; the best station in Europe for the yew *Taxus baccata.*

33. DAHOMEY

Listed Areas : two.

1. The ' W ' National Park.
2. Boucle de la Pendjari National Park.

General Introduction :

The administration of the Parks is the responsibility of the Service Eaux-Forêts-Chasse of the Ministry of Rural and Cooperative Development.

A short description of the second of the listed Parks was included in Part Two of the previous edition of the List.

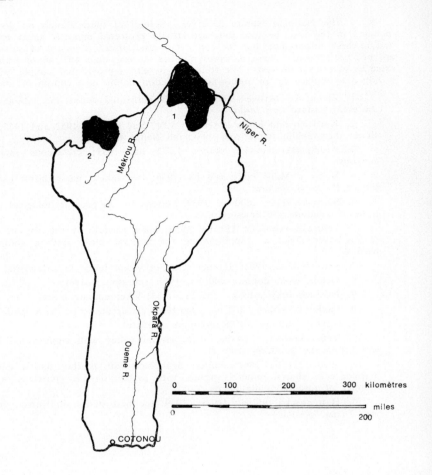

Details : application of criteria (II), general information (III) and description (IV) :

II.   1. THE 'W' NATIONAL PARK.

   a) Status : total protection.

   b) Area : 502,050 ha.

   c) Staff : 11 units. This is well below the standard laid down, but has been accepted on the grounds that much of the neighbouring country is completely devoid of inhabitants and only two sectors, 40,000 ha in the north and 60,000 ha in the south, are subject to a serious risk of poaching.

   d) Budget : U.S. $ 10,000, also well below the standard but the same considerations apply.

III.   *Date established :* 1954, having been a full game reserve and protected forest since 1952.

186

This Park, so named because it is situated on a double loop of the river Niger, is part of an international Park of which another 300,000 ha on the north are situated in the Niger Republic and 330,000 ha on the west in the Republic of Upper Volta. Formerly all three sections of the Park were operated jointly, access, for example, being by a single permit. Consideration was being given by the three Governments in 1965 to setting up a joint organisation for the co-ordination control of the whole area of approximately 1,135,000 ha.

Land tenure : state ownership.

Tourism : entry point is at Keremon to the south-west of the Park, whence a track leads to the Mekrou Falls at a place called Koudou (43 km), where it connects up with the track leading into the Upper Volta sector.

Altitude : 175-373 m.

a) A lateritic shield or peneplain of a mean height of about 250 m, dissected by a considerable number of rivers; mainly Soudanian type wooded savannah with a fire climax flora (the butter-tree *Butyrospermum, Parkia,* bastard mahogany *Khaya senegalensis,* etc.), verging towards the Sahelian type in the north, with fine gallery-forests (kola *Cola laurifolia, Kigelia aethiopica*) especially in the south along seasonal rivers. In the Dahomey sector the Park is traversed on a S.W.-N.E. line by the Atacora hills, the highest point of which reaches 373 m.

b) Elephant *Loxodonta africana,* buffalo *Syncerus caffer,* warthog *Phacochoerus aethiopicus,* the large antelopes of savannah, such as roan *Hippotragus equinus,* hartebeest *Alcelaphus buselaphus* and kob *Kobus kob*; baboon *Papio cynocephalus* and monkeys (*Cercopithecus* spp.); lion *Panthera leo,* caracal lynx *Felis caracal,* cheetah *Acinonyx jubatus,* jackal *Canis mesomelas;* hippopotamus and crocodile on the permanent waters.

2. BOUCLE DE LA PENDJARI NATIONAL PARK.

a) Status : total protection.

b) Area : 275,000 ha.

c) Staff : 9 units; below standard but only the south and south-eastern borders are inhabited and to the north the strict Faunal Reserve of Arly in Upper Volta constitutes a buffer zone.

d) Budget : U.S. $ 15,000, well above the criterion requirement.

Date established : 1961, having previously since 1954 been classified as a protected state forest and partial game reserve.

Land tenure : state ownership.

Tourism : there is a camp-site near the south-west border of the Park at Porga, which includes accommodation for 30 people. Three tracks totalling 250 km lead through the Park.

Altitude : about 175 m.

a) The alluvial plain of the Pendjari and its tributaries; grassland, with numerous pools which last through the dry season; there is a lateritic plateau, sprinkled with quartzite kopjes and wooded with guinean or soudano-guinean savannah; gallery-forest along the rivers.

b) The perennial water ensures a good varied fauna, similar to that of the 'W' National Park; elephant, hippopotamus, all the usual savannah antelopes except giant eland *Taurotragus derbianus,* warthog, baboon, lion, leopard; numerous birds (including crowned crane *Balearica pavonina,* marabou *Leptoptilos crumeniferus* and various herons).

DAHOMEY

V.   **Areas excluded :**

Some fifty protected forests, of which twenty-one are also game reserves :

Total area of protected forest ... ...   1,380,478 ha
Total area of game reserves ... ...   952,923 ha

About 600,000 ha of the game reserves are sufficiently well supervised to give an appreciable degree of protection to the typical fauna of the soudano-guinean savannah belt.

34. DENMARK

I.   **Listed Areas :** three.

1. Hansted.
2. Hirsholmene.
3. Vorsø.

General Introduction :

The basic legislation dating from 1917, provides for the establishment of reserves in which all natural associations are protected, excepting mammals and birds. However, special legislation of 1936, allowed mammals and birds to be brought within the scope of protection and this has been applied to the three reserves which have been accepted for the List.

The three reserves were not included in E/3436 or Part Two of the previous edition of the List, although certain other reserves were mentioned in Part Two.

Details : application of criteria (II), general information (III) and description (IV) :

1. HANSTED.

II.   *a)* Status : general protection.

b) Area : 3,000 ha.

c) Staff : supervision is provided by the State.

d) Budget : the Ministry of Agriculture's budget makes the necessary provision.

III.   *Date established :* 1930, revised 1940.

Land tenure : state ownership, the Reserve being under the management of the Reserves Committee of the Ministry of Agriculture.

Tourism : no accommodation. Access to the shore throughout the year, elsewhere from June to April only. A special permit has to be obtained to visit the area frequented by nesting birds, during the breeding season April-June. The are no motor roads, although proposals are under consideration.

Research : a small laboratory.

188

v.

Altitude : below 50 m.

a) Dunes, heath, marsh and lakes of the Jutland coast.

b) Bird sanctuary : several species of duck; only breeding place in Denmark of the golden plover *Pluvialis apricaria.* Roe deer *Capreolus capreolus* are numerous.

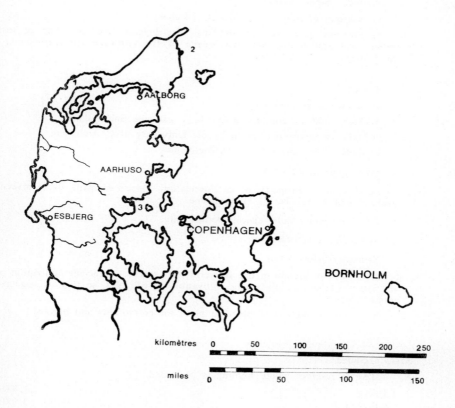

2. HIRSHOLMENE.

a) Status : general protection.

b) Area : the archipelago and protected zone include :

    (i) nine uninhabited islands ... ...   26.6 ha
    (ii) one inhabited island ... ...   13.5 ha
    (iii) open sea   300   ha

c) Staff : supervision by State employees.

d) Budget : no separate provision, but the over-all budget for ten scientific reserves including Hirsholmene and Vorsø is about U.S. $ 6,000.

189

DENMARK

III.   *Date established :* 1938, revised 1948.

Land tenure : the uninhabited islands are under state ownership. The Reserve is managed by the Ministry of Agriculture's Special Committee for Scientific Reserves.

Tourism : entry to the uninhabited islands only by special permit.

IV.   *Altitude :* below 50 m.

a) A group of islands with shingle beaches.

b) Breeding place of various birds, the biggest colonies being of terns, waders and guillemots : only nesting-site of the kittiwake *Rissa tridactyla* in the Kattegat.

3. VORSØ.

II.   *a)* Status : general protection.

b) Area : 300 ha, comprising one large and one small island.

c) Staff : supervision is given by the University of Copenhagen.

d) Budget : see under Nr. 2 Hirsholmene.

III.   *Date established :* 1934.

Land tenure : property of a Foundation associated with the University. Management as for No. 2 Hirsholmene.

Tourism : entry under special permit only.

Research : a laboratory.

IV.   *Altitude :* below 50 m.

a) Group of islands in the Horsensfjord : traces of ancient cultivation and the larger island was still under cultivation up till 1928, so that its vegetation is secondary.

b) Chiefly notable as a breeding place for cormorants and herons.

V.   **Areas excluded :**

A. — Twelve reserves where hunting is permitted :

Råbjerg	1,700 ha
Skallingen	3,500 ha
Anholt	800 ha
Randbøl	740 ha
Nørholm	350 ha
Hjerl	900 ha
Kongenshus	700 ha
Harrild	1,175 ha
Vindblaes	1,600 ha
Rebild	300 ha
Nymindestrømmen	450 ha
Lake Maribo	1,240 ha

190

B. — Ten reserves, several of comparatively large size (^{1}), where hunting is sometimes permitted and cultivation is still practised :

Borris (*) (°) ... ...   3,000 ha
Tipperne (*) (^{5}) . ...   450 ha
Klaegbanken (*) . ...   450 ha
Vejlerne ... ...   6,000 ha
Hesselø . ...   70 ha
Nakskov (*) . ...   200 ha
Stavnsfjord . ...   1,700 ha
West Amager island (°) ... ...   3 000 ha
Jordsand island and Waddensee (*) ... ... about 10,000 ha of the lake
                                                     along the German border
Felsted . ...   1,680 ha

35. DOMINICAN REPUBLIC

Listed Areas : one.

1. El Vedado Haina-Duey (**).

General Introduction :

Parks administration is the responsibility of the Forest Service, in consultation
with the advisory Commission for the Protection of Natural Resources set up
in 1963. The Commission is also responsible for any scientific research. There
is no specific tourist organisation.

The Dominican Republic was not included in E/3436 or Part Two of the
previous edition of the List.

Details : application of criteria (II), general information (III) and description (IV) :

1. EL VEDADO HAINA-DUEY.

a) Status : total protection. This is a state-owned wooded catchment area
set aside for the protection of the hydrographic basin on which the water
supplies of the capital depend; all occupation or exploitation by private persons

---

(^{1}) In addition there are some thirty smaller reserves where hunting is not
permitted.

(*) Hunting prohibited.

(°) Used for military purposes.

(^{5}) A famous biological station is situated on Tipperne.

(**) See map on page 180.

7

is therefore ruled out and hunting is forbidden. The relevant Law is No. 4991, the first Article of which forbids... " the felling or tapping of trees... cultivation, animal husbandry and the construction of dwelling-houses... ".

b) Area : 5,030 ha.

c) Staff : supervised by forest guards of the State Forest Service, the total strength of whom is 61.

d) Budget : covering salaries of staff.

III.   *Date established :* 1958.   " El Vedado " simply means " The Park ".

IV.   *Altitude :* 300-500 m.

a) Wooded catchments of the Haina and Duey rivers.

b) Small forest animals.

V.   **Areas excluded :**

A. — Two National Parks of large size :

1. Armando Bermúdez   ... ...   77,972 ha
2. José del Carmen Ramirez . ...   76,973 ha

Both these seem likely to qualify for inclusion in the List in due course. They are situated on the central mountain range, near the Pico Duarte (3,195 m), and the personnel available for their supervision comprises about 50 guards (" vigilantes ") stationed at six guard-posts.

Armando Bermúdez National Park has taken the place of the old Las Matas National Park (1933 : 20,000 ha), which was reorganised and enlarged in 1951, under Law No. 3107, containing a number of provisions which would allow the State to acquire lands included in the Park " in the public interest " and to forbid hunting and woodcutting. Later (under Laws 3841 of 1954 and 4389 of 1956), a limited area within the Park was declared " Strict Nature Reserve " and the legislation made further provision for elimination of human exploitation (" no-one is permitted to pursue any form of agriculture or animal husbandry... ") and also human occupancy (" The Executive Authority is hereby vested with the necessary powers to remove any families resident within the boundaries... "). In short the requisite legal basis would seem to have been provided and the way opened for its implementation within the framework of agrarian reform.

The same applies to the José del Carmen Ramirez National Park, which adjoins the Armando Bermúdez and was established in 1959 under Law No. 5066. Both areas are stated to be forest-covered, broad-leaved species at lower and *Pinus occidentalis* at higher altitudes. Wild pig have been introduced and bird life is plentiful.

B. — The following areas, though also the subject of various legal provisions, do not at present appear to meet the criteria :

3. Vedado Yaque del Norte.
1928 : 688 ha, extended to 6,491 ha in 1948.

4. Vedado El Puerto.
1947 : 26,000 ha; belonging to various proprietors.

5. Vedado alto de la Bandera.
1961 (" acquired in the public interest... ").

6. Vedado Diego de Ocampo.
   1962 ("acquired in the public interest... ").
7. Constanza Reserves : 1963.

C. — Areas proposed for reservation under the auspices of the Organisation of American States :
Los Altici, Isla Saona, Isabel de Torre and Boca de Juma.

36. ECUADOR

Listed Areas : one.

1. The Galapagos National Park.

General Introduction :

Ecuador was not included in E/3436 or Part Two of the previous edition of the List.

Details : application of criteria (II), general information (III) and description (IV) :

1. THE GALAPAGOS NATIONAL PARK.

   a) Status : strict protection (see under III below).
   b) Area : 10,000 ha.
   c) Staff : 2 units (see under III below).
   d) Budget : the staff salaries would satisfy the criterion.

   Date established : in 1934 a "National Park of the Galapagos Isles" was declared, comprising the islands of Isabella, Santa Cruz, Santiago, San Cristobal and Floreana. But it was not until 1963/1964 that, following an agreement between the Ecuador Government and the international "Charles Darwin Foundation for the Galapagos", a block of 100 km^2 was demarcated in the western part of Santa Cruz and put under the supervision of personnel of the Servicio de la Caza y Pesca, assisted by a guard in the employment of the Foundation and by a Conservation Officer provided for the Foundation by the New York Zoological Society. In effect, therefore, the reserve is under the supervision of the Charles Darwin Station.

   Land tenure : public ownership.

   Control of predators : the unique endemic fauna of the Galapagos, for the conservation of which the Santa Cruz reserve has been established, is under threat from poachers but also from feral domestic animals introduced by settlers. A scheme is afoot to bring the number of these introduced animals under control and for that purpose the Ecuadorian naval authorities, after informing the Director of the Charles Darwin Station, issue hunting permits authorising the killing of cattle, goats and pigs within the reserve.

   Future developments : the Charles Darwin Foundation nourishes the hope that it will be possible to extend to other islands the same degree of protection now applied to the western part of Santa Cruz.

ECUADOR

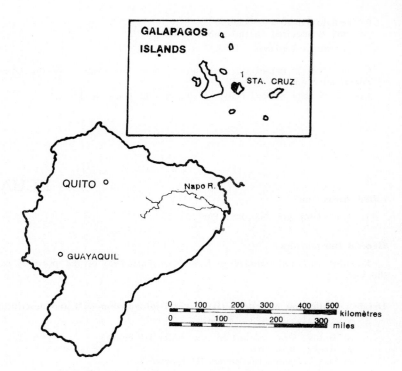

IV.   *Altitude :* sea level to 200 m.

a) South-west part of Santa Cruz (Indefatigable) island, situated in the centre of the archipelago; the vegetation zones comprise — primary forest of arborescent cactus (*Opuntia* and *Cereus*) along the seashore, thicket composed of aloewood *Cordia* bush, and finally damp forest of *Pisonia* and *Scalesia*, with ferns and mosses; the coastal sectors of Academy Bay, Tortuga Bay and the Fé are characterised by beaches of organogenous sand, rocky cliffs (" barrancos " formed by tectonic subsidence), considerable mangrove areas and some lagoons (noted for their flamingoes).

b) Important items include giant tortoise *Geochelone elephantopus porteri*, terrestrial and marine iguanas *Conolophus subcristatus* and *Amblyrhynchus cristatus*, flamingo *Phoenicopterus ruber*, pelicans *Pelecanus occidentalis*, herons *Nyctanassa violacea* and *Butorides sundevalli* and Darwin's fiches Geospizinae.

V.   **Areas excluded :**

Among the numerous projects for national parks and equivalent reserves under consideration or in the process of being implemented are :

1. Pululagua National Park.

Established 28 January 1966; primarily of geological interest, with a crater of 300 ha in area, the floor of which is under cultivation.

194

2. San Lorenzo Bay : a mangrove area.
3. Pastaza Gorge : a tourist attraction.
4. The Angel Paramo (Frailezon).
5. The three lagoons of Mojada : a site of historic interest; sport-fishing allowed.
6. The Surocucho Valley.
7. A section of the Andes summit ridge (" Ceja des Andes ").
8. The Cayapas Indian Reserve, extending over 50,000 ha and also serving as a natural reserve of the equatorial forest. At the end of August 1968 this area was given the status of a " Reserved Zone " under an Executive Decree. It is a strip of country, averaging 16 km in width, from the shore of the Pacific eastwards as far as Cotocachi, covering the western Cordillera, and its new status is the first stage towards development as a full National Park.

There were also (1967) two more ambitious projects under consideration, including the " Cayambe project ", for a belt of reserves along the line of the equator.

37. ETHIOPIA

Listed Areas : one.

1. Menagasha National Park.

General Introduction :

Responsibility for administering National Parks has recently been transferred from the Forest Department of the Ministry of Agriculture to a special Wildlife Conservation Department.

The Menagasha National Park was briefly described in E/3436 of the previous edition of the List.

Details : application of criteria (II), general information (III) and description (IV) :

1. MENAGASHA NATIONAL PARK.

a) Status : in effect a forest reserve and still the Forest Departement's responsibility.

b) Area : 3,000 ha, situated inside the Womara reserve of 25,000 ha.

c) Staff : 30 units.

d) Budget : the level laid down by the criterion would be exceeded by the staff salaries only. The total is quoted as U.S. $ 20,000.

Date established : not known : it was intended that this area should be upgraded to National Park status in 1958, by Imperial Proclamation, but this is apparently still pending.

Land tenure : state ownership.

Tourism : access by dry-season road only; some 28 km of road in the Park itself. No accommodation in the vicinity but plans are under consideration.

Research : a forest research station exists.

195

IV.   *Altitude :* 2,435-3,125 m.

a) Slopes of an ancient volcano, Mt. Wochocha; eucalyptus plantations at lower levels, then climax forest typical of the Ethiopian plateau, with pencil cedar *Juniperus procera* dominant and an admixture of *Podocarpus gracilior* and *Olea chrysophylla* (some attaining a height of 40 m); above 2,700 m is high altitude savannah of tree heath *Erica arborea, Rosa abyssinica, Hagenia abyssinica* and the St. John's wort *Hypericum lanceolatum.*

b) Monkeys including the local race of black-and-white colobus *Colobus polykomos,* baboon *Papio hamadryas,* Menelek's bushbuck *Tragelaphus scriptus meneleki* (found only in Ethiopia), leopard *Panthera pardus,* caracal *Felis caracal,* wild cat *Felis libyca;* plentiful birdlife.

V.   **Areas excluded :**

A. — There are three areas in the process of being established as National Parks, but not yet satisfying the ICNP criteria, which are sufficiently important and on which sufficient expenditure and organisational effort has already been

196

lavished as to merit a fairly full description. The stated aim of the Wildlife Conservation Department was to proceed in two stages, first in 1966 to establish a strict reserve status for the three areas and then to raise them to the rate of national parks as soon as a thorough investigation of the rights of local inhabitants has been completed and allows precise boundaries to be fixed.

The total extent of the three areas probably exceeds 100,000 ha, and the other details are as follows :

1. Simien Mountains.

A remarkable mountain massif reaching 5,000 m in altitude, situated 100 km north-east of Gondar. Afro-alpine vegetation, including tree heaths and giant lobelia. Habitat of the rare Walia ibex *Capra walie,* of which only 150 to 250 are reported to survive, and other rare or endemic species such as the Semien fox *Simenia (=Canis) simensis* and Gelada baboon *Theropithecus gelada.*

Six guards have already been appointed and the proposals for 1966-1967 were for a game warden and 27 guards; the 1966 budget was U.S. $ 65,000. A National Park of 15,000 ha was proclaimed on 31 October 1969.

2. Metahara or Awash.

Situated 150 km east of Addis Ababa, a reserve of some 120,000 ha has existed since 1961, but a complete overhaul of its boundaries and some removal of inhabitants was required before it could be declared a National Park, which was eventually done in 1969.

The Park marks the point where the Rift Valley debouches into the Danakil plains; a wide expanse of grassland interspersed with thorny thicket, from which the volcanic massif of Mt. Fantale emerges, with its unspoiled vegetation and a fine crater; the river Awash passes through a series of gorges.

The fauna includes oryx *O. beisa (=gazella),* Soemmering's gazelle *Gazella soemmeringi,* waterbuck *Kobus defassa,* greater and lesser kudu *Tragelaphus strepsiceros* and *imberbis,* Grevy's zebra *Equus grevyi* and leopard; there are proposals for introducing other species, such as the rare Swayne's hartebeest *Alcelaphus buselaphus swaynei* and Somali wild ass *Equus asinus somalicus,* which still exist not far outside the Park.

The 1966 estimates provided for a game warden, 34 guards and a budget of U.S. $ 80,000.

3. Maji or Omo.

An open plain with some areas more or less covered with thorn bush, between the Rift escarpment and the Omo river, some 180 km north of the north end of Lake Rudolf. Hunting has already been prohibited in an area of 160,000 ha and it is hoped that this sparsely inhabited area, which is full of game, can soon be accorded the status of a national park.

The fauna includes eland *Taurotragus oryx,* oryx, Grant's gazelle *Gazella granti,* Jackson's hartebeest, lesser kudu, buffalo *Syncerus caffer,* lion, leopard, cheetah *Acinonyx jubatus,* a few elephant and ostrich.

The 1966 estimates were intended to have covered a game warden, 45 guards and a budget of U.S. $ 120,000.

B. — Rift Valley Lakes National Park.

Now in the planning stage, this Park will enclose Lakes Abiata and Shala, protecting the important breeding colony of white pelican *Pelecanus onocrotalus* of Shala and the rich and varied avifauna generally. The total area will be about 70,000 ha.

C. — Bale Mountains.

A proposal for a National Park in this area was put forward in 1967 as a result of an investigation by Mr. Leslie Brown. Situated 240 km south of Addis Ababa and 940 km² in area, it would give protection to the mountain nyala *Tragelaphus buxtoni*. It is the main existing refuge of that species. Other endemic animals are the Semien fox, several species of birds, and a rodent which may be entirely new to science.

D. — Three proposed reserves :

1. Gambela.
2. Lake Chamo.
3. Danakil.

38. FALKLAND ISLANDS

I.
Listed Areas : two.
1. Kidney Island Nature Reserve
2. Cochon Island Nature Reserve.

General Introduction :

The legal basis of the reserve is provided by the Ordinance to make provision for the Establishment and Control of Nature Reserves, No. 8 of 27 May 1964.

The Falkland Islands were not included either in E/3436 or Part Two of the previous edition of the List.

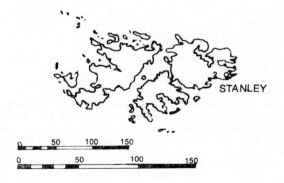

Details : application of criteria (II), general information (III) and description (IV) :

1. KIDNEY ISLAND NATURE RESERVE.

II.
a) Status : total protection; uninhabited; visits are strictly regulated and a permit is required.

b) Area : 29.5 ha, well below the criterion, but the scientific importance and degree of protection afforded justifies an exception.

c) and *d)* Staff and budget : administration and supervision carried out by the public services.

198

Date established : 1964.

Land tenure : public ownership.

Tourism : Access by sea; " a launch is available for tourists, conservationists and scientists ".

Altitude : sea-level to 16 m.

a) This small island lies on the east of the Falklands archipelago; its coast-line largely consists of cliffs, but there are also small sandy beaches as well as a strip of broken rock and boulder-strewn beach along the south and south-west shore. The characteristic vegetation is tussock-grass *Poa flabellata,* mixed with wild celery *Apium australa,* a rush *Carex trifioa,* a fern *Blechnum penna-marina* and, away from the shore, *Tillaea moschata* and thrift *Armeria macloviana.*

b) Sea-lion *Otaria byronia,* elephant seal *Mirounga leonina*; 24 of the 62 species of birds recorded as breeding in the Falklands have been found nesting on Kidney Island, including the rockhopper penguin *Eudyptes cristatus,* white-chinned petrel *Procellaria aequinoctialis,* sooty shearwater *Puffinus griseus,* a local race of grey-backed storm-petrel *Garrodia nereis chubbi,* king shag *Phalacrocorax atriceps albiventris,* tussock-bird *Cinclodes antarcticus* and Cobb's wren *Troglodytes musculus cobbi.*

2. COCHON ISLAND NATURE RESERVE.

a) Status : as for Kidney Island Nature Reserve (No. 1).

b) Area : 7.5 ha. Well below the criterion but inclusion justified by scientific interest and status.

c) and *d)* Staff and budget : as for Kidney Island Nature Reserve.

Date established : 1964.

Land tenure : public ownership.

Tourism : this is a strict nature reserve, not open to tourists.

Altitude : sea-level to 31 m.

a) Small island on the east of the archipelago, rising for the most part 15 to 20 m above the sea. Tussock is again the dominant plant; with thick patches of *Durvillea antarctica* and a belt of kelp *Macrocrystis pyrifera* in the inter-tidal zone.

b) Sea-lion; the 13 species of bird believed to breed are all found on Kidney Island with the exception of the " Johny Rook " *Phalcobaenus australis.*

Areas excluded :

A number of other Reserves, notably Flat Jason Island (368 ha), expected to be established under Ordinance No. 8 of 1964, but confirmation of which is still awaited.

Three Wild Animal and Bird Sanctuaries established in December 1964, totalling 256 ha, namely the Twins, Low Island and Beauchene; a further ten such sanc-tuaries are planned, but the status of these sanctuaries does not give full protection to the habitat or prohibit the pasturing of domestic stock.

199

I.   **Listed Areas :** two.

     1. Ravilevu Nature Reserve.
     2. Nandarivatu Nature Reserve.

General Introduction :

     The legal basis of the Reserves is provided by the Forest Ordinance of 1953. Responsibility for administration lies with the Conservator of Forests, Ministry of Natural Resources.

     Land tenure : Crown land.

     Tourism : no particular provision.

     Research : collections have been made for the herbarium of the Department of Agriculture; certain studies have been carried out, though not on a co-ordinated basis, by the scientists associated with the Fiji Society.

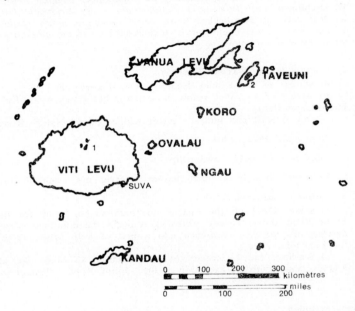

Details : application of criteria (II), general information (III) and description (IV) :

     1. RAVILEVU OR TAVEUNI NATURE RESERVE.

II.

     a) Status : according to an official statement of 29 July 1964, the Fiji Reserves " enjoy absolute protection against human exploitation of their natural resources and against any form of injury to the integrity of the area resulting from human activity ".

     b) Area : 3,972 ha.

     c) and *d*) Staff and budget : supervision is provided by the regular staff of the Forest Department.

Date established : 1959.

Tourism : access only allowed on foot.

Altitude : highest point 600 m.

a) Situated in the mountainous region of Taveuni Island; picturesque water-falls, narrow gorges; the venerated Tagimaucia plant *Medinella waterhousei* is found at high altitudes.

b) Contains a fair sample of the island fauna, including a notable green lizard, the flying fox or fruit bat and Pacific boa; the birdlife is varied and interesting, with such species as the orange dove *Chrysoena victor,* paradise flycatcher *Lamphrolia victoria* and jungle fowl *Gallus gallus* (presumably introduced).

2. NANDARIVATU NATURE RESERVE.

a) Status : as for Ravilevu Reserve (No. 1).

b) Area : 1,674 ha. The Reserve really consists of three separate areas, fairly close to one another (2-9 km apart), which are treated as a whole. They are :

Tomaniivi Nature Reserve	1,308 ha
Naqaranibuluti Nature Reserve	276 ha
Nandarivatu Nature Reserve	90 ha

The latter name has been adopted for the collective protected areas " as this is the usual name by which the locality is generally known ".

c) and *d)* Staff and budget : the three Reserves are situated in a strictly supervised Forest Reserve and cannot be entered except by a narrow winding road which is readily controlled by the local Forest Guards... " Our staff and other employees are constantly at work in areas adjacent to the Nature Reserve ".

Date established : Nandarivatu in 1956, the other two areas Tomaniivi and Naqaranibuluti in 1958.

Tourism : access by foot only along the winding Forest Reserve track ending at Nandarivatu.

Altitude : highest point 1,735 m.

a) Situated in the main island, 40 km north-west of the capital, Suva, the Reserves are in the heart of the Nandarivatu-Nadada Forest Reserve. A very mountainous area, with inaccessible ridges culminating in Mt. Victoria (1,735 m) in the Tomaniivi Reserve, which is noted for its rare orchids. In the Nandarivatu sector there is a block of virgin cowrie pine *Agathis vitiensis* forest.

b) Montane fauna, many wild pig; golden pigeon *Chrysoena luteovirens,* the lorikeet *Charmosyna aureicincta* and several birds of prey; very interesting insect-life.

Areas excluded :

Two very small Nature Reserves, Draunibota-Labiko (2.4 ha, 1959) and Vuo (1.2 ha, 1960).

Twenty Forest Reserves, of which the largest (11,160 ha, 1914) is in Taveuni Island.

I.   **Listed Areas :** twenty-four.

For names see table at the end of the General Introduction.

General Introduction :

Some departure from the mode of presentation adopted for the majority of other countries has seemed desirable in the case of Finland. In the first place the List comprises two quite distinct types of area, the National Parks, in which tourism is allowed and organised, and the Strict Natural Reserves where, with the exception of three Reserves in which certain paths are open to the public, visitors are only allowed under special permit. In respect of the criteria the position is as follows and explains the grounds on which the 24 areas have been accepted for the List (the previous edition of which, E/3436, only included the nine National Parks).

II.   *a*) Status : all 24 areas enjoy full protection, except that local exceptions have been made —

(I) to meet the administrative needs of particular areas;

(II) in the public interest; and

(III) to preserve certain traditional rights, such as the pasturage of reindeer in northern areas, the fishing and some hunting rights of the Laplanders and the control of predators which is still deemed necessary (unfortunately this latter exception means that the wolf and wolverine do not enjoy protection in any of the areas, whether National Park or Strict Natural Reserve, while bears are only protected seasonally from October to May in the country as a whole).

b) Area : as to *area,* certain Parks and Reserves which are considerably sub-standard in size have been retained at the special request of the Finnish authorities, because of their high scientific value.

c) and *d*) Staff and Budget : it has not proved possible to detail separately the full-time *staff* and annual *budget* allotted to each Park and Reserve. Many officers of the various administrative bodies concerned divide their time between several of the areas. Only one National Park (the Pallas-Ounastunturi of 50,000 ha) has two officers entirely to itself, and a further six (four Parks and two Reserves) have one each. But on the over-all average there is no doubt from the following figures that the criteria (one staff unit per 10,000 ha and the equivalent of U.S. $ 50 per 1,000 ha) are fully satisfied :

(I) in areas controlled by the Institute of Forest Reserves : 3.1 units per 10,000 ha and U.S. $ 259 per 1,000 ha.

(II) in areas controlled by the General Directorate of Forestry : 1.9 units per 10,000 ha and U.S. $ 79 per 1,000 ha.

III.   The *administrative responsibility* as indicated lies with the General Directorate of Forestry, which controls a total of 9,109,800 ha of forest land, 130,660 ha having the status of National Park or Strict Natural Reserve, and with the Institute of Forest Research with controls 133,570 ha, 61,680 ha of which is classed as Park or Reserve. The name given to the Strict Natural Reserves in Finland could be rendered as " Nature Park " or " Natural Park ".

Tourism : entry is unrestricted in all National Parks and is allowed on marked paths in the Sompio and Karkali Nature Parks and, subject to prior notification, in the Malla Nature Park. Sport-fishing is not allowed with rare exceptions and on special permit. There are hotels and skiing facilities. The National Parks most frequented are the Pallas-Ounastunturi, Oulanka and Pyhätunturi.

Scientific research : undertaken by the Universities and by the Institute of Forest Research. The latter maintains experimental stations in twelve of the areas, while Turku, Oulu and Helsinki Universities have each built their own research station, in the Kevo Nature Park, the Oulanka National Park and the Malla Nature Park respectively.

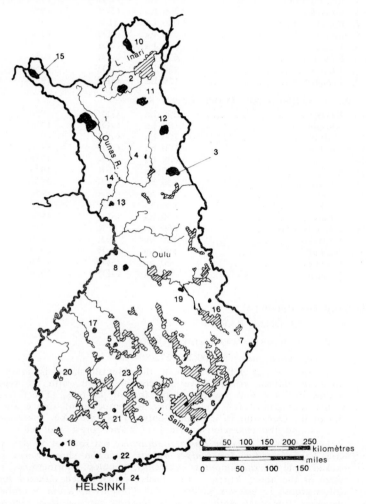

The following Table gives particulars of the 24 areas, set out in the two categories, in order of size. The controlling body (IFR=Institute of Forest Research, GDF=General Directorate of Forestry) is indicated, together with the date of establishment and the number of full-time permanent staff units, if any, allotted to each Park or Reserve.

203

FINLAND

Name	Area	Controlled by	Date established	Staff Units
A. — NATIONAL PARKS.				
1. Pallas-Ounastunturi	50,000 ha	IFR	1938	2
2. Lemmenjoki	38,500 ha	GDF	1956	1
3. Oulanka	10,700 ha	GDF	1956	1
4. Pyhätunturi	3,000 ha	IFR	1938	1
5. Pyhähäkki	1,010 ha	GDF	1956	—
6. Linnansaari	800 ha	GDF	1956	—
7. Petkeljärvi	650 ha	GDF	1956	1
8. Rokua	420 ha	GDF	1956	—
9. Liesjärvi	150 ha	GDF	1956	—
B. — NATURE PARKS (Strict Natural Reserves).				
10. Kevo	34,200 ha	GDF	1956	—
11. Sompio	18,100 ha	GDF	1956	—
12. Maltio	14,700 ha	GDF	1956	—
13. Runkaus	6,100 ha	GDF	1956	—
14. Pisavaara	5,000 ha	IFR	1938	1
15. Malla	3,000 ha	IFR	1938	1
16. Ulvinsalo	2,500 ha	GDF	1956	—
17. Salamanperä	1,270 ha	GDF	1956	—
18. Vaskijärvi	800 ha	GDF	1956	—
19. Paljakka	660 ha	GDF	1956	—
20. Häädetkeidas	560 ha	IFR	1956	—
21. Vesijako	120 ha	IFR	1956	—
22. Karkali	100 ha	IFR	1964	—
23. Sinivuori	60 ha	GDF	1956	—
24. Jussarö	40 ha	GDF	1956	—

IV.   **Detailed Description :**

A. — NATIONAL PARKS.

1. PALLAS-OUNASTUNTURI NATIONAL PARK.

Area and altitude : 50,000 ha, 272-807 m.

a) An area of fell (for which the Finnish name is *tunturi*) : Lapland mountain plateau, rising above the conifer forests, with the typical Lapland mixture of forest and peat-bog at the foot of the fells. The forest at the foot of the southermost fell, Pallastunturi, is composed of spruce and pine, while that of the Ounastunturi is of pine only. There are lakes, meres and numerous streams and the characteristic flora of Lapp forest and fell.

b) Mammals : reindeer *Rangifer tarandus*, red squirrel *Sciurus vulgaris*, blue hare *Lepus timidus*, fox *Vulpes vulpes*, common shrew *Sorex araneus*, red-backed vole *Clerithrionomys rufocanus*; reptiles : northermost point in the range of the adder *Vipera berus*; birds : rough-legged buzzard *Buteo lagopus*, willow-grouse *L. lagopus*, golden plover *Pluvialis apricaria*, whimbrel *Numenius phaeopus*, tree pipit *Anthus trivialis*, meadow pipit *Anthus pratensis*, waxwing *Bombycilla garrulus*, willow-warbler *Phylloscopus trochilus*, wheatear *Oe. oenanthe*, redstart *Ph. phoenicurus*, bluethroat *Luscinia svecica*, redwing *Turdus musicus*, Lapland bunting *Calcarius lapponicus*, brambling *Fringilla montifringilla*, redpoll *Acanthis flammea*, snow bunting *Plectrophenax nivalis*, Siberian jay *Perisoreus infaustus*.

2. LEMMENJOKI NATIONAL PARK.

Area and altitude : 38,500 ha, 123-601 m.

a) The Lemmenjoki river winds its way through a valley between the fells, often shut in by a very narrow gorge, elsewhere broadening into a series of narrow lakes, and fed by small tributaries plunging down through deep ravines. One of the latter, the Ravadsjoki, is famous for its waterfalls. The magnificent landscape includes at lower levels ancient forests of tall pines and, higher up, great expanses of heath and bare rocks.

b) Mammals : reindeer, common shrew, red-backed vole; birds : rough-legged buzzard, willow-grouse, golden plover, whimbrel, shore-lark *Eremophila alpestris,* tree pipit, meadow pipit, waxwing, willow-warbler, wheatear, redstart, bluethroat, redwing, Lapland bunting, brambling, redpoll, snow bunting; rarer species include whooper swan *C. cygnus*; brown bear *Ursus arctos* and wolf *Canis lupus.*

3. OULANKA NATIONAL PARK.

Area and altitude : 10,700 ha, 143-380 m.

a) A very wild region bordering the Oulankajoki river which flows into the White Sea. A fine landscape with rushing torrents, ravines, sandbanks, prairie and meadows full of flowers. The flora is specially interesting, species associated with the fells being also found in the coniferous forest zone.

b) Mammals : reindeer, red squirrel, blue hare, fox, common shrew, bank vole *Clethrionomys glareolus*; birds : black-throated diver *Gavia arctica,* mallard *Anas platyrhynchos,* wigeon *A. penelope,* pintail *A. acuta,* wood sandpiper *Tringa glareola,* tree pipit, meadow pipit, yellow wagtail *Motacilla flava,* willow-warbler, spotted flycatcher *Muscicapa striata,* song thrush *Turdus philomelos,* mistle thrush *T. viscivorus,* Siberian tit *Parus cinctus,* brambling, redpoll; rarer species include whooper swan, smew *Mergus albellus,* golden eagle *Aquila chrysaetos* and eagle-owl *B. bubo.*

4. PYHÄTUNTURI NATIONAL PARK.

Area and altitude : 3,000 ha, 300-540 m.

a) Comprises the southernmost of the great Finnish fells, with its steep flanks, deep ravines and bare rocks. These are quartzite formations, which accounts also for the comparative poverty of the fell flora. The isolated high Fell, well known for the magnificent views it commands, was a sacred place to the ancient Lapps. At its foot are spruce and pine forests and great stretches of peat-bog.

b) Mammals : common shrew, blue hare, red squirrel, bank vole, fox, stoat *Mustela erminea,* elk *A. alces* and reindeer; birds : rough-legged buzzard, willow-warbler, meadow pipit, spotted flycatcher, redwing, mistle thrush, Siberian tit, brambling, redpoll (despite the alpine character of much of the park, very few alpine species).

5. PYHÄHÄKKI.

Area and altitude : 1,010 ha, 159-193 m.

a) A sample of the original forest of southern Finland, with ancient pines over 250 years old (some of up to 450 years old). Peat-bogs, both open and wooded, and meres.

b) Mammals : common shrew, bank vole, red squirrel, blue hare, fox, elk; birds : tree pipit, yellow wagtail, chiffchaff *Phylloscopus collybita,* goldcrest *R. regulus,* pied flycatcher *Ficedula hypoleuca,* spotted flycatcher, redstart, robin *Erithacus rubecula,* great tit *Parus major,* chaffinch *Fringilla coelebs,* siskin *Carduelis spinus*; rare species : red-breasted flycatcher *Ficedula parva*; some unusual beetles, such as *Ips longicollis* and *Carphoborus minimus,* and the butterfly *Callimorpha menestriesi.*

6. LINNANSAARI NATIONAL PARK.

Area and altitude : 800 ha, 76-100 m.

a) A group of islands in the great Lake Saimaa. Their topography and coastline is very varied, with deep narrow coves, rocky outcrops, ravines and glens, and forests ranging from pines which can maintain themselves on bare rock to broad-leaved species in the valleys.

b) Mammals : common shrew, bank vole, red squirrel, blue hare, fox, elk, ringed seal *Pusa hispida* (breeding); birds : forest species including tree pipit, garden warbler *Sylvia borin,* willow warbler, spotted flycatcher, willow tit *Parus montanus,* and chaffinch; aquatic species, including mallard, goosander *Mergus merganser,* osprey *Pandion haliaëtus* (four pairs nest annually), herring gull *Larus argentatus,* common gull *L. canus* and common tern *Sterna hirundo.*

7. PETKELJÄRVI NATIONAL PARK.

Area and altitude : 650 ha, 140-150 m.

a) An infertile but beautiful part of Carelia, known as Karelara, containing pine forests, small hills calles " ôs ", lakes and islands (in which some damage has been caused by the trenches dug in the 1939-1940 war).

b) Mammals : common shrew, bank vole, red squirrel, blue hare, fox; birds : tree pipit, spotted flycatcher, redstart, Siberian tit, great tit, chaffinch and siskin.

8. ROKUA NATIONAL PARK.

Area and altitude : 420 ha, 130-197 m.

a) A long level ridge, varied in places by old fixed coastal dunes which stand up sharply in the otherwise flat and monotonous landscape. Crystal clear lakes and peat-bogs in the hollows, pine-sprinkled heaths covered with white moss.

b) Mammals : common shrew, blue hare, red squirrel, bank vole, fox, stoat, elk, reindeer; birds : tree pipit, spotted flycatcher, redstart, mistle thrush and chaffinch.

9. LIESJÄRVI NATIONAL PARK.

Area and altitude : 150 ha, 108-120 m.

a) A section of wooded country which has only a few inhabitants because of its infertility. Pine and spruce forests, some peat bogs; the Park includes part of the shore and islands of Lake Liesjärvi.

b) Mammals : common shrew, blue hare, red squirrel, bank vole, fox, stoat, elk, birds : tree pipit, chiffchaff, goldcrest, pied and spotted flycatchers, redstart, robin, great tit, chaffinch and siskin.

B. — NATURE PARKS or STRICT NATURAL RESERVES.

10. KEVO NATURE PARK.

Area and altitude : 34,200 ha, 74-551 m.

a) The great Kevoioki canyon; mainly characteristic birch forest of the fells, but also some pine forest along the river. In some places the vegetation of the canyon is comparatively rich and contains some rare species.

b) Mammals : reindeer, common shrew, bank vole; birds, numerous, including rough-legged buzzard, ptarmigan *Lagopus mutus,* golden plover, whimbrel, shore-lark, tree pipit, meadow pipit, waxwing, willow warbler, arctic warbler *Phylloscopus borealis,* wheatear, redstart, bluethroat, redwing, Lapland bunting, snow bunting, brambling and redpoll; rare species : gyr falcon *Falco rusticolus,* arctic fox *Alopex lagopus.*

11. SOMPIO NATURE PARK.

Area and altitude : 18,100 ha, 245-544 m.

a) The Nattastunturit fells, with expanses of bare rock, pine and spruce forest and great cordate peat bogs.

b) Mammals : common shrew, blue hare, red squirrel, bank vole, fox, stoat, elk, reindeer; birds : rough-legged buzzard, ptarmigan, golden plover, whimbrel, shore-lark, tree pipit, meadow pipit, waxwing, willow warbler, wheatear, redstart, bluethroat, redwing, Lapland bunting, snow bunting, brambling and redpoll.

12. MALTIO NATURE PARK.

Area and altitude : 14,700 ha, about 240-400 m.

a) Wooded hills, fells and peat bogs of southern Lapland.

b) Mammals : common shrew, blue hare, red squirrel, bank vole, fox, stoat, elk, reindeer; birds : black-throated diver, mallard, pintail, wigeon, wood sandpiper, tree and meadow pipits, yellow wagtail, willow warbler, spotted flycatcher, song thrush, mistle thrush, Siberian tit, brambling and redpoll.

13. RUNKAUS NATURE PARK.

Area and altitude : 6,100 ha, 99-160 m.

a) Includes two areas separated by large cordate peat bogs.

b) Mammals : common shrew, blue hare, red squirrel, bank vole, fox, stoat, elk, reindeer; birds : hen harrier *Circus cyaneus,* wood sandpiper, whimbrel, common snipe *Capella gallinago,* short-eared owl *Asio flammeus,* yellow wagtail and whinchat *Saxicola rubetra.*

14. PISAVAARA NATURE PARK.

Area and altitude : 5,000 ha, 135-220 m.

a) The slopes of Pisavaara hill are notable for the indications of ancient raised marine beaches. Primitive pine and spruce forests, peat bogs and a rich flora on the banks of the streams.

b) Mammals : common shrew and Laxmann's shrew *Sorex caecutiens,* bank vole, wood-lemming *Myopus schisticolor,* red squirrel, reindeer, elk, fox, blue hare; birds : tree pipit, willow warbler, chiffchaff, goldcrest, song thrush, chaffinch, brambling, siskin and Siberian jay.

15. MALLA NATURE PARK.

Area and altitude : 3,000 ha, 463-927 m.

a) High fell, with alpine vegetation which is botanically very rich due to the limestone.

b) Mammals : blue hare, red-backed vole, field voles (*Microtus oeconomus* and *agrestris*), Norwegian lemming *L. lemmus,* fox, stoat, elk, reindeer; birds : rough-legged buzzard, willow grouse, golden plover, whimbrel, shore-lark, house martins *Delichon urbica* (nesting in the cliffs of the ravines), meadow pipit, willow warbler, wheatear, redwing, brambling and snow bunting.

16. ULVINSALO NATURE PARK.

Area and altitude : 2,500 ha, 200-250 m.

a) Rather flat country covered by primitive pine and spruce forest and peat bogs.

b) Mammals : common shrew, bank vole, red squirrel, blue hare, fox, elk, brown bear; birds : great spotted woodpecker *Dendrocopus major,* tree pipit, chiffchaff, redstart, song thrush, willow tit, crested tit and chaffinch.

17. SALAMANPERÄ NATURE PARK.

Area and altitude : 1,270 ha, 180-195 m.

a) Pine forest and infertile peatland on the watershed between the lakeland plateau and the coast of the Gulf of Bothnia.

b) Mammals : common shrew, bank vole, red squirrel, blue hare, fox, elk; birds : tree pipit, yellow wagtail, spotted flycatcher, redstart, robin, great tit, chaffinch and siskin.

18. VASKIJÄRVI NATURE PARK.

Area and altitude : 800 ha, 53-61 m.

a) Raised bog.

b) Mammals : common shrew, blue hare, red squirrel, bank vole, fox, stoat, elk; birds : common crane *Grus grus,* curlew *Numenius arquata,* tree and meadow pipits, yellow wagtail and whinchat.

19. PALJAKKA NATURE PARK.

Area and altitude : 660 ha, 300-384 m.

a) The northern slopes of Paljakka mountain, covered with forest ranging from a rich ferny type of spruce forest at lower levels to the poorer forest of the summit, and interspersed with peat bogs.

b) Mammals : common shrew, blue hare, red squirrel, bank vole, fox, stoat, elk; birds : spotted woodpeckers, tree pipit, chiffchaff, redstart, song thrush, willow tit, crested tit and chaffinch.

20. HÄÄDETKEIDAS NATURE PARK.

Area and altitude : 560 ha, 149-155 m.

a) Raised bog.

b) Mammals : common shrew, blue hare, red squirrel, bank vole, fox, stoat, elk, birds : common crane, curlew, tree pipit, meadow pipit, yellow wagtail and whinchat.

21. VESIJAKO NATURE PARK.

Area and altitude : 120 ha, 131-168 m.

a) Mature spruce forest; some meres.

b) Mammals : common shrew, bank vole, red squirrel, blue hare, fox, elk; birds : chiffchaff, goldcrest, pied and spotted flycatchers, robin, great tit, chaffinch and siskin and, despite the small size of the Park, a number of specially interesting species, namely the osprey, pygmy owl *Glaucidium passerinum,* Ural owl *Strix uralensis* and red-breasted flycatcher.

22. KARKALI NATURE PARK.

Area and altitude : 100 ha, 32-80 m.

a) A sample of oak forest and its characteristic plants, at the extreme northern limit of its range. This is a rare type of vegetation in Finland.

b) Mammals : common shrew, blue hare, red squirrel, bank vole, fox, stoat, elk, reindeer; birds : garden warbler, willow warbler, pied and spotted flycatcher, fieldfare *Turdus pilaris,* blackbird *T. merula,* redwing, willow tit, great tit and chaffinch.

23. SINIVUORI NATURE PARK.

Area and altitude : 60 ha, 125-200 m.

a) Rich spruce forest and, along the streams, damp alder forest.

b) Mammals : common shrew, blue hare, red squirrel, bank vole, fox, stoat, elk; birds : chiffchaff, goldcrest, pied and spotted flycatchers, robin, great tit, chaffinch and siskin.

24. JUSSARÖ NATURE PARK.

Area and altitude : 40 ha, sea level to 10 m.

a) An archipelago in the Gulf of Finland, with a number of small islands, some covered with forest but the majority without any tree cover.

b) Noted for its sea-birds : eider *Somateria mollissima,* lesser black-backed gull *Larus fuscus,* common tern, arctic tern *Sterna paradisea,* razorbill *Alca torda,* and black guillemot *Cepphus grylle*; also tufted duck *Aythya fuligula.*

Areas excluded : nil.

41. FRANCE

I.   **Listed Areas :** twenty-nine.

    A. — NATIONAL PARKS :
1. La Vanoise National Park.
2. Port Cros National Park.

    B. — NATIONAL GAME RESERVES :
3. Chambord National Reserve.
4. Burrus National Reserve.
5. La Petite Pierre National Reserve.
6. Les Bauges National Reserve.
7. Bavella Sambucco Conca National Reserve.
8. Markstein National Reserve.
9. Cauterets National Reserve.
10. Chizé National Reserve.
11. Donzère-Mondragon Canal National Reserve.
12. Casabianda National Reserve.
13. Belval National Reserve.
14. La Pointe d'Arçay National Reserve.
15. Sainte-Opportune National Reserve.
16. Les Sept Iles National Reserve.

    C. — " RÉSERVES CYNÉGÉTIQUES D'INTÉRÊT NATIONAL ".
17. Le Mercantour National Game Reserve.
18. Le Pic du Midi d'Ossau National Game Reserve.
19. Etangs de l'Hérault National Game Reserve.

    D. — SPECIAL OR PRIVATE RESERVES :
20. The Camargue Zoological and Botanical Reserve.
21. Le Pelvoux Reserve or State Park.
22. Mont Vallier State Reserve.
23. Bure Aurouze Reserve.
24. Le Carlitte Reserve.
25. Le Combeynot Reserve.
26. Asco Federal Reserve.
27. Etangs des Impériaux Reserve.
28. Néouvieille Reserve.
29. The combined Biological and Artistic Reserves of the Forêt de Fontainebleau.

General Introduction :

Establishment of Reserves in France is usually effected under the provisions of a law enacted on 2 May 1930 and a Ministerial decree (Ministry of Agriculture) of 2 October 1951. As for the National Parks proper, their legal basis is a law enacted on 22 July 1960. There are several bodies which are also very concerned in the matter, such as the Commission Supérieure des Sites and the Conseil National de Protection de la Nature, which was set up in 1946. The latter is responsible to the Ministry for National Education and has also been delegated by the Commission Supérieure des Sites with responsibility for promoting the establishment of new reserves and co-ordinating the administration of existing reserves, especially those which are privately owned.

As indicated in section I above there are two classes of Game Reserve, the " Réserves cynégétiques nationales " and the " Réserves cynégétiques d'intérêt

210

national ", both of them established by decree of the Minister of Agriculture under the powers accorded by the Ministerial Decree of 2 October 1951. The main difference is that the so-called Game Reserves of National Interest are usually the administrative responsibility of the Hunting Federation of the Department in which they are situated and assisted financially by a grant from the Conseil Supérieur de la Chasse.

Other details of status, ownership and tourist and research facilities are given under each Park or Reserve. In the case of the Game Reserves there is in fact no provision for tourism, except occasionally by local initiative, and scientific studies are not co-ordinated or integrated.

Neither E/3436 nor Part Two of the previous edition of the List contained any information about France.

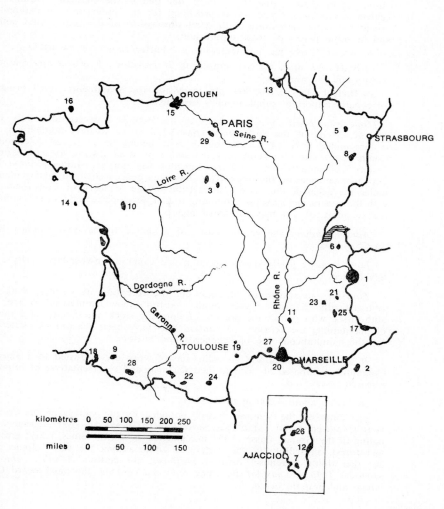

FRANCE

Details : application of criteria (II), general information (III) and description (IV) :

A. — NATIONAL PARKS.

1. LA VANOISE NATIONAL PARK (Savoie).

II. *a*) Status : the decision to include the Vanoise in the U.N. List was taken with some hesitation. A significant part of this National Park does not in fact satisfy the criterion of total protection. Although it contains some sectors which are free from agricultural, pastoral and forestry activities, all these are to be found elsewhere within the boundaries. Some of the alpine pasturage is, however, denied to sheep and goats, hunting is forbidden, though fishing is allowed under control, and some strict nature reserve areas are under consideration. In brief the status of the Park, like that of the German " Naturschutzgebiete ", can be summed up as providing for the prohibition of exploitation except for some agriculture, with strict supervision of this agricultural activity and in some places its total suppression.

b) Area : 52,839 ha, not including a " buffer zone " of 143,637 ha.

c) Staff : 38 units (1968), comprising 2 inspectors, 6 officers in charge of sectors and 30 wardens.

d) Budget : U.S. $ 200,000, plus provision for investments which brings in an equally important supplementary revenue.

III. *Date established :* the legal basis of the Park is a decree of 6 July 1963. The 52,839 ha of the Park proper has 3,717 ha of Reserve adjoining it and is surrounded by a 143,637 ha buffer zone belonging to the 29 neighbouring Communes. The idea is to give the status of strict reserve to small selected " islets " of land within the Park, but this has not yet (January 1968) been implemented, because the main effort has been concentrated on management — under the aegis of the Land Use division of the Ministry of Construction — with the general objective of promoting tourist development and so rehabilitating the economy of a rather run-down region.

Administration : the responsibility of a public or national Council based on Chambéry.

Land tenure : partly state ownership and Commune-ownership, partly privately owned.

Tourism : in course of organisation, the reception of visitors being now systematically planned. Cross-country ski-routes are maintained by the Park authorities, who permit the grazing of domestic stock specifically as a method of maintaining the ski-runs. Mountain huts have been adapted as shelters for for the simultaneous use of shepherds and visitors.

Research : planning and co-ordination of work are entrusted to a Scientific Committee composed of distinguished scientists and representatives of important research institutions.

IV. *Altitude :* about 1,000 m to 3,852 m.

a) Comprises the Vanoise massif, bounded by the valleys of the Arc and Isère (Maurienne and Tarantaise); several of the peaks are over 3,500 m culminating in the Grande Casse (3,852 m); glaciers, névés, moraines, lakes; grassland and forest, agriculture in the peripheral zone; among the rarer alpine plants are the alpine groundsel *Senecio uniflorus,* the milfoil *Achillea erba-rotta,* asphodel *Tofieldia pusilla,* the sedge *Kobresia caricina,* the hawksbeard *Crepis jubata* and *Sesleria ovata.*

b) Chamois *R. rupricapra*, ibex *Capra ibex*, varying hare *Lepus timidus*, marmot *M. marmota*, stoat *Mustela erminea*, fox *V. vulpes*; over 100 species of birds, including golden eagle *Aquila chrysaetos*, ptarmigan *Lagopus mutus* and rock partridge *Alectoris graeca*.

2. PORT CROS NATIONAL PARK (Var).

a) Status : in effect total protection, altough legally the situation is similar to that of the Vanoise National Park, No. A.1 above.

b) Area : an island of 685 ha, with a "Marine Protected Zone" some 600 m wide all round the island.

c) Staff : a chief warden and 3 assistants.

d) Budget : the criterion is covered by the salary of the warden.

Legal basis : a Decree of 14 December 1963.

Administration : by a public body based on Toulon, but with representatives frequently stationed on the island.

Land tenure : private property of two owners.

Tourism : not many visitors; access by launch.

Research : has been encouraged for the last 20 years by Dr. A. Balachowsky.

Altitude : sea level to 200 m.

a) An island of the Iles d'Hyères archipelago some 4½ km long by 2½ wide; the highly accentuated relief provides a variety of landscape — valleys, steep cliffs, coves and sandy beaches — and affords protection for a sample of the original western Mediterranean sea-coast flora and, in particular, the Aleppo pine *Pinus halepensis* with its very dense undergrowth typical of flint-land *maquis*.

b) A notable invertebrate and herpetological fauna and a varied avifauna (resting-place for migrants).

B. — NATIONAL GAME RESERVES.

3. — CHAMBORD NATIONAL RESERVE (Loir-et-Cher).

a) Status : as in the case of the Vanoise National Park, No. A.1 above, it has been necessary to waive in some degree the criterion requirements laid down by the ICNP, in order to fit in with the peculiar circumstances obtaining in France, a country in which the distribution of habitats and of private ownership of land is of ancient origin and highly diverse. Only in this way is it possible to include in the U.N. List some fourteen of the important National Game Reserves, in accordance with the selection made by the French authorities. However, most of the Reserves, Chambord included, are free from cultivation and are not used for pasturing domestic stock. Most of them are also forested, with forest exploitation, although practised under control by the State, and in none of them is hunting of any kind of animal by the general public allowed at any time. On the other hand game management procedures are applied, such as culling, capture of live animals and reduction of excess numbers of species regarded as harmful.

b) Area : 5,450 ha.

c) Staff : 9 units, comprising two "chefs de district" (C.D.) and seven "agents techniques" (A.T.) of the department of Eaux et Forêts.

d) Budget : U.S. $ 133,000, plus wardening expenses (1964 figure, as are all the others quoted below).

FRANCE

III. *Date established :* 1957.

Land tenure : State forest.

Hunting rights are confined to the Conseil Supérieur de la Chasse, which controls the Reserve through its Secretary-General; a C.S.C. Committee fixes annual hunting quotas (e.g. 134 red deer stags and does in 1964-1965).

IV. *Altitude :* 100 m.

a) Forest on the sandy and clay soils of the Sologne, with large stands of oak and birch, clumps of conifers (*Pinus sylvestris*) and coppice; some cultivation; marshes and meres with an interesting aquatic flora.

b) Red deer *Cervus elaphus* and roe deer *C. capreolus,* wild boar *Sus scrofa;* waterfowl include mallard *Anas platyrhynchos,* teal *A. crecca* and garganey *A. querquedula* among the ducks; geese and cranes on passage; lapwing *V. vanellus,* snipe *Capella gallinago* and grey heron *Ardea cinerea* in the marshy areas.

4. BURRUS NATIONAL RESERVE (Ariège).

II. *a)* Status : as for B.3 above.
b) Area : 4,387 ha.
c) Staff : two federal guards.
d) Budget : U.S. $ 1,700 plus salaries.

III. *Date established :* 1964.

Land tenure : property of Cellulose Company of Aquitaine.

Management : undertaken by the Hunting Federation of the Department, under C.S.C. authority.

IV. *Altitude :* 900-2,800 m.

a) Very rugged terrain, with forest (oak *Quercus,* beech *Fagus,* birch *Betula* and conifers), rocks, swards and lakes.

b) Ibex, wild boar, varying hare; ptarmigan, capercaillie *Tetrao urogallus.*

5. LA PETITE PIERRE NATIONAL RESERVE (Bas-Rhin).

II. *a)* Status : as for B.3 above.
b) Area : 4,289 ha.
c) Staff : 1 federal guard, 1 C.D. and 3 part-time A.T.
d) Budget : U.S. $ 11,150.

III. *Date established :* 1952 (6,082 ha), reduced to present size in 1961.

Land tenure : State forest (3,748 ha), Commune forest (540 ha).

Management : a 5-member management committee; D:rector : the Chief Engineer at Strasbourg.

IV. *Altitude :* 380 m.

a) Mixed forest on sandy soil (beech, pine, oak).
b) Red and roe deer, wild boar.

6. LES BAUGES NATIONAL RESERVE (Savoie and Haute-Savoie).

II. *a)* Status : as for B.3.
b) Area : 4,070 ha (2,390 in Savoie).
c) Staff : 4 guards provided by the C.S.C.
d) Budget : U.S. $ 18,500.

214

III. *Date established :* 1955.

Land tenure : state ownership, except for 126 ha belonging to the Department and managed as forest estate, and 24 ha belonging to the C.S.C.

Management : C.S.C.; Director : the Chief Engineer, Eaux et Forêts, Annecy.

V. *Altitude :* 1,000-2,260 m.

a) Typical woods, rocks and pasture of the Savoy landscape.

b) Mouflon *Ovis musimon* (introduced), roe deer, marmot, chamois, varying hare; ptarmigan.

7. BAVELLA SAMBUCCO CONCA NATIONAL RESERVE (Corsica).

a) Status : as for B.3.
b) Area : 3,901 ha.
c) Staff : two A.T.
d) Budget : U.S. $ 2,000 plus salaries.

III. *Date established :* 1950; enlarged 1960.

Land tenure : state forest (1,809 ha), Departmental forest (named Conca, acquired 1960; 2,092 ha).

Management : C.S.C., with a Director at Ajaccio.

V. *Altitude :* 500-1,300 m.

a) A very rugged area, with ilex *Quercus ilex* and larch *Larix europaea*, which was seriously damaged by fire in the summer of 1965.

b) Mouflon (Corsican race).

8. MARKSTEIN NATIONAL RESERVE (Haut-Rhin).

a) Status : as for B.3.
b) Area : 3,702 ha.
c) Staff : one C.D. and 6 A.T. on a part-time basis.
d) Budget : U.S. $ 6,000, plus salaries.

III. *Date established :* 1963.

Land tenure : State forest (1,094 ha), Commune lands (2,608 ha).

Management : a six member committee; Director : the Engineer at Guebwiller.

V. *Altitude :* 500-1,300 m.

a) Typical Vosges forest, with meadows and lakes.

b) Chamois (introduced), red and roe deer; capercaillie.

9. CAUTERETS NATIONAL RESERVE (Hautes-Pyrénées).

a) Status : as for B.3.
b) Area : 3,254 ha.
c) Staff : part-time federal guards.
d) Budget : U.S. $ 1,400 plus salaries.

III. *Date established :* 1958; altered in 1965.

Land tenure : a syndicate of the Communes of the Vallée de Saint-Savin owns 2,953 ha; the rest (300 ha) is State forest.

Management : Hunting Federation of the Department, under authority of the C.S.C.

IV. *Altitude :* 1,000-2,800 m.

a) Forest (conifers and coppice), pastures, rocks and lakes typical of the Pyrenees.

b) Chamois, varying hare; ptarmigan, capercaillie.

10. CHIZÉ NATIONAL RESERVE (Deux-Sèvres).

II. *a*) Status : as for B.3.

b) Area : 2,639 ha.

c) Staff : 1 C.D. and 1 part-time A.T.

d) Budget : U.S. $ 12,000 (including in 1964 an important capital investment).

III. *Date established :* 1964.

Land tenure : State forest.

Management : an eight member Committee with the Engineer at Niort as Director : the hunting rights are controlled by the C.S.C.

IV. *Altitude :* 75 m.

a) Forest on oolite soils (durmast *Quercus petraea,* mature stands and understory coppice, beech).

b) Roe deer, wild boar.

11. DONZÈRE-MONDRAGON CANAL NATIONAL RESERVE (Vaucluse/Drôme).

II. *a*) Status : very strictly protected; no visitors allowed.

b) Area : 1,812 ha.

c) Staff : 4 guards, one of them allocated exclusively to this Reserve.

d) Budget : U.S. $ 1,600, plus salaries.

III. *Date established :* 1954, by agreement between the C.S.C. and Compagnie Nationale du Rhône.

Land tenure : the Company holds a concession from the State over the Canal right of way.

Management : jointly by the C.S.C. and the Hunting Federations of Drôme and Vaucluse.

IV. *Altitude :* about 60 m.

a) A section of the Rhône valley plain along the Canal; plantations mainly of acacia.

b) Hare *Lepus europaeus*; red-legged partridge *Alectoris rufa,* pheasant *Phasianus colchicus,* mallard, teal; grey heron; lapwing, golden plover *Pluvialis apricaria,* curlew *Numenius arquata* and other large waders on migration.

12. CASABIANDA NATIONAL RESERVE (Corsica).

II. *a*) Status : as for B.3.

b) Area : 1,760 ha.

c) Staff : one federal guard.

d) Budget : U.S. $ 4,400, plus guard's salary.

III. *Date established :* 1948; given its present status in 1951.

Land tenure : owned by the Ministry of Justice, this being a penal settlement where the prisoners undertake some cultivation, but the greater part of the land is undisturbed reserve.

216

Management : a five-member Committee in collaboration with the C.S.C. and a Director at Ajaccio.

V.   *Altitude :* sea level to 65 m.

a) A section of the Corsican coast along the Tyrrhenian Sea, comprising grassland, arable land under cereals, woods (pine, cork oak *Quercus suber* and introduced eucalyptus), lagoons and marsh.

b) Red deer (local race), wild boar, hare; red-legged partridge, mallard, coot *Fulica atra*; teal, velvet scoter *Melanitta fusca*; turtle-dove *Streptopelia turtur*, quail *C. coturnix*, woodcock *Scolopax rusticola,* snipe; thrushes.

13. BELVAL NATIONAL RESERVE (Ardennes).

a) Status : this Reserve is designed specially for experimental work on the introduction, artificial rearing and the hunting of larger game species. Otherwise as for B.3.

b) Area : 915 ha.

c) Staff : one special guard and one A.T.

d) Budget : staff salaries would satisfy the criterion.

Date established : 1947, with subsequent modification in 1964, 1965.

Land tenure : entirely a State forest.

Management : a four-member Committee. Seven red deer were introduced in 1948 and had multiplied to five or six hundred in 1965, many of which have spread beyond the boundaries of the Reserve.

Altitude : 190 m.

a) Plateau composed of diorite-sand and Oxford clays supporting broad-leaved forest (durmast, with beech plantations).

b) Red and roe deer, Corsican mouflon (introduced), wild boar.

14. LA POINTE D'ARÇAY NATIONAL RESERVE (Vendée).

a) Status : as for B.3. No inhabitants.

b) Area : 550 ha.

c) Staff : one A.T. with additional supervision by coastguards, customs and police.

d) Budget : U.S. $ 1,000, plus salaries.

Date established : 1951, under a joint Decree of the Minister of Agriculture and Inscription Maritime.

Land tenure : State forest and Naval property.

Management : by the C.S.C. with the Engineer of La Roche-sur-Yon as Director.

Research : likely to become a research centre for I.N.R.A.

Altitude : sea level to 4 m.

a) A peninsula on the southern Vendée coast, where alluvial deposits have built up a spit of land parallel with the sea and between it and the mouth of a small river; this is now partly covered with pine woods, then dunes, marsh and low-lying areas, flooded by high tides, with salicornia, rush and mud flats.

217

b) Very plentiful birdlife — mallard, teal, curlew, black-tailed godwit *L. limosa,* knot *Calidris canutus,* grey plover *Charadrius squatarola,* harriers *Circus* spp., gulls, terns, etc.

15. SAINTE-OPPORTUNE NATIONAL RESERVE (Eure).

II.   *a*) Status : as for B.3.

b) Area : 146 ha, well below the criterion requirement, but accepted as this is a very important bird sanctuary and breeding-place of Anatidae.

c) Staff : one guard.

d) Budget : U.S. $ 7,250, plus guard's salary.

III.   *Date established :* 1958 with modifications in 1964.

Land tenure : owned by C.S.C.

Management : by C.S.C., with a Director.

IV.   *Altitude :* 2 m.

a) A stretch of woods, marshes and open water, which affords a suitable breeding-place for duck.

b) Waterfowl, especially mallard.

16. LES SEPT ILES NATIONAL RESERVE.

II.   *a*) Status : as for B.3. Uninhabited and fully protected.

b) Area : only 82 ha, but accepted because of the special standing of this sanctuary.

c) Staff : one federal guard.

d) Budget : U.S. $ 600, plus guard's salary.

III.   *Date established :* 1912, confirmed by the Inscription Maritime in 1950 and made over to the C.S.C. by a decree of 10 October 1961. Modified in 1965.

Land tenure and management : owned and operated by the Ligue Française pour la Protection des Oiseaux.

IV.   *Altitude :* sea level to 20 m.

a) An archipelago situated some kilometres off the Breton coast near Plou-manach and Perros-Guirec. To qualify for the title " Sept Iles " two rock-stacks have been dignified by the name of " islands ".

b) The rich avifauna includes about 30,000 puffins *Fratercula arctica,* gannets *Sula bassana,* 3,000 guillemots *Uria aalge,* 600 razorbills *Alca torda,* cormorants *Phalacrocorax carbo,* kittiwakes *Rissa tridactyla*; predators include herring gulls, 5,500 lesser black-back gulls *Larus fuscus,* greater black-backs *Larus marinus,* peregrine *Falco peregrinus,* raven *Corvus corax.*

C. — " RESERVES CYNEGETIQUES D'INTERET NATIONAL ".

17. LE MERCANTOUR NATIONAL GAME RESERVE (Alpes-Maritimes).

II.   *a*) Status : similar to that of B.3, but pertains to the rather special case of an uninhabited mountain ridge adjoining the Italian frontier over a distance of 120 km.

b) Area : 27,843 ha.

c) Staff : 7 federal guards.

d) Budget : U.S. $ 14,000 including the wardening.

Date established : 1953, with modifications in 1959 and 1964.

Land tenure : 26,177 ha belong to the Communes, State forest accounts for 1,000 ha and private property for a further 666 ha.

Management : by the Hunting Federation of the Department, the Director being the President of the Federation. The Reserve adjoins the Italian reserve of Valdieri-Entraque (Savoy dukedom).

Altitude : 1,500-3,061 m.

a) Very rugged country with forest of larch, spruce *Picea* and pine; alps, lakes, torrents and rocks; rare plants include the mountain pansy *Viola valderia* (=*cenisia* subsp.) and *Silene cordifolia.*

b) Chamois, mouflon, ibex, sika deer *Cervus nippon* (introduced), marmot varying hare; black grouse *Lyrurus tetrix,* ptarmigan, partridge *P. perdix* and rock partridge.

18. LE PIC DU. MIDI D'OSSAU NATIONAL GAME RESERVE (Basses-Pyrénées).

a) Status : as for B.3. A high altitude uninhabited area.

b) Area : 5,982 ha.

c) Staff : 3 guards.

d) Budget : U.S. $ 8,200.

Date established : 1956.

Land tenure : entirely owned by Communes and Commune syndicates.

Management : Hunting Federation of the Department with financial help from the C.S.C.

Altitude : maximum 2,885 m.

a) Typical Pyrenean landscape of forest, wasteland, pasture and rock.

b) Chamois, bear *Ursus arctos*; capercaillie.

19. ETANGS DE L'HÉRAULT NATIONAL GAME RESERVE (Hérault).

a) Status : as for B.3. Uninhabited.

b) Area : 651 ha, in several separate pieces.

c) Staff : one full-time and 2 part-time guards.

d) Budget : covering staff salaries only.

Date established : 1960, modified in 1962.

Land tenure : 327 ha owned by the Commune and 324 ha privately owned.

Management : Hunting Federation of the Department with financial help from the C.S.C.

Altitude : sea level.

a) A group of four lagoons separated from the Mediterranean by a sea-bank. The lagoons each constitute a reserve and their features are as follows :

The Réserve du Vacaran :

a) Salt marsh; mainly a stopping-place for migrant birds.

b) Stilt *H. himantopus,* avocet *Recurvirostra avosetta,* greater flamingo *Phoenicopterus ruber,* little egret *Egretta garzetta.*

The Réserve de l'Estagrol :

a) Fresh water lagoon; used both by nesting species and migrants.

b) Mallard, teal, tufted duck *Aythya fuligula* and coot breed.

The Réserve du Méjean :

a) Brackish water (communicating with the sea), at the western end of which is a marshy zone with sea-rush *Juncus maritimus* and salicornia.

b) Duck (mainly mallard), coot, moorhen *Gallinula chloropus* and other Rallidae; the Reserve is essentially a winter sanctuary from which most species emigrate in the spring.

The Réserve du Fond du Grau :

a) Marsh and open water at the south-east end of the Etang de Mouguio.

b) Again mainly a sanctuary for waterfowl, such as coot and mallard, during the shooting season.

D. — SPECIAL OR PRIVATE RESERVES.

20. THE CAMARGUE ZOOLOGICAL AND BOTANICAL RESERVE (Bouches-du-Rhône).

II. a) Status : this Reserve enjoys rather stricter protection than the Reserves listed in sections B and C above, due in part to the 75-year lease of the area granted to the Société Nationale de Protection de la Nature (SNPN) by the Compagnie Salinière de la Camargue.

b) Area : 9,366 ha.

c) Staff : a Director and SNPN wardens.

d) Budget : U.S. $ 9,000, plus salaries.

III. *Date established :* 1928, confirmed by Ministerial decree in 1956 and 1963.

Land tenure : property of the Société Péchiney (Compagnie Salinière de la Camargue), sub-let on a 75-year lease in 1959.

Management : SNPN (formerly the Société d'Acclimatation). In 1967 the Reserve was awarded the European Diploma for Nature Protection by the Council of Europe.

Tourism : the number of visitors has grown to a point where they have begun to threaten the integrity of some sectors of the Reserve.

Research : undertaken by the privately run Station biologique de la Tour du Valat. The Centre National de Recherche Scientifique maintains a laboratory. A number of publications on various aspects of the Reserve have appeared.

IV. *Altitude :* sea level to 5 m.

a) The southern part of the ancient Rhône delta, comprising low-lying ground and saline lagoons communicating with one another through shallow channels. The vegetation is stunted and monotonous, mainly composed of more or less halophilous species dominated by *Salicornia* spp. and sea lavender *Statice sinuata*; where the soil is less saline but still waterlogged are clumps of tamarisk *Tamarix gallica*; the drier not very saline soils are covered by the tall thick " maquis " of the Camargue, made up of a *Phillyrea angustifolia* association, semi-halophilous associations, tall herbs such as sea-rush and the couch grass *Agropyron pycnanthum* and grassy swards. The sandy flats support *Arthrocnemum* (=*Salicornia macrostachya*) and the dunes an *Agro-*

220

pyron junceum-Ammophila association, while the very old dunes of what was once the sea-bank have that Camargue speciality *Juniperus phoenicea.* In short the Reserve includes all the typical biotopes of the delta.

b) The birdlife is rich and varied, with several thousand pairs of greater flamingoes in the saline zone, large breeding colonies of terns, smaller and larger gulls, duck, avocet, redshank *Tringa totanus,* oystercatcher *Haematopus ostralegus* and Kentish plover *Charadrius alexandrinus,* and, in winter, many thousands of duck; in the less saline areas many other waterbirds nest (ducks, herons, little egret, squacco *Ardeola ralloides,* stilt) and also bee-eaters *Merops apiaster* and rollers *Coracias garrulus.*

21. LE PELVOUX RESERVE OR STATE PARK (Hautes-Alpes).

a) Status : a high altitude isolated mountain block which enjoys *de facto* total protection.

b) Area : 8,714 ha.

c) Staff : some part-time Agents Techniques (A.T.).

d) Budget : covering staff salaries.

Date established : 1913, confirmed by Ministerial Decrees in 1956 and 1965.

Land tenure : State ownership.

Management : Office of the Conservation des Eaux et Forêts at Grenoble.

Altitude : 1,500-4,102 m.

a) Mountain peak in the Oisans massif; forest (mountain pine *Pinus mugo,* larch, Siberian cedar *Pinus cembra,* green alder *Alnus viridis*), alps, crags and waterfalls.

b) Chamois, marmot, varying hare; blackcock, ptarmigan, golden eagle.

22. MONT VALLIER STATE RESERVE (Ariège).

a) Status : as for B.3 above; a higher altitude uninhabited region.

b) Area : 8,208 ha.

c) Staff : 2 Chefs de District (C.D.) and 4 A.T.

d) Budget : U.S. $ 300, plus staff salaries.

Date established : 1956, modified in 1965.

Land tenure : entirely State forest.

Management : Office of the Conservation des Eaux et Forêts at Saint-Gérons, assisted financially by the C.S.C. This Reserve is proposed as a nucleus of a National Park of the Eastern Pyrenees.

Altitude : 950-2,859 m.

a) A rugged section of the Pyrenean chain, with forest of beech, fir and mountain pine; high altitude pastures, lakes and tarns.

b) Chamois and other mountain animals.

23. BURE AUROUZE RESERVE (Hautes-Alpes).

a) Status : as for B.3; a high altitude uninhabited region.

b) Area : 6,560 ha.

c) Staff : some part-time federal guards.

d) Budget : covering staff salaries.

III.   *Date established :* 1956, modified in 1962 and 1965.

Land tenure : State ownership.

Management : this Reserve is shared between the neighbouring Communes and assigned for administrative purposes to local Hunting Clubs until 1968, after which there was no assurance that the arrangement will be maintained.

IV.   *Altitude :* 1,300-2,712 m.

a) Rugged Alpine terrain with woods, high level pasture, crags, lakes and springs.

b) Chamois, mouflon (introduced) and other mountain game animals.

24. LE CARLITTE RESERVE (Pyrénées-Orientales).

II.   *a*) Status : as for B.3; again a high altitude uninhabited zone.

b) Area : 5,717 ha.

c) Staff : part-time federal guards.

d) Budget : U.S. $ 2,500, plus staff salaries.

III.   *Date established :* 1956, with modifications in 1957, 1963 and 1965.

Land tenure : 2,150 ha of State forest, the remainder Departmental forest under lease for the financial benefit of the C.S.C.

Management : the Hunting Federation of the Department in collaboration with the C.S.C.

IV.   *Altitude :* about 2,000-2,921 m.

a) A section of the eastern Pyrenees mainly about 2,300 m in altitude, with forests of mountain pine, pastures, crags, lakes and streams.

b) Chamois, varying hare; capercaillie, ptarmigan.

25. LE COMBEYNOT RESERVE (Hautes-Alpes).

II.   *a*) Status : as for B.3; yet another high altitude uninhabited zone.

b) Area : 4,720 ha.

c) Staff : two federal guards.

d) Budget : U.S. $ 2,000, plus staff salaries.

III.   *Date established :* 1954, modified in 1962.

Land tenure : Commune-owned forest.

Management : Hunting Federation of the Department.

IV.   *Altitude :* 1,500-1,800 m.

a) Woods and meadows.

b) Chamois, ibex.

26. ASCO FEDERAL RESERVE (Corsica).

II.   *a*) Status : as for B.3.

b) Area : 2,900 ha.

c) Staff : part-time federal guards.

d) Budget : for staff salaries only

ND, Skaftafell N.P.　　　　　　　　　　　　　　(photo : E. Einarsson)

ND, Skaftafell N.P.　　　　　　　　　　　　　　(photo : E. Einarsson)

CEYLON, Wilpattu N.P.

(photo : F. Vollma

INDIA, Corbett N.P.

(photo : F. Vollma

ON, Ruhumu N.P.

(photo : F. Vollmar/WWF)

INDIA, Kaziranga W.L.S.

(photo : de Rahm)

JAPAN, Chubu-Sangaku N.P.

N, Akan N.P.

JAPAN, Fuji-Hakone-Izu N.P.

, Seto-Naikai N.P.

INDONESIA, Udjung Kulon R.   (photo : J. Vers

Date established : 1953.

Land tenure : Commune-owned forest.

Management : Hunting Federation of the Department.

Altitude : 800-1,900 m.

a) Situated in the valley of the Asco, and covered with larch (80 %) and maritime pine Pinus pinaster (20 %) forest.

27. ETANGS DES IMPÉRIAUX RESERVE (Bouches-du-Rhône).

a) Status : as for B.3.

b) Area : 2,777 ha.

c) Staff : wardened by the police force of the Commune of Les Saintes-Maries-de-la-Mer.

d) Budget : not reported.

Date established : 1964.

Land tenure : owned by the Department.

Management : the Commune of Les Saintes-Maries which leases the Etangs.

Altitude : sea level to 5 m.

a) This is a western extension of the Camargue Zoological and Botanical Reserve.

b) Flora and fauna similar to that of the Camargue, see B.20 above.

28. NÉOUVIEILLE RESERVE (Hautes-Pyrénées).

a) Status : total protection as a whole, with some sectors set aside as strict natural reserve.

b) Area : 2,100 ha.

c) Staff : one guard.

d) Budget : covering salary of guard.

Date established : 1935.

Land tenure : partly owned by the Commune and partly private, but leased to the managing Society.

Management : Société Nationale de Protection de la Nature.

Altitude : 1,750-3,092 m.

a) A section of the central Pyrenees, comprising a series of high peaks and some 25 lakes; high altitude flora, pastures, bare rock; there is a small forest at the foot of the Estibère valley (Scots pine, mountain pine, birch, aspen Populus tremula, willow Salix sp.).

b) High altitude fauna, including chamois, red squirrel Sciurus vulgaris; capercaillie, black grouse, vultures, eagles.

29. BIOLOGICAL AND ARTISTIC RESERVE OF THE FOREST OF FONTAINEBLEAU.

a) Status : no habitations; 140 ha are strict natural reserve and 411 ha managed reserve. No entry allowed.

b) Area : 551 ha.

c) and d) Staff and budget : provided by the State.

FRANCE

III.   *Date established :* control dates back to 1853, but in its present form, with 140 ha of strict natural reserve, the Reserve was established by a Ministerial decree of 9 October 1953.

Land tenure : State forest.

Management : the Research Station of the Ecole Nationale des Eaux et Forêts.

IV.   *Altitude :* 75-150 m.

a) Part of the watershed plateau of Paris, mainly composed of Beauce limestone and sand-calcites; the biological reserves contain beechwoods on flint and limestone respectively, park-like woods of durmast, rocky scrub-forest and birch; the managed or controlled part of the reserve contains some old timber.

b) Typical woodland fauna.

V.   **Areas excluded :**

As in the case of Germany, for which the selection has if anything had to be even more severe, it has been necessary to make an arbitrary choice of Reserves for inclusion in the List and to leave out a great number which do not really differ very greatly from those chosen. In the case of France there are some 1,700 " game reserves ", of which only 17 have been listed, and also a considerable number of reserves of varying status, some of which are quite well-known internationally (the Caroux and Lanzanier for example), but which cannot be accepted because they fall too far outside the criteria laid down by the ICNP. Some of the more important of these excluded areas are listed below :

A. — A new National Park has been set up by a Decree of 23 March 1967 (see Mont Vallier State Reserve, No. D.22 above, which it adjoins) :

1. Pyrénées Orientales National Park	46,000 ha

B. — Seven National Game Reserves :

2. Cadarache	1,605 ha
3. Saint-Lambert	815 ha
4. Basse-Seine	750 ha
5. Vaux-de-Cernay	391 ha
6. Génissiat	364 ha
7. Vaux, Baye and Gauffier	360 ha
8. Ile de Béniguet	81 ha

C. — Six Game Reserves " d'Intérêt National " :

9. Loire	1,100 ha
10. Gironde	550 ha
11. Marais de Gorge	505 ha
12. Chaillé-les-Marais	220 ha
12. Etang de Vitacker	80 ha
14. Bassin d'Arcachon	—

D. — Fifteen Private Reserves :

15. Caroux.
16. Lauzanier.

17. Mouline de Champsaur.
18. La Massane.
19. Ilots de la Baie de Morlaix.
20. Baie des Veys.
21. Ouessant and Molène.
22. Toulinguet.
23. Tas de Pois.
24. Cap Sizun.
25. Les Glenans.
26. Nar Hor.
27. Coast Reserves of St. Malo gulf.
28. Morbihan Reserves.
29. Ilots de Meaban.

E. — Thirty-two State Forest Reserves :

30. Lyons.
31. Saint-Germain.
32. Compiègne.
33. Retz.
34. Verzy.
35. Huelgoat.
36. Carnoet.
37. Fougères.
38. Noirmoutier.
39. La Perche.
40. Reno Valdieu.
41. Berce.
42. Blois.
43. Marly.
44. Malmaison.
45. Rambouillet.
46. Haslach.
47. Bois sauvage.
48. Saint-Nabor.
49. Saint-Antoine.
50. La Joux.
51. Saint-Trojan.
52. Châteauroux.
53. Tronçais.
54. La Grande-Chartreuse.
55. Montagne Noire.
56. Loubatière.
57. Rialsesse.
58. La Plaine.
59. La Gardiole.
60. La Sainte-Baume.
61. Ile Sainte-Marguerite.

In addition to the above, mention should be made of 18 Forest Reserves owned by Communes, totalling about 1,000 ha in area; 1,594 special approved reserves, totalling 380,724 ha; and, under new legislation enacted on 1 March 1967, the power given to set up " National Regional Parks" similar to the German " Naturparke " and the British " National Parks ".

FRANCE

OVERSEAS TERRITORIES

No areas have been accepted in respect of these territories. French Guyana, French Somaliland and New Caledonia are dealt with as separate countries and it is therefore only necessary to note here that —

A. — for Kerguelen, regulations have been made on the initiative of M. Aubert de la Rüe setting up two reserves, but no actual steps have been taken on the ground to implement this effectively;

B. — there are no Reserves in any of the islands of Oceania, the Antilles or Comoros, nor on Réunion.

42. FRENCH GUYANA

I. Listed Areas : nil.

V. Explanation :

No information has yet been received from the authorities who were consulted, but from private sources it appears that there is no area in the country corresponding to the criteria laid down by the International Commission on National Parks.

43. FRENCH SOMALILAND
(Afars and Issas)

I. Listed Areas : nil.

V. Explanation :

Again there has been no response from the authorities to requests for information, although it is known that some areas were classified as National Parks in or before 1939, namely :

The Dai Forest National Park	10,000 ha
The Maskali-Muscha Islands National Park	400 ha

In addition, two Reserves are known to have been proclaimed :

The Greater and Lesser Bara Reserve.
The Skoutir and Kourtimale Reserve.

However, according to private informants, it is clear that no staff has been appointed to supervise these four areas.

44. GABON

Listed Areas : two.

1. The Ofoué Strict Natural Reserve.
2. Okanda National Park.

General Introduction :

No recent information has been received from the Gabon authorities and neither of the areas or any mention of Gabon was included in E/3436 or Part Two of the previous edition of the List.

Details : application of criteria (II), general information (III) and description (IV) :

1. THE OFOUÉ STRICT NATURAL RESERVE.

a) Status : this is in accordance with the provisions laid down by the London Convention 1933 for strict reserves, but it is possible that mining operations are permitted in certain sectors.

b) Area : 150,000 ha.

c) and *d*) Staff and budget : no evidence of proper supervision, but it has been decided to retain the Reserve on the List because of its peculiar interest — still largely unexplored — and the fact that, according to local reports, it is entirely uninhabited.

Date established : 1946.

Management : vested theoretically in the Service des Chasses. No provision for tourism or research.

Altitude : not quoted, but probably c. 500 m.

a) No detailed description available, but the Reserve is situated on the left bank of the River Ofoué, after which it is named, is adjacent to the Equator and is wholly covered by dense humid tropical forest.

b) Doubtless the fauna includes most Gabon forest species, although there is some reason for believing that there are no bongo *Taurotragus eurycerus* or giant forest hog *Hylochoerus.*

2. OKANDA NATIONAL PARK.

a) Status : reported to conform with that of a National Park under the London Convention of 1933.

b) Area : 190,000 ha.

c) and *d*) Staff and budget : the same remarks apply as to the Ofoué Reserve.

Date established : 1946.

Management, etc. : as for Ofoué Reserve; the two areas are contiguous.

Ecologically similar to the Ofoué Reserve, which is immediately to the south. Elephants are said to be specially numerous in the National Park.

227

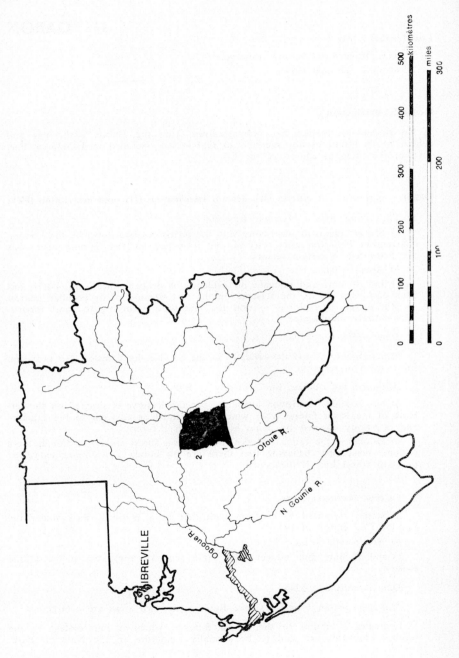

Areas excluded :

1. The Wonga-Wongue National Park, officially established on 20 November 1967 : 82,760 ha, extending from the Atlantic coast eastwards to Lake Azingo; staff comprises a Director and 17 guards; rain forest and savannah sectors, with a varied fauna.

2. The Lopé-Okanda Game Reserve, 150,000 ha, lying to the north of the two listed areas. A decree establishing it in the same year as the others (1946) does not, however, appear to have been offcially gazetted. Forested in the sector bordering the National Park, but with a gradual transition into savannah in the north. The fauna is reported to have a greater variety than that of the Ofoué Reserve.

45. GAMBIA

Listed Areas : nil.

a) **Explanation :**

The Ministry of Agriculture in a letter dated 18 September 1962, confirmed on 20 July 1963, states that " at present the Gambia does not possess any National Parks or Game Reserves as such, although 88 Forest Parks possessing an aggregate acreage of some 100,000 acres (40,467 ha) have been set aside ".

b) **Areas excluded :**

The ' Forest Parks ' mentioned above.

46. GERMAN FEDERAL REPUBLIC (¹)

Listed Areas : twenty-five.

A. — ' NATURSCHUTZPARKE ' :

1. Lüneburger Heide.
2. Siebengebirge.

B. — ' NATURSCHUTZGEBIETE ' :

3. Ammergebirge.
4. Königsseegebiet.

(¹) As an United Nations List, the present volume does not cover nature reserves of the German Democratic Republic, although they are numerous and well-run. Details of them can be found in " Die Naturschutzgebiete der Deutscher Demokratischen Republik " (262 pp.), published in 1964, at Berlin, by the Academy of Agronomic Sciences.

   5. Karwendel and Karwendelvorgebirge.
   6. Hochkienberg, Dürrnbachhorn, Sonntagshorn, Inzellerkienberg and
Staufen.
   7. Holzmaden.
   8. Isar River Valley.
   9. Mellumplate.
   10. Kühkopf-Knoblachsaue.
   11. Lister Dünen (Sylt).
   12. Die Lucie.
   13. Stadtwald Augsburg.
   14. Dümmer.
   15. Federsee.
   16. Eggstätt-Hemhofer Seenplatte.
   17. Mummelsee-Hornisgrinde.
   18. Schliffkopf.
   19. Weltenburger Enge.
   20. Wildseemoor.
   21. Grosser Arbersee and Arberseewand.

   C. — FOUR ADDITIONAL 'NATURSCHUTZGEBIETE', which although extremely
marginal cases are included at the request of the German authorities :
   22. Laacher See.
   23. Wollmatinger Ried.
   24. Neandertal.
   25. Breitachklamm.

General Introduction :
   The German Federal Republic presents one of the most difficult problems
for the present List, in that the strict application of the criteria would lead to
conclusions verging on the absurd. The fact is that in this country, throughout
which natural habitats certainly enjoy more careful and authoritative protection
than those of most other countries, assessment of the degree of total protection
accorded could lead to the unreasonable conclusion — taking into account the
density of population and extremely high level of industrial development — that
there is not a single area qualifying for inclusion in the List.
   For this reason the choice of areas, which has been made in consultation
with the German authorities, has had to be essentially subjective, since reference
to the objective criteria would clearly give quite the wrong impression. In making
the choice no attempt has been made to include for each area the usual comments
on its relationship to the criteria requirements. The aim has simply been to
present a full picture in keeping with the high place that the German Federal
Republic occupies in the field of interest of the present List. The twenty-five
selected areas are therefore dealt with on the understanding that, although admit-
tedly the criterion of full protective status cannot usually be satisfied, yet the
standard of supervision which each is accorded is certainly strict enough to be
quite adequate.
   In the particular case of the 'Naturschutzgebiete', their status can be described
as controlled management of natural features in such a way as to ensure the
maintenance of their variety, 'health' and beauty. Agriculture, forest exploitation, hunting, fishing etc. are practised within their boundaries, but controlled
and limited in accordance with scientifically established principles. Nevertheless
it is clear that certain sectors actually enjoy a totally protected status, because
they are uninhabited or have no exploitable resources or simply because of their
high altitude. This factor has therefore been taken into consideration in making

230

the selection, although it is not always one that can be readily and specifically applied to particular localities.

The general administration and development of the listed areas is sufficiently homogeneous for the relevant information to be summarised in this introductory section rather than detailed under each separate Park or Reserve.

Legislation : under the Constitution, the conservation of nature and safeguarding of sites and landscape fall within the competence of each of the eleven Länder. The Federal Government only has limited legislative powers, sufficient however to ensure that conservation efforts in each state are kept in harmony with other public interests and that at least a minimum area is set aside for reserves under general protection. These fall within the category of ' Naturschutzgebiete ', provision for establishing which is made in the relevant law.

Administration :

A. — The Lüneburger Heide Naturschutzpark is managed by a private organisation, the Verein Naturschutzpark E.V. Hamburg-Stuttgart, and by official representatives. In the same way the Siebengebirge Park is jointly administered by the public authorities and the Verschönerungsverein für das Siebengebirge.

B. — As previously indicated the management of the Naturschutzgebiete is entirely the responsibility of the Länder : under a decision of the Federal Constitutional Court in 1951, the Reichnaturschutzgesetz of 1935 ceased to have Federal application. It still applies in each of the Länder, without prejudice to State rights (decision of the Federal Tribunal on 1 October 1958) and subject to the exercise by Bonn of the general powers mentioned above under Legislation.

There is also a central organisation responsible for advising local authorities and organisations and for co-ordinating their work. This is the ' Bundesanstalt für Vegetations Kunde, Naturschutz und Landschaftspflege ' (B.A.V.N.L.), which is based at Bad Godesberg and is directly responsible to the Bundesministerium für Ernährung Landwirtschaft und Forsten.

Land tenure : the Verein Naturschutzpark owns some 5,000 ha of the Lüneburger Heath and the Verschönerungsverein 800 ha of the Siebengebirge. Most of the Naturschutzgebiete are public property, but some sectors are still in private ownership.

Tourism : organisational efforts have had little impact on the Naturschutzgebiete and have been mainly directed to the special areas designated as ' Naturparke ' (see Part V below), in which during the period 1956 to 1963, the equivalent of over 100 million dollars was invested on tourist facilities such as shelters, parking-places, paths and signposts. However the Lüneburger Heide Park, which dates back to 1910, was, in about 1955, brought within the scope of the Naturparke, despite its special status, and as such became the scene of an intensive tourist development effort. This included the imposition of strict regulations under which, for example, motor cars cannot be taken into many sectors, noise abatement measures (no transistor radios) are similarly applied and even entry on foot is forbidden in certain parts of the heath. This Park, incidentally, with No. 23 Wollmatinger Ried, was in 1969 awarded the Council of Europe's Diploma.

Scientific research : a number of German research organisations contribute to the scientific investigation of reserved areas and to putting into effect, with official backing, a co-ordinated policy on the control of such investigation. The B.A.V.N.L. is the principal central body responsible for such co-ordination and for the general integration of work in the over-all programme.

Only the two Naturschutzparke were described in E/3436 of the previous edition of the List.

232

Details : application of criteria (II), general information (III) and description (IV) :

For the reasons explained in the General Introduction above, reference is only made to heads II and III, where it is desirable to supplement the information already given.

A. — NATURSCHUTZPARKE.

1. LÜNEBURGER HEIDE (Lower Saxony).

a) Status : exploitation of natural resources is definitely restricted e.g. hunting and fishing are forbidden. Some agricultural pursuits continue, including the grazing of sheep, without which the heath would in fact cease to exist.

b) Area : 20,000 ha.

c) Staff : a senior forester and eight labourers are permanently employed in the Park, but supervision and maintenance involve many other part-time workers, some of them on a voluntary basis.

2,000 ha in the south-west of the Park are unfortunately used — and consequently devastated — as a tank practice ground by the British Army. Representations at an international level are seeking to remedy this situation.

Altitude : 70-169 m.

a) A landscape of heather moorland with underlying soils of glacial origin; juniper; since 1750, pine plantations have replaced some of the original vegetation. The authorities of the Reserve maintain a constant and, in view of the opposition, courageous fight to restrict these conifer plantation areas, in order to re-establish some of the ancient woodland of beech, oak, birch, etc. and also the heathland.

b) 40 species of mammal and 380 species of birds have been recorded : the sheep, which are encouraged for the purpose of keeping the heath in a stable condition, are of the Landes variety.

2. SIEBENGEBIRGE (the Rhineland of North Westphalia).

a) Status : rather nearer total protection than that of the Lüneburger Heath Park.

b) Area : 4,200 ha.

c) Staff : a State 'Forstmeister' and two foresters supplied by a private Society; also, during the summer, four mounted police.

Altitude : 60-460 m.

a) A region of hills of volcanic origin and with fairly steep slopes; 80 % of the surface is forest-covered, the remainder being vineyard; the orchidaceous flora is noteworthy.

B. — NATURSCHUTZGEBIETE.

3. AMMERGEBIRGE (Bavaria).

a) Status : because of its high altitude most of this reserve is free from all forms of exploitation.

b) Area : 27,000 ha.

Altitude : 2,000-2,500 m.

a) Mountain massif situated on the edge of a limestone section of the Alps; the forest is mainly very old and the meadows support sub-alpine and alpine flora according to altitude.

233

4. KÖNIGSSEEGEBIET (Bavaria).

II.   *a*) Status : only two or three thousand hectares are free from habitation and exploitation.
b) Area : 20,576 ha.

IV.   *Altitude :* 1,000-1,500 m.

a) Part of the Berchtesgaden Alps, with several lakes, including the Königssee and Obersee; a rich alpine flora.

5. KARWENDEL AND KARWENDELVORGEBIRGE (Bavaria).

II.   *a*) Status : virtually total protection due to altitude.
b) Area : 19,000 ha.

IV.   *Altitude :* 2,000-2,800 m.

a) A landscape ranging from riverside meadows to the high peaks of the Karwendel and its spurs in the Bavarian Alps near Garmisch-Partenkirchen; a rich alpine flora.
b) A good variety of alpine animals.

6. HOCHKIENBERG, DÜRRNBACHHORN, SONNTAGSHORN, INZELLERKIENBERG AND STAUFEN (Bavaria).

II.   *a*) Status : virtually total protection due to altitude.
b) Area : 9,500 ha in all.

IV.   *Altitude :* 1,800-2,000 m.

a) A very rugged area of calcareous ' prealpine ' ridges; the excellent alpine and sub-alpine flora includes such species as sow-bread *Cyclamen europaeum,* alpine rose *Rhodothamnus chamaecistus* and another plant typical of the eastern Alps, the cut spleenwort *Asplenium fissum.*

7. HOLZMADEN (Baden-Württemberg).

II.   *a*) Status : includes some hundreds of hectares which enjoy total protection.
b) Area : 8,000 ha.

IV.   *Altitude :* 600-800 m.

a) Contains some fine examples of fossilized flora and fauna of the Jurassic.

8. ISAR RIVER VALLEY (Bavaria).

II.   *a*) Status : except for some forest exploitation the flora and fauna are totally protected.

IV.   *Altitude :* 600 m.

a) Part of the valley of the Isar and its hinterland; meadows, Scots pine *Pinus sylvestris* forest and junipers along the river; exhibits the gradual occupation of the sands and gravels by vegetation, the stages in this process being remarkably clear-cut.
b) Birdlife is plentiful : many duck.

9. MELLUMPLATE (Lower Saxony).

II.   *a*) Status : about half the reserve is totally protected.
b) Area : 3,500 ha.

IV.   *Altitude :* 100-150 m.

a) Uninhabited meadowland between the mouths of the Jade and Weser rivers.

234

b) A nesting area for many coastal birds, including common and sandwich terns *Sterna hirundo* and *sandvicensis*, herring and common gull *Larus argentatus* and *canus*, and oystercatcher *Haematopus ostralegus*.

10. KUHKOPF-KNOBLACHSAUE (Hesse).

a) Status : total protection. Removal of fallen trees constitutes the only interference.
b) Area : 2,378 ha.

Altitude : 300 m.

a) Sample of the old Rhineland landscape, with forest and meadow.
b) Plentiful birdlife.

11. LISTER DÜNEN (SYLT) (Schleswig-Holstein).

a) Status : *de facto* total protection.
b) Area : 2,027 ha.

Altitude : sea level.

a) Remarkable area of moving dunes on the North Sea island of Sylt.
b) Good marine avifauna.

12. DIE LUCIE (Lower Saxony).

a) Status : virtually total protected.
b) Area : 1,800 ha.

Altitude : 50 m.

a) A section of a secondary valley in the glacial deposits of the ancient valley of the Elbe; marshy forest with especially rich bog vegetation.
b) The only nesting-place of the crane *Grus grus* west of the river Elbe.

13. STADTWALD AUGSBURG (Bavaria).

a) Status : as its name shows this is mainly a municipal forest reserved for recreational purposes, but there is a small section which enjoys total protection.
b) Area : 1,595 ha.

Altitude : 500 m.

a) A remnant of the original forest of the Lech, including the full transition from riverside meadow to coniferous forest and heath; due to the deepening of the river-bed the plant associations have undergone considerable changes.

14. DÜMMER (Lower Saxony).

a) Status : although shooting is allowed, other forms of exploitation are strictly controlled and this, with the fact that the Reserve provides an effective refuge for nesting waterfowl, has justified its inclusion in the List.
b) Area : 1,500 ha.

Altitude : 100 m.

a) A lake through which the river Hunte runs; reed-beds.
b) A remarkable place for birds and the most important sanctuary in north-west Germany for sea-birds and migrants. No less than eight species of duck breed : red-crested pochard *Netta rufina,* tufted duck, ferruginous duck and pochard, *Aythya fuligula, nyroca* and *ferina,* pintail, garganey, teal and shoveler, *Anas acuta, querquedula, crecca* and *clypeata;* bittern *Botaurus stellaris,* kestrel *Falco tinnunculus,* terns, ruff *Philomachus pugnax;* curlew and whimbrel *Numenius arquata* and *phaeopus* also occur and the reserve is a very important sanctuary for golden plover *Pluvialis apricaria.*

GERMAN FEDERAL REPUBLIC

15. Federsee (Bade-Württemberg).

II.
a) Status : totally protected.
b) Area : 1,410 ha.

IV.
Altitude : 400 m.
a) Sample of a silting lake-shore, exhibiting all the stages of the process from reed-bed to mosses covered with dwarf conifers.
b) Many water birds including grey heron *Ardea cinerea,* mallard *Anas platyrhynchos,* shoveler, garganey, marsh harrier *Circus aeruginosus,* bittern, snipe *Capella gallinago,* curlew, little crake *Porzana parva,* common tern *Sterna hirundo* and blackheaded gull *Larus ridibundus.*

16. Eggstätt-Hemhofer Seenplatte (Bavaria).

II.
a) Status : about 150 ha are under total protection.
b) Area : 1,008 ha.

IV.
Altitude : 600 m.
a) Landscape of glacial origin on the north-west of the Chiemsee, with many small lakes in the area of glacial deposits; a rich terrestrial flora and marshy heathland.

17. Mummelsee-Hornisgrinde (Bade-Württemberg).

II.
a) Status : full protection; no forest exploitation.
b) Area : 469 ha.

IV.
Altitude : 1,100 m.
a) A lake in a subsidence area of glacial origin, surrounded by primary forest.

18. Schliffkopf (Bade-Württemberg).

II.
a) Status : totally protected; no shooting or woodcutting allowed, but grazing of domestic stock is authorized on the outskirts of the area for a four-week period annually.
b) Area : 295 ha.

IV.
Altitude : 1,200-1,300 m.
a) Situated in the Black Forest, this Reserve comprises the interesting ' Missen ' landscape with mountain pine *Pinus mugo* forests on the plateau and glacially hollowed slopes; there are piles of rocks and peatland areas on the plateau, with a relict boreal flora.

19. Weltenburger Enge (Bavaria).

II.
a) Status : totally protected except for some woodcutting on the periphery.
b) Area : 257 ha.

IV.
Altitude : 400-450 m.
a) The steep valley of the Danube where it cuts through the Jura, with patches of forest.

20. Wildseemoor (Bade-Württemberg).

II.
a) Status : about 100 ha under total protection.
b) Area : 181 ha.

236

Altitude : 1,000 m.

a) Biologically an area of great interest, comprising the greatest area of marshy upland moss in the Federal Republic and the most notable example of this habitat type in the Black Forest; the flora has a pronounced arcto-alpine character and includes good stands of a dwarf variety of mountain pine.

b) The fauna is also markedly arcto-alpine, with many species of birds and a particularly varied selection of butterflies.

21. GROSSER ARBERSEE UND ARBERSEEWAND (Bavaria).

a) Status : 100 ha are totally protected.

b) Area : 157 ha.

Altitude : 700-900 m.

a) A relict glacial lake, with a rich flora and an important sample of fescue *Festuca* bog on its western shore; the lake is dominated by a wall of granite notable for the fine variety of firs it supports.

C. — ADDITIONAL NATURSCHUTZGEBIETE.

22. LAACHERSEE (Rheinland-Pfalz).

a) Status : total protection.

b) Area : 1,742 ha.

Altitude : 275 m.

a) A crater lake which is a good example of postglacial volcanic activity in western Europe : flora and fauna characteristic of recent volcanic soils.

23. WOLLMATINGER RIED (Bade-Württemberg).

a) Status : total protection. Awarded the Council of Europe's Diploma in 1969. Management of the meadow-land requires regular mowing.

b) Area : 430 ha.

Altitude : 400 m.

a) Part of the unique marshland of Lake Constance, with typical marsh vegetation, much influenced by fluctuations of water level.

b) The birdlife is particularly good, this being an important stopping place for migrants and wintering area for aquatic species, with a large variety of breeding species also, notably the red-crested pochard *Netta rufina*.

24. NEANDERTAL (Nordrhein-Westphalia).

a) Status : totally protected.

b) Area : 137 ha.

Altitude : 85 m.

a) The celebrated site where remains of *Homo neandertalensis* were disco-vered in 1856.

25. BREITACHKLAMM (Bavaria).

a) Status : total protection.

b) Area : 8 ha.

IV.   *Altitude :* 840-914 m.
           a) This is an outstanding 'natural monument', comprising a section of the remarkable Allgäu gorge which clearly shows the geological structure.

V.   **Areas excluded :**
       A. — About 900 other Naturschutzgebiete, which occupy a total area of a little less than 300,000 ha.

       B. — More than 6,000 Landschaftschutzgebiete, totalling nearly 3 million hectares in area or more than a tenth of the whole area of the Republic.

       C. — 40,000 'natural monuments'.

       D. — 35 'Naturparke', totalling 2 million hectares, which can be regarded as large zones of natural beauty with little urbanisation or industrialisation, where an effort is made to preserve this unspoilt character and to provide for the economic future of the inhabitants not only by agricultural development in the widest sense but also by systematically organising recreational opportunities and the healthy and rational use of leisure. In a densely populated country like Germany these Parks obviously have a considerable importance, but the criteria of selection laid down for the purpose of the present List do not allow them to be included, with the exception of the Lüneburger Heide and Siebengebirge, which are also reserves in keeping with the criteria. However, the general soundness of the organisation of these Parks and the beneficial effect which they undoubtedly confer on very large natural areas, justify giving their names and distribution below together with, in brackets, the area of each expressed in thousands of hectares :

       Baden-Württemberg : nil; *Bavaria :* Cham Waldmünchen (65), Mittl. Bayer. Wald (25), Bayerischer Spessart (90), Bayerischer Rhön (80), Vord. Bayer. Wald (80), Oberer Bayerischer Wald (145); *Hamburg :* Harburger Berger (4); *Hesse :* Hohen Vogelsberg (28), Bergstrasse-Odenwald (208), Meissner-Kaufunger Wald (42), Habichtswald (46), Hochtaunus (120), Hessischer Spessart (67), Hessische Rhön (40), Diemelsee (40); *Niedersachsen :* Münden (20), Harz (95), Solling-Vogler (50), Nördlicher Teutoburger Wald-Wiehengebirge (95), Südheide (56); *Nordrhein-Westphalia :* Nordeifel (134), Arnsberger Wald (45), Kottenforst (12), Rothaargebirge (113), Hohe Mark (101), Ebbe-Gebirge (66), Schwalm-Nette (41), Eggegebirge und Südl. Teutoburger Wald (63), Homert (37), Bergisches Land (57); *Rheinland-Pfalz :* Südeifel (40), Pfälzer Wald (179), Nassau (52), Rhein-Westerwald (37); *Schleswig-Holstein :* Lauenburgische Seen (40).

47. GHANA

I.   **Listed Areas :** one.
       1. The Mole Game Reserve.

       General Introduction :
       The Mole Reserve, together with a number of other areas which have had to be excluded, were cited in E/3436 of the previous edition of the List.

Details : application of criteria (II), general information (III) and description (IV) :

1. THE MOLE GAME RESERVE.

a) Status : total protection, six villages having been evacuated from the area and no inhabitants or exploitation now being allowed. It is proposed to amend the relevant legislation (Wildlife Preservation Act 1961) to confer the status of a National Park on the reserve and, in so doing, to take the opportunity of enlarging the protected area.

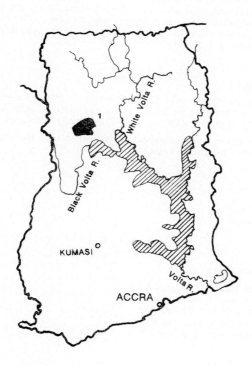

b) Area : 388,500 ha.

c) Staff : the establishment of 90 in 1964 had by 1966 been increased to 168 (3 senior assistant game-wardens, 4 assistant game-wardens, 2 senior game protection officers, 2 game protection officers, 2 senior rangers, 15 rangers, 5 senior game scouts, 65 game scouts, 55 game assistants and 15 game guards).

d) Budget : U.S. $ 50,000 (1962), $ 42,970 (including $ 27,740 for development) in 1967.

Date established : 1961.

Administration : responsibility of the Game and Wildlife Department of the Ministry of Forests.

Land tenure : state ownership.

Tourism : facilities include a rest-camp (25 beds) and a modern motel (50 beds), with a swimming-bath; there are 190 km of tracks.

IV. *Altitude :* 180-360 m.

a) A hilly region with Guinean-type savannah and gallery-forest along the rivers.

b) Elephant *Loxodonta africana,* lion and leopard *Panthera leo* and *pardus,* buffalo *Syncerus caffer,* various antelope (roan *Hippotragus equinus,* reedbuck *Redunca arundinum,* waterbuck *Kobus ellipsiprymnus,* Buffon's kob *Kobus kob,* bushbuck *Tragelaphus scriptus.* oribi *Ourebia oribi*); primates including colobus *C. polykomos* and baboon *P. papio*; reptiles : crocodile, Nile and Bosc's monitor lizards *Varanus niloticus* and *exanthematicus,* terrapin and river turtle (spp. not quoted); plentiful birdlife.

V. **Areas excluded :**

A. — Owabi Waterworks Game Reserve : 1,350 ha; excluded on the advice of the Ghanaian Government both on the grounds of size and because protection is inadequate, with no staff or budget especially allocated.

B. — Five Game Sanctuaries of insufficient status : Kommenda (203 ha); Aboma; Bia Shelterbelt; Bomfum; Onuem Bepo.

48. GREECE

I. **Listed Areas :** five.

1. Mount Parnes National Park.
2. Dias Island Reserve.
3. Guioura Island Reserve.
4. The Samarias Ravines Reserve.
5. Antimilos Island Reserve.

General Introduction :

A law promulgated in 1937, due largely to the initiative of the Hellenic Alpine Club, envisaged the creation of five National Parks each of which was to be of not less than 3,000 ha and supported by a 4,000 ha protective zone. Their administration was to be the responsibility of the Forest Service of the Ministry of Agriculture. However, of the various National Parks established under this law, only one has been given a protected status and standard of supervision which qualifies it for inclusion in the U.N. List. The 3,000 ha lower limit provided for in the law has, of course, also meant that a number of other Greek nature reserves cannot be termed National Parks.

Only one of the Listed areas, the Samarias Reserve in Crete (No. 4), was briefly described in E/3436 of the previous edition of the List, as also was one of the areas excluded — the Olympus National Park.

Details : application of criteria (II), general information (III) and description (IV) :

1. MOUNT PARNES NATIONAL PARK.

a) Status : no habitation, cultivation, hunting (other than fishing) or tree-felling (except in a few places and carried out by the Forest Service); grazing rights have at last, after long negotiations, been bought out and terminated; the right to cut and gather firewood still exists, but negotiations to redeem it are afoot. There is an unfenced strict nature reserve of 350 ha, also a fenced hunting reserve of 60 ha (to be increased to 120 ha). The mountain summit is occupied by a military radar station.

b) Area : 3,700 ha.

c) Staff : 4 units, including two for whom there is a statutory requirement.

d) Budget : U.S. $ 36,000.

GREECE

III.   *Date established :* 1953.

Land tenure : half the Park is state owned, a third the property of Mt. Parnes Monastery, and the remainder belongs to a tourist organisation which honours the protected status over part of its area, but elsewhere is indulging in the construction of some major facilities including a road.

Tourism : a large luxury hotel has been built on a spur of the mountain overlooking the plains which extend towards Hymettus and the Pentelikon.

IV.   *Altitude :* 300-500 m.

a) A mountain of Attica with rugged slopes and scattered Kermes oak *Quercus coccifera* and conifers.

b) Red and roe deer *Cervus elaphus* and *C. capreolus* and chamois *R. rupicapra* are being reared for release in the park.

2. DIAS ISLAND RESERVE.

II.   *a)* Status : total protection; an uninhabited island, closed to visitors. A campaign has to be waged against the excessive number of rabbits.

b) Area : 1,200 ha, which satisfies the criterion in Greece (where there are 64 inhabitants to the square km and the minimum is, therefore, 500 ha).

c) Staff : one guard, living alternately on the island and at Heraklion.

d) Budget : criterion satisfied by salary and expenses of the guard.

III.   *Date established :* 1938.

Land tenure : state ownership.

Tourism : not permitted, but up to three research workers can live at the guard's house.

IV.   *Altitude :* sea level to 268 m.

a) A rugged island with Mediterranean flora, such as mastic tree *Pistacia lentiscus, Juniperus foetidissima* and the *oleaster* subspecies of the olive *Olea europaea.*

b) The Cretan wild goat *Capra hircus aegagrus* has been introduced.

3. GUIOURA ISLAND RESERVE.

II.   *a)* Status : total protection; uninhabited island, no visitors allowed.

b) Area : 1,000 ha.

c) Staff : one guard.

d) Budget : criterion satisfied by salary, cost of sailing to and from island, patrols, etc.

III.   *Date established :* 1938.

Land tenure : state ownership.

Tourism : not permitted, but there are two shelters for persons in possession of special permits.

IV.   *Altitude :* sea level to 500 m.

a) A steep-sided island, 160 km from Volos, with typically Mediterranean vegetation, including Kermes oak, box *Buxus sempervirens,* mastic, juniper and olive.

b) Wild goat.

242

4. THE SAMARIAS RAVINES RESERVE (Crete).

a) Status : formerly allowed some habitation and limited cultivation but is at present being made more strict, a substantial sum of 6 million drachmas (U.S. $ 200,000) having been allocated in 1962 to pay for the necessary expropriations and to work towards total protection. Grazing of stock has already been entirely eliminated. The latest information (November 1966) is that the total amount allocated by that date had been brought up to 24 million drachmas.

b) Area : 800 ha, but an increase to 4,500 ha is under consideration.

c) Staff : 2 units.

d) Budget : in addition to the annual salary of the two wardens, there have been the large special allocations referred to above.

Date established : 1953. The Reserve is also referred to as the Coutsogerako and also the Lévka Ori (white mountains) reserve.

Land tenure : the original 800 ha have long been state owned. As already mentioned, substantial sums have been made available to bring a much larger area into public ownership, which is why in some quarters the reserve is already being referred to as a ' National Park '.

Tourism : no restrictions; accommodation is to be found in the neighbouring villages of Samaria, Agia Roumeli and Agios Loannis.

Altitude : 800-2,200 m.

a) A mountainous area with precipitous escarpments; the Mediterranean vegetation includes the funeral cypress *Cupressus sempervirens,* a variety of Aleppo pine *Pinus halepensis* var. *brutia,* Kermes oak and rock rose *Cistus* spp.

b) Cretan wild goat.

5. ANTIMILOS ISLAND RESERVE.

a) Status : total protection; an uninhabited island with no access for tourists. It is uncertain whether, as assumed here, another reserve, the Erimomilos Island Reserve (stated to have been established in 1962, to be 750 ha in extent and near sea level), is only a part of the Antimilos reserve or whether it is situated on a different and much smaller island closer to the main island of Milos. Some confusion is apparent in the details supplied by the Greek authorities and it is possible that two separate reserves should be listed, as was done in the case of the French version of this edition of the List.

b) Area : quoted as 800 ha, but probably nearer 2,000 ha.

c) Staff : a forest guard who lives on Milos.

d) Budget : covering salary and patrol expenses.

Date established : 1937.

Land tenure : the last private property was bought out in 1956 and the whole island is now state owned.

Tourism : not allowed and there is no accommodation even for research workers.

Altitude : sea level to 686 m.

a) Uninhabited island surrounded by steep cliffs; the Mediterranean vegetation includes juniper, mastic and rock rose.

243

b) Cretan wild goat have been introduced and crossed with domestic animals, becoming much too numerous so that measures are needed to control numbers. The same applies to rats (probably introduced accidentally) and to the cats which were introduced with the idea of keeping the rats under control.

V.   **Areas excluded :**

A. — Two National Parks : Olympus and Parnassus.

These two Parks, which were established in 1938 under the powers given by the 1937 Law quoted above, could not be kept protected during the War, with the result that the habitat was deforested, and otherwise exploited, and the fauna destroyed.

After the War the economic situation of the Communes in the neighbourhood of the Parks was so poor that it was considered impossible to compel the inhabitants to give up all occupation and exploitation of the areas, especially woodcutting and grazing of stock.

It seems that it would nevertheless still be possible to find and demarcate a thousand hectares in each of the Parks (which originally comprised 3,000 ha, plus 4,000 ha protective zone) and to make them into viable reserves, but although this is under consideration, it is clear that the two famous names of Olympus and Parnassus cannot yet qualify for inclusion in the List.

B. — The Pindus National Park.

In 1962 it was decided at Athens to undertake a survey in the Pindus mountain chain, on the borders of Thessaly and Epirus, where a very beautiful area estimated at 45,000 ha was thought to possess a combination of circumstances favourable to the creation of a great National Park, including an unspoilt landscape and not much pressure of human population. Three initial studies were financed by the Ministry of Co-ordination, which resulted in the selection and description of two perimeters, situated some fifty kilometres apart, and in the withdrawal of certain rights, notably that of woodcutting, which had been previously recognised by the State because of the bad economic situation of the local Communes, but which it was now in the position to cancel or buy out. The whole project is still going ahead and a preparatory Commission has been set up to bring it to a successful conclusion, but the stage has not yet been reached where the Pindus National Park can be justifiably included in the List.

C. — Twelve Reserves :

1. Mount Ainos (Cephalonia) . ...   2,500 ha
   It had been the original intention that this area should become the fifth of the five National Parks envisaged by the 1937 Law (together with Parnes, Samarias, Olympus and Parnassus), but its status and supervision have not yet been sufficiently restored from the damage caused by the War, to justify inclusion in the List.
2. Dérion (Thrace)   . ...   500 ha
3. Dragouteli (Chalcidice)   ...   .   2,500 ha
4. Kirkini (Thessalonica) . ...   2,500 ha
5. Skotina (Macedonia) ...   .   3,000 ha
6. Mavrovouni (Thessaly)   ...   .   3,000 ha
7. Mount Oeta (Thessaly) ...   .   3,000 ha
8. Mount Parnon (Peloponnese) ...   .   2,500 ha

9. Sapienza Island (off the S.W. Peloponnese) . ...   6,000 ha
   All the above eight areas are in fact merely hunting reserves, mainly for the protection of red deer.
10. Theodora Island (Crete) ... ...   70 ha
   This small island is of interest as the site of an effort to raise a stock of Cretan wild goats.
11. The Tsamliki Site (on the island of Mytilene or Lesbos). A petrified forest of 3,450 ha, made into a reserve in 1966.
12. The Nestos Marsh (on the Bulgarian frontier); also made into a reserve in 1966.

49. GUATEMALA

Listed Areas : four.

1. Rio Dulce National Park.
2. Santa Rosalia National Park.
3. Atitlan National Park.
4. Naciones Unidas National Park.

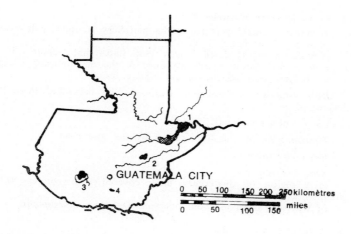

General Introduction :

The legislative basis for the Parks is a Law of 1949, authorising the Minister of Agriculture to apply certain conservation measures — restriction of wood-cutting, cultivation of slopes, grazing of stock, etc. — in selected zones. The areas are administered by the National Park Department of the Ministry of Agriculture's Direccion General Forestal.

The four listed parks, together with those excluded from the List, were described in E/3436 of the previous edition.

245

GUATEMALA

Details : application of criteria (II), general information (III) and description (IV) :

1. RIO DULCE NATIONAL PARK.

II.   *a*) Status : general protection, no hunting, wood-cutting or quarrying; no inhabitations.
  b) Area : about 20,000 ha; demarcation has not yet been completed.
  c) Staff : 2 supervisors and 2 forest guards.
  d) Budget : covering staff salaries.

III.   *Date established :* 1955.

  Land tenure : state ownership.

  Tourism : no organisation. Access by rail.

  Research : no systematic scientific work.

IV.   *Altitude :* 15 m.
  a) A flat region, with a hot damp climate, comprising Lake Izabel, the Rio Dulce and its mouth (where it enters the Atlantic near the ruins of San Felipe castle); luxuriant vegetation (giant trees, ferns, orchids); the plains are covered with mahogany *Swietenia mahogani,* Spanish cedar *Cedrela mexicana, Vochisia guatemalensis, Virola koschnyi* and *Calophyllum brasiliensis.*
  b) Whitetail deer *Odocoileus virginianus,* puma *Felis concolor,* the Central American tapir *Tapirus bairdii,* Central American spider monkey *Ateles geoffroyi,* North American raccoon *Procyon lotor;* rich tropical avifauna (toucans, egrets, etc.).
  c) Central American tapir.

2. SANTA ROSALIA NATIONAL PARK.

II.   *a*) Status : general protection; the periphery is under cultivation.
  b) Area : 4,061 ha.
  c) Staff : a report dated March 1966 states that " control is exercised by supervisors and forest guards stationed in the neighbouring villages ".
  d) Budget : staff salaries should meet criterion.

III.   *Date established :* 1956 (not included, like the other three Parks, in the Decree of 26 May 1955).

  Land tenure : national property.

  Tourism : no organisation; access by rail and road.

  Research : none.

IV.   *Altitude :* 320 m.
  a) A region of quaternary hills, covered with conifers (*Pinus oocarpa* dominant).
  b) Whitetail deer, raccoon, opossum *Didelphis marsupialis.*

3. ATITLAN NATIONAL PARK.

II.   *a*) Status : the law provides general protection, but it has only been possible for the area, which is fully inhabited and exploited for tourism, to be kept in the List in the light of information that quite close to habitations the natural associations have not been and are still not being seriously disturbed by man.
  b) Area : unknown; the park has never been demarcated.
  c) and *d*) Staff and budget : as for No. 2.

III.   *Date established :* 1955.

  Land tenure : municipal ownership, but not yet demarcated.

Tourism : the beauty of the lake, to which access is available by air and road, together with the folklore and traditions of the long-established Indian settlements on the shores, make this area a centre of the greatest attraction to tourists. There are a score of hotels, some of them very modern; lake excursions by boat are organised.

Research : no special facilities or activities.

Altitude : 1,558 m.

a) A mountainous region composed of basalts and andesite formations; Lake Atitlan is surrounded with active volcanoes, the slopes of which are covered by forest (pine, cypressus and oak), meadows, moss and lichen.

b) Whitetail deer, the eastern cottontail *Sylvilagus floridanus,* the squirrel *Sciurus deppei*; the endemic Atitlan or giant pied-billed grebe *Podilymbus gigas*.

c) Atitlan grebe.

4. NACIONES UNIDAS NATIONAL PARK.

a) Status : the law provides general protection, but in fact this area is only protected in the sense that it is kept for experimental work in reafforestation (eucalypts etc.) under the management of the School of Forestry. Its inclusion in the List is, however, deemed to be justified by the effectiveness of supervision.

b) Area : uncertain; 450 ha or, according to a report received in February 1966, 9,125 ha.

c) and *d)* Staff and budget : see under Status.

Date established : 1955.

Land tenure : state ownership.

Tourism : the town of Amatitlan is nearby and no special organisation is necessary; access by road with fine views over Lake Amatitlan.

Research : conducted by School of Forestry.

Altitude : 1,200-1,650 m.

a) A mountainous region with a comparatively cool climate; reafforestation with cypressus, eucalyptus and casuarina is being undertaken.

b) Eastern cottontail, eastern pocket gopher ('taltuza') *Geomys* sp., raccoon, grey fox *Urocyon cinereoargenteus*.

Areas excluded :

1. Cerro del Baúl National Park; 1955.

2. Cerro Miramundo National Park; 1956; 900 ha.

3. El Pino National Park or Estate; 1955; 518 ha; this is an old German-owned property used for grazing and other exploitation (saw-mill) and therefore degraded.

4. El Reformador National Park; 1955; situated in a built-up area.

5. La Laguna El Pino National Park; 1955.

6. Los Aposentos National Park; 1955; 45 ha.

7. Tikal National Park; 1955; 57,600 ha; chiefly of archeological interest. This Park might eventually be included in the List if adequate information could be obtained on its status, area, staff and budget, since it is stated to have an interesting fauna (puma, jaguar *Panthera onca,* ocelot *Felis pardalis,* agouti *Dasyprocta* sp., tapir, etc.).

I.   **Listed Areas :** one.

1. The Nimba Mountains Strict Natural Reserve.

General Introduction :

This Reserve was included and described in both E/3436 and Part Two of the previous edition of the List.

Details : application of criteria (II), general information (III) and description (IV) :

1. THE NIMBA MOUNTAINS STRICT NATURAL RESERVE.

II.   *a*) Status : the strict natural reserve status is weakened by the exception made for prospecting for minerals, with all that is inevitably involved in the

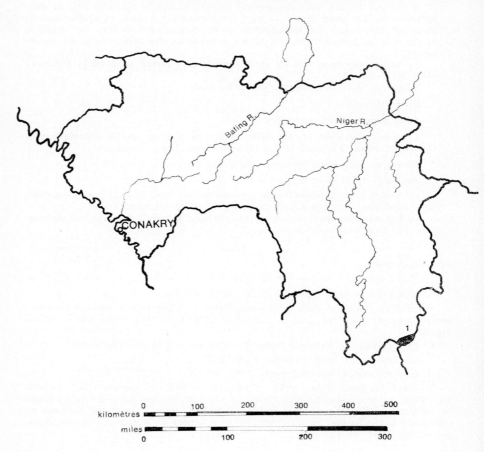

way of disturbances from the presence of prospectors (e.g. jeep tracks and the issue at Konakry of permits for sport-hunting which cover shooting in parts of the Reserve). The threat is accentuated by the proximity of the Liberian spurs of the Nimba, where the mining of iron ore is being undertaken by an international Mining Consortium. However, the latter is displaying an active interest in the protection of nature in that sector, which it is to be hoped may eventually be copied in Guinea.

b) Area : 13,000 ha.

c) Staff : 35 units, including 6 guards (1960).

d) Budget : of the order of U.S. $ 6,000.

Date established : 1944.

Administration : responsibility for supervision lies with the Regional Inspectorate of the department of Eaux et Forêts in collaboration with the I.N.R.D.G. (Institut National de Recherches et de Documentation de Guinée), the latter also being responsible for scientific work in the Reserve.

Land tenure : state ownership.

Tourism : none, in view of the Strict Natural Reserve status.

Research : the I.N.R.D.G. maintains the Nimba Mountains National Scientific Station, which comprises a laboratory, library and equipment, but is not permanently staffed, although visiting research workers often use it. A large number of publications have appeared (over 100 titles), mostly in the form of papers in the I.F.A.N. Bulletin and Memoranda.

Altitude : 500-1,752 m.

a) The Nimba Mountains are a narrow rectangular barrier running south-west to north-east, about 50 km in length, rising in the middle of an extensive plateau; the plinth of the ridge is at a ruling level of 1,000-1,200 m. The mountains are encircled with forest, tending on the northern side to break down into patches of savannah, but above this the rectangular summit ridge, some 15 km in length, is covered with a type of low bush, often called high-altitude grassland or prairie. On the south-west up to 700 or 800 m is dense primary forest of an ombrophile or mesophile type and secondary forest dominated by oil-palms; tongues of this forest go as high as 1,200 m or more, in the form of gallery-forest along the drainage lines. The north-eastern slopes, which are strongly lateritic, are dominated by tropophile forest — between 900 and 1,750 m mainly grassland savannah (in which the dominant grass *Loudetia kagerensis* HUBBARD is typical) and stunted prairie on the laterite shields, while between 1,500 and 1,600 m there are remnants of forest with such species as the closely related fruiting trees of the myrtle family, *Syzygium staudtii* and *Eugenia leonensis*, and in the beds of the ravines good stands of the tree-fern *Cyathea mannii*. Among rarer species is the heath *Blaeria mannii*, which is found on the rocky scarps of the summit ridge. Altogether the Guinean sector of the Nimba Mountains Reserve is generally considered by naturalists to be the most interesting.

b) Chimpanzee *Pan troglodytes*, a pygmy race of buffalo *Syncerus caffer*; the viviparous toad *Nectophrynoides occidentalis* (endemic).

Areas excluded : nil.

I.   **Listed Areas :** one.

      1. The Kaieteur National Park.

General Introduction :

    Administration : the responsibility of the Commissioner for the Interior exercised through the Commission of Lands and Mines.

The Park was listed in E/3436 of the previous edition.

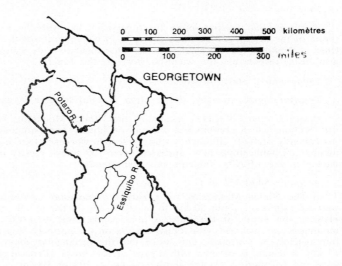

Details : application of criteria (II), general information (III) and description (IV) :

    1. THE KAIETEUR NATIONAL PARK.

II.   *a*) Status : total protection is accorded by the Kaieteur National Park Ordinance " ... unlawful to hunt and disturb animal life, to gather flora, to disturb the soil by mining or construction... ".

    b) Area : 11,655 ha.

    c) Staff : three units.

    d) Budget : U.S. $ 1,700 (B.W.I. $ 3,000).

III.   *Date established :* 1929.

    Land tenure : public ownership.

    Tourism : access is by water (Potaro river) and by air; accommodation for fifty persons.

    Research : no specific organisation.

IV.   *Altitude :* 100-500 m.

    a) Forested area bordering the Potaro, Mure Mure and Elinku rivers, famous in particular for the Kaieteur Falls (225 m high); the heavy soils of the gorges

250

support humid tropical forest and the sandy soils dry forest, dominated by the wallaba tree *Eperua*; savannah on the plateaux above the gorges. *Bauhinia* and *Utricularia humboldti* occur near the Falls.

b) Jaguar *Panthera onca*, ocelot *Felis pardalis*, tapir *Tapirus terrestris*, deer, sloths, opossum *Didelphis* sp., otter *Lutra* sp.; a rich avifauna; toucans, parrots, trumpeter *Psophia* sp., curassow *Crax* sp., tinamou *Crypturellus variegatus*.

Areas excluded : nil.

52. HAITI

Listed Areas : nil.

Explanation :

No replies to official enquiries have been received from Port-au-Prince, but in a report presented by the Forest Section of the Department of Natural Resources and Rural Development (Damien, Haiti) to a symposium of the Latin-American Committee on National Parks, one reads... " but without pessimism it is believed that a great effort has still to be made before National Parks are established ".

53. HONDURAS

Listed Areas : nil.

Explanation :

No reply has been received from the authorities or individuals consulted in letters adressed to Tegucigalpa. The nil return is based on information supplied by visitors to the country.

54. HONG KONG

Listed Areas : nil.

Explanation :

Although the previous edition of the List, E/3436, referred briefly to six protected areas, the exclusion of these from the present List is justified by a statement made at the Bangkok Conference on Conservation of Nature and Natural Resources held in December 1965.

According to this, there is a great need for strict protective measures in still quite extensive wild or rural areas, 86 % if the 1,031.5 km² of the territory, part of which is very rugged and covered with grassland, scrub and woodland. Only such measures could prevent the total disappearance of the fauna, which is a prey to hunters and poachers, and are particularly required to protect the catchments of the domestic water-supplies of the built-up areas which have had an increase of more than a million inhabitants in the last ten years. Regulations exist, but they are not enforced.

Several projects for Reserves are under consideration. Despite the small area and enormous population of Hong Kong, there is a distinct possibility that, in order to provide a recreation area for the citizens, a national park of some tens of thousands of hectares could be established in the Sai Kung peninsula (on the extreme east of the New Territories). It would be divided into three zones, one of which would be given protection fully up to the standards laid down by the ICNP.

Other projects under consideration include :

Sharp Island (due east of Sai Kung).
Tung Lung Island (east of Hong Kong Island).
Mai Po Marshes (on the north-western frontier).
Lantau (the largest island of the archipelago, situated due west of Hong Kong Island : a reserve is planned at the western end).
Stonecutters' Island (harbour area).
Tai Mo Shan (summit area of this, the highest, peak in the New Territories).

55. HUNGARY

I. **Listed Areas** : six.

    A. — NATIONAL PARKS.
      1. Tihany National Park.

    B. — RESERVES.
      2. Little Balaton Reserve.
      3. The Baradla Stalagmite Cave, Aggtelek-Jósvafö.
      4. The Cave of Peace.
      5. Szalajka Valley.
      6. Lake Velence.

General Introduction :

Legislative basis : Legal Decree No. 18 of 1961, Conservation of Nature, enacted by the Praesidium of the Hungarian People's Republic and brought into effect by Governmental decree No. 23/1962/VI.17.

Administration : the responsibility of a National Office for Nature Conservation operating under the supervision of the Council of Ministers. Its duties are defined as all action relevant to nature conservation, including the proclamation and cancellation of natural reserves, and it keeps an eye on the maintenance, conservation and administration of everything pertaining to a reserved area. It is also responsible for publishing the results of conservation activities and studies and for disseminating the principles of conservation among the general public. Except where otherwise provided, the actual management of reserves falls, in the first instance, on the agricultural section of the executive committee of the local departmental Council concerned (e.g. of Budapest). The National Office thus plays a secondary, supporting role in management matters.

Land tenure : all the Reserves and a considerable section of the Tihany National Park are under state ownership.

Tourism : except for the scientific Reserves (Little Balaton, Lake Velence), systematically organised and encouraged in many of the others (e.g. the Szalajka Valley). Visits are accompanied by guide-lecturers for educational purposes and numerous pamphlets are distributed or sold to tourists. Conferences are often held.

Scientific research : carried out by the national scientific institutions (universities and museums), under the general direction of the National Office for Nature Conservation and at centres built through its initiative (land-research laboratories, etc.).

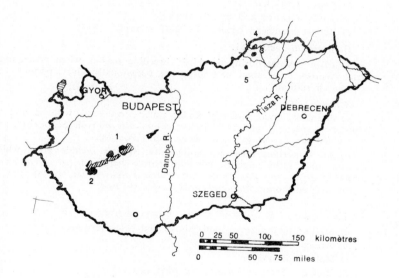

Details : application of criteria (II), general information (III) and description (IV) :

A. — NATIONAL PARKS.

1. TIHANY NATIONAL PARK.

   a) Status : total protection, except for certain user rights in the vicinity of Tihany village which is situated within the Park.

   b) Area : 1,100 ha.

   c) Staff : a Director and two wardens.

   d) Budget : criterion covered by staff salaries.

253

III.   *Date established :* 1952.

Tourism : the Park is open to tourists, for whom paths are provided. There are a number of historic and prehistoric (bronze age) sites; also a research station.

IV.   *Altitude :* 232 m.

a) A volcanic region with an extinct mud-volcano, old geyser cones, hot springs and lakes, which projects as a peninsula into Lake Balaton. Some cultivation and forest exploitation are carried on by the Tihany villagers.

b) There is nothing unusual about the fauna, the protection of which is not a particular aim of the Park.

B. — RESERVES.

2. LITTLE BALATON (KISBALATON) RESERVE.

II.   *a)* Status : strict natural reserve, even visits for scientific purposes being subject to special permit. A limited amount of reed and sedge cutting is however still allowed.

b) Area : 1,403 ha.

c) Staff : a factor and two wardens.

d) Budget : criterion covered by staff salaries.

III.   *Date established :* 1951.

Tourism : except during the birds' breeding season, when protection is very strict, visitors other than naturalists are occasionally given permits. There is a research station.

IV.   *Altitude :* 105 m.

a) A marsh area, formerly under water; reed-beds, willows and meadows (dominant species : reeds *Phragmites communis,* bulrush *Schoenoplectus lacustris,* reedmace *Typha* spp. and sedge *Carex riparia*).

b) An important area ornithologically; species include great white heron *Egretta alba,* little egret *E. garzetta,* purple heron *Ardea purpurea,* squacco heron *Ardeola ralloides,* spoonbill *Platalea leucorodia,* glossy ibis *Plegadis falcinellus,* cormorant *Phalacrocorax carbo sinensis.*

3. THE BARADLA STALAGMITE CAVE, AGGTELEK-JÓSVAFÖ.

II.   *a)* Status : total reserve, both above and below ground.

b) Area : 778 ha.

c) Staff : one warden.

d) Budget : criterion covered by staff salary.

III.   *Date established :* 1951 as far as the cavern itself is concerned; 1958 for the environs of the entrance.

Tourism : control of visitors to the cave is in the hands of the Tourist Office (IBUSZ) of the local government of Borsod-Abauj-Zemplén, conservation being the responsibility of the National Office. There is a biological research station in the cave.

IV.   *Altitude :* 350 m.

a) The cavern is 15 km in length, with numerous side-galleries and formations of a typical karstic type.

b) Common cavernicolous fauna.

4. THE CAVE OF PEACE (BEKEBARLANG).

a) Status : total protection.

b) Area : 643 ha.

c) Staff : one warden.

d) Budget : criterion covered by staff salary.

Date established : 1953 (the date of its discovery).

Tourism : this cave is in the same area as the Baradla Cave (No. 3 above) and is under the same management and control.

Altitude : 370 m.

a) Calcareous formations similar to those of the neighbouring Baradla Cave.

b) Common cavernicolous fauna.

5. SZALAJKA VALLEY.

a) Status : total protection.

b) Area : 558 ha.

c) Staff : one warden.

d) Budget : criterion covered by staff salary.

Date established : 1955.

Tourism : visited by a very large number of tourists every year.

Altitude : highest point 959 m.

a) A mountainous area traversed by a stream with numerous falls and calcareous tufa formations : beechwoods in the valley and oakwoods on the drier slopes, with bracken Pteris aquilinum along the river banks. There is a palaeo-lithic site.

b) The fauna consists of common small species.

6. LAKE VELENCE.

a) Status : strict natural reserve, entry by permit only.

b) Area : 420 ha.

c) Staff : a factor and one warden.

d) Budget : criterion covered by staff salaries.

Date established : 1958.

Tourism : a few visitors are allowed in this Reserve.

Altitude : 104 m.

a) A lake surrounded by reed-beds.

b) An important ornithological area, the great white heron being the most prized of the 28 breeding species.

Areas excluded :

Some 18 Reserves, which were named and described in the previous edition of the List, E/3436, are excluded by the fact that they are all smaller in size than the standard laid down by the International Commission on National Parks.

255

9

HUNGARY

At the conference of the European Continental Section of the International Council for Bird Preservation held at Balatonzemes in May 1968, the Minister of Agriculture announced the decision to establish a new National Park in the Hortobágy area of the Hungarian *puszta*. As probably the most important central European breeding and feeding area for waders, herons and birds of prey, as well as being a resting-place for vast numbers of migratory geese, the importance of this park cannot be exaggerated and, when establishment is complete and the details available, it will certainly merit an honourable place in the List.

56. ICELAND

I.   **Listed Areas :** two.

1. Thingvellir National Park.
2. Eldey Nature Reserve.

General Introduction :

Details of a third area, which probably now qualifies for inclusion in the List, the Skaftafell National Park, have not yet been obtained. A project for supporting the establishment of this Park by the purchase of land was launched by the World Wildlife Fund in 1962 and a report by the Secretary-General of the Fund dated 11 April 1967 states that it has been completed. Pending information on the various points relevant to inclusion in the List, the new Park, which has been described as one of the largest individual conservation achievements in Europe of recent years, is retained in Section V.

Both the areas accepted for the List were included in Part Two of the previous edition.

Details : application of criteria (II), general information (III) and description (IV) :

1. THINGVELLIR NATIONAL PARK.

II.   *a)* Status : in principle one of total protection, but some qualifications have to be made. Thus, though there is no cultivation, some haymaking is practised and, in places, there are exploited conifer plantations; there is shooting during the winter in some sections of the Park and the lake is fished. A stricter regime is reported to be proposed and certainly needs to be applied if this area is to be kept in the List.

b) Area : 4,000 ha.

c) Staff : one superintendent.

d) Budget : U.S. $ 25,000.

III.   *Date established :* 1928.

Legislative basis : a Parliamentary decision made in 1928. The Park does not come within the ambit of the more recently (1956) enacted Protection of Nature Act.

256

Administration : in the hands of a special committee elected by the Althing (Parliament) and presided over by the Chief State Architect. The National Council for Nature Protection has nothing to do with the administration of this National Park, the siting of which was mainly influenced by the desire to give the status of a National Sanctuary to the famous and historic spot where the Icelandic chiefs first met in council in the year 930 A.D.

Land tenure : state ownership.

Tourism : this Park is a great tourist attraction, with no restriction on entry. There is no accommodation in the Park but Reykjavik is only 50 km away.

Research : not specifically organised.

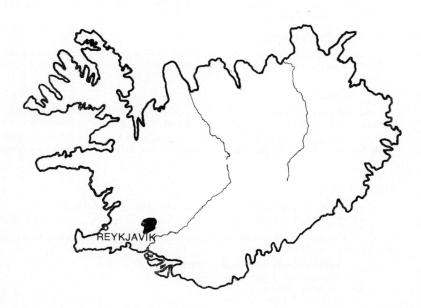

Altitude : 103-140 m.

a) Part of a very fine volcanic landscape, comprising a tectonic trench overlaid with successive lava flows and split by fissures, typical of the post-glacial era; this ' graben' formation is bounded on the west by a fault in which the displacement or ' throw' is no less than 40 m high, resulting in the famous falls of the River Oxara; the level ground between the faults is largely covered by dwarf birch *Betula,* while the woolly-fringed moss *Rhacomitrium lanuginosum* is also a feature of the vegetation.

b) The Thingvallavatn, Iceland's largest lake, which borders the reserve, contains large numbers of trout *Salmo trutta.*

257

2. ELDEY NATURE RESERVE.

II.   *a*) Status : total protection.

b) Area : 1.5 ha; the reserve has nevertheless been accepted for the List, at the request of the Icelandic authorities, because of its high biological importance.

c) Staff : no full-time supervision is provided, but the island is inspected from time to time from the air.

d) Budget : covering supervision as indicated above.

III.   *Date established :* 1940.

Legal basis : a special act of parliament in 1940; the Nature Reserve status was conferred in 1960 under the Protection of Nature Act of 1956.

Administration : by the seven member National Council for Nature Protection set up by the 1956 legislation.

Land tenure : state ownership.

Tourism : the problem of visitors to this precipitous and inaccessible little island does not arise. No special arrangements have been made for research work.

IV.   *Altitude :* sea level to 77 m.

a) This small rocky island with its precipitous cliffs lies 14 km to the south west of Reykjanes, the south-westernmost point of the main island.

b) The gannet *Sula bassana* here has its biggest breeding colony (11,000 nests) in Iceland. This was also the last refuge of the extinct great auk *Alca impennis*.

V.   **Areas excluded :**

A. — Projects nearing completion (see General Introduction) :
1. Skaftafell National Park ... ...   500,000 ha

B. — Projects which are to be implemented when the Skaftafell Park has been established :
2. Jökulsa Canyon National Park.
3. Thjorsarver Nature Reserve.
4. Hellisey Nature Reserve.
5. Surtsey Nature Reserve ... ...   270 ha

C. — Partial Reserves :
6. Thjorsardalur . ...   12,500 ha, established 1938.
7. Thorsmörk ... ...   1,500 ha, established 1925.
8. Hallormstaour ... ...   600 ha, established 1905.
9. Asbyrgi ... ...   320 ha, established 1928.
10. Vaglir ... ...   300 ha, established 1909.

Listed Areas : fourteen.

Assam	1. Manas Wild Life (¹) Sanctuary.
	2. Kaziranga Wild Life Sanctuary.
Bihar	3. Hazaribagh National Park.
Gujarat	4. Gir Wild Life Sanctuary.
Kerala	5. Periyar Wild Life Sanctuary.
Maharashtra	6. Taroba National Park.
Madhya Pradesh	7. Kanha National Park.
	8. Shivpuri National Park.
Tamilnadu (Madras)	9. Mudumalai Wild Life Sanctuary.
Mysore	10. Bandipur Wild Life Sanctuary.
Rajasthan	11. Sariska Wild Life Sanctuary.
	12. Jaisamand Wild Life Sanctuary.
Uttar Pradesh	13. Corbett National Park.
West Bengal	14. Jaldapara Wild Life Sanctuary.

General Introduction :

Due to the population density in most of India and to the need for the greatest possible utilisation of the country's natural resources, it has not usually been possible to establish natural reserves of any great size nor to ban completely the exploitation of forest cover in national parks and equivalent reserves. For this reason, where with the agreement of the Indian authorities areas have been accepted for the List and credited with 'total protection', it must be understood that this status, though rather more strictly maintained in the National Parks than in the Wild Life Sanctuaries, does not necessarily exclude the exploitation of forests at least in certain zones and under scientific control; the term 'exploitation' includes forest management and re-planting. In order to offset the disturbance caused by these activities, provision is made for certain areas to be kept strictly protected, which are known as "inner sanctuaries" or "abhayaranya". In theory grazing of domestic stock is forbidden in the national parks and sanctuaries but in practice is difficult to suppress.

The establishment and administration of national parks and equivalent reserves in India is constitutionally the prerogative of each State.

Nevertheless the central Government of the Indian Union took certain steps in 1957 to promote some degree of uniformity and in particular to ensure that any 'National Park established in a State must justify that title'. For this purpose a 'Model Bill for the constitution of National Parks' was proposed, in order to serve as a basis for enactments by the various local legislatures. In 1964, a 'National Parks Policy' and 'Standards for National Parks in India' were drawn up, approved and communicated to all State Governments and it was decided that only those protected areas which conformed to the standards laid down and were approved by the central organisation known as the Indian Board for Wild Life, could be upgraded to the status of National Parks by State legislation.

At the central government level the Ministry of Food and Agriculture has the responsibility for all problems affecting "national parks, reserves, wild animals and forests". Its chief adviser is the Inspector General of Forests and there is an Indian Board for Wild Life, which was responsible, in particular, for drawing up a definition of 'National Park' at its inaugural session in 1952 (reconstituted 1969).

(¹) The Indian authorities prefer 'Wild Life' to the single word 'Wildlife'.

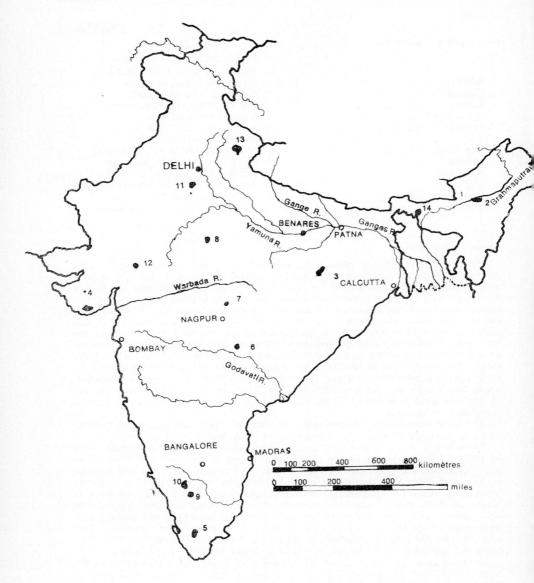

The States also have consultative bodies equivalent to the Wild Life Board and most of them also employ a State Wild Life Officer and in some areas have already established a Wild Life Department. In Rajasthan no Wild Life Officer has been appointed and no separate Department has been established, as distinct from the State Forest Department; however, some members of the State Wild Lif

Board have been appointed as Honorary Game Wardens for the various sanctuaries (including one Chief Wild Life Warden).

In general the difference between a National Park and a Sanctuary is simply one of the method by which it was created, national parks being set up by an Act of the State Legislature and sanctuaries by an executive order.

The land of the Parks and sanctuaries is usually state-owned forest-land. Provision is made for tourists who are encouraged. As for research, Universities and similar institutions are the operative bodies although the Indian and State Boards for Wild Life endeavour to secure co-ordination.

All the fourteen listed areas were included in the previous edition of the List, E/3436.

Details : application of criteria (II), general information (III) and description (IV) :

1. MANAS WILD LIFE SANCTUARY (Assam) ([1]).

   a) Status : general protection.
   b) Area : 27,195 ha.
   c) Staff : 57 units, including 8 Forest Guards and 22 Game Watchers.
   d) Budget : U.S. $ 3,100, about $ 2,000 of it for staff salaries (1966-1967).

   Date established : 1928, enlarged in 1965.

   Tourism : also known as the North Kamrup Sanctuary and under consideration for being raised in status to a National Park; no staff are specially allocated for tourist promotion.

   Altitude : 75-225 m.

   a) Situated north of the Brahmaputra in the foothills near the Bhutan border; the northern part is forested, the south has grassy plains and reed-beds.
   b) Great Indian rhinoceros *Rhinoceros unicornis,* buffalo *Bubalus bubalis,* gaur *Bos gaurus,* hog deer *Axis porcinus,* muntjac *Muntiacus muntjak,* black bear *Selenarctos thibetanus,* tiger *Panthera tigris*; plentiful birdlife.
   c) The great Indian rhinoceros.

2. KAZIRANGA WILD LIFE SANCTUARY (Assam).

   a) Status : general protection.
   b) Area : 42,994 ha, plus a no-shooting buffer-zone of 16,825 ha.
   c) Staff : 122 units, including 21 Forest Guards and 26 Game Watchers.
   d) Budget : U.S. $ 7,250, of which $ 3,300 is allocated to salaries (1966-1967).

   Date established : 1908.

   Tourism : this sanctuary, also, is under consideration by the Government for National Park status; two guest-houses just outside the park and a rest camp; within its boundaries; jeepable tracks; game viewing on elephant-back.

   Altitude : averaging 75 m.

   a) South bank of the Brahmaputra river, largely covered in herbage.

([1]) There is no doubt that the immediately adjoining Manas Sanctuary of the Kingdom of Bhutan should have a place in the List as soon as full details are available. Established in July 1966 and extending over 41,934 ha of forested foothills, it is of great scientific interest, not least as the habitat of the unique golden langur *Presbytis geei.*

b) Great Indian rhinoceros, elephant *Elephas maximus*, buffalo, hog deer, muntjac, swamp deer or barasingha *Cervus duvauceli*, wild pig *Sus scrofa*, tiger, leopard *Panthera pardus*, bear.

c) Great Indian rhinoceros, swamp deer.

3. HAZARIBAGH NATIONAL PARK (Bihar).

II.

a) Status : general protection.

b) Area : 18,636 ha; originally 38,828 ha, but half has been excised for administrative reasons.

c) Staff : 14 units, including 10 Forest Guards.

d) Budget : U.S. $ 6,400 (inclusive of salaries).

III.   *Date established :* 1955.

IV.   *Altitude :* 480-600 m.

a) Hills covered with dense jungle, mainly of sal trees *Shorea robusta*.

b) Tiger, leopard, sloth bear *Melursus ursinus*, muntjac, wild pig, hyaena *H. hyaena*, sambar *Cervus unicolor*; peafowl *Pavo cristatus*, red jungle-fowl *Gallus gallus*, green pigeon *Crocopus phoenicopterus* and partridges.

4. GIR WILD LIFE SANCTUARY (Gujarat).

II.

a) Status : total protection, no shooting allowed.

b) Area : 126,422 ha.

c) Staff : forest guards under a Superintendent.

d) Budget : there are still no funds specifically allocated.

III.   *Date established :* with full sanctuary status from 18 September 1965.

Tourism : accommodation consists of a 15-bed Forest Guest House; there are also vehicles to transport visitors in search of the lions.

IV.   *Altitude :* 61-122 m.

a) Arid stunted jungle.

b) Lion *Panthera leo persica*, leopard, sambar, wild pig, sloth bear, hyaena, nilgai *Boselaphus tragocamelus*, chinkara *G. gazella bennetti*, chital or spotted deer *A. axis*, four-horned antelope *Tetracetus quadricornis*; many species of birds including large number of peafowl.

c) Asiatic lion (the greater part of the surviving world population of this subspecies).

5. PERIYAR WILD LIFE SANCTUARY (Kerala).

II.

a) Status : general protection (the Sanctuary comprises the catchment of a reservoir); sport-fishing is allowed in the lake.

b) Area : 77,000 ha.

c) Staff : 77 units, including 26 guards.

d) Budget : U.S. $ 38,500, of which $ 14,500 is allocated to staff salaries (1966-1967).

III.   *Date established :* 1940.

Tourism : the sanctuary is under consideration by the Government for conversion into a National Park; most of the staff is occupied with tourist promotion duties — including taking visitors' boat-trips on the reservoir, guides, interpretative services and if necessary going to the aid of anyone in difficulties. There are four two-roomed rest-houses, well-equipped and well-sited; four 'machan' for observing game; a first-class hotel and two bungalows with accommodation for 64 people. There are plans for more hotels and a landing-ground.

Altitude : 914-1,828 m.

a) Surroundings of an artificial reservoir, with bays, promontories and islands, wooded hills, valleys and grassy plains.

b) Elephant, gaur, sambar, muntjac, tiger, sloth bear, wild pig and black langur *Presbytis johni*; plentiful bird-life, including hornbills and grey jungle fowl *Gallus sonneratii*.

6. TAROBA NATIONAL PARK (Maharashtra).

a) Status : general protection.

b) Area : 11,654 ha. There is also a 15,000 ha protected zone surrounding the Park, in which shooting is prohibited.

c) Staff : 10 units, all members of the Forest Service.

d) Budget : U.S. $ 9,000 (of which $ 2,000 covers staff salaries).

Date established : as a sanctuary 1935, upgraded to National Park in 1955.

Tourism : a Forest Rest House and a Guest House, each with two comfortable apartments; there is a vehicle for viewing the Park equipped with spotlights, microphone and radio; four observation towers.

Altitude : averaging 335 m.

a) Fairly thick jungle surrounded by plains and lakes.

b) Tiger, leopard, sambar, chital, gaur; crocodiles.

7. KANHA NATIONAL PARK (Madhya Pradesh).

a) Status : general protection, but there is a village, the Kanha Forest village, in the middle of the Park and poaching is rife during the rains when motorised patrols cannot operate.

b) Area : 31,826 ha.

c) Staff : 6 units, including 2 foresters and 2 guards.

d) Budget : U.S. $ 7,500 (1964-1965).

Date established : as a Sanctuary under the title of the Banjar Valley in 1935, raised to National Park status with an area of 25,109 ha in 1955; and enlarged to its present size in 1964.

Tourism : there is a good comprehensive network of motor-tracks, but they cannot be used during the rains (July-November). There are two Forest Rest Houses with 4 apartments each; a cook is provided and food can be obtained. Guides, two game-viewing 'machan' or observation towers, dark-room. There is no charge for entry, but a small charge of U.S. cents 40 per day is made for the use of rest houses. Elephant-back excursions are arranged. An air landing-strip has been surveyed and cleared, but is not yet authorised for use.

Altitude : 525-870 m.

a) Comprises part of the upper Banjar valley, with hills and lakes, scattered 'sal' forests, big grassy plains, bamboo thicket on the hills.

b) Swamp deer or barasingha of the distinct subspecies *branderi* (favouring drier country), sambar, gaur, chital, blackbuck *Antilope cervicapra,* tiger, leopard; many species of birds, including peafowl, red jungle-fowl, grey jungle-fowl and several species of quail.

c) Barasingha.

8. SHIVPURI NATIONAL PARK (Madhya Pradesh).

II.
a) Status : general protection. This in effect continues the strict conservation which the area enjoyed when it was the private shooting-reserve of the Maharaja of Gwalior.

b) Area : 15,799 ha.

c) Staff : 7 units, including 3 Wild Life Watchers.

d) Budget U.S. $ 3,600 (1964-1965).

III.
Date established : 1955, under the name of Madhya Bharat National Park; became the Shivpuri National Park in 1959, simultaneously with the creation of the new State of Madhya Pradesh.

Tourism : various facilities for tourists are in the process of acquisition, such as the George Castle and Sultan Hotel Shooting Box, belonging to the Maharaja of Gwalior, the Sakkya Sagar Sailing Club, in private ownership, etc. Tigers can be photographed from the 'Shooting Box'. There are paddle-canoes and motor-canoes on the lake, picnic sites, an excellent road network and, in short, a very promising future from the tourist point of view.

IV.
Altitude : 390-480 m.

a) A region of hills and valleys in the Vindhyan range, with dry deciduous 'sal' jungle and some grassy plains.

b) Tiger, leopard, sloth bear, hyaena, sambar, chital, four-horned antelope, blackbuck, nilgai and chinkara; wild pig; numerous birds.

9. MUDUMALAI WILD LIFE SANCTUARY (Madras, now Tamilnadu).

II.
a) Status : general protection.

b) Area : 32,116 ha.

c) Staff : 31 units (3 Rangers, 10 Forest Guards and 18 Reserve Watchers).

d) Budget : U.S. $ 13,550 (1966-1967).

III.
Date established : 1940. The Sanctuary is under consideration for conversion to National Park status.

Tourism : there is a plan to build a " 20-room dormitory " in the Reserve; in the meantime there are three well-equipped rest houses (running water, refrigerator, good cooks, etc.). Elephant-back excursions are arranged. There are some 160 km of motor-track. A charge is made for entry. The best seasons for a visit are between February and May or September and November. The Sanctuary has an excellent reputation both in India and abroad.

IV.
Altitude : 914-1,260 m.

a) Situated not far from Bandipur Sanctuary (No. 10 in the List), but with a considerably higher rainfall and thicker jungle.

b) Elephant, gaur, tiger, leopard, sloth bear, chital, muntjac, sambar, four-horned antelope, hyaena, monkeys, squirrels, jackal *Canis aureus*, jungle cat *Felis chaus*, wild pig, otter *L. lutra*, crocodile, python *P. molurus*; very good birdlife, including peafowl, grey jungle-fowl, partridges and spurfowl *Galloperdix* sp., many birds of prey and song-birds.

10. BANDIPUR WIAD LIFE SANCTUARY (Mysore).

a) Status : general protection.

b) Area : 5,695 ha. In a letter of the 16 January 1965, the Secretary to the Government of Mysore quoted this figure, but added that proposals were on hand to extend the area. The Sanctuary forms part of Venugopal Wild Life Park, established in 1941, which extends over 310 sq.miles (80,244 ha), the figure quoted in the previous edition, E/3436, of the List.

c) Staff : 40 units, including 7 Game Watchers.

d) Budget : U.S. $ 22,000 including salaries.

Date established : 1941.

Tourism : there are plans to extend the reserve and to give it National Park status; at present none of the staff are specially allocated to tourist promotion duties.

Altitude : 1,020-1,223 m.

a) Somewhat stunted and sparse forest of teak *Tectona grandis* and various kinds of sandalwood, especially *Santalum album*; hills.

b) Elephant, sloth bear, tiger, leopard, sambar, chital, muntjac, gaur; plentiful birdlife including peafowl and jungle-fowl.

11. SARISKA WILD LIFE SANCTUARY (Rajasthan).

a) Status : general protection.

b) Area : 49,182 ha.

c) Staff : 20 units, including 8 Game Watchers.

d) Budget : U.S. $ 10,000, inclusive of staff salaries.

Date established : 1955, and re-declared in August 1958 under the Rajasthan Wild Animals and Birds Protection Act 1951.

Tourism : easy access by motor vehicle; observation towers (with a good chance of seeing tigers at a bait); the Sanctuary also has considerable archaeological interest, notably the Garh Temples (dating from 1,000 A.D.) and the Kankwari Fort. There are several forest rest-houses, equipped with electricity and a new tourist lodge (14 beds), opened in 1968.

Altitude : about 360 m.

a) Valleys and hills, covered with forest of *Anogeissus pendula*, the resinous *Boswellia serrata* and, in the valleys, ' dhak ' or flame-of-the-forest *Butea monosperma*; along streams the male bamboo *Dendrocalamus strictus*.

b) Tiger, leopard, sambar, chinkara, wild pig, four-horned antelope, nilgai, chital, palm civet *Paradoxurus hermaphroditus*, small Indian civet *Viverricula indica*, caracal *Felis caracal*, ratel *Mellivora capensis*, porcupine *Hystrix indica*, hyaena; peafowl, spurfowl and many other species of birds.

12. JAISAMAND WILD LIFE SANCTUARY (Rajasthan).

II.
    a) Status : general protection.

    b) Area : 5,267 ha.

    c) Staff : 14 units, including 12 Game Watchers.

    d) Budget : U.S. $ 3,000, including staff salaries (1966-1967).

III.
    Date established : 1955 (under the Rajasthan Wild Animals and Birds Protection Act of 1951).

    Tourism : facilities include good boating on the lake, which is overlooked by a beautifully situated resthouse.

IV.
    Altitude : 420 m.

    a) An area of hills and valleys, heavily wooded with mainly thorny species and bamboo on the hills; typical species of the jungle are the ' dhok ' *Anogeissus pendula, Boswellia serrata*, the Indian silk-cotton tree *Salmalia malabarica* and flame-of-the-forest.

    b) Tiger, leopard, sloth bear, sambar, chital, four-horned antelope, chinkara, wild pig; grey partridge *Francolinus pondicerianus*, spurfowl, quail, migratory duck in winter, minivets and other woodland birds.

13. CORBETT NATIONAL PARK (Uttar Pradesh).

II.
    a) Status : in theory total protection since 1955, but in several sectors the right to cut firewood still persists, which involves the presence of men and domestic stock; expulsion of the latter is rendered more difficult for reasons connected with religious beliefs. The general situation has considerably deteriorated recently in the west of the Park due to construction work on a barrage across the Ramganga river. The resulting reservoir will put about 50 km^2 of the Park under water, the trees in this area being scheduled for removal before the water rises. As a result of this development and the clearance of the timber, the western part of the Park is being disturbed by large numbers of people.

    b) Area : 52,547 ha; the disturbances noted under the previous sub-section have been offset by the recent inclusion in the Park of several adjacent " shooting blocks " which have brought the size of the Park from 32,375 ha up to the present size.

    c) Staff : 26 units, including 1 Wild Life Warden, 3 Assistant Wild Life Wardens and 14 Wild Life Guards.

    d) Budget : U.S. $ 15,000, covering maintenance of the Park, the Park roads and buildings, and staff salaries.

III.
    Date established : 1935, under the name of the Hailey National Park; re-named in 1957.

    Tourism : long-established organisation, but still being developed; it was expected that some U.S. $ 60,000 would be spent. Thus comfortable accommodation, which is plentiful (including 13 Forest Rest-Houses or tourist camps — Dhikala Camp being the most important), is being extended. Elephant-back excursions are arranged; there are observation towers, guides, sport-fishing, a " tiger training programme ", film shows, etc.

    Arising from the building of a large artificial lake on the west of the Park, a number of new developments are being planned, although it is hoped that the hotel-complex proposed for construction on the shores of the lake will be situated outside the Park boundaries.

IV.
  Altitude : 459-914 m.

  a) A broad valley and hills, with extensive grassy plains. The vegetation includes the shisham *Dalbergia sisso,* flame-of-the-forest, sal and the silk-cotton tree. There is a steep gorge through which the Ramganga river winds and the ravines are full of brackens, orchids and climbing tropical plants.

  b) Tiger, leopard, sloth bear, elephant, chital, sambar, hog deer, muntjac, wild pig, hyaena, jackal; red jungle-fowl, peafowl, black partridge *F. franco-linus*; osprey *Pandion haliaetus,* many song-birds; crocodile *Crocodilus palustris* and gharial *Gavialis gangeticus.*

  14. JALDAPARA WILD LIFE SANCTUARY (West Bengal).

II.
  a) Status : general protection.

  b) Area : 10,464 ha.

  c) Staff : 55 units, including 11 Forest Rangers or Deputy Forest Rangers and 20 Forest Guards.

  d) Budget : U.S. $ 20,000, of which $ 13,000 is allocated to salaries.

III.
  Date established : 1941; this Sanctuary, also, is under consideration for National Park status.

  Tourism : there is a tourist lodge and a second one is planned; riding elephants are available.

IV.
  Altitude : averaging 61 m.

  a) Riverine forest along the river Torsa and its tributaries; tall grass and scattered forest of simul and shisham.

  b) Great Indian rhinoceros, leopard, sambar, barasingha or swamp deer, a few elephant, tiger and bear. The rich birdlife includes peafowl and jungle-fowl.

  c) Great Indian rhinoceros (still a population of c. 80), barasingha (c. 12).

V.
  Areas excluded :

  1. One Sanctuary, namely the Bharatpur Bird Sanctuary, also known as the Keoladeo Ghana Bird Sanctuary, in Rajasthan, which like all the areas included in the List except those already given National Park status, was recommended in December 1963 for upgrading to a National Park, by the Indian Board for Wild Life. It is of about 2,800 ha and established in 1956, but in a letter dated 2 January 1965 the Indian authorities indicated that it does not yet qualify for inclusion in the List.

  2. One area in Maharashtra, near Bombay (forest-land, protecting part of the catchment of the city's water supplies). Its establishment under the name of 'Borivli National Park' was being very actively pursued at the end of 1969 : status - like that of many other sanctuaries in India, e.g. forest exploitation now ceased, but domestic stock yet to be withdrawn, etc.; size 6,929 ha; staff - a forest officer and 3 rangers (specially trained) plus 16 guards under a superintendent; budget to be fixed (but staff salaries should largely satisfy criterion); tropical moist deciduous woodland (sea level to 453 m); a few leopard and muntjac (re-introduction of other species planned); monkeys and birdlife plentiful.

3. Seventy-two Sanctuaries are listed by the Indian Board for Wild Life, but, except in the case of the 14 selected for the U.N. List, they are not considered to meet the criteria laid down for selection. Their distribution State by State is as follows :

Andhra Pradesh	6	Madras (Tamilnadu)	1
Assam	3	Manipur	1
Bihar	8	Mysore	3
Gujarat	1	Orissa	4
Himachal Pradesh	4	Punjab	5
Kashmir	([1]) 3	Rajasthan	5
Kerala	2	Uttar Pradesh	12
Madhya Pradesh	9	West Bengal	5

58. INDONESIA

I. **Listed Areas :** forty-one.

    A. — NATURE RESERVE.

        1. Udjung Kulon-Panaitan Nature Reserve.

    B. — RESERVES OF OVER 500 HA :

a) Java :
2. Nusa Barung.
3. Lautan Pasir, Tengger.
4. Kawah Idjen, Merapi.
5. Rawa Danau.
6. Ranu Kumbolo.
7. Tjibodas, Gunung Gede.
8. Nusakambangan.
9. Pulau Sempu.
10. Kawah Papandajan.
11. Ardjuna-Lalidjiwa.

b) Sumatra :
12. Gunung Indrapura (Kerintji).
13. Rimbopanti.
14. Krakatau mountain.

c) Kalimantan (Borneo) :
15. Pandang Luwai.

([1]) In December 1966, it was proposed to raise the status of one of the Kashmir reserves, the Dachigam sanctuary, to that of a national park in order to give adequate protection to the fast disappearing ‘ Kashmir stag ’, a race of red deer, *Cervus elaphus hanglu*, which is an IUCN ‘ Red Book ’ endangered species. But recent information does not suggest that the proposal has yet been effectively implemented.

d) Sulawesi (Celebes) :

    16. Gunung Tangkoko, Batuangus.
    17. Panua.

C. — Reserves of less than 500 ha :

a) Java :

    18. Pulau-Dua.
    19. Pulau-Bokor.
    20. Pulau-Rambut.
    21. Saobi.
    22. Ranu Darangan.
    23. Sigogor.
    24. Gunung Djagat.
    25. Takokak.
    26. Tjigenteng-Tjipanti.

b) Sumatra :

    27. Rafflesia Serbödjadi.
    28. Dolok Tinggi Radja.
    29. Sibolangit.
    30. Rafflesia.
    31. Despatah I/II.
    32. Tjawang I/II.
    33. Dolok Saut.
    34. Dusun Besar.
    35. Batang Palupuh.

c) Kalimantan (Borneo) :

    36. Mandor.

d) Sulawesi (Celebes) :

    37. Mas Popaja Radja.
    38. Tanggala.
    39. Bantimurung.
    40. Napabalano.

e) Maluku (Moluccas) :

    41. Gunung Api.

General Introduction :

The situation in respect of criteria and general administration, tourism, etc., is rather uniform and, therefore, can largely be dealt with by way of introduction rather than repeated for each of the 41 Listed areas.

a) Status : all the areas are fully protected — " absolute legal protection and freedom from other rights " — and no settlement, exploitation or hunting is allowed.

b) Area : the size of each reserve is quoted in the detailed list, the criterion being satisfied in each case except for the 24 reserves listed as Nos. 18-41, which have been included at the special request of the Indonesian Government, reasons being given to justify the exception in each case.

269

c) Staff : for the important Udjung Kulon reserve a staff of 40 is allocated and, as its total area is 41,150 ha, approximately meets the criterion. Of the other reserves only No. 12 Gunung Indrapura in western Sumatra exceeds 10,000 ha (12,530 ha) and the Government states that in each case the supervision is undertaken on a part-time basis only by " the staff of the proper Forest Districts " although " usually one special officer for Nature Conservation " is appointed in addition to the Forest Officers. In fact, despite the efforts of Central Government and of the local supervisory staff, control of poaching is not always effective and in several cases peripheral zones are being steadily eroded by settlement and other human exploitation to which it has not been possible to call a complete halt.

d) Budget : for Udjung Kulon in Java, where there are over 50 inhabitants per km^2, the criterion would demand an annual expenditure of U.S. $ 8,000, but in fact in 1963 the total was increased to $ 25,000, $ 8,000 covering supervision and the remainder for maintenance and development. For the other 40 reserves it has not been possible to quote figures area by area, especially as most of the staff is part-time, but the authorities state that " the budget spent annually for supervision is proportionally at just the same rate as for Udjung Kulon ". In fact to satisfy the criterion it could even be at a lower rate, since where population density exceeds 50 to km^2 $ 500 per 500 ha is deemed sufficient.

III.   *Administration :* the Division of Nature Conservation and Wild Life Management of the Forestry Department of the Directorate of Forestry and Agrarian Affairs is responsible for all areas.

Land tenure : the land of all reserves pertains to the State.

Tourism : so far efforts have mainly been directed to the Udjung Kulon reserve, with a view to facilitating visits for scientific purposes; lodging is available on the two islands in the reserve, Handuleum and Peutjang, and also in the vicinity of the watchtowers at Tjigenter and Tjiudjongkulon; guides are provided to accompany visitors.

270

Scientific research: began in 1925 and many botanical and zoological studies have been published.

Indonesia was dealt with briefly in the previous edition of the List, E/3436.

Details : application of criteria (II), general information (III) and description (IV) :

A. — NATURE RESERVE.

1. UDJUNG KULON NATURE RESERVE (1921).

   b) Area : 41,150 ha.

   Altitude : sea level to 480 m.

   a) Peninsula and island at the western extremity of Java, of volcanic origin and difficult of access; lagoons, dune formations, primary forest dominated by *Ficus* species. The south-west of the area is rugged, the rest being composed of low hills and plateaux. The vegetation is rich with many endemic species, this being the last relict of low-level forest in Java : *Intsia bijuga,* a great deal of *Barringtonia* and the last few examples of the nearly extinct dipterocarp *Vatica bantamensis.*

   b) Javan rhinoceros *Rhinoceros sondaicus,* chevrotain *Tragulus javanicus,* barking deer *Muntiacus muntjak;* local races of banteng *Bos banteng,* tiger *Panthera tigris,* leopard *Panthera pardus;* birds include the green peafowl *Pavo muticus.*

   c) Javan rhinoceros and Javan tiger.

B. — RESERVES OF OVER 500 HA.

a) **Java.**

2. NUSA BARUNG (1920).

   b) Area : 6,000 ha.

   Altitude : sea level to 313 m.

   a) Vegetation includes *Cordia subcordata,* sago-palm *Cycas revoluta, Pterocymbium, Tarenna incerta, Ficus* spp. and nicker bean *Entada scandens.*

   b) Timor or rusa deer *Cervus timoriensis,* giant squirrel *Ratufa bicolor albiceps,* the two-banded monitor *Varanus salvator;* birds include the red junglefowl *Gallus g. bankiva* and brown booby *Sula leucogaster.*

3. LAUTAN PASIR, TENGGER (1919).

   b) Area : 5,250 ha.

   Altitude : 2,100-2,500 m.

   a) Sandy plain situated on Tengger mountain, with steppe vegetation including the rare heath-like *Styphelia pungens.* The astonishing landscape is a tourist attraction.

   b) No information.

4. KAWAH IDJEN, MERAPI (1920).

   b) Area : 2,560 ha.

271

IV.   *Altitude :* about 2,250 m.

a) A locality of great scientific and aesthetic interest, with a very beautiful crater lake and casuarina forest.

b) Banteng, deer.

5. RAWA DANAU (1921).

II.   b) Area : 2,500 ha.

IV.   *Altitude :* 325 m.

a) Forest in a marshy fresh-water zone with such species as *Elaeocarpus littoralis, Glochidion manogynum, Alstonia spathulata,* pitcher-plant *Nepenthes mirabilis,* flame tree *Erythrina* sp., the sedge *Cladium crassum* and another cyperaceous species, the very rare *Thoracostachyum pandanophyllum.*

b) This is regarded as mainly a bird reserve.

6. RANU KUMBOLO (1921).

II.   b) Area : 1,342 ha.

IV.   *Altitude :* 2,400 m.

a) One of the highest nature reserves in Java, with a remarkable mountain lake of which the characteristic shore vegetation and fauna are of rather special interest.

b) No information.

7. TJIBODAS, GUNUNG GEDE (1925).

II.   b) Area : 1,040 ha.

IV.   *Altitude :* 1,400-3,050 m.

a) This reserve, which is administered by the National Institute of Biology, is situated in a mountainous zone on the eastern slopes of the volcanoes of west Java, and is of interest chiefly for its flora but also for its geological formations and water-falls; it contains one of the richest types of humid tropical forest with trees attaining the height of 60 m, notably the famous west Javan *Altingia excelsa.* A botanic garden is maintained and much visited.

b) Formerly leopard, but the species has now almost disappeared; the avifauna is very rich.

8. NUSAKAMBANGAN (1937).

II.   b) Area : 928 ha.

IV.   *Altitude :* sea level to 250 m.

a) Vegetation includes the venerated lettuce tree *Pisonia silvestris*; *Rafflesia patma* also occurs.

b) The fauna is generally distinct from that of the rest of Java, but the reserve is also another refuge for banteng.

9. PULAU SEMPU (1928).

II.   b) Area : 877 ha.

272

Altitude : sea level to 375 m.

a) Primary forest containing some rare species.

b) Typical Javanese fauna; no details available.

10. KAWAH PAPANDAJAN (1924).

b) Area : 844 ha.

Altitude : 1,500-2,600 m.

a) Volcanic crater with a specialised flora; sulphur springs occur and the reserve is a tourist attraction.

b) Fauna comprises common species; no details available.

11. ARDJUNA-LALIDJIWA (1928).

b) Area : 580 ha.

Altitude : 1,300-2,000 m.

a) Volcanic landscape with the alpine vegetation characteristic of such areas in eastern Java. Rare plants include the rubiaceous *Coprosma sundana* and *Styphelia pungens* and the area is of great botanical interest.

b) The typically Javanese fauna includes the Timor deer and barking deer.

b) **Sumatra.**

12. GUNUNG INDRAPURA (KERINTJI) (1929).

b) Area : 12,530 ha.

Altitude : highest point 3,800 m.

a) The highest mountain in Sumatra, with characteristic montane flora and fauna. Plant species include rhododendrons, the cudweed *Gnaphalium longifolium, Senecio sumatrana* and, another composite, the everlasting *Anaphalis javanica.*

b) There is a possibility that one or two Sumatran rhinoceros *Didermocerus sumatrensis* still survive in this area; the mountain goat or goral *Naemorhedus goral,* of a distinctive Sumatran race, and elephant are found.

c) Sumatran rhinoceros.

13. RIMBOPANTI (1932).

b) Area : 3,500 ha.

Altitude : 750 m.

a) Stated to have good forest and fauna.

b) No details, but said to be composed of common species.

14. KRAKATAU MOUNTAIN (1919).

b) Area : 2,500 ha.

Altitude : sea level to 813 m.

a) Volcanic island of the Sunda straits, well-known because of the studies carried out on the recolonisation by plants and animals of the lavas extruded in the great eruption.

b) Reticulated python *P. reticulatus* and the two-banded monitor.

273

c) Kalimantan (Borneo).

15. PADANG LUWAL (1934).

II.   *b*) Area : 1,080 ha.

IV.   *Altitude :* sea level to 100 m.

a) Landscape and flora typical of a volcanic region. The plant species include peeling bark *Tristania* sp., *Podocarpus* sp., the conifer *Dacrydium* sp., whortleberry *Vaccinium* sp., orchids and ferns *Hydnophytum* spp., and the famous pitcher-plants *Dischidia* sp., and *Nepenthes* sp.

b) The characteristic fauna of this volcanic area includes some interesting parrots such as the blue-crowned dwarf parakeet *Loriculus galgulus.*

d) Sulawesi (Celebes).

16. GUNUNG TANGKOKO, BATUANGUS (1919).

II.   *b*) Area : 4,446 ha.

IV.   *Altitude :* sea level to 1,370 m.

a) Shrubby vegetation.

b) Babirusa *Babyrousa babyrussa,* anoa *A. depressicornis*; birds include the maleo, a rare species of Megapodidae, *Macrocephalon maleo.*

c) Anoa, maleo.

17. PANUA (1938).

II.   *b*) Area : 1,500 ha.

IV.   *Altitude :* sea level to 20 m.

a) Situated on a coastal plain, the reserve is designed as a special sanctuary for the maleo.

b) and *c*) Maleo.

C. — RESERVES OF LESS THAN 500 HA.

a) Java.

18. PULAU-DUA (1937).

II.   *b*) Area : 46 ha, together with Nos. 19 and 20.

IV.   *Altitude :* sea level to 8 m.

a) Coral island covered with mangroves and enclosing lagoons with many species of fish.

b) Important breeding colonies of egrets, ibises (including the glossy ibis *Plegadis falcinellus* and the sacred ibis *Threskiornis melanocephala*), cormorants ducks and storks. Only nesting place in Java of the spoonbill *Platalea* sp

19. PULAU-BOKOR (1921).

II.   *b*) Area : 46 ha, together with Nos. 18 and 20.

274

Altitude : sea level to 10 m.

a) Coral island with heavy forest.

b) A bird sanctuary especially for migration studies; species include the pink imperial fruit pigeon *Ducula rosacea,* much more rarely, the pied imperial pigeon *Myristicivora bicolor* and the spangled drongo *Dicrurus hottentottus.*

20. PULAU-RAMBUT (1939).

b) Area : 46 ha, together with Nos. 18 and 19.

Altitude : sea level to 10 m.

a) Coral island with heavy forest.

b) Largely of interest as a bird sanctuary; both species of ibis mentioned under No. 18 above are found.

21. SAOBI (1926).

b) Area : 430 ha.

Altitude : sea level to 100 m.

a) A zoogeographically remarkable locality. The orchidaceous flora is noteworthy.

b) Deer; birds include endemic species and races such as the green-billed malkoha *Rhopodytes kangeanensis* and northern coucal *Centropus sinensis kangeanensis* and several megapodes or scrubfowl including *Megapodius freycinet* subsp.

22. RANU DARANGAN (1936).

b) Area : 378 ha.

Altitude : 525-750 m.

a) A massif with a peculiar ecology due to climate. The mountain flora is of special interest and includes the fern *Gleichenia* and pitcher-plant *Nepenthes* sp.

b) No information.

23. SIGOGOR (1936).

b) Area : 190 ha.

Altitude : 1,400-1,500 m.

a) Forest of a type which is restricted to this part of Java; the orchidaceous flora includes a rare *Cypripedium.*

b) Leopard, Javan pig *Sus verrucosus.*

24. GUNUNG DJAGAT (1954).

b) Area : 187 ha, together with Nos. 25 and 26.

Altitude : not known.

a) Climax bush of a low altitude type.

b) No information.

25. TAKOKAK (1919).

II.   *b*) Area : 187 ha, together with Nos. 24 and 26.

IV.   *Altitude :* 1,000-1,200 m.
            a) Interesting high altitude vegetation, including the fine timber tree *Altingia* sp.
            b) Crab-eating macaque *Macaca irus*, Javan pig; many species of birds.

26. TJIGENTENG-TJIPANTJI (1919).

II.   *b*) Area : 187 ha, together with Nos. 24 and 25.

IV.   *Altitude :* 1,300-1,600 m.
            a) Mainly of botanic interest.
            b) No information.

b) **Sumatra.**

27. RAFFLESIA SERBÖDJADI (1936).

II.   *b*) Area : 300 ha.

IV.   *Altitude* not known.
            a) Habitat of one of the *Rafflesia* species.
            b) Orang-utan *Pongo pygmaeus*.
            c) Orang-utan.

28. DOLOK TINGGI RADJA (1934).

II.   *b*) Area : 167 ha.

IV.   *Altitude :* 425 m.
            a) Travertine terraces; hot springs.
            b) Crab-eating macaque, Javan pig.

29. SIBOLANGIT (1934).

II.   *b*) Area : 115 ha.

IV.   *Altitude :* 300-500 m.
            a) Of considerable botanic interest, with flora typical of northern Sumatra. The reserve is in fact managed as a botanic garden.
            b) The fauna is composed of common species; no details available.

30. RAFFLESIA (1937).

31. DESPATAH I/II (1932).

32. TJAWANG I/II (1932).

II.   *b*) Area : this group of small reserves totals 72 ha.

276

Altitude : 1,500-2,250 m.

a) Habitat of *Rafflesia arnoldi.*

b) Common species; no details available.

33. DOLOK SAUT (1924).

b) Area : 39 ha.

Altitude : 1,800 m.

a) The original habitat of *Pinus merkusii.* The underwood is composed of the fern *Gleichenia linearis.*

b) No information.

34. DUSUN BESAR (1936).

b) Area : 12 ha.

Altitude : 750-1,500 m.

a) Lake. Surrounding vegetation notable for the orchid *Vanda hookeriana.*

b) Avifauna composed chiefly of aquatic species.

35. BATANG PALUPUH (1930).

b) Area : 4 ha.

Altitude : appproaching 2,000 m.

a) Habitat of *Rafflesia arnoldi.*

b) Common species; no information.

c) **Kalimantan (Borneo).**

36. MANDOR (1936).

b) Area : 195 ha.

Altitude : 1,250 m.

a) Sandstone area with xeromorphic flora and several different orchids including *Vanda* sp.

b) Proboscis monkey *Nasalis larvatus.*

d) **Sulawesi (Celebes).**

37. MAS POPAJA RADJA (1939).

b) Area : 160 ha.

Altitude : sea level to 50 m.

a) Comprises three islands, Mas, Popaja and Radja. There is a rare species of tree *Adina fagifolia,* belonging to the cinchona sub-family of the Rubiaceae.

b) A species of marine turtle is said to breed.

38. TANGGALA (1936).

b) Area : 125 ha.

IV.
　　　　Altitude : 750-1,000 m.
　　　　a) Interesting both scientifically and as a beauty spot.
　　　　b) Anoa (tending to become extinct locally), Timor deer.
　　　　c) Anoa.

　　　　39.　BANTIMURUNG (1919).
II.
　　　　b) Area : 10 ha.
IV.
　　　　Altitude : 150-175 m.
　　　　a) Of geological interest, with its caverns and subterranean watercourses.
　　　　b) The tailless black ape *Cynopithecus niger,* anoa; an important invertebrate fauna.
　　　　c) Anoa.

　　　　40.　NAPABALANO (1919).
II.
　　　　b) Area : 9 ha.
IV.
　　　　Altitude : 900 m.
　　　　a) Natural teak *Tectona grandis* forest.
　　　　b) No information.

　　　　e) **Maluku (Moluccas).**
　　　　41.　GUNUNG API.
II.
　　　　b) Area : 80 ha.
IV.
　　　　Altitude : sea level to 650 m.
　　　　a) Volcanic islet.
　　　　b) Many species of seabirds nest; boobies *Sula* (3 species), terns (3 species), frigate-birds (1 species) and tropic-bird *Phaethon* (1 species, probably the white-tailed *P. lepturus*).

V.　　**Areas excluded :**
　　　　Fifty-three nature reserves of small size (of which the name, area and a brief description were given in the previous edition of the List, E/3436).
　　　　Twenty-two Nature Parks, a type of reserve which only aims to give protection to the fauna and not to the habitat as a whole. These total :

　　　　150,000 ha in Java; where they include the Baluran reserve (25,000 ha).
　　　　1,540,000 ha in Sumatra; where they include the famous Löser Game Reserve which affords a sanctuary for the rhinoceros.
　　　　650,000 ha in Kalimantan (Borneo); and
　　　　100,000 ha in the Sunda archipelago.

　　　　These latter areas, if supervision could be made effective, would nevertheless have considerable importance since they contain such animal species as the Sumatran rhinoceros, orang-utan, gibbons and Komodo dragon *Varanus komodoensis.* Strict measures in the Sunda islands for the protection of the Komodo dragon and in all areas for the strengthening of protection afforded to orangs and gibbons would certainly commend themselves.

278

Apart from the above, it has seemed advisable for the present to exclude from the List the vast area of 320,000 ha in West Irian (formerly New Guinea), which used to go by the name of the Lorentz Natuurmonument. No administrative measures or supervision are currently in operation for the maintenance of this long-established Sanctuary; indeed it seems even possible that the legal basis for its protection has been formally rescinded.

Finally, it must be noted that a report recently received indicates that, as recommended above, a sector of the famous Komodo islands, Padar or Rintjah, has in fact been set aside as a reserve and closed, it is said, to the public, since October 1965. But details are not yet to hand which would allow this important new addition to be included in the List.

59. IRAN

Listed Areas : nil.

Explanation :

1. Iranian laws provide for the creation of 'Protected Regions', in which rights of exploitation and usage are restricted but not eliminated. For example hunting and fishing are allowed in them under a special permit issued by the Game and Fish Department in Tehran and, similarly, cultivation, grazing of stock and woodcutting are subject to specific authorisation by the Ministry of Agriculture and the Department of Hunting. The exercise of such rights makes it impossible to regard the 'Protected Regions' of the country as falling within the category established by the ICNP criteria. At the end of 1965 there were in fact eleven of these 'Protected Regions' in Iran, totalling some 600,000 ha.

2. There is also legal provision for the creation of 'Wild Life Parks'. These, in contrast to the Protected Regions, are on public land held by the Game and Fish Department. Cultivation and grazing are proscribed, but hunting and fishing are still allowed under certain conditions, so that once again they have to be excluded from the present List. However, in fact, at the present moment, there is only one of these areas, situated in the north-east of Iran between the towns of Bojnourd and Gonbad Kabus. Named after His Majesty the Shah, it extends over some 100,000 ha and encircles a mountain range of which about half is under dense forest. Among the animals recorded in the area are urial sheep, ibex, leopard, bear, the maral (or local race of Red Deer) and a few tigers of the Caspian race, together with a notable avifauna.

This Wild Life Park would seem perhaps to merit inclusion in the List and it is only with some hesitation, on the basis of official advice (date 4 April 1965) that hunting still takes place in the area, that it has been decided that for the present it must be omitted.

3. Also to be noted is an announcement made at an IUCN Technical Meeting in Ankara (October 1967) that the Iranian Game and Fish Department had "set aside 8,000 ha of important reedbed and marshland on the south side of the Mordab (Caspian littoral) as a refuge; hunting, fishing, reed cutting and other activities will be prohibited or carefully controlled to allow for maximum security with special emphasis on wildfowl ".

279

I.   Listed Areas : nil.

V.   Explanation :

There has been no official reply to enquiries, but the authorities of the Baghdad Natural History Museum report that " no Game Parks, Nature Reserves or Bird Sanctuaries are in existence, although their creation is envisaged in the law ".

Deserving mention is the ' Army Canal Gardens ', about 510 ha in extent and approximately 26 km long by 200 m wide, located to the east of Baghdad City. This area is in effect a public park, " opened to serve as a public recreation-ground and to moderate the weather ".

61. **IRELAND**

I.   Listed Areas : one.

1. Bourn Vincent Memorial Park.

General Introduction :

The Park was included in the previous edition (E/3436) of the List.

Details : application of criteria (II), general information (III) and description (IV) :

1. BOURN VINCENT MEMORIAL PARK.

II.   *a)* Status : for the most part totally protected, but a small (120 ha) section is set aside for blood-stock rearing under State control. There is also, in limited areas, an annual game cull (deer, woodcock) and some fishing. Japanese sika deer have been introduced for sporting purposes. There are patches of cultivation.

b) Area : 4,250 ha.

c) Staff : 39 units.

d) Budget : the equivalent of nearly U.S. $ 60,000.

III.   *Date established :* 1932 (the Bourn Vincent Memorial Park Act).

Administration : by a group of Commissioners (of Public Works) responsible to the Minister of Finance.

Land tenure situation : land generously donated by Senator A. R. Vincent, Mr. M. W. B. Bourn and Mrs. Agnes Bourn and now the property of the State.

Tourism : access unrestricted to pedestrians, cyclist and horse-drawn vehicles.

Scientific research : no specific organisation.

IV.   *Altitude :* maximum 750 m.

a) A landscape consisting of lakes surrounded by woods and dominated on the east and west by hills varying between 500 and 750 m (highest in the neighbourhood of the Killarney lakes); shallow Pleistocene deposits on ancient red sandstone in the south and carboniferous limestone in the north; some cultivation. The original forest comprises strawberry tree *Arbutus unedo,* durmast oak *Quercus petraea* and yew *Taxus,* while the Killarney or bristle fern *Trichomanes speciosum* is found in damper localities; the Mangerton mountains are particularly rich in bryophytes. Mediterraneo-lusitanian elements are well-represented in the flora, having been enabled to extend to this region by the high rainfall and absence of low temperatures.

b) The Park provides a refuge for the indigenous red deer *Cervus elaphus scoticus* LÖNNBERG, which has developed slight subspecific differences in the last 200 years, and also for Japanese sika *Cervus nippon,* introduced in 1844.

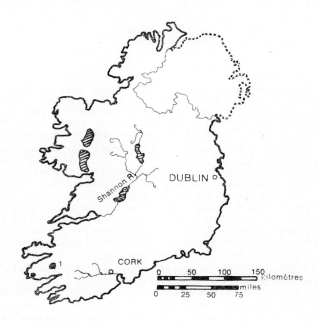

Areas excluded :

1. Phoenix Park, established 1925 . ...   700 ha
A walled Park used for recreation, horse racing, polo, etc.

A number of ornithological reserves, including :

2. North Bull Island . ...   1,390 ha
3. Rosslare Strand (Wexford) . ...   160 ha
4. Rahasane Turlough (Galway) ... ...   120 ha
5. Cork Lough.
6. The Skelligs : two rocky islets in the Atlantic, where some 10,000 pairs of gannets nest.
7. Cambay Island ... ...   247 ha

281

I. **Listed Areas :** thirteen.

1. Mount Meron Nature Reserves.
2. Mount Carmel National Park and Nature Reserves.
3. Wadi Shorek Nature Reserves.
4. The Ein Gedi Nature Reserve.
5. The Wadi Tabor Nature Reserve.
6. The Wadi Bezet Nature Reserve.
7. The Wadi Amud Nature Reserve.
8. The Wadi K'ziv Nature Reserve.
9. Mount Gilboa Nature Reserves.
10. The Wadi Dishon Nature Reserve.
11. Huleh Swamp Nature Reserve.
12. The Solelim Forest Nature Reserve.
13. The Eilat Gulf Nature Reserve.

General Introduction :

The total budget available to the Nature Reserves Authority in 1965-1966 amounted to some U.S. $ 250,000, allocated as follows : general administration $ 50,000 : pay of 12 motorized guards and grants to associations, such as the Society for the Protection of Nature, which contribute to the supervision of reserves, $ 50,000 : equipment $ 120,000; miscellaneous (publicity etc.) $ 30,000.

Legislation : a law enacted in August 1963, provides for the proclamation of natural reserves and national parks. It set up a consultative Council, the National Parks Authority, directly responsible to the Prime Minister, and another independent body responsible to the Minister of Agriculture, the 'Nature Reserves Authority'. When a Nature Reserve is 'proclaimed', the exercise of all human rights of exploitation in the area, of which the boundaries are specified, is provisionally suspended, subject to final confirmation by act of the supreme Executive. Several of the Reserves listed had still not been formally proclaimed in February 1966, but their total protection is already ensured by regulations under the Wild Animals and Wild Plants Act, pending proclamation.

Administration : the Nature Reserves and National Parks are administered respectively by the Nature Reserves Authority (with a staff of 30) and the National Parks Authority. To date the latter only controls three National Parks, one of them being the listed Carmel Park.

Land tenure : about 90 % of the land in Israel is in public ownership, including the whole of that comprised in the natural reserves.

Tourism : the two 'Authorities' are responsible for tourist organisation. In practice recreational needs are regarded as the sole objective in the National Parks and also a principal objective in the Nature Reserves, although in the latter scientific objectives, with conservation measures, are also taken into account. Visitors are, however, generally restricted to the paths and picnicking is only allowed in specified localities.

Research : the Nature Reserves Authority has already undertaken, in collaboration with the Society for Nature Protection, a number of research projects on such subjects as waterfowl, birds of prey and, in the desert areas, dorcas gazelles. Other projects were being planned for 1966-1967. In September 1965 an Institute of Nature Protection and Ecology was set up in Tel Aviv University.

Only a short account of Israel, with description of four areas (two of them now excluded) appeared in Part Two of the previous edition of the List.

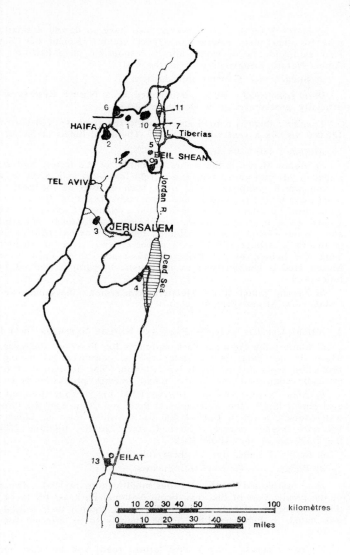

Details : application of criteria (II), general information (III) and description (IV) :

1. MOUNT MERON NATURE RESERVES (Upper Galilee).

   a) Status : total protection except for an enclave of some 2,000 ha in which a village with its arable land and pastures is situated.

   b) Area : 10,500 ha, 8,500 being totally protected with no dwellings, wood-cutting, picking of flowers or fruit, cultivation or hunting allowed.

283

c) Staff : 3 units, who, however, also have to devote a small part of their time to other small reserves in Upper Galilee (Kerem ben Zimra, Bar-Am, Paar etc.) and one of whom also is responsible on a half-time basis for the Amud Nature Reserve (No. 7 in the List).

d) Budget : see General Introduction.

III.   *Date established :* 1955, administered as a Nature Reserve since 1965 and officially proclaimed on 9 December 1965.

Tourism : there is a road almost up to the summit of Mount Meron. Some 120,000 visitors a year visit the area. There are hotels at Safad, 20 km away.

IV.   *Altitude :* 480-1,208 m.

a) Mount Meron is the highest mountain of the region, and exhibits various stages of Mediterranean vegetation, from low bush and heath to a climax association which comprises some trees, such as two of the pear family *Sorbus trilobata* and *Pyrus syriaca*, and also many beautiful flowers, some of them quite rare, including the small-flowered cyclamen *Cyclamen orbiculatum* (also known as *vernum* and *coum*), *Sternbergia spaffordiana, Hyacinthus orientalis* and various orchid species, including the lizard orchid *Himantoglossum.* Also in the Park, Mount Hillel has a rather different type of Mediterranean flora, being the habitat of *Juniperus phoenicea* and peony *Paeonia mascula,* while Mount Hod is characterised by its Karstic topography derived from Turonian limestones.

b) Typical fauna of the Mediterranean region : the salamander is especially common on Mount Meron.

2. Mount Carmel National Park and Nature Reserves (near Haifa).

II.   *a*) Status : the National Park embraces the Reserves and even those sectors which do not have reserve status can be considered as having the level of protection demanded by the ICNP criterion. The movement of visitors is systematically controlled and in the actual reserves protection is complete.

b) Area : western Carmel reserve 1,500 ha, in four divisions : the western escarpment, the Galim watercourses, Beth and Oren, and the Oren and Bustan watercourses; northern Carmel 500 ha, to which may be added the 50 ha of the river Nesher reserve; eastern Carmel 220 ha; totalling 2,270 ha out of the 7,000 ha of the whole Park.

c) Staff : 2 units, one of them full-time.

d) Budget : see General Introduction.

III.   *Date established :* 1956. Various modifications in 1964. The administration of the greater part of the area, being National Park, is still being set up, while the Reserves are already maintained as such, though their formal proclamation was stated, in February 1966, to be unlikely to be effected for another year or two.

Tourism : access is by several tarmac roads and the Park receives a large number of visitors : hotel accommodation at Haifa.

IV.   *Altitude :* 50-528 m.

a) The Mount Carmel region, overlooking the Mediterranean, falls into a number of distinct sections :

(i) On the east, ' maquis ' composed of the Kermes oak or grain tree *Quercus* ' *calliprinos* ' (=*coccifera*), *Phillyrea media* and the Mediterranean medlar *Crataegus azarolus*;

284

(ii) On the north, slopes typical of those with a northern exposure : habitat of Bourbon lily *Lilium candidum,* the laurestinus *Viburnum tinus* and Judas tree *Cercis siliquastrum*;

(iii) On the west, deep narrow valleys : carob (*Ceratonia*)-*Pistacia* association merging gradually into Kermes oakwoods *Quercus coccifera* (var. *calliprinos* and *palaestina*), with some fine examples of Aleppo pine *Pinus halepensis* forest and typical plants of grey calcareous soils, such as broom *Genista* spp., as well as the parasitic *Cytinus hipocistis*;

Coastal sector, stabilised dunes with carob woods and the mastic tree *Pistacia lentiscus,* also tamarisk *Tamarix gallica*; saline springs.

b) Birds of prey, including the spotted eagle *Aquila clanga*, frequent the northern cliffs; the rock dove *Columba livia*, herring gull *Larus argentatus*, other gulls and terns are found on the coast.

3. WADI SHOREK NATURE RESERVES (Judaea).

a) Status : total protection.

b) Area : 990 ha.

c) Staff : 2 units, who also supervise the Judaean hills area generally.

d) Budget : see General Introduction.

Date established : one section proclaimed on 10 June 1965, the remainder awaiting proclamation (as at February 1966).

Tourism : access is by a secondary road and footpaths. Several hundred visitors each year : accommodation in Jerusalem hotels 30 km away.

Altitude : 300-725 m.

a) Geologically and botanically a typical example of the Judaean hills landscape, with bare slopes, cliffs and wooded hills.

b) No information.

4. THE EIN GEDI NATURE RESERVE (Dead Sea).

a) Status : total protection.

b) Area : 850 ha (a proposal for a new ' Judaean Desert' Reserve of 3,000 ha, taking in the present Reserve, is under consideration).

c) Staff : 3 units, occasionally assisted by the staff of a local Youth Hostel and Field Studies Centre.

d) Budget : see General Introduction.

Date established : formal proclamation was being prepared in February 1966.

Tourism : access is by one main road and footpaths; 200,000 visitors a year. Youth Hostel.

Altitude : from 392 m a.s.l. down to 200 m below sea-level.

a) An oasis with an unique flora, for example the helleborine *Epipactis veratrifolia,* the Biblical ' mustard' *Salvadora persica* and *Moringa aptera.*

b) A varied and abundant fauna includes the desert partridge *Ammoperdix heyi,* Tristram's grackle *Onychognathus tristramii* and the Nubian ibex *Capra ibex nubiana* (formerly a ' Red Book' species, now considered to be out of danger of extinction).

285

5. THE WADI TABOR NATURE RESERVE (Lower Galilee).

II.   *a*) Status : total protection.

b) Area : 800 ha.

c) Staff : 2 part-time units, of whom one is responsible for various other small reserves and also the Wadi Amud (No. 7) and the other spends part of the time supervising the Mount Gilboa reserves (No. 9).

d) Budget : see General Introduction.

III.   *Date established :* maintained as a reserve since 1964, soon to be formally proclaimed (as at February 1966).

Tourism : access is by footpaths. Several hundred visitors a year; hotel accommodation at Tiberias, 30 km away.

IV.   *Altitude :* from 116 m a.s.l down to 250 m below sea level.

a) Geological formations dating from the late Tertiary, with springs and typical streamside vegetation; *Acacia albida* is common.

b) The Arabian gazelle *Gazella g. arabica* is more frequent here than in most other areas.

c) Arabian gazelle.

6. THE WADI BEZET NATURE RESERVE (Western Galilee).

II.   *a*) Status : total protection.

b) Area : 765 ha.

c) Staff : shares 2 units with the K'ziv reserve (No. 8) and a group of other small reserves nearby.

d) Budget : see General Introduction.

III.   *Date established :* maintained as a reserve since 1962, formal proclamation being prepared (February 1966).

Tourism : a road reaches the edge of the reserve, thence access by footpath. 10,000 visitors a year; hotel accommodation at Naharia, 20 km away.

IV.   *Altitude :* 100-600 m.

a) A meandering watercourse with its banks covered in thick Mediterranean 'maquis' of the more northerly type; many fern species including *Pteris longi folia* and *Dryopteris rigida*.

b) Birds of prey nest on the cliffs and the 'maquis' is the habitat of small carnivores, such as the stone marten *Martes foina* and the small-spotted genet *G. genetta*.

7. THE WADI AMUD NATURE RESERVE (Upper and Lower Galilee).

II.   *a*) Status : total protection.

b) Area : 720 ha.

c) Staff : 2 units, one shared with the Mount Meron Reserves (No. 1) and the other with the Wadi Tabor Reserve (No. 5).

d) Budget : see General Introduction.

III.   *Date established :* administered as a reserve since 1964, one part was formally proclaimed on 9 December 1965 and the proclamation of the rest was expected as at February 1966, to follow shortly.

A, Meru N.P.

(photo : Ch. A. Vaucher)

KENYA, Tsavo N.P.

(photo : F. Vollma

A, Masai Mava R.   (photo : M. Kaplan)

KENYA, Tsavo N.P.

(photo : M. Kaplan)

MEXIQUE, In. M. Hidalgo y Castilla N.P.   (photo : E.)

MEXIQUE, Iztaccihuatl-Popocatepetl N.P.   (photo : E

ERLANDS, Veluwezoom N.P.

(photo : Vereeniging tot behoud van Natuurmonumenten)

NETHERLANDS, Veluwezoom N.P.   (photo : Vereeniging tot behoud van Natuurmor

Tourism : main roads lead to the boundaries of the reserve, thence access by footpath. 80,000 visitors a year, hotel accommodation at Safad and Tiberias, both 10 km away.

Altitude : from 500 m. a.s.l. dropping to 200 m below sea-level.

a) The region exhibits the gradual transition from Mediterranean-type vegetation (including myrtle *Myrtus communis*) to steppe vegetation with the thorny jujube *Ziziphus spina-christi*.

b) The rock dove and little swift *Apus affinis* nest freely and there are some 15 pairs of raptors, griffon vulture *Gyps fulvus* and Bonelli's eagle *Hieraaetus fasciatus*.

8. THE WADI K'ZIV NATURE RESERVE (Western Galilee).

a) Status : total protection.

b) Area : 650 ha.

c) Staff : 2 units, shared with Wadi Bezet reserve (No. 6).

d) Budget : see General Introduction.

Date established : maintained as a reserve since 1958, formal proclamation being prepared (February 1966).

Tourism : access by footpaths only. 50,000 visitors a year; hotel accommodation at Naharia, 20 km away.

Altitude : 200-567 m.

a) A gorge cutting deep into the plateau, along the bottom of which the oriental plane *Platanus orientalis* occurs typically, and on the steep slopes there is a fine sample of ' maquis ', with Judas tree and Syrian maple *Acer syriacum*.

b) Many birds of prey nest on the cliffs, such as buzzards *Buteo* spp.

9. MOUNT GILBOA NATURE RESERVES.

a) Status : total protection.

b) Area : 610 ha, made up of Gibborim reserve 280 ha, Barkan 300 and Lapidim 30.

c) Staff : two units shared with the Wadi Tabor reserve (No. 5) and some other small reserves nearby.

d) Budget : see General Introduction.

Date established : maintained as a reserve since 1960, formal proclamation in course of preparation.

Tourism : access by secondary roads. 10,000 visitors a year; no hotel accommodation in the vicinity.

Altitude : from 497 m a.s.l. down to 100 m below sea-level.

a) A cross-section of Turonian, Senonian and Eocene geological formations, covered with vegetation ranging from transitional forest dominated by carob or locust tree *Ceratonia siliqua* to an Irano-Turonian type. The only habitat of *Iris haynei*; *Tulipa systola* is fairly common.

b) No information.

10. THE WADI DISHON NATURE RESERVE (Upper Galilee).

II.	*a)* Status : total protection.

b) Area : 600 ha.

c) Staff : one full time; two others shared with nine small reserves in the vicinity.

d) Budget : see General Introduction.

III.	*Date established :* maintained as a reserve since 1962, formal proclamation in course of preparation.

Tourism : access by a main road crossing the reserve, footpaths; 15,000 visitors a year; hotels 15 km away.

IV.	*Altitude :* no information.

a) A good example of Galilean geological formations ranging from Lower Senonian to Middle Eocene, with their associated vegetation. Rare plants include *Iris lorteti* and *Sternbergia spaffordiana.*

b) Raptorial birds, including griffon vulture and eagle owl *Bubo bubo.*

11. HULEH SWAMP NATURE RESERVE (Upper Galilee).

II.	*a)* Status : total protection.

b) Area : 308 ha, which is smaller than demanded by the criterion for a country of 110 persons per km²; retained at the special request of the Israel authorities, as a last surviving sample of the Huleh swamp.

c) Staff : one for supervision and a number of others for tourist purposes.

d) Budget : see General Introduction.

III.	*Date established :* maintained as a reserve since 1962, formal proclamation in course of preparation.

Tourism : a main road leads to the area, which has many footpaths and offers excursions by boat. 20,000 visitors a year; hotel accommodation 15 km away.

IV.	*Altitude :* 70 m.

a) A remnant of the old Huleh marshes, with their characteristic fauna and flora; the water level is artificially maintained by a barrage. The typical aquatic plant associations include papyrus and waterlilies *Nuphar* spp.

b) Otter *L. lutra,* lynx *Felis lynx,* wild pig *Sus scrofa*; nesting place of common tern *Sterna hirundo,* black-winged stilt *H. himantopus* and grey and purple herons *Ardea cinerea* and *purpurea.*

12. THE SOLELIM FOREST NATURE RESERVE (western Lower Galilee).

II.	*a)* Status : total protection.

b) Area : 300 ha, not satisfying the criterion but retained because of special phytosociological interest.

c) Staff : part-time only.

d) Budget : see General Introduction.

III.	*Date established :* proclamation expected shortly (as at February 1966).

Tourism : access is by road to the borders of the reserve, but to date there are no visitors and no hotels.

Altitude : 175-264 m.

a) 'Parkland' type of vegetation, with Valonia oak *Quercus macrolepsis* (al. *aegilops* or *ithabunensis*) and storax *Styrax officinalis,* representing a climax on the grey soils of the Eocene limestones.

b) No information.

13. THE EILAT GULF NATURE RESERVE (Red Sea).

a) Status : total protection.

b) Area : 100 ha, but retained in the list because of the unusual interest of the coral reef.

c) Staff : 3 units, who also patrol the southern Negev desert area.

d) Budget : see General Introduction.

Date established : proclaimed on 10 September 1964.

Tourism : a main road leads to the confines of the reserve, which is visited by 100,000 people a year; hotel accommodation at Eilat.

Altitude : sea level.

a) Coral reef.

b) Typical tropical reef fauna.

Areas excluded :

A. — About 120 reserves of small size, which are maintained in the same way as the 13 listed reserves and, as mentioned above, are in many cases supervised jointly jointly with the latter.

B. — Two National Parks, in which the standard of protection does not yet conform to the ICNP criterion :

Arbel National Park . ...   1,192 ha
Jarmaq National Park ... ...   8,800 ha

63. **ITALY**

Listed Areas : seven.

A. — NATIONAL PARKS :

1. Gran Paradiso National Park.
2. Stelvio National Park.
3. Abruzzo National Park.
4. Circeo National Park.

B. — STRICT NATURE RESERVES :

5. Cossogno or Val Grande Reserve.
6. Sasso Fratino Reserve.
7. Poggio Tre Cancelli Reserve.

ITALY

General Introduction :

The text of this Notice, subject to some rearrangement, is largely a literal translation of a document in Italian submitted by the authorities in Rome. Only the four National Parks were included in the previous edition, E/3436, of the List.

As at January 1966, drafts of new basic legislation, two governing National Parks and one for Strict Nature Reserves, were under study by Parliament. They were also of concern to the Parliamentary Commission of Inquiry set up to advise on the safeguarding and stabilisation of the country's historical and artistic heritage and the landscape, which was due to complete its work at the end of November 1965.

No actual law has to be invoked to give the status of a Strict Nature Reserve to any land in public ownership; it may be simply effected by a decision of the Administrative Authority for State Forests (A.S.F.D.).

Details : application of criteria (II), general information (III) and description (IV) :

A. — NATIONAL PARKS.

1. GRAN PARADISO NATIONAL PARK.

a) Status : total protection. There are a few inhabitants. The Board of Administration permits the killing as a biological and sanitary measure of a quota of ibex and chamois which are not in fact kept under sufficient control by their natural predators. The Park guards are responsible for reporting the presence and whereabouts of these surplus animals.

b) Area : 62,000 ha.

c) Staff : 62 guards, sworn in and allocated to the Senior officers (one for each valley), foremen and wardens; all are under the supervision of an Inspector.

d) Budget : 110 million lire or about $ 175,000. This has recently been increased to $ 236,800, shared by the State, the province of Torino and the Val d'Aosta.

Date of establishment : a Hunting Zone was declared as long ago as 1836 and in 1856 became the Royal Hunting Reserve of the Gran Paradiso; legal constitution by decree followed in 1922 and, by a Law of 5 August 1947, the Park attained its present status of an Autonomous Organisation, based at Turin and run by an Administrative Council and a Director-Superintendent (a University Professor).

Land tenure : the Organisation of 'PNGP' owns 2,435 ha, 2,214 ha are state-owned and 51,000 ha belong to the Communes and private persons, of which some 3,800 ha have been leased to the PNGP.

Five kilometres of the western boundary of the Park on the Franco-Italian frontier adjoin the French National Park of the Vanoise, co-operation with which is being developed.

Tourism : the PNGP Autonomous Organisation does not own or manage any tourist accommodation, but 4 alpine huts, 2 chalet-restaurants and eleven camp-sites are available for visitors. There are hotels in the villages in the vicinity of the Park. Access is unrestricted and there are 30,000 to 40,000 visitors a year.

Scientific research : the scope of research work covers the study of pedological, agrarian and climatological problems affecting the mountain economy and inhabitants of the Park, full assistance to qualified experts, students and trainees working for the Organisation, and the mounting of special campaigns to study particular Park problems or recruitment of qualified research workers for that purpose. A special 'Commission on Biological Equilibrium' has been set up for the Park.

Altitude : 1,200-4,061 m.

a) The Park extends along the upper Val d'Aosta, to the south of the centre of which the Gran Paradiso massif rises. The terrain is typically alpine with numerous glaciers, slopes mantled by conifers (larch *Larix decidua,* silver fir *Abies alba* and other species) and pastures interspersed with rocks and screes.

b) Ibex *Capra ibex,* chamois, stoat and weasel *Mustela erminea* and *nivalis,* common and varying hare *Lepus europaeus* and *timidus*; golden eagle.

2. STELVIO NATIONAL PARK.

a) Status : total protection, although in the ten years ending 1962, a fairly large number of deer were allowed to be shot. Except within limits defined by regulations, the pasturing of livestock is forbidden, all exploitation of pastures and woodlands being subject to approval by the Authority administering the Park. The existing cultivation of some pieces of arable land, comprising about 1 per cent of the total area, is authorised strictly in accordance with the conditions laid down by the ICNP in its ' prescribed principles '. There are some hydroelectric dams.

b) Area : 57,772 ha (37,589 ha having been recently excised, despite the fact that the boundaries had been fixed).

c) Staff : a Director (a Chief Inspector of the State Forest Service), 15 permanent guards, a Secretariat Assistant (also from the State Forest Service) and 8 other guards and employees of the State and Alto Adige-Trentino Forest Services, who are posted to the Forest divisions which comprise part of the Park area.

d) Budget : U.S. $ 4,000 (2.5 million lire), in addition to emoluments and salaries of staff. This amount has recently been increased by law to about U.S. $ 80,000, still excluding staff salaries.

III.   The Administrative Office of the Park, situated at Bormio (Sandrio Province), is responsible to the State Forest Department. This is in fact one of the two Parks coming directly under the aegis of the Ministry of Agriculture and Forests.

Date established : 1935, brought under the present regulations in 1951.

Administration : for some considerable time a project has been under study for altering the Park boundaries, by an extension up the catchment area of the Spöl torrent, to bring them into direct contact with those of the Swiss National Park. The proposed modifications would also involve the exclusion of zones in which large numbers of people are living. This plan, which had still not reached its final stages in January 1966, could help eventually to establish a vast faunal reserve in the heart of south central Europe.

Land tenure : 42 % in the ownership of the State and of the Alto Adige-Trentino Region; 45 % owned by the Communes and other local organisations; 13 % in private hands.

Tourism : some well-appointed hotels, 5 ski-schools, ski-lifts and excellent communications inside the Park, which is surrounded by many quite important centres such as Tubre, Glorenza, Spondigna, Lasa, Silandro and Laces in Bolzano Province, Bagni di Robbi and Pejo in Trento Province, and S. Caterina, Valfurva, S. Nicolo and Bormio in Sondrio Province. The growth of the hotel industry in these places during the last few years has been quite phenomenal. There are no restrictions on access to the Park, the flow of visitors on holiday or in transit being very active; from June to October, particularly, many places are crammed with young people from all over Italy and abroad. The central part of the Park offers facilities for long stays both in summer and winter.

IV.   *Altitude :* 650-3,899 m.

a) The rugged massif of the Ortles-Cevedale group constitutes the Alps of the Alto-Adige, with Mt. Cevedale itself as the highest point. From it radiate five ridges divided by deep valleys with rushing rivers. There are no less than 111 glaciers, large and small, in the Park. Meadows and fields are mainly concentrated in the valley on the right bank of the Adige. Coniferous forests (especially larch) find favourable climatic conditions on the mountain flanks and exhibit all the stages of their vegetational succession.

b) A count carried out between the Adamello and the Brenta, quite near the Park boundaries, produced a total of 15 brown bears *Ursus arctos*, 800 red deer *Cervus elaphus*, 3,000 chamois *R. rupicapra*, 4,000 roe deer *C. capreolus*, 4,000 marmots *M. marmota*; 80 golden eagles *Aquila chrysaetos* and many montane game-birds.

3. ABRUZZO NATIONAL PARK.

a) Status : total protection, except for wood-cutting and other forestry exploitation, which is controlled by the Park's administrative Authority. There are plans for creating some strict reserves in the interior of the Park. At the moment supervision is exercised by the Ministries of Agriculture and Forests, Public Works, Education and the Interior, but a management plan for the whole Park is under consideration. This would envisage the creation of an outer zone to include the 7 villages at present within the Park plus the area just outside the Park, on its eastern boundary, along the Sangro valley.

b) Area : 29,160 ha, of which 95 ha were due, from the beginning of 1967, to be designated as strict reserve (Colle di Licco; Alfadena).

c) Staff : Chairman of the Administrative Council; Secretary; a State Forest Service Inspector (head of the Inspectorate for the District of Pescasseroli, where the management of the Park is based); an Assistant-Secretary, stationed at Rome; 2 wardens; 8 guards. As soon as the new Law awaiting approval has been promulgated, which provides for an increased State subsidisation of the Park organisation, the number of guards will also be increased. In addition there are 23 employees or guards of the State Forest Service posted to 12 Forest Stations with total or partial jurisdiction within the Park boundaries.

d) Budget : 25 million lire or about U.S. $ 40,000, which has been increased to 75 million or $ 120,000 under the provisions of the Law which was on the way to being promulgated in December 1965.

Date established : set up by Royal Decree in 1923 and a law enacted on 12 July of that year, and maintained as an Autonomous Organisation until 1933, when it came under the State Administration of Public Forests, reverting to the status of an Autonomous Organisation in 1950.

Administration : now undertaken by the Autonomous Organisation, the status of which, like that of the other National Parks, is to be incorporated under the new basic Law awaiting approval.

Land tenure : the greater part of the Park is the property of the Communes who actually hold 96 % of the forested areas (66 % of the total). Since 1947 the State has gradually acquired some 1,003 ha, mostly just outside the Park but 113 ha inside its boundaries. Some level areas, not planted up with trees, previously used as pastures, have been sold for building, but the extension of this practice has now been forbidden.

Tourism : there is a network of tracks sufficient for the modest traffic requirements. There are 3 hotels and 3 *pensione* at Pescasseroli and another 3 hotels and 12 *pensione* in the immediate vicinity of the Park. Every effort is being made to bring unrestricted camping under control and provide for obligatory camp-sites at places where they cannot cause damage to the Park. As previously stated, supervision is exercised by no less than four Ministries, which leads to obvious difficulties.

The Park has been awarded (1968) the Council of Europe's 'Diploma' for European National Parks.

ITALY

IV.   *Altitude:* highest point 2,247 m, the area designed as strict reserve lying between 1,300 and 1,795 m.

a) The Park comprises a section of the Abruzzi Apennines, with a sharply undulating typically glacial relief, especially along the Sangro valley with its glacier-filled cirques and stretches of ordinary moraine interspersed with great fault blocks and Karstic phenomena. There are also some cultivation patches in the valley. The upland forests are dominated by beech.

b) Brown bear and chamois of the distinct Abruzzi races (*Ursus arctos marsicanus* and *Rupicapra r. ornata*), wolf *Canis lupus,* fox *V. vulpes,* wild cat *Felis silvestris*; golden eagle, white-backed woodpecker *Dendrocopos leucotos,* collared flycatcher *Ficedula albicollis,* snow finch *Montifringilla nivalis.*

4. CIRCEO NATIONAL PARK.

II.   *a)* Status : in theory total protection, but the forests are exploited subject to the agreement of the Park administration and crops are allowed to be cultivated. It was in fact at first considered that this Park should be excluded from the List on the following grounds : presence of some 8,000 inhabitants, cultivation, reclamation involving the alteration of former stagnant marshes into land fit for human economic exploitation, sale of building plots, issue of licences for hunting in the Park, and intensive touristic development (30,000 to 40,000 visitors a year). However, retention in the List was finally decided at the express wish of the Italian authorities who wrote : " Until the Circeo National Park is abolished by the abrogation of the Law which instituted it (Royal Decree No. 285 of 25 January 1934), the Government feels that it cannot be properly omitted from the world list of National Parks ". It has recently been reported that a port has been constructed on the Lake of Paolato to serve an industry established in that section of the Park.

b) Area : 7,445 ha.

c) Staff : a Director (Chief Inspector of the State Forest Service); 3 employees and guards of the same Service and 6 other full-time guards.

d) Budget : 10 million lire or about U.S. $ 16,000, in addition to emoluments and salaries, recently increased to $ 22,400.

III.   *Date established:* 25 January 1934 by Royal Decree.

Administration: by the State Administration of Public Forests.

Land tenure: 3,360 ha in state ownership, 1,351 ha in Communal ownership and 2,732 ha in private hands.

Tourism: of the three Communes, Latina, Sabaudi and S. Felice Circeo, the two last provide remarkably attractive tourist facilities. The great touristic development of the area is explained by its notable road network and its situation near the main route between Rome and Naples.

IV.   *Altitude:* highest point (the Circeo headland) 541 m.

a) Situated on a low rather level plain bounded by the Laziali hills, the Lepini and Ausoni mountains and the Tyrrhenian sea. Forests of holm oak *Quercus ilex* and cork oak *Quercus suber* occupy some 3,783 ha.

b) Wild boar *Sus scrofa,* fox, pine and stone marten *M. martes* and *foina* weasel, hare, fallow deer *D. dama.*

B. — STRICT NATURE RESERVES.

5. COSSOGNO or VAL GRANDE NATURE RESERVE (Novara).

II.   *a)* Status : a strict nature reserve as defined in the London Convention for Africa (1933), with no inhabitants and access only for scientific purposes.

294

b) Area : about 1,000 ha, but boundaries had not yet been finally fixed in December 1965.

c) Staff : still to be appointed from the Canton Forest Department Guards.

d) Budget : still under discussion with the responsible authorities at Rome as at the end of 1965.

Date established : 1965.

Administration : Public Forest Service.

Land tenure : publicly owned forest land.

Tourism : no provision anticipated, access being limited to those concerned with scientific research and general supervision.

Altitude : 700 to 2,100 m.

a) Alpine coniferous and broad-leaved forest.

b) Chamois, eagles.

6. SASSO FRATINO RESERVE (Forli).

a) Status : total protection.

b) Area : 45 ha, plus a 50 ha buffer zone.

c) Staff : covered by the staff of the State Forest of which the Reserve forms part.

d) Budget : covered by the funds available for the State Forest.

Date established : 1965.

Administration, land tenure and tourism : as for No. 5.

Altitude : 900 to 1,500 m.

a) Typical forest of the central Apennines.

b) Apennine fauna.

7. POGGIO TRE CANCELLI RESERVE (Grosseto).

a) Status : total protection.

b) Area : 50 ha, plus a 49 ha buffer zone.

c) Staff : covered by the staff of the State Forest of which the Reserve forms part.

d) Budget : covered by the funds available for the State Forest.

Date established : 1965.

Administration, land tenure and tourism : as for No. 5.

Altitude : 160-280 m.

a) Mediterranean ' maquis ' area.

b) Typical fauna of the maquis.

Areas excluded :

The new National Park of Calabria, established by Decree No. 503 of 2 April 1968; 18,000 ha, but split into ten different zones which are separated by an average distance of 50 km. Morevover, each zone is itself subdivided into four parts : *a*) a strict nature reserve, *b*) an area in which wildlife species are raised under semi-captive conditions to replenish the stock, *c*) a woodland and grassland zone, and *d*) a treeless zone; administered by the Ministry of Agriculture and Forests, this Park enjoys an annual State grant of $ 240,000, plus an allocation from the national Forest Department budget.

Two new strict Nature Reserves, set up by a Ministerial Decree in February 1967 :

    1. Campolino Reserve (Pistoia Province) : 60 ha; 1,691-1,808 m in altitude.

    2. Colle di Licco Reserve (situated within the Abruzzo National Park, No. 3 above) : 95 ha; altitude 1,300-1,795 m.

One Reserve which is being established in Calabria.

One proposed Reserve being planned in Sardinia.

Several other State Forests, to which it is intended to give the status of strict Nature Reserves.

One very fine private Reserve, of about 3,000 ha, at Miemo in Tuscany, the strict supervision of which on a thoroughly scientific basis is ensured by the owner. There have been some successful animal introductions into this area, notably of mouflon and especially of francolin. The Reserve must be excluded from the U.N. List because hunting is practised as a method of controlling the numbers of game species. Its status nevertheless closely approximates to that of the National Hunting Reserves in France.

64. IVORY COAST

I.   **Listed Areas :** two.

    1. Nimba Mountains Strict Nature Reserve.

    2. Bouna Faunal Reserve and Protected Forest.

General Introduction :

The two listed Reserves were described in Part Two of the previous edition of the List, which also mentioned three of the areas (numbered 3-5 in Section V below) now excluded.

Details : application of criteria (II), general information (III) and description (IV) :

    1. NIMBA MOUNTAINS STRICT NATURE RESERVE.

II.   *a*) Status : total protection.

    b) Area : 5,000 ha.

    c) Staff : two.

    d) Budget : about U.S. $ 1,000 per year.

III.   *Date established :* 1944, by a decree which simultaneously established a 13,000 ha reserve in the immediately adjacent area of Guinea.

    Administration : the Reserve is protected by the Forest Service and scientific supervision is entrusted to the Institut Français d'Afrique Noire (I.F.A.N.).

Land tenure : state ownership. It should be noted that the Nimba Mountains massif extends into three countries, the Ivory Coast, Guinea and Liberia. In Liberia the Government has never followed the example of the former French authorities by applying measures of strict protection and in fact the Liberian sector of the mountain is being actively exploited for iron ore by an international consortium, the ore being railed to the coast by a railway opened in 1963. As the working-face is already at 600 m, the whole sector is in danger of destruction within a few years.

Tourism : not permitted.

Scientific research : undertaken by I.F.A.N. principally from a research station established in the Guinean sector.

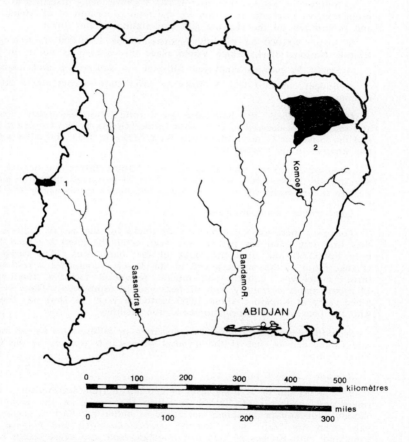

Altitude : 500 to 1,752 m.

a) Mountain massif rising to an average level of 1,200 m above the surrounding peneplain, with heavy rain — or semi-rain — forest up to 700 or 800 m and secondary forest dominated by oil-palms; forest patches extend to 1,200 m,

297

often in the form of gallery forest in the drainage lines. At higher levels there is graminaceous savannah on the lighter soils and rather poor grassland on the lateritic shields.

b) Chimpanzee, buffalo *Syncerus caffer,* warthog *Phacochoerus aethiopicus,* bushbuck *Tragelaphus scriptus,* forest duikers *Cephalophus dorsalis, niger* and *guevei mawelli,* leopard *Panthera pardus,* golden cat *Felis aurata,* civet *Viverra civetta,* otter *Lutra lutra,* bushbaby *Galago senegalensis,* potto *Perodicticus potto*; pythons; rarest species is the viviparous batrachian *Nectophrinoides occidentalis.*

2. BOUNA-KOMOE FAUNAL RESERVE AND PROTECTED FOREST (Yao Saraka).

II.

a) Status : less assured than that of No. 1 above, being described as " general protection, with specific provision for the total protection of all animal species and prohibition on the clearing and exploitation of the forest ".

b) Area : 900,000 ha recently reported to be 1,140,000 ha (incorporating Komoe National Park) which would place this reserve as no. 1 on the list.

c) Staff : 56 persons employed full-time on supervision and maintenance.

d) Budget : in 1963 U.S. $ 40,000 to cover staff salaries and $ 20,000 for equipment.

III.

Date established : the boundaries of a future Northern Ivory Coast park and reserve were decreed in 1926, with further Orders by the Governor in 1942, and the Governor General of French West Africa in 1953, the latter setting up the Reserve in its present form.

Administration : by the Hunting and Nature Protection Service of the Ministry of Agriculture's Water and Forests Department, though some modification is now being considered of the arrangements for managing the Reserve.

Land tenure : state ownership.

Tourism : there are some 500 km of tracks for the use of visitors, though they are only open for part of the year, after the grass has died back or been burnt off and until the break of the main rains. The camp-area at Ouango-Fitini at the northern end of the Reserve comprises a resthouse and three ' motel-type ' cabins, with modest restaurant facilities, totalling some 14 rooms and a dormitory with 42 beds and 10 camp-beds. There is a small 6-bed camp at Kapkin. About 1,000 visitors a year. A start has been made with the provision of information/education facilities.

Scientific research : no special organisation or publications so far, but separate cabins can be put at the disposal of research workers at the Ouango-Fitini Camp.

IV.

Altitude : 250-650 m.

a) A peneplain of a ruling level of 250-300 m from which rises a series of ridges and inselbergs of 500-650 m along the course of the Komoe river. Woody Guinean-type savannah and karite or butter-tree *Butyrospermum* savannah, open dry ' sau ' and ' somon ' (*Isoberlinia doka* and *Uapaca somon*) woodland, with patches of very dry woodland and also dense stands of forest marking the site of former villages; gallery forest, swamps and meadows occur along the Komoe.

b) The typical fauna of the Guinean savannah comprises hartebeest *Alcelaphus buselaphus,* roan *Hippotragus equinus* and kob *Kobus kob,* among larger antelopes, oribi *Ourebia ourebi* and bushbuck among smaller species, warthog, buffalo, elephant *Loxodonta africana,* hippopotamus *H. amphibius,* lion *Panthera leo,* leopard, spotted hyaena *C. crocuta* and baboon *P. papio.*

Areas excluded :

1. Banco National Park.

Established in 1953, a Protected Forest, with an arboretum and forest research station, which is the headquarters of the Ivory Coast Forest School. As such it serves as an experimental centre for high forest silviculture, species of particular economic value being artificially encouraged by planting and clearing, and, therefore, does not meet with the requirements for inclusion in the U.N. List, although qualifying in other respects (e.g. a staff of six for its 2,900 ha). It is a popular excursion area for the inhabitants of Abidjan, which is situated only a few kilometres away.

2. Sassandra or Tai Reserve.
425,000 ha, established 1956.

3. Asagny Reserve.
A hunting reserve of 30,000 ha, offering conducted hunting parties.

4. The Elephant Plain.
A partial reserve of 20,000 ha.

65. JAMAICA

Listed Areas : nil.

Explanation :

A letter of 28 January 1968 refers to some very small areas which are well-protected and of some scientific interest, namely :

The Botanical Gardens at Hope, Castleton, Cinchona and Bath.

The ' Beauty Spots ' of Bamboo Grove and Fern Gully.

These areas cannot, however, be included because the Botanical Gardens are essentially artificial plantations, while the Beauty Spots, although maintained in " an almost pristine or wild state ", are too small in relation to the criterion of 500 ha for a country which averages 160 inhabitants to the square kilometre.

Additionally, the island possesses a number of forest reserves, mostly dating from legal enactments of 1937 and 1941 and totalling 96,000 ha in extent or about 8.5 % of the surface of Jamaica. The relevant regulations applying to these areas, however, only prohibit shooting.

A sanctuary in which all animals would be fully protected was created in 1947 on the Healthshire Hills, but its status and other details of its present condition are not known.

I. **Listed Areas :** twenty-three.

1. Daisetsuzan National Park.
2. Bandai-Asahi National Park.
3. Jo-Shin-Etsu Kogen National Park.
4. Chubu Sangaku National Park.
5. Nikko National Park.
6. Fuji-Hakone-Izu National Park.
7. Chichibu-Tama National Park.
8. Shikotsu-Toya National Park.
9. Akan National Park.
10. Towada-Hachimantai National Park.
11. Aso National Park.
12. Seto Naikai National Park.
13. Yoshino-Kumano National Park.
14. Kirishima-Yaku National Park.
15. Ise-Shima National Park.
16. Hakusan National Park.
17. Shiretoko National Park.
18. Minami-Alps National Park.
19. Daisen-Oki National Park.
20. Unzen-Amakusa National Park.
21. Saikai National Park.
22. Rikuchu Kaigan National Park.
23. San-in Kaigan National Park.

General Introduction :

II. With reference to the information elsewhere summarised in Section II of the List, the situation in Japan, with its population density generally exceeding 250 inhabitants to the square kilometre, has posed some difficult problems in the application of the criteria laid down by the ICNP, comparable to those which have arisen, for example, in the case of Germany. Strict application of the criteria, which envisaged the recognition of those parts of the world's biotopes which have been effectively set aside from human exploitation in order to conserve them in what is judged to be a suitable state of natural balance, would have had the effect of giving a quite false idea of the vast, coherent and praiseworthy efforts of the Japanese authorities towards " the protection of places of scenic beauty and also, through the promoted utilisation thereof, a contribution to the health, recreation and culture of the people ".

The problem can be set out in a schematic way as follows, further details of certain developments being given, in the second part of this Introduction, under Section III :

1. In the face of the veritable flood of human activity in Japan — agricultural, industrial and urban —, certain areas or ' natural parks ' have been defined where, for the future, the flood can be dammed or canalised under legal sanction, mainly with a view to recreation and public health (it is the Minister of Health and Welfare who is responsible for these areas) but also, as far as possible, to preserve samples of natural biotopes deemed to be scientifically important.

300

2. These 'natural parks' fall into three categories, the National Parks proper, quasi-National Parks and the Natural Parks of the Prefectures (cf. the definitions in Section III below). Most of these areas satisfy the criteria of size and effective

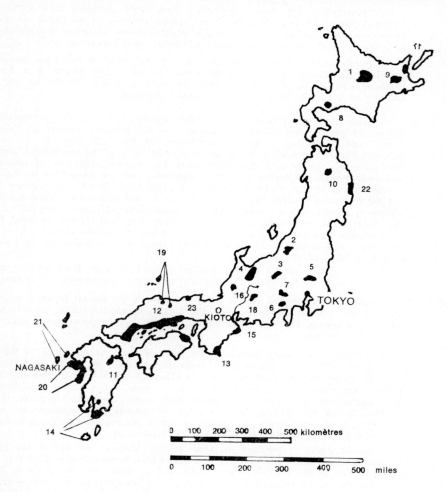

management. Thus for the 2,600,000 ha occupied by the National Parks and quasi-National Parks, the budget criterion for a densely populated country would have demanded an annual expenditure of about U.S. $ 500,000, whereas in fact, in 1965, expenditure totalled the equivalent of U.S. $ 1,500,000 (50,000 on supervision and administration and the rest on equipment). On the other hand, none of these Parks, with the exception of very small sections, enjoy the degree of absolute protection defined by the ICNP criterion. On the whole, therefore, they resemble the British 'National Parks' and the 'Natural Parks' of Germany, which have not been kept in the List, or still more perhaps what some countries call 'areas subject to landscape management regulations'.

3. Nonetheless, the basic Law of 1 June 1957 provides that within the National Parks and quasi-National Parks certain sections, to be known as special protection areas, can be put under much stricter control, involving the prohibition of domestic stock, wood-cutting, plant-collecting, animal-trapping, etc.

4. Furthermore, increasing use is in fact being made of this legal provision, so much so that although in 1960 there were no more than 40,000 ha in Special Protection Areas, by the end of 1965 the total exceeded 165,408 ha and the addition of a further 197,738 ha was "under planning".

To sum up, it has been decided after consultation with the authorities in Tokyo, to present this rather full account of the Japanese system of 'Natural Parks' and to include, somewhat arbitrarily, in the U.N. List all 23 of the National Parks proper, even though no more than 10 % of the two million hectares they comprise can be said in fact to meet the requisite standards of protection and even though the degree of control exercised over the remainder of the area is very similar to that which in the case of comparable British and German areas has led to exclusion from the List. It should be noted that this decision equally arbitrarily results in the omission of the 'quasi-National Parks', despite the fact that their status, while perhaps rather less firm than that of the National Parks proper, also provides for the creation of 'special protection areas'. It is also noted that almost all the 23 National Parks listed were included in the previous edition, E/3436, of the List.

For the above reasons in the detailed account of each Park set out below only the area is quoted under the marginal heading II (application of criteria).

III.   To avoid repetition and in order fully to elaborate the special Japanese situation, most of the general information on the legal and administrative aspects of the Parks, land tenure, tourism and scientific research can be conveniently dealt with in this Introduction.

Legislation: as already mentioned the basis of the 'natural parks' is the Law of 1 June 1957, which places them under the Minister of Health and Welfare. Also by virtue of this Law the latter is officially assisted by a 'Natural Parks Deliberative Council', on which provision is made for a strong representation of scientific interests. Three non-governmental bodies collaborate actively, though unofficially, in the framing and execution of natural park management policy, namely: the National Parks Association of Japan, the Nature Conservation Society of Japan and the People's Holiday Village Association.

National Parks proper are declared by the Minister on the advice of the Council and are administered by a National Parks Bureau of the Ministry. The same applies to the quasi-National Parks, but in their case the initiative comes from the Prefectures concerned, which also play a large part in their administration. Finally, as the name indicates, the category of 'Natural Parks of the Prefectures' is entirely within the competence of the latter to establish.

Administrative organisation: the combination of zones of varying status within a National Park or quasi-National Park has been indicated above. Every sector of a Park, unless it is made the subject of stricter regulations, is basically a "common", "general" or "ordinary" area, in which people may live and exploit the natural resources, but where, even if they own the land, they are prohibited by Article 20 of the Law from erecting buildings, interfering with volcanic strata and indulging in any kind of publicity unless they have previously given notice to the Governor of the Prefecture. Next comes the " developed area ", as determined by the Minister, in which the enjoyment of the public is safeguarded by prohibitions on rubbish-dumping, pollution of the atmosphere, disturbance of peace and quiet by loud-speakers, and so on. Similar prohibitions apply to the next category, the " special areas ", which the Minister is also empowered to demarcate in National Parks and quasi-National Parks and to which additional restrictions may apply, all human activities being subject to Ministerial approval. Finally, within these " special areas " the Minister may designate " special protection areas " still more strictly controlled.

One of the main differences between the National Parks proper and the quasi-National Parks, apart from the fact that the initiative for the creation of the latter lies with the Prefectures, is that the powers for establishing " special protection areas " in the quasi-National Parks has been less often used, only 2.6 % of their area having been so designated up to the end of 1965. The following table shows the very variable proportion of the different kinds of zone as between the two categories :

NATIONAL PARKS :

Special Protection Areas : as at the end of 1965 … … … … … …	7 %
Special Protection Areas : under consideration . … … … … … …	5 %
Special Areas … … … … … … … … … … … …	56 %
Common Areas . … … … … … … … … … … …	32 %

QUASI-NATIONAL PARKS :

Special Protection Areas . … … … … … … … … … …	3 %
Special Areas … … … … … … … … … … … …	59 %
Common Areas . … … … … … … … … … … …	38 %

Land tenure : in the National Parks proper about 62 % of the land is state-owned, 17 % public land and 21 % in private ownership, the equivalent percentage for the quasi-National Parks being 43 %, 17 % and 40 % — another indication of the comparatively weaker status of the second category.

Tourism : a great effort is made to encourage the use of the national parks by the public as places for rest, recreation, acquiring an interest in natural science and spiritual inspiration. Ten museums have been established, conducted tours are arranged and conferences are organised for visitors, especially during the period 21 July to 20 August as part of the so-called " Movement for communion with Nature ". The number of visitors bears witness to the success of these endeavours : in 1964, 162,920,000 people (including 230,592 foreigners) visited the National Parks and 84,891,000 the quasi-National Parks. A great range of facilities has been provided, especially in the " common areas ", for lodging, feeding and amusing tourists, although in fact this is only partly due to public enterprise, two-thirds of the $ 43,000,000 spent in 1962 on such developments in the natural parks as a whole having been private investment. This is of course a typical manifestation of the fact that people who own or live in areas in which other forms of economic exploitation are restricted claim the right to benefit and increase their incomes through the hotel and tourist industries.

Scientific research : a great deal of work is undertaken by the staff of the National Parks Bureau, members of the Natural Parks Council, the universities and other scientific institutions. Co-ordination, at least so far as publication of the results of this work is concerned, is assured by the National Parks Association of Japan.

Details : application of criteria (II), general information (III) and description (IV) :

1. DAISETSUZAN NATIONAL PARK (Hokkaido).

II. *b)* Area : 231,929 ha, with five Special Protection Areas (S.P.A.) of 10,970, 7,933, 3,464, 9,018 and 3,808 ha (none up to 1965).

III. *Date established :* 1934.

Tourism : numerous villages, the best ski runs in Japan on Mt. Tokachi, mountaineering, hot springs — " the greatest primeval park in Japan ".

IV. *Altitude :* 400-2,290 m.

a) Comprises the Ishikari mountain range and its assemblage of volcanic features : many lakes, gorges and waterfalls; ancient coniferous forest, alpine meadows.

b) Asiatic black bear *Selenarctos thibetanus japonicus,* Japanese macaque *Macaca fuscata,* northern pika *Ochotona hyperborea yesoensis,* chipmunk *Tamias sibiricus lineatus*; pine grosbeak *Pinicola enucleator,* three-toed woodpecker *Picoides tridactylus,* black woodpecker *Dryocopus martius.*

2. BANDAI-ASAHI NATIONAL PARK (Honshu).

II. *b)* Area : 189,661 ha in three separate sections, with S.P.A. totalling 17,139 ha in 1969 and expected to be increased by three more zones (1,026 ha).

III. *Date established :* 1950.

General : many villages, sulphur mining, forest exploitation, considerable areas of cultivation, artificial lake with hydroelectric installation.

Tourism : spas, mountaineering, ski-ing, sport-fishing, camping, conducted tours.

IV. *Altitude :* 100-2,128 m.

a) Extremely rugged terrain caused by volcanic activity and a very large earth movement in prehistoric times : they are still active volcanoes and lakes formed by volcanic action. The mountain slopes are covered with broad-leaved and coniferous forests. A notable plant is *Rhododendron fauriae* FRANCHET of the variety *nemotoanum* NAKAI.

b) Black bear, macaque, Japanese serow *Capricornis crispus*; many song-birds.

3. JO-SHIN-ETSU KOGEN NATIONAL PARK (Honshu).

II. *b)* Area : 188,915 ha, with 8 S.P.A. planned, totalling 10,082 ha in 1969.

III. *Date established :* 1949.

General : the Park itself is virtually uninhabited but there is a high population round its borders. Sulphur mining.

Tourism : highly developed, with more visitors than any other Park except Fuji-Hakone. Mountaineering, ski-ing, camping, riding.

IV. *Altitude :* 550-2,542 m.

a) The Mt. Tanigawa range extends along the north-east of the Park, while in the south there are plateaux and volcanoes, the most active of which is

Mt. Asama; many hot springs. The characteristic vegetation comprises the larch *Larix leptolepis* MURRAY, the broad-leaved birch *Betula platyphylla* SUKATCHEV and *Rhododendron japonicum* SURING.

b) Black bear, macaque, serow; song-birds.

4. CHUBU SANGAKU NATIONAL PARK (Honshu).

b) Area : 169,768 ha, including, in 1969, 63,522 ha of S.P.A. which covers various mountain massifs and two valleys and constitutes the largest S.P.A. in the country.

Date established : 1934.

General : part of the ' Japanese Alps ', with few inhabitants; hydroelectric barrages.

Tourism : many mountain huts, mountaineering, camping, ski-ing.

Altitude : 400-3,190 m.

a) A high mountain region, hence the name Japanese Alps, comprising both extinct and active volcanoes, gorges and glacial erosion. There are forests, alpine meadows and eternal snows. An interesting plant is *Chosenia arbustifolia* A. SKVORTSOV, a type of dwarf willow originally attributed to *Salix*.

b) Black bear, macaque, serow; golden eagle *Aquila chrysaëtos*, the mountain hawk-eagle *Spizaetus nipalensis,* ptarmigan *Lagopus mutus*; song-birds.

5. NIKKO NATIONAL PARK (Honshu).

b) Area : 140,698 ha, in three sections, of which the 14 S.P.A. in 1969 totalled 9,805 ha.

Date established : 1934.

General : there is a hydroelectric installation on Lake Chuzenji. Sulphur mining.

Tourism : vehicles can reach several points at a very high altitude. Many temples including the famous Toshogu Shrine. Spas, camping, ski-ing, organised excursions especially to the hot springs. A Wilderness Area at Oze.

Altitude : 300-2,578 m.

a) A volcanic landscape, with cones and crater lakes alternating, broadleafed and coniferous forest (some of the cedars about 300 years old), alpine meadows, waterfalls. A notable plant is the butterwort *Pinguicola racemosa* MIYOSHI.

b) Black bear, macaque, serow, sika *Cervus nippon centralis*; many species of birds, especially passerines, and some colourful insects.

6. FUJI-HAKONE-IZU NATIONAL PARK (Honshu).

b) Area : 122,309 ha, of which in 1969 the 17 small S.P.A. comprised 2,013 ha, but two additional large S.P.A. of 1,404 and 3,692 ha and 11 small ones totalling 842 ha are planned.

Date established : 1936, subsequently enlarged in 1938, 1955 and 1964.

General : it is scarcely necessary to remark on the role which Mt. Fuji has always played in the religious, social and artistic life of Japan. The inhabitants of the Park are mainly those concerned with the tourist industry, but there are some farmers and fishermen.

Tourism : by far the most frequently visited of the Parks, with about 20 million visitors a year. Facilities for them are elaborate : accommodation, camping sites, tourist trails, etc.; hot springs.

IV.　　*Altitude :* sea level to 3,776 m.

a) The volcanic profile of this Park includes the region of Mt. Hakone, the Izu peninsula with its hot springs, a string of seven islands (Izu Schichito) with their crater-lakes, lava cliffs and more hot springs, and Mt. Fuji itself of which the lower slopes are clothed in forest (azaleas, cherries, pines).

b) Sika, macaque, wild pig *Sus scrofa leucomystax,* Japanese dormouse *Glirulus japonensis;* the goshawk *Accipiter virgatus,* the fruit-pigeon *Columba janthiria,* the Japanese auk or murrelet *Synthliboramphus wumizusume* and other sea-birds such as the white-faced shearwater *Puffinus* (=*Calonectris*) *leucomelas;* passerines.

7. CHICHIBU-TAMA NATIONAL PARK (Honshu).

II.　　*b)* Area : 121,600 ha, with no S.P.A. in 1969 but two small ones planned, totalling 1,001 ha.

III.　　*Date established :* 1950.

General : the forest is exploited. An artificial lake forms part of Tokyo's water-supply.

Tourism : mountaineering is being rapidly promoted, camping, fishing, over 5 million visitors a year.

IV.　　*Altitude :* 200-2,600 m.

a) A mountain region of sedimentary rocks, deeply dissected by water courses; there is a bamboo zone and then, in succession, ancient pine forest, and mixed forest of firs, spruces *Picea* spp. and *Tsuga* spp, and pines.

b) Black bear, sika, serow, wild pig; passerine birds.

8. SHIKOTSU-TOYA NATIONAL PARK (Hokkaido).

II.　　*b)* Area : 98,660 ha, with in 1969 five S.P.A. totalling 1,408 ha.

General : many inhabitants and some farming. Hydroelectric installation.

Tourism : mountaineering, ski-ing, canoeing, sport-fishing, camping : the hot springs are a special attraction. Between 4 and 5 million visitors a year.

IV.　　*Altitude :* 80-1,893 m.

a) A region which is full of volcanic features, with some old forests including the beautiful forest of 'Yezo' fir around Lake Shikotsu; good alpine flora.

b) Brown bear *Ursus arctos yesoensis,* red squirrel *Sciurus vulgaris orientalis,* the sable *Martes zibellina brachyura,* the varying hare *Lepus timidus ainu.*

9. AKAN NATIONAL PARK (Hokkaido).

II.　　*b)* Area : 87,498 ha, with in 1969 four S.P.A. totalling 8,445 ha.

306

Date established : 1934.

General : inhabited by some groups of the aboriginal Ainu tribe. There are hydroelectric installations and a railway traverses the Park.

Tourism : mountaineering, ski-ing, hot springs and spas, fishing, water-sports and conducted tours.

Altitude : 120-1,502 m.

a) The volcanic region of eastern Hokkaido, with active volcanoes, numerous lakes and caldera lakes (Akan, Kutcharo and Mashu) and hot springs; in the caldera areas there is old coniferous forest, with rhododendrons, azaleas and birch trees.

b) Brown bear, sable, squirrel, stoat *Mustela erminea orientalis,* raccoon dog *Nyctereutes procyonoides albus,* sika, chipmunk *Tamias sibericus lineatus*; pine grosbeak, great grey shrike *Lanius excubitor,* black woodpecker, the eagle-owl *Bubo blakistoni; Aegagropila sauteri* KÜTH, a sponge, is also noted, but probably in error.

10. TOWADA-HACHIMANTAI NATIONAL PARK (Honshu).

b) Area : 83,351 ha, with seven S.P.A. in 1969, totalling 9,422 ha.

Date established : 1936, modified in 1956.

General : hydroelectric installations, sulphur mining.

Tourism : plentiful accommodation; ski-ing, camping, mountaineering, canoeing, conducted tours.

Altitude : 500-2,041 m.

a) In the north of the Park there is a double caldera, the bottom of which is occupied by a lake and the Hakkoda volcanic cones; around the lake and and the Oirase river which flows out of it, there is some mature broad-leaf forest; on the slopes of the volcanoes conifers and alpine flora. The Hachimantai sector of the Park comprises a string of volcanoes and a plateau covered with ancient conifer forests.

b) Black bear, macaque, serow, dormouse, badger *Meles meles anakuma.*

11. ASO NATIONAL PARK (Kyushu).

b) Area : 73,060 ha, with S.P.A. totalling 1,063 ha in 1969 and two more planned, of a total of 3,756 ha.

Date established : 1934.

General : the low lying central area is highly populated (60,000 people) with farms, domestic stock and plantations.

Tourism : more than 2 million visitors a year. A railway traverses the Park, through which also passes the finest ' Parkway' of Japan; there is also a network of tourist roads; conducted tours, mountaineering.

Altitude : 220-1,788 m.

a) A sunken crater or caldera of Aso volcano, surrounded by other mountains and volcanoes, some still active : erosion is often very pronounced on the slopes of the volcanoes; there are stretches of grassland, alpine meadows and volcanic cinder zones.

b) Sika, macaque, black bear; plentiful bird life.

12. SETO NAIKAI NATIONAL PARK (on the Inland Sea).

II.   *b)* Area : 65,925 ha, with three small S.P.A. totalling 370 ha (1969).

III.   *Date established :* 1934.

General : there are fishing villages along the shores and on the 600 or s(
islands and islets in the Park.

Tourism : a pilgrimage area; tourist recreations include yachting, canoeing
swimming, sport-fishing, camping and mountaineering.

IV.   *Altitude :* sea level to 932 m.

a) Nearly 600 islands and islets and part of the main shore of Honshu an(
Shikoku; forest of black pines; rapids.

b) Macaque, sika, wild pig; the sealion *Neophoca cinerea* (*Neophocaen*
phacoenoides auct.).

13. YOSHINO-KUMANO NATIONAL PARK (Honshu).

II.   *b)* Area : 55,936 ha; no S.P.A. in 1969, but four small ones planned, total
ling 967 ha.

III.   *Date established :* 1936.

General : the area contains a number of historic sites and is frequented b
itinerant priests of a mountain sect. There is a hydroelectric barrage.

Tourism : spas, water-sports.

IV.   *Altitude :* sea level to 1,915 m.

a) The northern sector is notable for its cherry trees; the south comprise
mountain ridges and plateaux, with thick forest, gorges and waterfalls, alon
a geological fault line which, with its upthrust and sunken blocks, can be see
very clearly along the sea coast.

b) sika, black bear, serow; passerine song-birds.

14. KIRISHIMA-YAKU NATIONAL PARK (Kyushu).

II.   *b)* Area : 55,231 ha, with S.P.A. totalling 10,793 ha in 1969 and anoth(
six, totalling 2,514 ha, under planning.

III.   *Date established :* 1934, enlarged in 1964.

General : lightly inhabited and not much exploited. There are some famo(
temples.

Tourism : mountaineering, camping; hot springs.

IV.   *Altitude :* 200-1,700 m.

a) The region comprises 23 volcanoes, several of them active, others extin(
and containing calderas; hot springs, evergreen forest on the slopes and azale
Rhododendron kiusianum scattered along the summits. The mainland Cape Sac
sector has a subtropical vegetation, while the offshore island of Yakushin
has some original forest of Japanese cedar *Cryptomeria japonica* D. DON date
as 3,000 years old (now under threat of felling for its valuable timber).

b) Japanese dormouse, macaque, wild pig, sika; the brown booby *Su*
leucogaster, the white-rumped copper pheasant *Phasianus soemmeringii ijm(*
and roller *Eurystomus orientalis*; song-birds and other passerines.

308

15. ISE-SHIMA NATIONAL PARK (Honshu).

b) Area : 52,036 ha, with one 500 ha S.P.A. proposed (none in 1969).

Date established : 1946.

General : a large population of fishermen and producers of cultured pearls. Since the very earliest times in the history of Japan Ise-Shima has been a national religious centre for Shintoism.

Tourism : over 5 million visitors a year : mountaineering, yachting.

Altitude : sea level to 553 m.

a) The archipelago of the Shima peninsula, composed of palaeozoic, mesozoic and tertiary sedimentary formations.

b) No information.

16. HAKUSAN NATIONAL PARK (Honshu).

b) Area : 47,402 ha, with one S.P.A. (1969) of 18,080 ha.

Date established : 1962 (before which it was a ' quasi '-National Park).

General : there are ancient temples. Anti-erosion works have been undertaken.

Tourism : this Park is difficult of access except on foot. Mountaineering is permitted in the S.P.A. or Wilderness Area.

Altitude : highest point 2,702 m.

a) A mountain chain of about 2,000 m in altitude with many volcanic features; old forest of *Abies mariesii, Fagus crenata* BLUME and *Quercus crispula*; alpine flora and permanent snow at higher levels.

b) Sika (subsp. *centralis*), macaque, black bear, serow; golden eagle, Japanese hawk-eagle, ptarmigan.

17. SHIRETOKO NATIONAL PARK (Hokkaido).

b) Area : 41,375 ha, with in 1969 four S.P.A. totalling 21,317 ha.

Date established : 1964.

General : the wildest Park in Japan, with very few inhabitants, visited mainly by mountaineers.

Altitude : sea level to 1,600 m.

a) The Chishima volcanic range; lakes, swamps, mature forest of white and silver firs and of yew *Taxus cuspidata*.

b) Red fox *Vulpes v. schrencki*, stoat, steller's sealion *Eumetopias jubatus*, Californian sealion *Zalophus californianus*, brown bear, sika (subsp. *yesoensis*); white-tailed sea-eagle *Haliaetus albicilla*, Steller's sea-eagle *Haliaetus pelagicus*; many bird species are found on the cliffs along the sea.

18. MINAMI ALPS NATIONAL PARK (Honshu).

b) Area : 35,799 ha, with in 1969 four S.P.A. totalling 9,181 ha.

Date established : 1964.

General : a representative sample of a mountain National Park. There is a little forest exploitation.

IV. *Altitude :* about 3,000 m.

a) A high mountain zone, with rocky pinnacles and cliffs; virgin boxwood forest; some silver fir, spruce *Picea yezoensis* and alpine flora.

b) Sika (subsp. *centralis*), macaque, wild pig, serow; golden eagle, Japanese hawk-eagle, ptarmigan.

19. DAISEN-OKI NATIONAL PARK (Honshu).

II. *b*) Area : 31,927 ha, with in 1969 thirteen small S.P.A. totalling 1,433 ha.

III. *Date established :* 1936, the Oki sector added in 1953.

General : there is forest exploitation and new planting in some areas. Religious monuments of a kind which commands special veneration and protection.

Tourism : mountaineering, ski-ing.

IV. *Altitude :* sea level to 1,723 m.

a) Includes many islands of the central part of the coast of the Sea of Japan, most of them bounded by cliffs and averaging about 250 m in height. The Park also contains several mountains, including Mt. Daisen which is a conical peak; grassy plains and, at higher levels, pine forest, beech, alpine meadows and permanent snow. Noted for occurrence of the yew *Taxus cuspidata* SIEB. et ZUCC. var. *nana* REHD.

b) Japanese hare *Lepus brachyurus okiensis*; many birds, especially song-birds and such sea-bird species as the white-faced shearwater and the black-tailed gull *Larus crassirostris*.

20. UNZEN-AMAKUSA NATIONAL PARK (Kyushu).

II. *b*) Area : 25,600 ha in two sections, of which in 1969 S.P.A. comprise 608 ha.

III. *Date established :* 1934.

General : the Unzen sector has few inhabitants, but there are many villages in the Amakusa sector. The Park contains the ruins of some of the earliest Christian missions in Japan.

Tourism : camping, mountaineering, horse-riding, golf; hot springs.

IV. *Altitude :* sea level to 1,360 m.

a) The northern, Unzen, sector includes the massif of Mt. Fugendake and some other volcanic peaks, and numerous hot springs; azaleas, box-trees and fine forests of broad-leaf species, many species of heath. The Amakusa sector which is in effect an archipelago, presents a more gentle landscape.

b) Sika (subsp. *nippon*); blue-winged pitta *Pitta brachyura*, shelduck *Tadorna tadorna* (wintering); song-birds and other passerines.

21. SAIKAI NATIONAL PARK (Kyushu).

II. *b*) Area : 24,324 ha with in 1969 three small S.P.A. totalling 55 ha.

III. *Date established :* 1955.

General : people have settled in the Park within recent years, but there are some small uninhabited islands which are effectively safeguarded from disturbance.

Tourism : despite its comparatively small size the Park is popular with tourists and there are over 2 million visitors a year. Access is largely by water.

Altitude : sea level to 568 m.

a) A portion of the coast facing continental China which has been partially submerged, leaving numerous small islands and the volcanic Goto archipelago with its bays and cliffs.

b) No information.

22. RIKUCHU KAIGAN NATIONAL PARK (Honshu).

b) Area : 11,584 ha, with in 1969 seven small S.P.A. totalling 454 ha.

Date established : 1955, enlarged in 1964.

General : access to the Park is difficult, since it mainly consists of a 140 km stretch of rugged sea coast inhabited by a few fishermen.

Altitude : sea level to 500 m.

a) The cliffs along the 140 km Pacific coastline are 100 m high and composed of tertiary rocks in the north, and 250 m high in the south, where they are mainly of cretaceous and palaeozoic origin, interspersed with small sandy bays. The coast is covered with conifer and broad-leaf woods and marks the northern limit of the flora of the warmer temperate climatic zone.

b) Serow, sika (subsp. *centralis*); notable for its sea birds, including Swinhoe's fork-tailed petrel *Oceanodroma monorhis,* the Madeiran fork-tailed petrel *Oceanodroma castro,* white-faced shearwater and black-tailed gull.

23. SAN-IN KAIGAN NATIONAL PARK (Honshu).

b) Area : 8,996 ha, with in 1969 five small S.P.A. totalling 556 ha.

Date established : 1964.

Altitude : sea level to 250 m.

a) A sea-coast Park, with various kinds of reef, many headlands, islands and islets and, in general, interesting geological features of basaltic type; cliffs, caves and dunes.

b) Macaque; sea birds; white stork *Ciconia ciconia.*

Areas excluded :

A. — As explained in the first part of the Introduction, 24 ' Quasi '-National Parks, totalling 593,831 ha in area, most of which were included in the previous edition, E/3436, of the List.

B. — 240 Parks of the Prefectures, totalling 1,816,753 ha (1965 figures).

C. — 5 small strict nature reserves, 141 geological reserves, 515 botanical reserves, 109 zoological reserves, 93 forest reserves and 285 areas known as Wild-life Sanctuaries, which altogether total 84,780 ha or an average of 74 ha for each of these 1,148 reserves.

I.   **Listed Areas :** nil.

V.   a) **Explanation :**
         A letter dated 7 September 1963 from the Jordanian Government confirmed
that at that date no national parks or equivalent reserves existed in the country.
         However, shortly before this Second Edition of the List went to press, the
first information was received of an area which will certainly merit inclusion as
soon as conditions prevail which allow it to be properly established — namely
the Azraq Desert National Park.
         The creation of the Azraq Desert National Park was announced in an official
document dated 26 July 1965 and followed recommendations of the British Jordan
Expedition of 1963.   The main features of the Park were described as follows :

         Situation : 100 km east of Amman in the area of Jordan projecting between
Syria and northern Saudi Arabia.

         General designation : a scenic-scientific-historical area.

         Area : 400,000 ha, including a large oasis.

         Administration : by the Division of National Parks and Historic Monuments
of the Jordan Tourism Authority.

         Supervision : no details given, but known to be in course of organisation.

         Description : the oasis included in the Park and therefore to be protected, has
the only permanent water in a desert area of some 3 million hectares and as
such is a powerful attraction to migratory birds.   The surrounding desert is of
three types : salt desert, calcareous and basaltic.   The Park contains an historic
monument — a fort dating from Roman times and used in 1917 by T. E. Lawrence
during the Arab Revolt.

         Tourism : no facilities yet established, but they are being planned.

         b) **Other Areas excluded from the List :**
         A. — Forest land, amounting to 52,676 ha and in private ownership, which is
de facto forest reserve and well supervised.

         B. — Three other National Parks are proposed by the Royal Hashemite Govern-
ment, of which the first two were also recommended by the British Jordan
Expedition 1963, and plans for establishing and maintaining them are under
consideration.

         1. WADI RUM NATIONAL PARK.
         In the south-west of the country, near the Saudi-Arabian border and not far
from the northern end of the Gulf of Aqaba.   The area would be about 100,000 ha
It includes some fine mountain and desert landscapes; access only by four-wheel
drive vehicles, camels or horseback.

         2. THE PETRA AND RIFT VALLEY NATIONAL PARK.
         At the south end of the Dead Sea on the frontier with Israel.   The area would
be about 140,000 ha.   Includes the " world famous spectacular Nabatean city
carved in the cliffs and a portion of the great Afro-Asian Rift Valley ".   There is
a resthouse near Petra and a campsite on the spot.

312

3. AJLUN FOREST NATIONAL PARK.

A recreational area, west of Jerash, containing the firwoods which occupy the slopes of Jordan's highest mountain.

C. — The Qumran National Historic Monument.

Created in 1965, half way between Amman and Jerusalem and some 4 miles from the Dead Sea Hotel. The area is about 800 ha and is administered by the Division of National Parks and Historic Monuments of the Jordan Tourism Authority. Its purpose is to safeguard the sites where the Essenes prepared and hid the famous Dead Sea Scrolls.

D. — Two other Historic Monuments are in course of establishment :
1. Jerash National Historic Monument (120 ha).
2. Samaria-Sybastin National Historic Monument (40 ha).

68. KENYA

Listed Areas : twelve.

A. — NATIONAL PARKS :
1. Tsavo National Park.
2. Meru National Park.
3. Aberdare National Park.
4. Mount Kenya National Park.
5. Mount Elgon National Park.
6. Nairobi National Park.
7. Nakuru National Park.

B. — COUNTY COUNCIL GAME RESERVES (formerly known as African District Council Reserves) :
8. Masai Mara Game Reserve.
9. Isiolo Buffalo Spring Game Reserve.
10. Samburu Uaso Nyiro Game Reserve.

C. — OTHER RESERVES :
11. South-west Mau Nature Reserve.
12. Marsabit National Reserve.

General Introduction :

Administration :

a) the National Parks are administered by a Board of Trustees set up under Ordinance No. 9 of 1945 as amended in 1964.

b) The County Council Game Reserves are controlled by County Council By-laws, as regards land use and human activities, while game aspects are dealt with by the Game Department under the Wild Animals Protection Act.

c) The Nature Reserves are declared and administered by the Forest Department under the Forest Act, but the Chief Game Warden has to be consulted on faunal problems. The Marsabit National Reserve is administered by the National Parks authorities.

Land tenure : all the land is in public ownership.

KENYA

Tourism : organised by the Board of Trustees in the National Parks, though concessions for the management of one or two of the Tourist Lodges have been granted to private enterprise. The County Councils are responsible in their Reserves, but are assisted by the Game Department and have also granted some concessions. There is no special organisation in the other Reserves.

The first seven of the Listed Areas were included in the previous edition of the List, E/3436 and Part Two.

Details : application of criteria (II), general information (III) and description (IV) :

A. — NATIONAL PARKS.

1. TSAVO NATIONAL PARK.

II.
    a) Status : strict protection, no inhabitants and no exploitation allowed except for one isolated mine and the piping of water to Mombasa from the Mzima springs.

    b) Area : 2,080,000 ha.

    c) Staff : 204 units.

    d) Budget : U.S. $ 144,000 (£ 60,000).

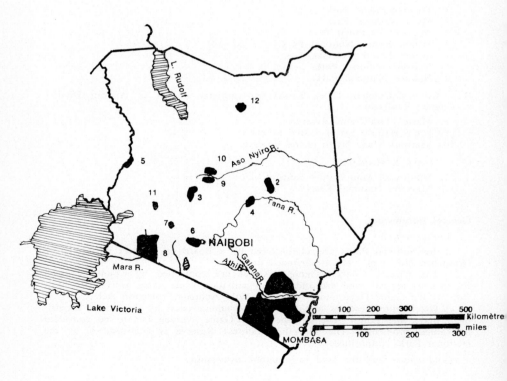

314

Date established : 1948.

Tourism : 800 miles of motorable track; many airstrips; three safari-lodges, at Kilaguni, Kitani and Aruba; 40,000 visitors in 1964-1965.

Altitude : 600-2,600 m.

a) A semi-arid plateau, covered with thick thorn bush, many baobabs *Adansonia digitata,* euphorbias and acacias; there are volcanic cones, with old lava streams, and mountain ranges in the western part of the Park, where the Mzima springs are also situated.

b) The main reserve for the typical Kenya fauna, including elephant *Loxodonta africana,* buffalo *Syncerus caffer,* black rhinoceros *Diceros bicornis,* lion and leopard *Panthera leo* and *pardus,* hippopotamus and many species of antelope such as lesser kudu *Tragelaphus imberbis* and the beisa or fringe-eared oryx *Oryx gazella.* The Park has been the scene of a serious phenomenon, the problem presented by an excessive increase in its elephant population.

c) Black rhinoceros.

2. MERU NATIONAL PARK.

a) Status : no exploitation or occupancy allowed.

b) Area : 103,600 ha.

c) Staff : in 1966, County Council : 1 warden and 20 full-time rangers; Game Department : 1 warden and 30 game-scouts (part-time or for general supervision) and no doubt maintained or increased under National Parks management.

d) Budget : U.S. $ 26,400 (£ 11,000) in 1964.

Date established : 1960; upgraded to National Park from Game Reserve in 1967.

Tourism : access by road and two airstrips. Accommodation at Leopard Rock Lodge (20 beds) and Kenmare Lodge (12 beds); camping sites. Some 300 miles of motor-tracks run through the Reserve. 812 visitors in 1963.

Altitude : 300-1,320 m.

a) The greater part of the Reserve is covered with more or less dense bush, but there are some open grasslands, swamps and clumps of forest.

b) A good selection of East African mammals, including lesser kudu, bushbuck, eland, duiker, Jackson's hartebeest, beisa oryx, Grevy's zebra *Equus grevyi,* reticulated giraffe, black rhinoceros, lion, leopard, cheetah *Acinonyx jubatus,* hippopotamus, warthog *Phacochoerus aethiopicus.*

c) Black rhinoceros.

3. ABERDARE NATIONAL PARK.

a) Status : strict protection.

b) Area : 59,050 ha.

c) Staff : 138 units shared with No. 3 below.

d) Budget : U.S. $ 42,240 (£ 17,600) shared with No. 3.

Date established : 1950.

Tourism : one main road runs through the Park, with branching secondary roads. One Lodge, the famous ' Treetops ' hotel. 16,420 visitors in 1964-1965.

315

IV.

Altitude : 2,000-4,000 m.

a) The vegetational stages comprise montane mesophile forest, bamboos, *Hagenia* and *Hypericum* woodland and, from about 3,300 m, an afro-alpine zone with peat-bogs.

b) Elephant, buffalo, black rhinoceros, bongo *Taurotragus eurycerus* (not numerous), waterbuck *Kobus ellipsiprymnus,* bushbuck *Tragelaphus scriptus,* giant forest hog *Hylochoerus meinertzhageni,* leopard, duiker *Cephalophus* sp., black-and-white colobus *Colobus polykomos.*

c) Black rhinoceros.

4. MOUNT KENYA NATIONAL PARK.

II.

a) Status : strict protection.

b) Area : 58,790 ha.

c) Staff : 138 units shared with No. 2.

d) Budget : U.S. $ 42,240, shared with No. 2.

III.

Date established : 1949.

Tourism : three motorable tracks go as far as the snow-line. The only accommodation is the hut of the 'Mountain Club of Kenya'. Visitors are not very numerous.

IV.

Altitude : 3,300-5,194 m.

a) An ancient volcanic cone with signs of glaciation (moraines) down to 3,000 m. The vegetation belts comprise : below the Park proper, mesophile montane forest dominating *Themeda* grassland; also below the Park and up to about 3,200 m bamboo; alpine zone from 3,300-4,500 m, with giant groundsel *Senecio* sp. and lobelias divided into a lower and upper zone at the 3,860 m level. Above 4,500 m, glaciers and permanent snow fields.

b) Elephant, buffalo, black rhinoceros, bongo (a few), bushbuck, blue duiker *Cephalophus monticola,* giant forest hog, colobus monkey, leopard.

c) Black rhinoceros.

5. MOUNT ELGON NATIONAL PARK.

II.

a) Status : strict protection.

b) Area : about 15,000 ha.

c) Staff : in 1966, Forest Department : a Forest Officer and the large subordinate staff responsible for the Mt. Elgon forest; Game Department : 1 warden and 20 part-time game scouts, and no doubt maintained or increased under National Parks management.

d) Budget : no known.

III.

Date established : 1958 to 1964, under the Forest Act; upgraded to National Park in 1967.

Tourism : tracks and paths have been developed mainly for supervisory purposes.

IV.

Altitude : lies roughly between the 1,500 and 2,500 m contours. The summit of Mt. Elgon is 4,321 m.

a) Occupies the eastern flank of the mountain; contains a fine sample of *Podocarpus,* damp forest with some African mahogany *Khaya senegalensis,* bamboo.

b) Elephant, buffalo, leopard; noted for its variety of forest duikers of which the taxonomy is not yet fully understood.

6. Nairobi National Park.

a) Status : no cultivation, wood-cutting, hunting or fishing allowed, but eight families of Somali herdsmen have been allowed to remain for the last 30 years and possess about 20 cattle and 25 sheep apiece.

b) Area : 11,400 ha.

c) Staff : 120 units.

d) Budget : U.S. $ 70,800 (£ 29,500).

Date established : 1946.

General : crucially important to this Park is the protection which could be given by the implementation of a plan to set up the Ngong Hills County Council Game Reserve in the area immediately to the west.

Tourism : about 100 miles of motor tracks, no accommodation (but Nairobi is very near). Great number of visitors, 105,000 in 1964-1965.

Altitude : 1,500-1,800 m.

a) Open-type upland plateau, with some bush and woody savannah (dominated by acacia species) and on the western border some dry forest.

b) Fauna of the Masai Plains : lion, leopard, a few black rhinoceros, buffalo, zebra *Equus burchelli,* impala *Aepyceros melampus,* eland *Taurotragus oryx,* wildebeest *Connochaetes taurinus,* Thomson's and Grant's gazelles *Gazella thomsoni* and *granti;* waterbuck, hartebeest *Alcelaphus buselaphus,* giraffe *Giraffa camelopardalis;* Masai ostrich *Struthio camelus,* kori bustard *Choriotis kori,* secretary-bird *Sagittarius serpentarius,* Hartlaub's lourie *Turacus hartlaubi,* speckled and blue-naped colies *Colius striatus* and *macrourus.*

c) Black rhinoceros.

7. Nakuru National Park.

a) Status : strict protection.

b) Area : 4,660 ha.

c) Staff : 13 units, plus some unpaid helpers.

d) Budget : U.S. $ 7,200 (£ 3,000).

Date established : 1961.

Tourism : there is a track along one side of the Lake. No accommodation, but Nakuru is very close. The number of visitors is growing.

Altitude : 1,750 m.

a) A salt lake of the Great Rift Valley.

b) 370 species of birds, notably the greater and lesser flamingoes *Phoenicopterus ruber* and *Phoeniconaias minor* which fluctuate in numbers (1,250,000 counted on one date in 1961).

B. — COUNTY COUNCIL GAME RESERVES.

8. MASAI MARA GAME RESERVE.

II.
a) Status : 64,750 ha are fully protected, with no exploitation or habitations; the rest is open to grazing by cattle, sheep and goats, though the wild fauna is protected.

b) Area : 151,300 ha.

c) Staff : County Council provides 1 assistant warden and 20 full-time rangers, Game Department 1 senior warden and 35 game scouts (part-time but ensuring adequate supervision).

d) Budget : U.S. $ 28,800 (£ 12,000).

III.
Date established : 1961 (includes the former Mara National Reserve, established in 1950 with an area of 64,750 ha).

Administration : by a Committee appointed by the Narok County Council.

Tourism : In the completely protected central 64,750 ha area, there are 160 km of motor track; the main road traversing the Reserve leads to the Serengeti National Park in Tanzania. Airstrip. Accommodation in the 40-bed Keekorok Lodge at the centre of the Reserve and camping sites on the periphery. 1,848 visitors in 1963.

IV.
Altitude : 1,500-1,650 m.

a) A vast plain dissected by strips of riverine vegetation along the drainage lines; some acacia forests and thickets especially on the hills. The Mara river runs through the Reserve.

b) Thomson's and Grant's gazelles are numerous, giraffe, buffalo, black rhinoceros, Burchell's zebra, elephant, warthog, lion, leopard, cheetah, hunting-dog *Lycaon pictus,* wildebeest and many antelope species, including topi *Damaliscus korrigum* and roan *Hippotragus equinus* which do not occur in any other Kenya Parks.

c) Black rhinoceros.

9. ISIOLO BUFFALO SPRING GAME RESERVE.

II.
a) Status : strict protection like No. 10 which it adjoins.

b) Area : 19,425 ha.

c) Staff : County Council, 6 full-time rangers; Game Department, 1 warden and 35 game-scouts (part-time or general supervision).

d) Budget : U.S. $ 12,000 (£ 5,000).

III.
Date established : 1964.

General : this Reserve forms a single unit with the Samburu Uaso Nyiro Game Reserve (No. 10) on the other side of the river, but as it lies in a different County Council area (Isiolo), its control is vested in a different authority.

Tourism : about 160 km of track which are connected with those of the neighbouring Reserve by a bridge over the Uaso Nyiro river. Airstrip. No accommodation (visitors stay at the Samburu Lodge). Camping site.

IV.
Altitude : 1,300 m.

a) On the south bank of the Uaso Nyiro, opposite the Samburu Uaso Nyiro Game Reserve of which it is in effect an extension, since the river is narrow enough to allow animals to cross it freely.

318

b) The large number of species includes spotted and striped hyaena *C. crocuta* and *H. hyaena,* serval *Felis serval,* leopard, lion, cheetah, elephant, Burchell's and Grevy's zebras, black rhinoceros, warthog, reticulated giraffe, bushbuck, eland, buffalo, both races of waterbuck, beisa oryx, klipspringer *O. oreotragus,* dikdik *Madoqua* sp., impala, gerenuk *Litocranius walleri,* Grant's gazelle, hunting-dog and crocodile; birds are very numerous, ranging from the Somali or blue-necked race of ostrich to waxbills *Estrilda* spp.

c) Black rhinoceros.

10. SAMBURU UASO NYIRO GAME RESERVE.

a) Status : total protection, no exploitation or occupancy.

b) Area : 10,360 ha, with a surrounding Controlled Area of 129,500 ha, where hunting is prohibited, and with the Isiolo reserve, No. 9 adjoining.

c) Staff : County Council : 1 assistant warden and 10 full-time rangers; Game Department : 1 senior warden and 35 game-scouts (part-time or for general supervision).

d) Budget : U.S. $ 19,200 (£ 8,000).

Date established : 1962.

Tourism : airstrip; about 160 km of track; confortable lodge accommodating 34 visitors, of whom there were 4,424 in 1963.

Altitude : 1,300 m.

a) With the Isiolo Buffalo Spring Reserve forms the only protected area in the arid region typical of northern Kenya; plains covered with open savannah of the Sahelian type, where the dominant grass is *Cynodon plectostachyus* and various species of acacia are the dominant trees.

b) The fauna is very similar to that of the Isiolo reserve (No. 9 above) and contains the same species, though the vulturine guineafowl *Acryllium vulturinum* is worth special mention among the birds.

C. — OTHER RESERVES.

11. SOUTH-WEST MAU NATURE RESERVE.

a) Status : total protection, treated as a strict nature reserve.

b) Area : 42,570 ha.

c) Staff : Forest Department : a Forest Officer and the large staff responsible for the south-western sector of the Mau Forest; Game Department : one full-time game scout.

d) Budget : not known exactly, as it forms part of the general departmental provision.

Date established : 1961, under the Forest Act.

Tourism : as the Reserve is administered as a strict Nature Reserve, there is no provision for visitors and motorable tracks are restricted to the minimum necessary for supervision.

Altitude : 2,400-2,700 m.

a) Part of the high primary forest of the Mau, dominated by cedar *Juniperus procera* and *Podocarpus* in an undisturbed climax, with some stands of bamboo and a number of open glades. The principal objective of the Reserve is to protect the bongo of which it contains the largest concentration in East Africa.

b) Bongo, yellow-backed duiker *Cephalophus silvicultor,* golden cat *Felis aurata* and brush-tailed porcupine *Atherus africanus* (elsewhere unknown in Kenya); also elephant, buffalo, leopard, giant forest hog.

12. MARSABIT NATIONAL RESERVE.

II.
a) Status : strict protection; may possibly be declared as a National Park.
b) Area : 14,250 ha.
c) Staff : 10 units.
d) Budget : U.S. $ 5,140 (£ 2,100).

III.
Date established : 1950, under National Parks administration.

Tourism : airstrip; a small Lodge (six beds)

IV.
Altitude : 1,200-1,950 m.

a) A volcanic massif covered in forest.

b) Many large mammals, including elephant and greater kudu *Tragelaphus strepsiceros.*

V.   **Areas excluded :**

A. — Three National Parks of very small size, which are of purely historic or archaeological interest; but mentioned in the previous edition, E/3436, of the List :
1. Olorgesaille National Park ... ...   21 ha.
2. Gedi National Park . ...   42 ha.
3. Fort Jesus National Park ... ...   2 ha.

B. — Masai Amboseli County Council Game Reserve (326,000 ha).

The inclusion of this area in the List (a good description of it is given in Part Two of the previous edition) has been deemed incompatible with the fundamental principle laid down in the criterion of ' strict conservation ', due to the concessions which have had to be made to the local Masai tribesmen, notably in regard to the grazing of their stock. One must express the hope — particularly in the case of such a world famous area as Amboseli — that measures may be taken to confer a sufficiently strict status of protection on at least one or more specific sectors of what at present can only be regarded as a partly protected area. The Kajiado County Council, which is responsible for the Reserve, has in fact already applied certain ' by-laws ' prohibiting cultivation and restricting grazing in some sectors (notably those which constituted the former National Reserves of Ngong and West Chyulu, 117,845 and 37,550 ha, respectively, established in 1961). But these measures do not yet go far enough to justify the restoration of Amboseli to the U.N. List.

C. — Watumu Fish Protection Area.

This area does not yet fully correspond to the objective of a ' Marine Park ', only certain methods of underwater fishing being prohibited. However, it has since been reported that in March 1968, two proper Marine Parks were established : the first at Watamu itself (1,165 ha) and the other at Malindi (583 ha). They should make an interesting addition to the next edition of the List.

320

69. KOREA (South) ([1])

Listed Areas : nil.

Explanation :

The Republic of Korea has made a great effort to strengthen the conservation of the country's natural resources and to set aside certain areas as nature reserves or national parks. A 'Bureau of Management for Cultural Treasures' has been charged with promoting implementation of measures contained in an 'Act for Cultural Property Preservation', which provides particularly for the creation of national parks and equivalent reserves. A National Park Commission was set up in 1967.

Following a report presented to the Government by Dr. George C. Ruhle in 1966, the first National Park, Chiri-san, of 43,890 ha, was declared in December 1967 and a management and development plan completed a year later. In December 1968, three more National Parks were added : Han-ryo on the coast, 34,660 ha, Kyeryong-san, 6,010 ha and Kyongju, 10,210 ha. The first of these consists of six separate sections, covering the places of greatest scenic beauty and most important historic monuments. The third is also divided into three sections, one on the coast, the other two in mountain areas. Development plans are in preparation for all Parks and three additional Parks were created in 1970 : Hanran-san in Jeju, 8,180 ha, Sorak-san, 20,640 ha, and Sokni Mountains, 6,000 ha, while three more will receive careful consideration at a future date. So far none of these parks are properly staffed.

There are therefore good grounds for hoping that the names of some Korean National Parks will soon qualify for inclusion in the next edition of the U.N. List. In the Republic as a whole there are, however, already some 111 protected areas, made up of 30 zoological, 78 botanical and 3 geological reserves.

70. KUWAIT

Listed Areas : nil.

Explanation :

The information on Kuwait is still only derived from foreign sources, since no reply has been received from the Kuwait Government.

71. LAOS

Listed Areas : nil.

Explanation :

According to a statement made by the Laotion delegation at the Conference on the Conservation of Nature and Natural Resources in South-East Asia, held at Bangkok in November-December 1965, no area in Laos fulfilled the criteria laid down by the ICNP.

([1]) North Korea, which is not yet a member of the U.N., also has a number of Reserves, such as the Natural Park of Mount Chilbo.

There are nevertheless several regions in the country which, by virtue of their biological interest and the relatively untouched state of their natural associations, would be eminently suitable for the creation of nature reserves. Study of them has already begun, but the political situation is not ot present favourable to progress in the matter or to concrete results.

According to information received in September 1969, 10 Forest reserves actually exist (151,500 ha) which will be up-graded into national parks. However the effectiveness with which they are supervised varies from place to place, though hunting is sometimes forbidden. Unfortunately, people are at present in possession of abnormal quantities of firearms, to which the wild fauna very often falls victim.

The largest forest reserves are :

Dong Xieng Thong (42,500 ha);
Dong Heua Xao (26,000 ha);
Dong Veunekham (20,000 ha);

and there is also a project for part of the well-known Plain of Jarres (Thra Ninh and Xieng Khuang).

72. LEBANON

I.   **Listed Areas :** nil.

V.   **Areas excluded :**

A. — A dozen cedar-woods which survive in the country and receive strict protection, by virtue not only of the control exercised by the authorities but also of the deep respect in which the people hold the tree which is the badge of their country.

Special mention may be made of the place known as ' The Cedars ' at a height of 1,900 m near Bécharré, where there is a stand of 400 trees, a dozen of them over a thousand years old. Other cedar-woods along the Lebanon range cover a total area of about 800 ha, all but 200 ha in the north of the country, at Kammoua, Emmamine, Ehden, Hadeth etc., the southern woods being at Ain Zhalta, Maasser Chouf and Barouk. There is a U.N. Special Fund/F.A.O. Project for establishing a national cedar forest of 2,000 ha near the three last-mentioned places and for introducing into it a selection of wild animals, mouflon, roe deer and sika, but the main difficulty is first to get rid of domestic goats.

B. — There are various other plans for establishing national parks falling within the scope of the national Plan for the development of hunting and fishing. The top priority is the ' Barouk National Park ', which would comprise a 10×30 km (30,000 ha) piece of country along the Lebanon range and adjoining the F.A.O. cedar-forest project. Next in importance is the ' Kamouha Forest National Park ' in the north of the country, some 40,000 ha in area, and finally two much smaller reserves :

Terbol National Park, east of Zahlé, 200 ha.
Raselain National Park, on the coast near Tyre, 100 ha.

The development plan envisages the provision of some 410,000 Lebanese pounds (U.S. $ 150,000) for the establishment of these four National Parks.

73. LESOTHO

Listed Areas : nil.

Explanation :

The last report received, a statement by the Permanent Secretary for Agriculture, Maseru, dated 11 January 1965, gave a nil return of National Parks and Game Reserves.

74. LIBERIA

Listed Areas : nil.

a) Explanation :

Referring to areas for which the legal basis is the 'Act for the Conservation of the Forests of the Republic of Liberia, 1953', the Department of Agriculture and Commerce at Monrovia reported in a letter dated 20 July 1964, that "these National Park Reserves have been only planned and mapped... the Bureau (of Forest Conservation) is hopeful to carry out its plan at a propitious moment to make these Reserves operational".

b) Areas excluded :

The three proposed Reserves mentioned above are :

1. Mount Wutivi National Park Reserve. In north-western Liberia, with an estimated area of 6,000 ha.
2. Bokoma National Park Reserve : 2,920 ha.
3. Tiempo National Park Reserve. In south-eastern Liberia, with an estimated area of 13,000 ha.

75. LIBYA

Listed Areas : nil.

a) Explanation :

The previous edition of the List contained no reference to Libya and requests for precise information addressed to the authorities in Tripoli have met with no response. A letter from the Acting Under Secretary of State of the Ministry of Agriculture, dated 17 December 1962, did however refer to various "green belt" areas set aside for visitors and tourists, but gave no indication that they constitute areas in which forest exploitation has been halted or in which human settlement, hunting or fishing is prohibited.

b) Areas excluded :

The Green Mountain area of Cyrenaica is reported to contain 'nature parks' at Bakour, Rekab, El-mary (Barce), Wadi El-Kuf, Cyrene, and in the region of Ras El-Halal and Tulmitha.

323

In Tripolitania there are forest remnants near Tripoli itself and along the coast. In the Fezzan, the Ein Kary area is celebrated for its hare and dorcas gazelle hunting.

These 'management zones' are said to amount to a total of 20,000 ha and to be visited by some 25,000 people a year.

76. LUXEMBOURG

I.   **Listed Areas :** nil.

V.   **Areas excluded :**

The Germano-Luxembourgeois Park.

Established in 1963 and with 32,000 ha within the boundaries of the Grand Duchy and the remaining 40,000 in the German Federal Republic, this area, for reasons explained under Part V of the chapter on Germany (No. 46 in the List), where the 'Nature Parks' are discussed, has an insufficient degree of protection to justify its inclusion in the List. However, there is some prospect that eventually strict nature reserves, though of small size, will be established within the Park.

Mention may also be made of the plan under consideration for setting up a 400 ha nature reserve in the vicinity of the artificial lake created by the barrage near Esch-sur-Sure.

77. MALAGASY REPUBLIC (Madagascar)

I.   **Listed Areas :** thirty-one.

A. — STRICT NATURE RESERVES :

1. Tsingy du Bemaraha.
2. Ankarafantsika.
3. Andohahela.
4. Zahamena.
5. Marojejy.
6. Tsaratanana.
7. Andringitra.
8. Tsingy de Namoroka.
9. Tsimanampetsotsa Lake.
10. Betampona.
11. Lokobe.

B. — NATIONAL PARKS :

12. Isalo National Park.
13. Ambre Mountain National Park.

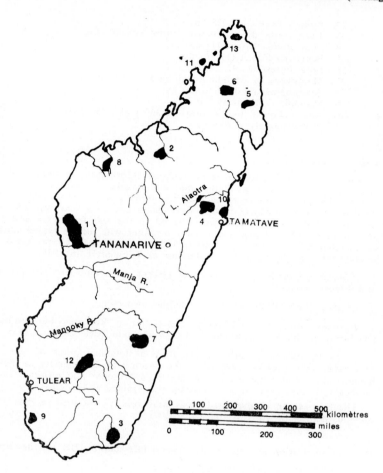

C. — SPECIAL RESERVES :

N.B. — Since no details except size are available for these reserves, the area of each is quoted in this section of the List.

14. Ambatovaky Forest (60,050 ha).
15. Marotandrano Forest (42,200 ha).
16. Manongarivo Forest (35,250 ha).
17. Analamena Forest (34,700 ha).
18. South Anjahanaharibe Forest Massif (32,090 ha).
19. Kalambatitra Massif (28,255 ha).
20. Ambohijanahary Forest Massif (24,750 ha).
21. Katsijy Forest (18,800 ha).

325

MALAGASY REPUBLIC (Madagascar)

22. Ankara Forest (18,225 ha).
23. Tampoketsa d'Analamaitso Forest (17,150 ha).
24. Mangerivola Forest (11,900 ha).
25. Bemarivo Forest (11,575 ha).
26. Bora Forest (8,491 ha).
27. Maningozy or Mandihalohaloha Forest (7,900 ha).
28. Andranomena Forest (6,420 ha).
29. Manombo Massif (5,320 ha).
30. Ambre Forest (two sections : 3,360 and 1,450 ha).
31. Ambohitantely (3,453 ha).

General Introduction :

II.   For most of the listed areas no separate information in respect of the application of the criteria is available and only a general indication of the situation can be given in a preface to each of the three sections into which the areas are divided. Recent unofficial reports have given rise to a fear that the supervision of many of the reserves has been relaxed in the last few years and IUCN has already expressed a strong hope that the matter will receive urgent attention, has co-operated in a project for a survey and reassessment of all protected areas and is sponsoring a Conservation Conference at Tananarive in 1970.

III.   *Administration :* all three classes of reserve are administered by the Water and and Forest Service.

    Land tenure : all the land is in public ownership.

    Tourism : not permitted in the Strict Nature Reserves, but gradually being developed in the two National Parks, which date back only to 1958 and 1962.

    Scientific research : work, mainly from a botanical point of view, has been undertaken in the reserves ever since the creation of the majority of them in 1927, being at first under the control of the Paris Museum and reflected in numerous publications, especially those issued by the Malagasy Academy.

    The first eleven of the listed areas were briefly described in Part Two of the previous edition of the List.

Details : application of criteria (II), general information (III) and description (IV) :

A. — STRICT NATURE RESERVES.

II.   *a)* Status : the degree of protection is exceptionally strict in theory, all entry and *a fortiori* exploitation by ordinary people being prohibited and even scientific work being carefully controlled in order to ensure that nothing is done which could disturb the fauna and flora. Unfortunately, in practice, some areas are poorly supervised and subject to disturbance by man and domestic stock. Several of the reserves are flanked by buffer zones. Up till 1964 there were twelve Reserves, but Masoala, officially listed as No. II, has been opened for forest exploitation and has been recently cancelled.

    b) Area : all the eleven listed Reserves, except No. 11 Lokobe, exceed the minimum of 2,000 ha required by the criterion in a country of which the population density is 9 to the square kilometre. The Lokobe Reserve has, however, been retained in the List, at the suggestion of the Malagasy Government, " because of its special interest as the only remaining sample of forest in the Sambirano and Nosy-Be Island region ".

c), d) Staff and Budget : the largest of the Reserves No. 1 (officially IX) Tsingy du Bemaraha should under the criterion, as applied to its area of 152,000 ha, have a staff of fifteen and a budget of the order of U.S. $ 7,500 a year. In fact its permanent staff is very small (only two technical officers of the Water and Forest Service) and its budget is only a third of what it ought to be, so that it is hardly surprising that it is reported to be periodically subjected to poaching, incursions by domestic stock and grass fires. However, for the time being, the failure to satisfy the criteria may be ignored, although there is a risk that this area and the equally disturbed area No. 2 may have to be removed from the List in a future edition, unless a considerable improvement can be effected. For three of the ten Reserves, the actual figures, at least for the budget, approach the correct level, as the following Table shows :

No.	Staff		Budget ($)	
	Criterion	Actual	Criterion	Actual
4 (III)	6	1	2,900	1,800
2 (VII)	6	2	3,050	2,700
3 (XI)	6	2	3,050	2,600

The remaining 7 Reserves very nearly reach or in some cases exceed the criteria :

No.	Staff		Budget ($)	
	Criterion	Actual	Criterion	Actual
10 (I)	1	1	200	1,600
6 (IV)	4	3	2,250	3,700
7 (V)	3	3	1,750	3,500
11 (VI)	1	1	100	1,400
8 (VIII)	2	1	1,200	1,600
9 (X)	1	1	750	1,300
5 (XII)	5	3	2,400	3,800

1. TSINGY DU BEMARAHA, Reserve IX.

a), c), d) : See prefatory notes above.

b) Area : 152,000 ha, plus buffer-zone of 6,450 ha.

Date established : 1927.

Altitude : 75-700 m.

a) A limestone region with lapiaz, caverns and fissures from which underground rivers break out; primary forest of the tropical trophytic type of western Madagascar and a xerophytic flora (Liliaceae, aloes, orchids, Leguminosae, Euphorbiaceae).

b) The remarkably rich fauna includes grey gentle lemur *Hapalemur griseus,* red-fronted lemur *Lemur macaco rufus,* sportive lemur *Lepilemur mustelinus ruficaudatus,* fat-tailed lemur *Cheirogaleus medius,* lesser and Coquerel's mouse lemurs *Microcebus murinus* and *coquereli,* fork-marked mouse lemur *Phaner furcifer* and Verreaux's sifaka *Propithecus v. verreauxi.*

c) Grey gentle, red-fronted and fat-tailed lemurs, Coquerel's and fork-marked mouse lemurs, and Verreaux's sifaka.

2. ANKARAFANTSIKA, Reserve No. VII.

a), c), d) : See prefatory notes.

b) Area : 60,520 ha, plus buffer zone of 9,139 ha.

III.   *Date established :* 1927-1958.

IV.   *Altitude :* 75-390 m.

a) Sandy plateau covered with the tropophytic flora typical of western Madagascar; primary and secondary deciduous forest, western-type gallery forest, Leguminosae and Myrtaceae especially well represented. This block of country was under occupation in the 19th and early 20th Century and there was a good deal of clearing.

b) An easily accessible area but with a good number of species including the brown lemur *L. fulvus,* the mongose lemur *L. m. mongoz,* the sportive lemur, the fat-tailed lemur, the lesser mouse lemur, the western woolly avahi *Avahi laniger occidentalis* and Coquerel's sifaka *Propithecus verreauxi coquereli.*

c) Mongoose and fat-tailed lemurs, western woolly avahi and Coquerel's sifaka.

3. ANDOHAHELA, Reserve No. XI.

II.   *a), c), d)* : See prefatory notes.
b) Area : 76,020 ha.

III.   *Date established :* 1939.

IV.   *Altitude :* 120-1,956 m.

a) Evergreen primary and secondary high and lower level forest of the south-eastern region. In the Mandrare sector there is a sample of primary and secondary deciduous forest typical of southern Madagascar and also some remnants of the transitional type deciduous forest which occurs on western slopes of the western region. Owing to this conjunction of different vegetational associations, the flora is particularly rich and varied.

b) Little is known of the fauna but the following species have been recorded : ring-tailed lemur *L. catta,* weasel lemur *Lepilemur mustelinus* subsp., lesser mouse lemur, fat-tailed lemur and Verreaux's sifaka.

c) Weasel lemur, Verreaux's sifaka.

4. ZAHAMENA, Reserve No. III.

II.   *a), c), d)* : See prefatory notes.
b) Area : 73,160 ha, plus buffer zone of 24,800 ha.

III.   *Date established :* 1927.

IV.   *Altitude :* not quoted.

a) Vegetation of the eastern escarpment with high level evergreen tropical forest, primary and secondary; zones of bamboo and of virgin forest hung with lichens.

b) The remarkable fauna includes grey gentle lemur, ruffed lemur *L. variegatus,* brown lemur, a race of weasel lemur, greater dwarf lemur *Cheirogaleus major,* lesser mouse lemur, eastern woolly avahi *Avahi laniger orientalis,* diademed sifaka *Propithecus d. diadema* and indris *Indri indri.*

c) Grey gentle lemur, indris.

5. MAROJEJY, Reserve No. XII.

II.   *a), c), d)* : See prefatory notes.
b) Area : 60,150 ha.

III.   *Date established :* 1952.

Altitude : 90-2,137 m.

a) Geologically a highly fragmented area, with a great altitudinal range and hence microclimatic variation; it is the only mountainous area in Madagascar in which every stage of typical vegetation of the eastern region can be found, from those of the low 100 m level up to those of over 2,100 m in altitude; very many species of palms, ferns, orchids and Acanthaceae.

b) Little is known of the fauna, but among the species recorded are the brown lemur, lesser mouse lemur, greater dwarf lemur and a distinct race (*candidus*) of the diademed sifaka.

6. TSARATANANA, Reserve No. IV.

a), c), d) : See prefatory notes.
b) Area : 48,622 ha, plus buffer zone of 81,940 ha.

Date established : 1927.

Altitude : 160-2,887 m.

a) A mountain massif covered with evergreen primary and secondary forest of low and high level types; virgin forest with lichens, heath-type associations, a flora rich in endemic species with many orchids.

b) Except for the fossa *Cryptoprocta ferox*, which occurs in most of the reserves, the fauna is little known, but includes black lemur *L. macaco* subsp., a weasel lemur, greater dwarf lemur and lesser mouse lemur.

c) Black lemur.

7. ANDRINGITRA, Reserve No. V.

a), c), d) : See prefatory notes.
b) Area : 31,160 ha, plus buffer zone of 11,100 ha.

Date established : 1927.

Altitude : 1,000-2,658 m.

a) Very broken country, in which many rivers have their source; evergreen primary and secondary forest; heath-type and herbaceous vegetation typical of this high altitude, with a xerophytic flora on the rock faces.

b) Fauna is not well-known, but includes ring-tailed lemur and diademed sifaka.

8. TSINGY DE NAMOROKA, Reserve No. VIII.

a), c), d) : See prefatory notes.
b) Area : 21,742 ha, plus buffer zone of 94 ha.

Date established : 1927.

Altitude : 180-370 m.

a) Limestone area with lapiaz, caves and a Vauclusian spring; tropical deciduous primary forest, characteristic of the western region of Madagascar, with some areas partially destroyed as a result of grass burning in the 19th Century; some fine ebony trees.

b) The rich fauna includes grey gentle, red-fronted, mongoose and fat-tailed lemurs, lesser mouse lemur, western woolly avahi, Decken's and crowned sifakas *Propithecus verreauxi deckeni* and *coronatus*.

c) All species named above except lesser mouse lemur.

9. TSIMANAMPETSOTSA LAKE, Reserve No. X.

II.   *a*), *c*), *d*) : See prefatory notes.
         b) Area : 43,200 ha.

III.   *Date established :* 1927.

IV.   *Altitude :* 10-160 m.

     a) Limestone plateau, with a large swallow-hole, covered in the xerophytic bush of south-western Madagascar, including some shrubby associations where the soil is sandy; the southern flora comprises many euphorbia species.

     b) The remarkably rich fauna, which is a fine sample of the typically sub-desertic fauna of southern Madagascar, includes ring-tailed and sportive and fat-tailed lemurs, lesser, Coquerel's and fork-marked mouse lemurs, and Verreaux's sifaka. One of the most important breeding-places for birds in Madagascar : among the many waterbird species coming to nest here are both greater and lesser flamingo *Phoenicopterus ruber* and *Phoeniconaias minor*.

     c) Fat-tailed lemur, Coquerel's and fork-marked mouse lemurs, Verreaux's sifaka.

10. BETAMPONA, Reserve No. I.

II.   *a*), *c*), *d*) : See prefatory notes.
         b) Area : 2,228 ha, plus buffer zone of 1,840 ha.

III.   *Date established :* 1927, but was a Forest Reserve since 1909.

IV.   *Altitude :* 275-550 m.

     a) A sample of the natural low altitude biotopes of the eastern region in the neighbourhood of Tamatave, with evergreen primary and secondary forest.

     b) The remarkably rich fauna includes grey gentle, ruffed, brown, weasel and greater dwarf lemurs, lesser mouse lemur, eastern woolly avahi and diademed sifaka.

     c) Grey gentle lemur.

11. LOKOBE, Reserve No. VI.

II.   *a*), *c*), *d*) : See prefatory notes.
         b) Area : 740 ha, with buffer zone of 439 ha; see preface for justification of inclusion.

III.   *Date established :* 1927, the buffer zone in 1933.

IV.   *Altitude :* sea level to 550 m.

     a) A sample of the natural low altitude vegetation of the Nosy-Be sector of the Sambirano region, containing the only surviving remnant of the Nosy-Be forest, an evergreen primary and secondary tropical forest with has an important hydrological function; the slopes were partly cleared in the 19th Century.

     b) An interesting island fauna includes the black lemur *L. m. macaco,* the Nosy-Be weasel lemur *Lepilemur mustelinus dorsalis* and the lesser mouse lemur.

     c) Black lemur and Nosy-Be weasel lemur.

B. — NATIONAL PARKS.

II.   *a*) Status : total protection, though grazing of domestic stock is allowed in some parts of the larger of the two parks. The National Parks are distinguished from the Strict Nature Reserves by virtue of the fact that tourism is specifically encouraged in them.

c), *d)* Staff and Budget : to satisfy the criteria these two parks ought to have a total staff of forty and a budget of the order of U.S. $ 25,000. A fair proportion of the personnel is in fact covered by those paid from the central Budget, but the number is brought up to the requisite level by those paid from provincial funds. The Malagasy Government has given assurances that the two Parks can be justifiably retained in the U.N. List.

12. ISALO NATIONAL PARK.

    a), *c)*, *d)* : See prefatory notes above.
    b) Area : 81,540 ha.

Date established : 1962.

Tourism : easy access, on the main road from Tananarive to Tulear; tourist facilities are being developed.

    Altitude : 800-1,082 m.

    a) A decayed mountain massif, with sheer scarps, deeply entrenched gorges and many springs at the foot of the cliffs; a landscape at once majestic and picturesque; remains of human occupations of considerable historic interest. The flora comprises a mixture of species typical of both western and eastern regions, with many endemics confined to this massif. There are remnants of a peculiar transitional fauna and flora of great scientific interest.

    b) Not remarkable for its vertebrate fauna, but little is really known of the species which occur.

13. AMBRE MOUNTAIN NATIONAL PARK.

    a), *c)*, *d)* : See prefatory notes above.
    b) Area : 18,200 ha.

Date established : 1958.

Tourism : becomes practically inaccessible by car during the rainy season; the rest-camp at the road staging-post at Les Roussettes offers accommodation and is often used by scientists visiting the area.

    Altitude : 380-1,475 m.

    a) An ancient volcano, with many small craters on its flanks, several of them containing crater-lakes : thick evergreen forest, comprising both high-altitude associations and moss and lichen-festooned virgin forest; there are fine stands of mature trees, on which many species of epiphytes are found, and also tree-ferns.

    b) Fauna little known, but the grey gentle lemur, Sanford's lemur *L. macaco sanfordi,* the crowned *L. mongoz coronatus,* the lesser mouse lemur, weasel lemur and fork-marked lemur have been recorded.

    c) All species mentioned under *(b)* except the lesser mouse lemur.

C. — SPECIAL RESERVES.

    a) Status : exploitation of forest products, hunting and fishing are prohibited, and customary rights have been annulled. Access is unrestricted.

    b) Area : the 18 reserves, as listed in Section I, all exceed the criterion level of 2,000 ha, ranging from 4,810 ha up to 60,050 ha.

Administration : by the Department of Forestry and Game of the Ministry of Natural Resources.

Land Tenure : public ownership.

Tourism : the park is open throughout the year; access from two airports, at Rumpi, 110 km away, and Nikuzu, 185 km away; accommodation for 26 visitors in two well-equipped lodges; the park is served by a good network of roads. The introduction of sport-fishing in 1965 was on the basis of a seven-month season, September to the end of March.

Scientific research : in 1963-1964 the area was the subject of intensive ecological study for the purpose of setting it up as a National Park. This was carried out by a Professor of the State University of New York.

IV.   *Altitude :* 900-2,565 m.

a) The Nyika montane massif, comprising a great variety of vegetational associations, ranging in accordance with altitude from woody savannah to high level grassland, with some pieces of evergreen forest also as the upper levels.

b) Zebra *Equus burchelli,* eland *Taurotragus oryx,* sable and roan antelope *Hippotragus niger* and *equinus,* klipspringer *O. oreotragus,* hartebeest *Alcelaphus buselaphus,* reedbuck *Redunca arundinum,* buffalo *Syncerus caffer,* lion and leopard *Panthera leo* and *pardus.*

V.   Areas excluded :

Five Game Reserves, in which only the fauna is protected and where, despite a not inconsiderable effort at supervision, rather heavy poaching still sometimes occurs. They are :

Kasungu Game Reserve; 204,800 ha, established in 1956, where " it should be feasible to control poaching with vigorous patrolling ".

Nkhota-Kota Game Reserve; 170,000 ha, established in 1956 (" heavy encroachment by cultivators ").

Majete Game Reserve; 18,000 ha, established in 1960 (" heavy poaching ").

Mwabvi Game Reserve; 15,000 ha, established in 1954 (" has been subject to heavy poaching in the past ").

Lengwe Game Reserve; 12,800 ha, 7 guards; established in 1956 (" heavy population pressure "); well-known and important as the main refuge of the nyala *Tragelaphus angasi*; its future is under some threat from works connected with a proposed irrigation scheme.

The Government is determined to make every effort to strengthen the supervision and perhaps the protective status of these five reserves, which could well result in their inclusion in the U.N. List. As far as the suppression of poaching is concerned the situation in the Kasungu Reserve looks most hopeful, since there is already a staff of 28, a Game Ranger, a Wildlife Biologist and 26 Game Guards, and a budget of U.S. $ 11,200. Similarly the Mwabvi Reserve, with " its relatively light population ", existing staff of seven and U.S. $ 2,500 budget, only needs some tightening up its protective status to qualify without difficulty for the List. The great scientific importance of the Lengwe reserve has also been recognised by the Government and it is hoped that development proposals in the adjacent area will be modified accordingly.

79. MALAYSIA
(includes the States of Malaya, Sabah and Sarawak)

Listed Areas : four.

a) Malaya :
1. Taman Negara (formerly King George V) National Park.
2. Templer Park.

b) Sabah :
3. Kinabalu National Park.

c) Sarawak :
4. Bako National Park.

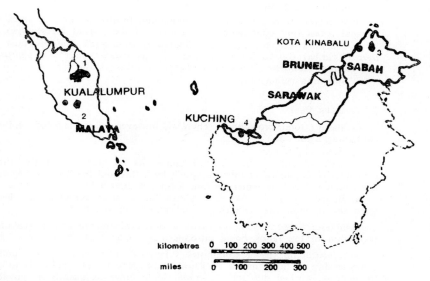

General Introduction :

There is nothing to add to the details which follow, except to note that all four areas were described in the previous edition, E/3436, of the List.

Details : application of criteria (II), general information (III) and description (IV) :

a) **Malaya.**

1. TAMAN NEGARA NATIONAL PARK.

a) Status : total protection; occupancy, cultivation and domestic livestock prohibited, but sport-fishing is allowed in one or two places.
b) Area : 434,340 ha.
c) Staff : 62 units (as compared with 44 required by the criterion).
d) Budget : U.S. $ 41,000 (as compared with $ 22,000 under the criterion).

MALAYSIA

III.   *Date established :* 1938 (under the name of King George V National Park).

Administration : by a Board of Trustees which includes, among others, the Sultans of Pahang, Kelantan and Trengganu. The Board appoints the Chief Game Warden who runs the Park. The headquarters are at Kuala-Tahan, where the superintendent, his assistant and the greater part of the staff are based. There are five guard-posts.

Land tenure : public ownership.

Tourism : air landing-ground, paths, ' up-river ' lodges which visitors reach by boat, along the navigable rivers. There is also a modern Rest-House and chalets, with 16 beds. Tourism is building up and a " park brochure " has been published, but much of the area still remains inaccessible.

Scientific research : undertaken by the University of Malaya, which maintains a field laboratory at Kuala Tahan.

IV.   *Altitude :* 120-2,150 m.

a) A region of plateau, hill and mountain, mostly covered by thick humid tropical forest (but containing no examples of the coastal forest type).

b) Elephant *Elephas maximus,* Sumatran rhinoceros *Didermocerus sumatrensis,* sambar *Cervus unicolor,* tapir *Tapirus indicus,* gaur *Bos gaurus,* tiger and leopard *Panthera tigris* and *pardus.*

c) Sumatran rhinoceros.

2. TEMPLER PARK.

II.   *a*) Status : total protection. There is, however, an enclave of exploitation, containing a tin mine.

b) Area : 1,200 ha.

c) Staff : 5 units, which is well above the requirements of the criterion : in a heavily populated country in which both this and the Taman Negara Park are situated, the requirement is one man per 10,000 ha.

d) Budget : U.S. $ 2,100, also above the criterion requirement. Royalties from the tin-mine are devoted to the running of the Park.

III.   *Date established :* 1955, originally a botanical reserve and recreation area, protection of the fauna being introduced at a later stage.

Administration : by a Committee (' Friends of Templer Park ') under the chairmanship of the Minister of Rural Development. The policy is to get the tin deposits worked out and the mine closed down as quickly as possible.

Land tenure : public ownership.

Tourism : no accommodation, but a canteen and trails for visitors.

Research : no museum or other particular activities, but there is a plan for a small zoo.

IV.   *Altitude :* 98-544 m.

a) The region bears the mark of old mining operations; vegetation comprises numerous bush associations and forest on the higher slopes.

b) The fauna includes a number of amphibians, such as the interesting torrent-frog *Staurois larutensis,* reptiles, such as various species of the *Draco* lizard, birds (drongos, hornbills, the fairy blue bird *Irena puella* etc.) and other small animals characteristic of Malayan hills and plains. Larger animals include tiger and tapir.

336

b) **Sabah.**

3. KINABALU NATIONAL PARK.

a) Status : total protection.

b) Area : 69,000 ha.

c) Staff : one full-time Park Warden, 1 park ranger, 9 assistant park rangers, 3 drivers, 12 park artisans, 5 clerical and administrative staff and a peace corps volunteer; also, on a part-time basis, personnel of the Department of Forests and Agriculture.

d) Budget : U.S. $ 66,000, plus staff salaries.

Date established : 1964, under the Sabah National Park Ordinance.

Administration : by a Board of Trustees, comprising the Permanent Secretary for Natural Resources (Chairman), two other officers and three private individuals appointed by the State Government. The every day administration is undertaken by the Warden. Headquarters are at Tenompok, from which the main route to the summit of Kinabalu starts.

Land tenure : public ownership.

Tourism : trails and four mountain huts are available for visitors and further improvements are being made, including provision of simple equipment in the huts and a 20-bed hostel. Access is by air (landing-ground at Ranau, 15 km from the Park entrance) or by road [4 hours from Kota Kinabalu (formerly Jesselton)].

Altitude : about 300 metres to the summit of Kinabalu at 4,104 m.

a) Dated by geologists to the Miocene, the mountain has a flora which is apparently of much more ancient origin, comprising a variety of elements : *Dipterocarpus* forest typical of the Malaysian region, then between 1,300 and 3,000 m a mixed forest of austral conifers (*Agathis, Dacrydium, Phyllocladus*), myrtles (*Leptostermum*), Cunoniaceae, Eurasian oaks, laurels and tea-trees (Theaceae, e.g. *Schima* sp., *Ternstroemia*); above 3,000 m thickets and herbaceous vegetation of species related to those found in China and the Himalayan region (e.g. *Photinia, Pygaeum, Rubus, Potentilla, Daphniphyllum*) or in Australia - Tasmania - New Zealand (e.g. *Ranunculus lowii, Drimys, Patersonia, Euphrasia* and many ferns).

b) Gibbon *Hylobates* spp., orang-utan *Pongo pygmaeus,* probably a few Sumatran rhinoceros, sambar, Bornean pig *Sus barbatus,* shrew-faced ground squirrel *Rhinosciurus* sp., civet; numerous kinds of birds typical of all altitudes.

c) Orang-utan, Sumatran rhinoceros (?).

c) **Sarawak.**

4. BAKO NATIONAL PARK.

a) Status : total protection, except that the right to cut wood on the borders of the Park is retained by the inhabitants of one village.

b) Area : 2,550 ha.

c) Staff : 2 units.

d) Budget : U.S. $ 4,950.

Date established : 1957, extended in January 1960.

Administration : by a Board of Trustees, appointed under a section of Ordinance No. 17 of 1954.

Land tenure : public ownership.

Tourism : access by sea, no roads in the Park, but a network of footpaths; a rest-house and two bungalows; a guidebook already in its second enlarged and improved edition (1965), though the growth of tourism is quite recent.

337

Research : supervised by the Curator of the Sarawak Museum and the Forest Department.

IV.　　　　*Altitude :* sea level to 240 m.

a) A peninsula with sandstone cliffs overlooking the sea and sandy bays; mangrove, various other coastal and alluvial vegetation associations, such as mixed dipterocarp forest, heavy ' Kerenga ' or ' padang '-type forest and bushy areas.

b) Malaysian and plumbeous dolphins *Sousa borneensis* and *plumbea,* Bornean pig, chevrotain *Tragulus* sp., monkeys such as the proboscis *Nasalis larvatus*; the varied birdlife includes sea-eagles *Haliaetus* sp., harriers *Circus* sp., paradise flycatcher *Tchitrea* sp., woodpeckers (e.g. a local race of the three-toed golden-backed woodpecker *Dinopium javanense*).

V.　　**Areas excluded :**

a) Malaya : various game reserves including the 50,000 ha Krau Game Reserve.

b) Sabah : nil.

c) Sarawak : a large number of proposed reserves of which it was stated, in January 1966, that some had reached the stage of being " approved by the Government : preliminary proclamation issued ". Those included in the Sarawak Development Plan 1964-1968 are :

Gunong Mulu National Park	61,900 ha
Matang National Park	2,180 ha
Gunong Gading National Park	3,283 ha
Sabah National Park	1,216 ha
Pelagus Rapids National Park	5,200 ha
Similajau National Park	3,750 ha
Lambir National Park	4,000 ha
Sungei Dalam National Park	510 ha
Loagan Bunut National Park	5,180 ha
Niah National Park	3,000 ha

80.　**MALDIVE ISLANDS**

I.　　**Listed Areas :** nil.

V.　　**Explanation :**

No contact has yet been made with the Maldivian Government. In view of the fact that only 210 out of the 1,067 islands and islets are inhabited and that many interesting seabirds and other marine species have been reported from this archipelago, which extends over 800 km north from the equator, it is to be hoped that one result of the current survey of oceanic islands being undertaken by the International Biological Programme will be the selection and creation of one or more reserves qualifying for inclusion in the List.

338

Listed Areas : one.

1. La Boucle du Baoulé National Park.

General Introduction :

A description of the Park was given in Part Two of the previous edition of the List.

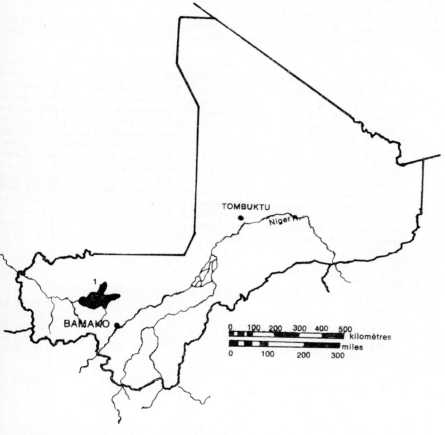

Details : application of criteria (II), general information (III) and description (IV) :

1. LA BOUCLE DU BAOULÉ NATIONAL PARK.

a) Status : total protection. There are four small villages on the southern boundary.

b) Area : 350,000 ha.

c) Staff : 12 units (departmental provision of the Ministry concerned in 1964). This is well below the criterion level, but is accepted as sufficient in the light of the fact that there are few inhabitants in the surrounding area, that access is impracticable for five months of the year and that poaching is at a low level (though it occurs in the north of the Park).

d) Budget : U.S. $ 3,000 for maintenance; a capital provision of $ 40,000 a year for the two years 1962-1963 and 1963-1964 was also budgeted.

III.   *Date established :* 1954.

Administration : by the Division des Eaux et Forêts of the Ministry of Development.

Land tenure : public ownership.

Tourism : there is a rest-camp at Missira and two other hotel/rest-camp are situated not far from the Park, which contains 400 km of motorable tracks.

IV.   *Altitude :* about 300 m.

a) A flat sandstone plateau, with broken country on the south and east, where there is a range of mountains interspersed with steep kopjes and dissected by long parallel clefts with vertical walls. The northern part is more feature-less and the west is also much less rugged than the south, with broad plains of sandy clays and some lateritic outcrops. Despite the few inhabitants, the vegetation has been rather impoverished by the bush-fires which occurred before the area was protected. In the gallery forests especially along the Baoulé the borassus palm is the dominant species. Elsewhere the dominants are *Combretum pterocarpus, Anogeissus, Gardenia, Bauhinia, Terminalia* and *Cassia sieberina,* while bastard mahoganies *Khaya senegalensis, Pterocarpus erinaceus, Ziziphus, Acacia seyal, Balanites,* red-water tree *Erythrophloeum misrauthum, Cola cordifolia, Sarcocephalus* and *Dialium* also occur. In the east of the Park are a few stands of kapok (Bombacaceae), *Isoberlinia* spp. and *Afzelia africana.*

b) The wildlife is plentiful and consists mainly of elements of the Soudanian fauna, such as gazelle, bushbuck, hartebeest, kob, topi, roan, hippopotamus. Derby eland, buffalo and elephant still occur but are getting more and more rare.

V.   **Areas excluded :**

A. — Five Faunal Reserves (where animals are totally protected) :

Bodinko	193,000 ha.
Fina	136,000 ha.
Keniabaoulé	67,500 ha.
Sousan	37,000 ha.
Talikourou	13,900 ha.

B. — One Protected State Forest :

Kongossombougou	92,000 ha.

82. MALTA

I.   **Listed Areas :** nil.

V.   **Explanation :**

According to outside sources of information there are no national parks on the island. There has been a proposal for a reserve at Ghadira in the north western peninsula, but it would be difficult in this small overcrowded island to meet the criterion in respect of size.

Listed Areas : one.

1. Mauritanian Islands Strict Nature Reserve.

General Introduction :

No information on Mauritania was included in either E/3436 or Part Two of the previous edition of the List.

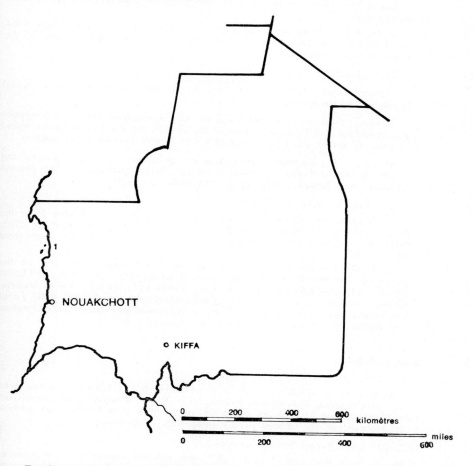

Details : application of criteria (II), general information (III) and description (IV) :

1. MAURITANIAN ISLANDS STRICT NATURE RESERVE.

a) Status : total protection. There is a complete prohibition on all hunting, whatever the weapons or other methods employed, on the introduction of any

341

species, collecting, forestry, agricultural or mineral exploitation, and on any act calculated to harm or disturb the fauna and flora. Nevertheless, exceptions are permissable in the case of companies engaged in oil exploration and exploitation.

b) Area : slightly less than 10,000 ha and comprising " the off-shore island territories of the Islamic Republic of Mauritania between 19° and 21° N. and 16° and 17° W. ".

c) Staff : supervision is carried out by the personnel of the Service des Eaux et Forêts, the men stationed at Atar and Nouakchott respectively taking turns on this duty.

d) Budget : a letter from the Foreign Affairs Ministry dated 4 June 1964 stated that it was impossible to give even approximately an estimate of the actual annual expenditure.

III.   *Date established :* not known.

Administration : by the Service des Eaux et Forêts of the Ministry of Rural Economy and Co-operation.

General : these are uninhabited islands, only occasionally visited by Imraguen and Saint-Jean Bay fishermen. One of the islands, Arguin, has still some traces — ruins of a fort and old cultivation — of former Portuguese occupation.

Research : the scientific investigation of the island was largely carried out by the Reverend Father de Naurois, results being published in the journal '*Alauda*' (e.g. fifteen species of nesting birds recorded).

IV.   *Altitude :* sea level to 15 m.

a) A group of islands and islets, sand and sandstone, emerging from the deep water off the Mauritanian coast : some of them are bounded by cliffs others by beaches running into vast mudflats; halophytic vegetation dominated by salicornia.

b) Large breeding colonies of several tens of thousands of birds of the following species : long-tailed cormorant *Phalacrocorax africanus*, gull-billed tern *Gelochelidon nilotica,* royal, common, bridled and little terns *Sterna maxima hirundo, anaethetus* and *albifrons,* slender-billed and grey-headed gulls *Larus genei* and *cirrocephalus,* spoonbill *Platalea leucorodia,* grey heron *Ardea cinerea* reef heron *Egretta gularis,* flamingo *Phoenicopterus ruber.*

V.   **Areas excluded :**

1. Lévrier Bay Strict Faunal Reserve.

This Reserve of 310,000 ha acts as a protective buffer zone on the mainland for the neighbouring Mauritanian Islands Strict Nature Reserve. All animals are fully protected but " customary rights of usage other than hunting are allowed to be exercised in the interest of the indigenous inhabitants ".

2. El Agher Partial Faunal Reserve.

Set up by a decree of 21 June 1937, this Reserve consists of two sections (*a*) a very remote, uninhabited area which is full of game but receives no supervision; and (*b*) a more accessible area between the towns of Kiffa and Aioun-el Atrouss in which the main objective is the preservation of a herd of some forty elephants.

342

Listed Areas : two.
1. Bel-Ombre Reserve.
2. Macabe-Mare Longue Reserve.

General Introduction :
Both the above areas, together with a number of others now excluded from the List, were briefly described in the previous edition E/3436. They were then referred to as 'National Reserves', but under a recent revision of the legislation are in the process of being renamed 'Nature Reserves'. Compared with the Macabe-Mare Longue Reserve, which completely meets all the criteria laid down by the ICNP, No. 1, the Bel-Ombre Reserve, can be considered as only marginally qualified for inclusion.

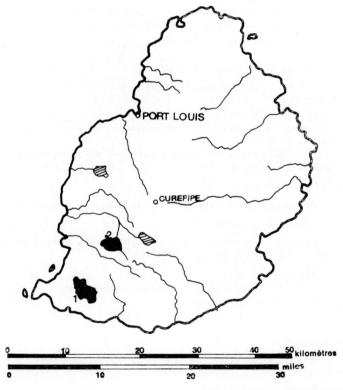

Details : application of criteria (II), general information (III) and description (IV) :
1. Bᴇʟ-Oᴍʙʀᴇ Rᴇsᴇʀᴠᴇ.
  a) Status : total protection. No hunting, fishing or disturbance of the flora allowed.
  b) Area : 919 ha.

343

c) Staff : according to the authorities the hunting and fishing rights given in a Crown estate adjoining the Reserve imply an obligation on those who hold them to ensure proper supervision in the Reserve itself.

d) Budget : funds are provided for "expenditures in connection with the treatment of small experimental plots in the Reserve".

III.   *Date established :* 1951.

Administration : by the Ministry of Education and Cultural Affairs, Port Louis.

Land tenure : public ownership.

Tourism : this Reserve is inaccessible and not visited by tourists.

IV.   *Altitude :* 240-480 m.

a) Climax forest characteristic of moderate altitudes, dominated by the Bois de Natte and with ebony *Diospyros reticulata* on the lower slopes.

b) Wild pig, deer and monkeys.

2. MACABE-MARE LONGUE RESERVE.

II.   *a*) Status : total protection (under Section 12 (1) of a 1944 Ordinance Cap. 282 of the Laws).

b) Area : 507 ha.

c) Staff : Government officers supervise the area on a part-time basis by periodic patrols.

d) Budget : covers the above supervision, the relevant section of the budget actually providing for one post at U.S. $ 2,100 per year.

III.   *Date established :* 1951.

Administration : by the Ministry of Education and Cultural Affairs.

Land tenure : public ownership.

Tourism : accessible by forest roads, which can be used by the public, including a few tourists, subject to permission.

IV.   *Altitude :* 510 m.

a) Climax forest of the plateau on laterite soils.

b) Wild pig, deer, monkeys.

V.   **Areas excluded :**

A. — Two areas which "do not meet requirements since they are not supervised and no budget is made available for supervision and control " :

1. Round Island (159 ha).

It is a great pity that this does not meet the requisite conditions, since it constitutes the last refuge for a small but unique fauna, particularly in respect of its reptiles, which include two species of snake of the Boa family that in their archaic features would bid fair to rival the famous Coelocanth.

2. Sainte-Marie-Cocotte (164 ha).

344

B. — Five other reserves too small in size to meet the criterion:
3. Cabinet (18 ha).
4. Corps de Garde (91 ha).
5. Ferrier (1.5 ha).
6. Petrin (69 ha).
7. Pouce (69 ha).

85. MEXICO

Listed Areas : thirteen.
1. La Malinche.
2. Zoquiapan.
3. Iztaccihuatl-Popocatepetl.
4. Pico de Orizaba.
5. Bosencheve.
6. Cofre de Perote.
7. Lagunas de Chacahua.
8. Lagunas de Zempoala.
9. Desierto de Los Leones.
10. Insurgente Miguel Hidalgo y Costilla.
11. El Chico.
12. El Tepeyac.
13. Desierto del Carmen.

General Introduction :

Administration : responsibility of the Subsecretaria Forestal y de la Fauna of the Secretaria de Agricultura y Ganaderia.

Land tenure : a great effort is being made by the State to acquire all lands comprised in National Parks, but purchases and expropriations are inevitably expensive and likely to take some considerable time before they are complete. The detailed situation is recorded under each Park.

Tourism : entry to National Parks is unrestricted : several million visitors (3 m. in 1962) visit the Parks as a whole each year and bring in a certain amount of revenue through parking-fees, etc.

Research : encouraged by the Instituto Mexicano de Recursos Naturales y Reno-vables and by the Sociedad Mexicana de Historia Natural.

All the listed Parks and most of those excluded from the List were described in E/3436 of the previous edition of the List.

Details : application of criteria (II), general information (III) and description (IV) :
1. LA MALINCHE.

a) Status : total protection, except that certain sections are still privately owned and the demarcation of boundaries is still incomplete.

b) Area : 41,711 ha.

c) Staff : 4 units.

d) Budget : U.S. $ 1,700 (21,120 pesos).

345

III.   *Date established :* 1938.

Land tenure : the remaining privately-owned sectors are subject to controls.

Tourism : access by the road from Mexico City to Puebla and Tlaxcala.

IV.   *Altitude :* highest point 4,461 m.

a) This Park was established to protect La Malinche volcano and the vegetation of its slopes, which is characteristically composed of *Pinus* and *Abies :* there has been considerable deforestation. The high altitude climate is very mild for Mexico.

b) No information.

2. ZOQUIAPAN.

II.   *a*) Status : complete protection.

b) Area : 20,454 ha.

c) Staff : 3 units.

d) Budget : U.S. $ 2,100 (27,040 pesos).

III.   *Date established :* 1930.

Land tenure : State ownership.

Tourism : access from the Mexico City to Puebla road, 50 km from Mexico City.

IV.   *Altitude :* 2,500-3,000 m.

a) High altitude climate and a flora influenced by comparatively low temperatures : *Pinus* and *Abies* forest.

b) No information.

346

3. Iztaccihuatl-Popocatepetl.

a) Status : complete protection, but some private property; boundary demarcation still in progress.

b) Area : 25,679 ha.

c) Staff : 9 units.

d) Budget : U.S. $ 3,200 (39,560 pesos).

Date established : 1935.

Land tenure : expropriation of privately-owned land is in hand.

Tourism : access from the village of Amecameca, on the Mexico City to Cuautla road; some innes in the park.

Altitude : highest point 5,451 m.

a) Two volcanoes, their summits under permanent snow : *Pinus* (of many species) and *Abies* forest on the slopes.

b) Birds include vermilion flycatcher *Pyrocephalus rubinus,* curved-bill thrasher *Toxostoma curvirostre,* house-finch *Carpodacus mexicanus,* tufted flycatcher *Myiarchus tyrannulus,* violet-crowned humming bird *Amazilia verticalis,* red-faced warbler *Cardellina rubrifrons,* russet nightingale thrush *Catharus aurantiirostris,* brown-throated wren *Troglodytes brunneicollis,* red-eyed towhee *Pipilo erythrophthalmus,* Mexican chickadee *Parus sclateri* and red-backed junco *Junco caniceps.*

4. Pico de Orizaba.

a) Status : complete protection, but boundaries not yet demarcated.

b) Area : 19,750 ha.

c) Staff : 3 units.

d) Budget : U.S. $ 1,400 (17,040 pesos).

Date established : 1936.

Land tenure : expropriation under compensation of the privately-owned land is planned.

Tourism : access from the Mexico City to Puebla road.

Altitude : 2,000-5,762 m.

a) A volcano capped by permanent snow; *Abies* and *Pinus* forest on the slopes.

b) No information.

5. Bosencheve.

a) Status : complete protection, but see below under ' land tenure '; demarcation of boundaries not yet complete.

b) Area : 15,000 ha.

c) Staff : 4 units.

d) Budget : U.S. $ 2,000 (26,640 pesos).

Date established : 1940.

Land tenure : state ownership, except for some private properties which, however, are subject to control.

Tourism : access is by the Mexico City-Morelia-Guadalajara road between km 127 and 147.

IV.   *Altitude :* averages 3,000 m.

a) Comprises a lake (Laguna del Carmen) and the slopes of the Cerro de Zacatones : conifers *Pinus* sp. and *Abies religiosa* are dominant.

b) The Park was established in the interests of the protection of the birds around the lake shore, especially migrants; species include the yellow rail *Coturnicops noveboracensis,* clapper rail *Rallus longirostris* and Mexican duck *Anas fulvigula diazi.*

6. COFRE DE PEROTE.

II.   *a)* Status : complete protection, but some privately-owned sectors although boundaries have been fully demarcated.

b) Area : 11,700 ha.

c) Staff : 2 units.

d) Budget : U.S. $ 900 (11,000 pesos).

III.   *Date established :* 1937.

Land tenure : the areas still in private ownership are subject to controls

Tourism : access by unsurfaced branch road from Perote on the Mexico City to Veracruz highway.

IV.   *Altitude :* highest point 4,282 m.

a) A volcano, the lower slopes of which are covered by coniferous *Pinus, Abies* and *Cupressus,* mixed with some alder and oak *Alnus* and *Quercus.*

b) No information.

7. LAGUNAS DE CHACAHUA.

II.   *a)* Status : complete protection, but demarcation of boundaries still to be undertaken.

b) Area : 10,000 ha.

c) Staff : 3 units.

d) Budget : apparently about U.S. $ 2,000.

III.   *Date established :* 1937.

Land tenure : State ownership.

Tourism : access by air or sea, but the construction of a road is under consideration.

IV.   *Altitude :* 100 m.

a) Mangroves surrounding lagoons and backed by forest chiefly composed of ceiva (silk-cotton) *Bombax* sp., ebony *Brya ebenus,* cedar *Cedrela,* caoba (mahogany) *Swietenia* and velvet tamarind *Dialium* sp.

b) Deer, wild pig; many seabirds, ducks, pelicans and herons.

8. LAGUNAS DE ZEMPOALA.

II.   *a)* Status : complete protection, but demarcation of boundaries still to be undertaken.

b) Area : 4,669 ha.

c) Staff : 6 units.

d) Budget : U.S. $ 2,400 (31,920 pesos).

I.

Date established : 1936.

Land tenure : expropriation of private property in hand.

Tourism : access from the village of Tres Cumbres on the Mexico City to Cuernavaca road.

7.

Altitude : about 3,500 m.

a) Volcanic lakes, surrounded by pine forests of several *Pinus* species, both pure stands and mixed with oak and alder. *Abies religiosa* also occurs.
b) No information.

9. DESIERTO DE LOS LEONES.

a) Status : complete protection.
b) Area : 1,900 ha.
c) Staff : Forest Department supervision.
d) Budget : provided by the Department.

Date established : 1917.

Land tenure : municipal property.

Tourism : access from the Mexico City to Toluca and the Mexico City to San Angel Tetelpa roads.

Altitude : averages 3,000 m.

a) Forests mainly of *Abies, Cupressus* and *Quercus,* with in addition a good many *Prunus, Salix* and *Senecio* species.
b) No information.

10. INSURGENTE MIGUEL HIDALGO Y COSTILLA.

a) Status : complete protection.
b) Area : 1,836 ha.
c) Staff : 9 units.
d) Budget : U.S. $ 4,000 (50,000 pesos).

Date established : 1936.

Land tenure : expropriation of private property in hand.

Tourism : access by the Mexico City to Toluca road at 34 km from Mexico City.

Altitude : averages 3,000 m.

a) A valley filled with *Abies religiosa*; many springs; an artificial lake; some areas freed from private rights.
b) Many birds, including tufted flycatcher, buff-breasted flycatcher *Empidonax fulvifrons,* slate-throated redstart *Setophaga* sp., golden-crowned kinglet *Regulus satrapa,* brown-throated wren, grey cactus wren *Campylorhynchus* sp., rufous-capped brush finch *Leucosticte* sp., pine siskin *Spinus pinus,* collared towhee *Pipilo aberti,* whip-poor-will *Caprimulgus vociferus.*

11. EL CHICO.

a) Status : complete protection, but the mining village of Chico is still included within the Park boundaries.
b) Area : 1,835 ha.
c) Staff : 5 units.
d) Budget : U.S. $ 3,150 (38,160 pesos).

III.   *Date established :* 1898.

Land tenure : State ownership.

Tourism : access from Chico on the Mexico City to Pachuca Real del Monte road.

IV.   *Altitude :* 2,500-2,900 m.

a) Mountains covered in forest of which the principal species are *Abies religiosa, Pinus, Cupressus, Juniperus* and *Quercus* spp.

b) No information.

12. EL TEPEYAC.

II.   *a)* Status : complete protection, but boundaries not yet demarcated and some land is privately-owned.

b) Area : 1,420 ha (rather below criterion requirement).

c) Staff : 8 units.

d) Budget : U.S. $ 2,800 (35,000 pesos).

III.   *Date established :* 1937.

Land tenure : State ownership, but there are also private properties although these are subject to controls.

Tourism : access from the Mexico City to Pachuca road, 7.5 km from Mexico City.

IV.   *Altitude :* upwards of 2,200 m.

a) The interest of this Park lies more in the protection it enjoys than in the natural vegetation, since it is in fact part of the Sierra de Guadaloupe at present being reafforested with eucalypts.

b) No information.

13. DESIERTO DEL CARMEN.

II.   *a)* Status : complete protection.

b) Area : 529 ha only, but kept in the List despite its size, as a particularly well-known National Park which is well administered.

c) Staff : one unit.

d) Budget : U.S. $ 700 (9,000 pesos).

III.   *Date established :* 1942.

Land tenure : State ownership; the Park is well-demarcated and sign posted.

IV.   *Altitude :* 2,200-2,500 m.

a) A comparatively cool highland area, with dense forests of *Quercus, Pinu* and *Cupressus.*

b) No information.

EALAND, Tongariro N.P.   (photo : Nat. Publicity Studios)

EALAND, Egmont N.P.   (photo : Nat. Publicity Studios)

NEW ZEALAND, Arthurs Pass N.P.

(photo : Nat. Publicity

EALAND, Mount Cook N.P.　　　　　　　　　　　　　　　　　　(photo : Nat. Publicity Studios)

EALAND, Fiordland N.P.　　　　　　　　　　　　　　　　　　(photo : Nat. Publicity Studios)

POLAND, Bialowieza N.P.

RHODESIA, Kyle Dam R. (photo : R.

RHODESIA, Matopos N.P. (photo : B. S

ESIA, Wankie N.P.

(photo : M. Graut-Parke)

RHODESIA, Rhodes Inyanga N.P.

(photo : Ministry of Inf

Areas excluded :

The 35 National Parks excluded are :

A. — Nine of considerable size, which are ruled out on the grounds that their status and especially standard of supervision and budget fall well below those laid down in the ICNP criteria for selection.

1. Sierra de San Pedro Martir	... ...	63,000 ha
2. Canon del Rio Blanco	... ...	55,690 ha
3. Pico de Tancitaro	... ...	29,315 ha
4. El Corrogon .	... ...	25,000 ha
5. El Tepozteco (Tepokzeco) .	... ...	24,000 ha
6. Los Marmoles	... ...	23,500 ha
7. Volcan (Nevada) de Colima	... ...	22,000 ha
8. Benito Juarez	... ...	2,700 ha
9. El Potosi	... ...	2,000 ha

B. — Twenty-two which fall below the minimum size requirement of 2,000 hectares.

10. Cacahuamilpa.
11. Garnica.
12. Ajusco.
13. A. de Humboldt.
14. Tlalpam.
15. Chapultepec.
16. Las Campanas.
17. Molino de Flores.
18. Xicotencatl.
19. Los Remedios.
20. Padierna.
21. Estrella.
22. Sabinal.
23. Cupatitzio.
24. Insurgente Morelos.
25. Sacromonte.
26. Los Novillos.
27. Camecuaro.
28. Rayon.
29. Contador.
30. Molino de Belem.
31. El Historico Coyoacan : 584 ha.

C. — Four of which it has been impossible to obtain satisfactory proof that the criterion of effectiveness is respected.

32. Cumbres de Monterrey	... ...	246,500 ha
33. Nevado de Toluca	... ...	67,000 ha
34. Lagunas de Montebello	... ...	6,022 ha
35. Cumbres de Majalca .	... ...	4,773 ha

I.   **Listed Areas :** nil.

V.   **Explanation :**

Despite many efforts it has not yet been possible to obtain official or even semi-official information on the position which Mongolia should properly occupy in this new edition of the U.N. List. Questioned verbally on the subject at the General Conference of UNESCO in 1964, Mr. Pountsagyn Tseren Tsoodol, then Secretary-General of the Mongolian National Commission to UNESCO, stated that there were in fact a number of National Parks and Nature Reserves in his country, for which the Academy of Sciences was responsible. One of these is known to be the Bogdo-Ula Reserve (125,000 ha) in the north-east of the country, which includes the 2,257 m Choybalsan-Ula mountain, the lower slopes of which are covered in forests which constitute the most southerly example of Mongolian *taiga*. Unfortunately it has not yet been possible to obtain full details of this and other areas which may well qualify for the List.

I.   **Listed Areas :** one.

1. Tazzeka National Park.

Details : application of criteria (II), general information (III) and description (IV) :

1. TAZZEKA NATIONAL PARK.

II.   *a*) Status : protection is almost total. There is no human occupation except at a radar installation on the highest point of the Park, currently used for relaying Moroccan radio and television programmes; however this relay station only has one man to look after it and its buildings have been carefully designed so as not to spoil the charm of the site. Cultivation, grazing, hunting and fishing are all prohibited and there is no wood-cutting except for the occasional removal of decaying trees in order to discourage the spread of fungal or other cryptogamic diseases. There is little poaching, game animals being rare and the Park being the protected centre of the much larger permanently reserved area which surrounds the whole of it.

b) Area : 580 ha. This is below the criterion requirement (Morocco having an average population density of 26 inhabitants to the km²), but inclusion seems justified by the high interest of the area. In fact the two tribes within whose territory the Park is situated have a population density of 43 and 53 respectively, per km², but despite this and despite the importance attached by these tribesmen to their herds of cattle, sheep and goats, the prohibition on the use of the Park for grazing is strictly, though sometimes rather reluctantly, respected.

c) Staff : three officers of the Water and Forest Service, on a part-time basis but regular roster; a fire-watcher is posted at the summit station for the four months 1 July to 1 November; recently a small Post has been esta-

352

blished by the Forest Service on a new forest track which runs along the northern boundary of the Park.

d) Budget : no specific provision, but the services specified above are covered.

Date established : 1950, under the powers given by Royal Edict and Vizier's Decree, on 11 and 25 september 1934, respectively.

Land tenure : State forest-land, free of all incubus of customary rights.

Tourism : an 8 km branch track from a tourist circuit route gives access to the summit; no construction of tourist facilities in the Park has been permitted, but there is a holiday camp for young people about 15 km away and also a buffet-restaurant open periodically. No specific information/education facilities. About 200 visitors a year.

Scientific research : not specially organised, but a botanical study, by L. Emberger, has been published and reference can also be made to a review of the flora prepared for the Excursion of the VIIIth International Botanical Congress by C. Sauvage and published by the Scientific Institute of Morocco in 1956; to the geobotanical research on cork-woods in Morocco (also published by the Institute, Botanical Series No. 21, Rabat 1961); and to the geological studies by Mr. Mori of the Mines and Geology Service at Rabat.

Altitude : 1,700-1,980 m, the summit of the mountain tending to be under snow from December to April.

a) An area of mainly botanical interest with a number of endemic species. The cedars (*Cedrus atlantica*) are separable from those of the Rif and Atlas, but with more of the characteristics of the former and, though now a scarce and relict species, are maintaining themselves very well. There is good natural regeneration on south-facing slopes, where the stands of seedlings and young

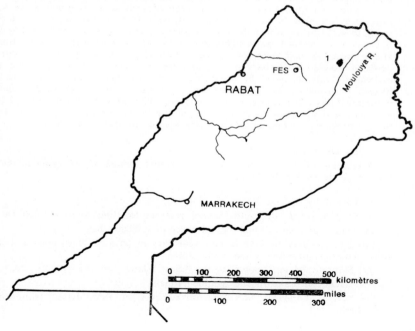

353

trees are very thick, but much less so on northern and eastern slopes where snow may fall from November to April. Though much of the woodland is immature, the old trees, which are not very tall and, from the forestry point of view, often form a rather patchy and uneven canopy, are very picturesque and photogenic.

b) Wild pig *Sus scrofa* numerous, leopard *Panthera pardus* occasional in winter, hare *Lepus atlanticus,* rabbit *Oryctolagus cuniculus* and Barbary partridge *Alectoris barbara* fairly abundant.

V.   **Areas excluded :**

1. The Toubkal National Park (36,000 ha).

There are no villages or human habitations in the Park and no permanent inhabitants, but during the summer it is visited by large numbers of wandering shepherds and their flocks. From spring-time onwards the upland pastures are under heavy pressure from animals which trample the soil when it is still moist and soft, and as a consequence erosion is aggravated and at the same time the vegetational cover becomes modified with progressive elimination of more palatable species. The forests which are found at lower altitudes on the borders of the Park are not subjected to regular exploitation but suffer a good deal of damage from frequent slashing and pollarding, although it cannot be said that their survival is seriously threatened. More serious, however, are the depredations of poachers which have resulted in several animals having become scarce or in some cases having quite disappeared; similarly the fish fauna of the rivers has suffered a marked decrease.

This failure to observe the regulations applied to the Park when it was established in 1942, under the provisions of the Royal Edict of 1934, which set out the conditions required for the conservation of such areas, is much to be regretted since it is an area of great interest. It consists in effect of a high mountain rising to 4,167 m, of which the lower slopes are covered with very old ilex *Quercus ilex* woods, succeeded by junipers *Juniperus thurifera* at higher levels, finally by alpine meadows and numerous screes. Formerly, the mountain had some good herds of Aoudad or Barbary sheep *Ammotragus lervia,* but this species has become exceedingly rare as have the mountain gazelle *Gazella g. cuvieri* and the striped hyaena *H. hyaena.* As for the leopard *Panthera pardus.* which used to haunt the mountain forests, it has completely vanished. The flora presented and still presents a pronounced tendency to endemism, but the effects of over-grazing are reflected in the progressive elimination of many species in this category.

2. La Deroua Reserve (200 ha).

A remnant of the botanical associations once typical of the Tadla plains before they were developed by irrigation.

3. Partial or Special Reserves :

(i) 87 permanent 'de facto' faunal reserves totalling some 284,000 ha.

(ii) 380 legally constituted faunal reserves (200,000 ha).

(iii) Khnifiss Bay Reserve (a bird sanctuary in an area of swamps and lagoons with numerous breeding waders and duck).

(iv) Skhirate Island, known as the 'Bird Island' on the Atlantic coast.

(v) Affenourir Lake in the Middle Atlas.

(vi) Several botanical sites (the olive-groves of Beni-Mellal, palm-groves of Marrakesh, etc.).

Listed Areas : two.
1. Rhinoceros Sanctuary, Chitawan District.
2. Sukla Phanta Sanctuary, Khanchanpur District.

General Introduction :
Nepal was not included in the previous edition of the List. The legal basis for reserves in the country is provided by the Wild Animal (Protection) Act and the Forest Department of His Majesty's Government of Nepal is responsible for their administration. When the two Listed Areas are formally declared to be 'Wildlife Sanctuaries', there is special legal provision for giving them the status of 'National Parks' by a separate Act of the legislature in each case. A Bill for the Chitawan Rhinoceros Sanctuary had already been drafted by the end of 1966.

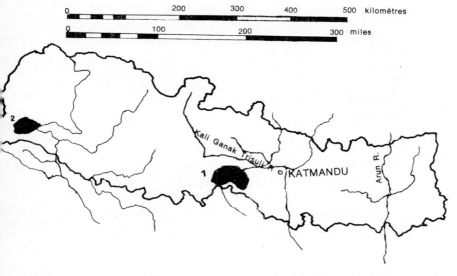

Details : application of criteria (II), general information (III) and description (IV) :
1. CHITAWAN RHINOCEROS SANCTUARY.

a) Status : total protection (" certainly in the category of fully protected reserves ").

b) Area : about 80,000 ha (Chitawan Sanctuary : 62,160 ha; King Mahendra National Park : 15,540 ha; plus a small Royal Shikar Reserve in between, of unknown size).

c) Staff : 1 wildlife officer, 1 assistant officer, 4 subahdars, 146 wildlife guards, 22 hawalders, 4 clerks.

d) Budget : U.S. $ 23,500 (235,000 Nepalese rupees) in 1968-1969.

Date established : part of the present sanctuary was declared in 1959 as the " King Mahendra National Park ", but without a specific Act or other legal provision for according it this status. From 1959 to 1962 there was a period

355

of considerable friction with the local people, during which they put the eastern end of the area under cultivation, but control was reasserted in 1963 and, in the following year, H.M. King Mahendra gave instructions for this area, together with the area south of the river Rapti, which is the main habitat of the rhinoceros, to be given sanctuary status. The boundaries were to be demarcated and some villages evacuated, increasing the total sanctuary area from about 350 km² to about 800 km². In 1965, this work was completed by the termination of all human occupancy and the resettlement of some 4,000 people elsewhere.

Tourism : " Tiger Tops Hotel ".

IV. *Altitude :* about 350 m.

a) Part of the Siwalik Hills, foothills of the Himalaya, overlooking the Ganges plain; between the hills and the main Himalayan range there is a series of transverse valleys called « duns » and the Park is situated at the western end of a typical « dun », through which the Rapti river flows and near the confluence of the Rapti and Rue. Along these rivers extensive marshland forms the characteristic habitat of the rhinoceros, the vegetation being chiefly composed of sugar cane *Saccharum* spp., the silk-cotton tree *Bombax malabaricum,* the cutch-tree *Acacia catechu, Bauhinia* sp., sisham *Dalbergia sissoo* and sal *Shorea robusta.*

b) Great Indian rhinoceros *Rhinoceros unicornis,* elephant *Elephas maximus,* tiger and leopard *Panthera tigris* and *pardus,* black bear *Selenarctos thibetanus,* sambar *Cervus unicolor,* gaur *Bos gaurus,* chital *A . axis,* muntjac *Muntiacus muntjak,* wild pig *Sus scrofa,* crocodile *Crocodilus palustris* and gharial *Gavialis gangeticus.*

c) Great Indian rhinoceros.

2. SUKLA PHANTA SANCTUARY.

II. *a)* Status : total protection.
b) Area : 12,500 ha.
c) Staff : 1 wildlife officer, 2 subahdars, 40 wildlife guards.
d) Budget : U.S. $ 8,950 (63,840 Nepalese rupees) in 1965-1966.

III. *Date established :* as at January 1966 not yet formally declared as a Sanctuary, but accorded full protection under the Wild Animals (Protection) Act. The final work of demarcation by the end of that year.

Tourism : one forest rest house; jeepable roads.

IV. *Altitude :* about 180 m.

a) Part of the Terai region of the Ganges plain; sal forest, swamps and grassy plains calls " phantas ". An excellent sample of the typical vegetation of south-west Nepal.

b) Swamp deer *Cervus duvauceli* (numerous), tiger, leopard, elephant, blackbuck *Antilope cervicapra,* sambar, hog deer *Axis porcinus,* muntjac, chital, wild pig.

c) Swamp deer.

V. **Areas excluded :**

Proposed reserves :

Tappu Sanctuary;
Royal Shikar Reserves (include 9 different reserves).

356

Listed Areas : eighteen.

A. — RESERVES.

1. Veluwe Randmeren and the Zwarte Meer.
2. Boschplaat.
3. Schorren achter de Polder Eendracht op Texel (includes the new Texel reserves for seals).
4. Kobbeduinen.
5. Geul and Westerduinen.
6. Dwingelosche and Kraloër Heide.
7. Strabrechste Heide.
8. Kampinasche Heide.
9. Oostvoornse Duinen.
10. Biesbosch.
11. Naardermeer.
12. Hulshorster Zand.
13. Oostelijke Maasdalhelling.
14. Fochtelooër Veen.

B. — NATIONAL PARKS.

15. Hoge Veluwe.
16. Veluwezoom.
17. De Wieden.
18. Kennemerduinen.

General Introduction :

Administration : some of the Dutch reserves are run by the public authorities, mainly by the Departments of Agriculture (Staatsbosbeheer) or Education (O.K.W. Afdeling Oudheidkunde en Natuurbescherming), others by private bodies, of which the most important is also the oldest (1905) — the Vereeniging tot Behoud van Natuurmonumenten in Nederland (V.B.N.). It has not been possible to obtain a breakdown of the staff and budget of each area, but the authorities vouch that all the listed areas are effectively maintained and supervised. No information is available as to the year in which each of the reserves was established.

As indicated in section I, four of the eighteen listed areas have the title of 'National Park', which means no more than they are rated as State property, though two of them, No. 16 Veluwezoom and No. 17 De Weiden, are in fact entirely under the control of the V.B.N. except for certain roads.

Land tenure : the relevant legislation makes it obligatory for all land to be acquired by the State or private organisations, as the case may be.

Tourism : due to the population density of the Netherlands, the highest in the world, all the protected areas are open to visitors, though, as indicated below, a few contain limited sectors treated as strict nature reserves and, conversely, others have been deliberately organised and equipped for mass recreational purposes.

Scientific research : many ecological and systematic studies have been undertaken in the Reserves, most often within the integrated programme of the Institute of Ecological Research for Nature Protection (R.I.V.O.N.).

The Netherlands was not included in the previous edition of the List.

Details : application of criteria (II), general information (III) and description (IV) :
A. — RESERVES.

    1. VELUWE RANDMEREN AND THE ZWARTE MEER.

II.   *a*) Status : total protection applies only to 1,500 ha of the Zwarte Meer.
    b) Area : 5,500 ha.
    c) and *d*) Staff and Budget : see General Introduction.

III.   *Administration :* management and supervision are undertaken by a special
Foundation.

358

a) The Zwarte Meer is a lake originating from the development of the North-East Polder.

b) Many water birds, notably the bearded reedling *Panurus biarmicus*.

2. BOSCHPLAAT.

a) Status : total protection. Strictly supervised measures are taken to control rabbits.

b) Area : 4,400 ha.

c) and *d*) Staff and Budget : see General Introduction.

Administration : by Government departments.

a) Comprises the dunes, beaches and sandy flats of the Frisian island Terschelling and demonstrates the successive stages in the occupation of bare saline areas by halophilous vegetation. Plant species recorded include : the purslanes *Halimione portulacoides* and *pedunculata*, the scurvy grasses *Cochlearia anglica and danica*, sea lavender *Limonium vulgare*, the orache *Atriplex glabriuscula*, rockrose *Helianthemum guttatum*, fen orchid *Liparis loeselii*, sea holly *Eryngium maritimum*, sea bindweed *Calystegia soldanella*, bog rush *Schoenus nigricans*, grass of Parnassus *Parnassia palustris*, early marsh orchid *Orchis strictifolia*, fragrant orchid *Gymnadenia conopsea*, bearberry *Arctostaphylos uvaursi*, crowberry *Empetrum nigrum* and large cranberry *Oxycoccus macrocarpus*.

b) The small colony of spoonbills *Platalea leucorodia*, established since 1962, is a notable feature of the plentiful birdlife.

3. SCHORREN ACHTER DE POLDER EENDRACHT OP TEXEL.

a) Status : total protection. Includes a special reserve for seals.

b) Area : 3,000 ha.

c) and *d*) Staff and Budget : see General Introduction.

Administration : by the V.B.N.

a) The " slikkes " and " schorrels " (saltings subject to tidal influence) of the north-east coast of the island of Texel, with typical halophilous vegetation.

b) An important breeding-station for terns, black-headed gulls *Larus ridibundus*, avocets *Avosetta recurvirostra*, etc. and very important as a refuge for migratory waders such as knot *Calidris canutus*, dunlin *C. alpina*, bar-tailed godwit *Limosa lapponica*, brent goose *Branta bernicla*, etc.

4. KOBBEDUINEN.

a) Status : total protection, but shooting is occasionally allowed under strict control.

b) Area : 2,400 ha.

c) and *d*) Staff and Budget : see General Introduction.

Administration : by Government departments.

a) The eastern part of the island of Schiermonnikoog, comprising vast sand flats, with dune formations in which depressions holding both fresh and brackish water occur.

b) No information.

5. GEUL AND WESTERDUINEN.

II.　　　*a)* Status : total protection, but shooting is occasionally allowed under strict control.

b) Area : 1,680 ha.

c) and *d)* Staff and Budget : see General Introduction.

III.　　*Administration :* by Government departments.

IV.　　　*a)* In the south-west part of the island of Texel, an expanse of dunes, with channels, "windkuilen" ("wind-holes" or depressions caused by wind) and and some heathy areas in which *Juniperus communis* occurs.

b) A dike and fresh-water lagoon in the south of the reserve is an important breeding place for birds, particularly the herring gull *Larus argentatus*; there are some spoonbills.

6. DWINGELOSCHE AND KRALOËR HEIDE.

II.　　　*a)* Status : total protection, but shooting is occasionally allowed under strict control.

b) Area : 1,200 ha, in two sections of 835 and 365 ha respectively.

c) and *d)* Staff and Budget : see General Introduction.

III.　　*Administration :* the V.B.N. and State are jointly responsible, the former for maintenance, the latter for supervision.

IV.　　　*a)* A sample of the original heathland of Drenthe Province, of a type rather rare in Western Europe with its mixture of numerous pools and dry heath. The flora includes spotted orchid *Orchis maculata*, *Arnica* and the marsh lungwort *Pulmonaria* sp.

b) Black-headed gulls nest in some of the marshy areas, but need to be controlled, for their numbers tend to become excessive; blackcock *Lyrurus tetrix*; curlew *Numenius arquata*.

7. STRABRECHTSE HEIDE.

II.　　　*a)* Status : total protection.

b) Area : 1,200 ha.

c) and *d)* Staff and Budget : see General Introduction.

III.　　*Administration :* by Government departments.

IV.　　　*a)* A landscape of heath and upland mosses typical of the Brabant region; interesting aquatic habitats.

b) Rich in birdlife. The gudgeon *Gobio fluviatilis* occurs in the waters.

8. KAMPINASCHE HEIDE.

II.　　　*a)* Status : total protection, but shooting sometimes allowed under strict control.

b) Area : 1,106 ha.

c) and *d)* Staff and Budget : see General Introduction.

III.　　*Administration :* by the V.B.N.

IV.　　　*a)* A sample of the semi-natural landscape of the Campine, of which there is little left; dry and damp heathlands, pools, marshes and forests, with a rich and varied flora including skull-cap *Scutellaria*, great burnet *Sanguisorba offi-*

cinalis, marshland ragworts *Senecio* spp. and, more rarely, quill-worts *Isoetes* spp. and species, such as whortleberries *Vaccinium* sp. and the spike-rush *Eleocharis,* characteristic of peatlands.

b) Many species of birds, including bittern *Botaurus stellaris,* black-headed gull, curlew, blackcock.

9. OOSTVOORNSE DUINEN.

a) Status : total protection with occasional exceptions.

b) Area : 1,042 ha, made up of Voornse Duinen 742 ha and Duinen van Oostvoorne 300 ha.

c) and *d)* Staff and Budget : see General Introduction.

Administration : by a private organisation.

a) Old and modern dune formations, with some small lakes and damp depressions, in which gentians and orchids occur; eglantine *Rosa rubiginosa,* barberry *Berberis vulgaris* and orchids on the dunes.

b) Black-headed gull, blackcock, shelduck *T. tadorna,* tufted duck *Aythya fuligula.*

10. BIESBOSCH.

a) Status : total protection in some sectors which have the status of strict nature reserves and in which only limited exploitation such as reed- and osier-cutting is allowed.

b) Area : 800 ha.

c) and *d)* Staff and Budget : see General Introduction.

Administration : by Government departments.

Tourism : alongside the strict nature reserves, other areas have been specially developed for recreation purposes.

a) Extensive water-bodies, osier-beds and rushy areas make this a typically freshwater marshy biotope, quite unusual in the Brabant region.

b) Many birds, including several pairs of night-herons *N. nycticorax.*

11. NAARDERMEER.

a) Status : total protection, but controlled shooting, mainly of duck, is sometimes allowed.

b) Area : 751 ha.

c) and *d)* Staff and Budget : see General Introduction.

Administration : by the V.B.N. Contains a sector classified as strict nature reserve.

a) Contains a wide range of lake and marsh vegetation; several orchids occur.

b) Among the many breeding birds, spoonbills, purple herons *Ardea purpurea,* cormorants and black terns *Chlidonias niger* are the most important.

12. HULSHORSTER ZAND.

a) Status : total protection.

b) Area : 279 ha.

c) and *d)* Staff and Budget : see General Introduction.

III.   *Administration :* by the V.B.N.

Tourism : no restrictions on entry of visitors.

IV.   *a)* Situated to the south-east of the Amersfoort-Zwolle railway, this is a remnant of a once large area of shifting sand, now mainly stabilised by trees. Of considerable archaeological and entomological interest.

b) No information.

13. OOSTELIJKE MAASDALHELLING.

II.   *a)* Status : total protection in the two areas, Bunderbosch and Savelbosch, of which this Reserve is composed.

b) Area : Bunderbosch 55 ha, Savelbosch 174 ha, total 229 ha.

c) and *d)* Staff and Budget : see General Introduction.

III.   *Administration :* by Government departments.

Tourism : rapidly increasing in the Savelbosch sector.

IV.   1. Bunderbosch sector :

a) A remarkable broad-leaved forest, with a rich flora including great horsetail *Equisetum telmateia,* pendulous sedge *Carex pendula,* golden saxifrage *Chrysosplenium* sp., large bittercress *Cardamine amara,* goldilocks *Ranunculus auricornus* and herb paris *Paris quadrifolia.* There are many springs on the hillsides.

2. Savelbosch sector :

a) Varied and well-developed forest land, enclosing a prehistoric site, with not many flowering plants; yellow wood-anemone *Anemone ranunculoides,* man orchid *Aceras anthropophorum,* hard shield-fern *Polystichum lobatum.*

b) Animals said to be scarce in the Savelbosch, but no other details.

14. FOCHTELOOËR VEEN.

II.   *a)* Status : total protection.

b) Area : 209 ha.

c) and *d)* Staff and Budget : see General Introduction.

III.   *Administration :* by the V.B.N.

Tourism : admission strictly reserved for members of V.B.N.

IV.   *a)* Typical saturated peat-bog, rare in N.W. Continental Europe.

b) Great grey shrike *Lanius excubitor,* common snipe *G. gallinago,* Montagu's harrier *Circus pygargus,* blackcock.

B. — NATIONAL PARKS.

15. HOGE VELUWE NATIONAL PARK.

II.   *a)* Status : total protection, but controlled shooting sometimes allowed.

b) Area : 5,700 ha.

c) and *d)* Staff and Budget : see General Introduction.

362

Administration : by a special Foundation.

Tourism : very active, with full organisation and facilities for mass recreation.

a) Conifer and broad-leaf woods, heaths, lakes.

b) Roe deer *C. capreolus,* red deer *Cervus elaphus,* wild pig *Sus scrofa,* fox *V. vulpes*; mouflon *Ovis musimon* introduced in 1921 — a sign of human interference with the ecosystem; many birds, including blackcock, black wood-pecker *Dryocopus martius*; white-tailed sea-eagles *Haliaetus albicilla* have been recorded in several winters.

16. VELUWEZOOM NATIONAL PARK.

a) Status : total protection, but controlled shooting allowed at times and also some exploitation of forest produce.

b) Area : 4,490 ha.

c) and *d)* Staff and Budget : see General Introduction.

Administration : by the V.B.N.

Tourism : very active.

a) Loess deposits and moraines cut by rivers; heaths, mixed broad-leaf and coniferous forest.

b) Deer, fox, wild pig, badger *M. meles* (one earth); blackcock, common buzzard *B. buteo,* black woodpecker.

17. DE WEIDEN NATIONAL PARK.

a) Status : one sector kept as strict nature reserve, some other sectors open to various exploitations, such as reed-cutting, and three controlled duck-shoots.

b) Area : 2,500 ha in the V.B.N. section, plus 1,000 ha in a State-owned section known as the Overyssel.

c) and *d)* Staff and Budget : see General Introduction.

Administration : jointly exercised by the State and the V.B.N.

Tourism : yachting.

a) An important group of lakes and marshes, with some peat and traces of ancient occupation. Recorded plants include the sedges *Carex buxbaumii, aquatilis* and *diandra,* fen violet *Viola stagnina,* narrow smallreed *Calama-grostis neglecta,* bladderwort *Utricularia intermedia,* grass of Parnassus, marsh fleawort *Senecio congestus,* cranberry *Oxycoccus palustris,* marsh sow-thistle *Sonchus palustris.*

b) Many birds, including cormorants *Phalacrocorax carbo* and purple herons.

18. KENNEMERDUINEN NATIONAL PARK.

a) Status : a good example of a ' zoned ' area, with some parts totally protected, controlled shooting in others and others actively developed for tourism.

b) Area : 1,240 ha.

c) and *d)* Staff and Budget : see General Introduction.

Administration : by a special Foundation.

Tourism : very active in limited sectors of the Park; camping sites.

IV.   *a*) A sample of the Dutch coastal dune areas along the North Sea near Harlem; the varied flora is typical of that of sandy calcareous soils.

b) A great variety of nesting and migratory birds.

V.   **Areas excluded :**

The official list furnished by the Dutch Government of protected areas of over 100 ha in size comprises 112 names, including the 18 listed above. Some 94 are therefore omitted plus some hundreds of others of smaller size. Among the omissions are several quite large areas which, in agreement with the Dutch authorities, are judged to be under too intense tourist pressure to allow the ICNP criterion of effective protection to be sufficiently satisfied : for example —

De Veluwemeer (4,000 ha).
Het Gooisch Nature Reserve (1,918 ha).
Ventjagersplaat (1,270 ha).

These, with a number of other reserves, must also be excluded because they are in the area affected by the Delta Plan development works.

90. NEW CALEDONIA

I.   **Listed Areas :** nil.

V.   **Explanation :**

The authorities consulted have not yet responded. It is known that a number of projects have been under consideration in the past, but no measures have apparently been taken to implement plans for five reserves which have been mentioned — the Plaine des Lacs, Mt. Humboldt, Mt. Panié, Unia and Poumé.

91. NEW ZEALAND

I.   **Listed Areas :** ten.
1. Fiordland National Park (South Island).
2. Urewera National Park (North Island).
3. Mount Aspiring National Park (South Island).
4. Arthur's Pass National Park (South Island).
5. Westland National Park (South Island).
6. Mount Cook National Park (South Island).
7. Tongariro National Park (North Island).
8. Nelson Lakes National Park (South Island).
9. Egmont National Park (North Island).
10. Abel Tasman National Park (South Island).

General Introduction :

In the smaller islands under New Zealand Administration there are at present no areas which qualify for inclusion in the List. Shooting and sport-fishing (introduced species only, under a permit system) are allowed in some parts of most of the National Parks, but under strict supervision and, with these localised exceptions, the Parks enjoy a fair standard of protection, indigenous fauna and flora being totally protected everywhere.

The legal basis of the National Parks is the National Park Act of 1952, which set up a National Parks Authority of New Zealand and a National Park Board. The executive body is the Department of Lands and Surveys, while Tourism and and Scientific Research are, respectively, the responsibility of the Department of Tourism and Publicity and the Department of Scientific and Industrial Research in conjunction with the Universities.

All the land of the Parks is in public ownership except for part of No. 2, Urewera (q.v.) and all the Parks, except the newly created No. 3, Mt. Aspiring National Park, were described in the previous edition E/3436 of the List.

365

NEW ZEALAND

Details : application of criteria (II), general information (III) and description (IV) :

1. FIORDLAND NATIONAL PARK.

II.
a) Status : protected generally, with one specially protected "wilderness area " of 11,664 ha. The Park may be impaired by a hydroelectric project.

b) Area : 1,223,654 ha (including the wilderness area).

c) Staff : 11 units, which is well below the requisite level, but the considerations which justify the inclusion of the Park are : entirely uninhabited character of the region, difficulty of access, the possibility (of which good use is made) of applying effective supervision by air and water and, in addition, the fact that voluntary or temporary assistance is given by personnel employed on campaigns to control undesirable introduced species (opossums, wild goats, wapiti and red deer), as well as by scientific staff.

d) Budget : U.S. $ 73,280, as compared with a criterion level of $ 60,000 (1968-1969 figures).

III.
Date established : 1904.

Tourism : two hotels, motels, camping sites, mountain huts; mountaineering, sport-fishing, shooting, trips by air.

IV.
Altitude : sea level to 2,460 m.

a) A South Island mountain landscape, with typical glacial relief (glaciers, lakes, rivers, waterfalls) and numerous fiords; the lower slopes are forest covered (*Nothofagus* or southern beech), above which are subalpine associations, alpine meadows and a snow zone.

b) Many birds, including the takahe *Notornis mantelli,* of which this is the last surviving habitat, and the owl parrot or kakapo *Strigops habroptilus*; wapiti *Cervus canadensis,* red deer *Cervus elaphus* (both introduced); seals in the fiords.

c) Takahe, kakapo.

2. UREWERA NATIONAL PARK.

II.
a) Status : total protection. Some small Maori communities still live around Lake Waikaremoana, their folklore and traditions being the subject of special measures of protection.

b) Area : 199,523 ha.

c) Staff : 6 units, below the criterion, but sufficient for effective management, including eradication of introduced animals considered to be harmful.

d) Budget : U.S. $ 38,490 (1968-1969 figure).

III.
Date established : 1954.

Land tenure : the Lake and some adjacent land is Maori-owned.

Tourism : a hotel, a ' motor camp ', mountain huts; sport fishing and shooting.

IV.
Altitude : 575-1,300 m.

a) Mountain zone densely covered with mixed forest; many precipices, waterfalls and lakes.

b) Many birds, including the kiwi *Apteryx* sp.; some introduced mammals including ' opossum ' (the brush-tailed phalanger *Trichosurus vulpecula*), wild goat, red deer and wild pig.

366

3. MOUNT ASPIRING NATIONAL PARK.

a) Status : total protection.

b) Area : recently reported to be 272,797 ha, which would place this park as No. 2 in the List.

c) Staff : 4 units, including the former Supervisor of National Parks, Mr. R. W. Cleland, who in 1966 elected to return to park work in the field.

d) Budget : U.S. $ 27,590 (1968-1969).

Date established : 1964.

Tourism : a hotel and mountain huts; mountaineering, shooting, trips by air.

Altitude : 350-2,850 m.

a) Comprises part of both the western and eastern slopes of the Southern Alps. Glaciers. Thick forest; extensive river valleys.

b) A good sample of the indigenous avifauna; red deer and ' opossum ' have been introduced.

4. ARTHUR'S PASS NATIONAL PARK.

a) Status : total protection, especially of a ' wilderness area ' of 12,100 ha.

b) Area : 98,371 ha.

c) Staff : 7 units.

d) Budget : U.S. $ 39,720 (1968-1969).

Date established : 1929.

Tourism : mountain refuges and huts, motels; mountaineering, skiing, shooting; there is a museum.

Altitude : 600-2,250 m.

a) Another sample of the Southern Alps, with marked glacial morphology (glaciers, corries, moraines, tills of boulder-clay); on the eastern slopes, up to about 1,350 m, *Nothofagus* beech forest; subtropical rain forest on the western slopes, the strictly protected ' wilderness area ' referred to in Section II being composed of a mixture of both; above this is a rather impenetrable subalpine zone, then high altitude tussock-grassland and rocky outcrops.

b) The birds include the mountain parrot or kea *Nestor notabilis,* which is quite plentiful, and the large grey kiwi *Apteryx haastii,* in the more remote areas; red deer, chamois *R. rupicapra* and ' opossum ' have been introduced.

5. WESTLAND NATIONAL PARK.

a) Status : total protection.

b) Area : 91,804 ha.

c) Staff : 7 units, slightly below criterion but similar arguments as applied to No. 1, Fiordland, especially the uninhabited nature of the country, justifiy retention in the List, having regard also to the very adequate budget.

d) Budget : U.S. $ 45,987 (1968-1969), as compared with a criterion requirement of $ 4,000.

Date established : 1960.

Tourism : two hotels, ' motor-camps ', mountain huts; mountaineering, skiing, trips of the glaciers, sightseeing by aeroplane, shooting.

IV.

Altitude : sea level to 3,300 m.

a) Comprises part of the western foothills of the Southern Alps from sea level to 3,300 m; many lakes, rivers, waterfalls; the Fox and Franz-Josef glaciers; thick subtropical rain-forest up to 1,000 m.

b) Chiefly of interest for its birds; red deer and chamois introduced.

6. MOUNT COOK NATIONAL PARK.

II.

a) Status : total protection.
b) Area : 70,002 ha.
c) Staff : 11 units (above the criterion).
d) Budget : U.S. $ 63,027 (1968-1969).

III.

Date established : 1953.

Tourism : a hotel, motels, camp-sites, mountain huts; mountaineering, skiing, shooting, trips by air.

IV.

Altitude : 750-3,700 m.

a) A section of the Southern Alps, which includes seventeen peaks of over 3,000 m in height and many glaciers (e.g. the 29 km long Tasman glacier); subalpine and alpine zones of vegetation, leading up to the snow zone.

b) All the mammals are introduced species, the most notable being mountain goats or tahr *Hemitragus* sp. and chamois; the indigenous birds include the mountain parrot or kea *Nestor notabilis*.

7. TONGARIRO NATIONAL PARK.

II.

a) Status : total protection, with special protection for two 'wilderness areas' totalling 14,800 ha.
b) Area : 67,404 ha.
c) Staff : 13 units, compared with a criterion level of 7.
d) Budget : U.S. $ 111,754 (1968-1969).

III.

Date established : 1894.

Tourism : a hotel, motels, 'motor-camp', mountain huts and refuges; skiing, shooting, sport-fishing.

IV.

Altitude : 600-2,150 m.

a) A mountain zone which includes the three volcanoes, Mt. Ruapehu (semi-active, with a warm water crater-lake), Mt. Ngaurohoe (the most active volcano in New Zealand) and the extinct Mt. Tongariro; the only glaciers of North Island are in the Park; tussock-grassland surrounds the mountains, of which the lower slopes are forested (*Podocarpus*) and the upper clothed in subalpine vegetation.

b) The forest has a good avifauna; red deer, 'opossum' and wild pig have been introduced.

8. NELSON LAKES NATIONAL PARK.

II.

a) Status : general protection, with special protection for a 'wilderness area' of 3,480 ha and an 'animal study area' of 27,500 ha.
b) Area : 57,112 ha.
c) Staff : 5 untis (criterion : 6).
d) Budget : U.S. $ 47,630 (1968-1969).

Date established : 1956.

Tourism : a motel, camp-sites, mountain huts; skiing, shooting, sport-fishing.

Altitude : 450-2,350 m.

a) Two lakes surrounded by mountains thickly covered up to 1,230 m by forest of *Nothofagus* beech.

b) Abundant indigenous birdlife; red deer, chamois and ' opossum ' have been introduced.

9. EGMONT NATIONAL PARK.
a) Status : total protection.
b) Area : 33,377 ha.
c) Staff : 5 units.
d) Budget : U.S. $ 47,970 (1968-1969).

Date established : 1900.

Tourism : three hotels, mountain huts; skiing and mountaineering.

Altitude : sea level to 2,475 m.

a) Comprises the volcanic cone of Mt. Egmont and its surroundings; many waterfalls; the vegetational stages range from dense sub-tropical forest to the snow zone (about 1,800 m), through zones of grassland, sphagnum bog and bare rock.

b) The many indigenous birds include the kiwi; entomologically very interesting; introduced species are wild goat and ' opossum ', but no deer.

10. ABEL TASMAN NATIONAL PARK.
a) Status : total protection.
b) Area : 18,265 ha.
c) Staff : 3 units (criterion : 2).
d) Budget : U.S. $ 20,240 (1968-1969).

Date established : 1942.

Tourism : only camping facilities and huts; shooting, boating.

Altitude : sea level to 1,100 m.

a) A coastal area on Tasman Bay, including beaches and coves, mountainous terrain and inshore islands; apart from some dunes, marshes and rain forest with many epiphytes, most of the Park, at least nine-tenths, consists of various kinds of *Nothofagus* beech forest.

b) Many birds, including the pigeon *Hemiphaga novaeseelandiae,* long-tailed cuckoo *Eudynamis taitensis,* ' robin ' *Petroica australis,* white-faced heron *Ardea novaehollandiae,* terns, southern skua *Catharacta skua lonnbergi* and ' dove-petrel ' or broad-billed prion *Pachyptila vittata*; fur seals and sea lions are elements of the important marine-life of the Park.

Areas excluded :

29 partial or special reserves for fauna or flora, many of them bird-sanctuaries, totalling 178,771 ha in area.

927 scenic reserves or historic sites, totalling 270,733 ha. These reserves were established under the Reserves and Domain Act of 1953 and, since 1961, have been managed and supervised by the National Parks Authority.

369

I.   **Listed Areas :** nil.

V.   **Explanation :**

Information received many years ago gives the impression that plans were formerly under consideration for enacting a law which would provide a basis for the promulgation of National Parks in regions of biological or geological interest in Nicaragua. Various names were mentioned, such as the volcanoes of Momotombo, Masaya and Mombacho, and the small islands in Lake Granada.

No news had been received of the implementation of these plans until, just at the time when the List for the present edition had been closed (March 1966), an official communication was received from Managua, confirming the general position, as outlined above, but also stating that on 3 February 1941, a decree numbered 163 had in fact been promulgated to establish, in the public interest, a 100 hectare National Park in a place named Las Piedrecitas.

93.   **NIGER**

I.   **Listed Areas :** one.

1. The ' W ' National Park.

General Introduction :

This Park, which was included in Part Two of the previous edition of the List, extends to the south-east into Dahomey (502,050 ha) and to the south-west into Upper Volta (330,000 ha). It is named after the double loop of the Niger river on which it is situated. A plan to create a single authority to administer the whole 1,130,000 ha area was submitted for the consideration of the three Governments in 1965. The Niger sector is at present administered by the Ministry of Rural Economy.

Details : application of criteria (II), general information (III) and description (IV) :

1. The ' W ' National Park.

II.   *a)* Status : total protection.

b) Area : 300,000 ha.

c) Staff : 7 units, well below the criterion level but just acceptable.

d) Budget : U.S. $ 14,000, which meets the criterion.

III.   *Date established :* 1954, having been classified as a total faunal reserve and state forest a year earlier.

Land tenure : public ownership.

Tourism : active from December to the end of April, the rest of the year being ruled out by the heavy rains, when the Park is closed; there is a rest-camp at Tapoa on the north-west border, with accommodation for 32; 226 km of motorable track in the Park : landing ground for aircraft up to DC 3 size; 860-1,000 visitors a year.

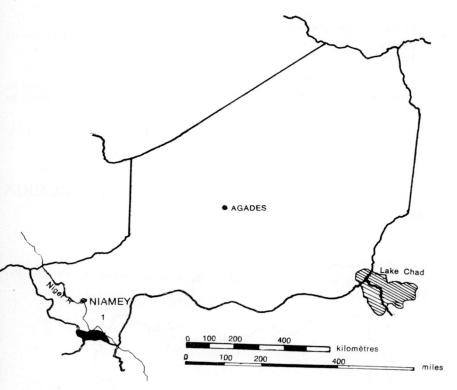

Altitude : about 250 m.

a) A lateritic shield or peneplain, deeply dissected by watercourses, which results in prehistoric gorges such as those of Tapoa and Mekrou and the rapids of Barou; Soudanian-type wooded savannah with a fire-climax flora (*Butyro-spermum, Parkia,* bastard mahogany *Khaya senegalensis,* etc.); in the north tends towards the Sahelian-type savannah; some fine gallery forests (*Cola laurifolia, Kigelia aethiopica*), especially along the seasonal rivers in the south. The main hills, the Atacora range, are in the Dahomey sector.

b) Elephant *Loxodonta africana,* buffalo *Syncerus caffer,* warthog *Phaco-choerus aethiopicus,* the larger antelopes of savannah country such as roan *Hippotragus equinus,* hartebeest *Alcelaphus buselaphus,* topi *Damaliscus korri-gum* and kob *Kobus kob*; monkeys (*Cercopithecus* spp.); lion and leopard *Panthera leo* and *pardus,* caracal *Felis caracal,* cheetah *Acinonyx jubatus,* jackal *Canis mesomelas*; hippopotamus and crocodile on the permanent waters.

371

V. **Areas excluded :**

A. — One total faunal reserve, established in 1962 on the north-west border of the ' W ' National Park, as a protective buffer zone. Although entry is by permit only, no control is exercised other than the prohibition of hunting.

B. — Two reserves in the north central region of Agades (Aïr), in the first of which game enjoys protection and the supervision is strict :

Tadress . ... 4,400,000 ha
Termit.

C. — Two other reserves :

Gadabegi, established by Decree No. 3206 of 22 December 1956 ...   76,000 ha
Tamou . ... 50,000 ha

94. NIGERIA

I. **Listed Areas :** one.

1. Yankari Game Reserve.

General Introduction :

No Nigerian areas were described in the previous edition, E/3436 and Part Two, of the List.

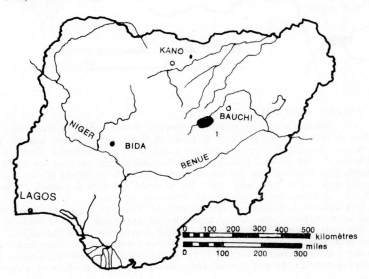

Details : application of criteria (II), general information (III) and description (IV) :

1. YANKARI GAME RESERVE.

   a) Status : general protection, both as a forest reserve and as a ' no shooting ' area. No human occupancy, cultivation or grazing of animals allowed.

   b) Area : 182,160 ha.

   c) Staff : 15 units (a warden and 14 scouts or guards).

   d) Budget : no information available.

   Date established : 1956.

   Administration : by the Bauchi Local Authority.

   Tourism : 200 km of motorable track; a rest-camp in the north of the reserve; tourist traffic was increasing (1967).

   Altitude : not quoted, but probably a little less than 500 m.

   a) Guinean savannah of the northerly type, very thick bush in places and swampy in the inundation zones of the rivers, where there are grassy plains and groundwater forests; hot springs; ancient cisterns hollowed out in the sandstone for storing water.

   b) Elephant *Loxodonta africana*, hippopotamus *H. amphibius*, various antelopes such as roan *Hippotragus equinus*, waterbuck *Kobus ellipsiprymnus* and bushbuck *Tragelaphus scriptus*; giraffe *Giraffa camelopardalis*, lion and leopard *Panthera leo* and *pardus*; crocodiles.

Areas excluded :

1. Borgu Game Reserve (about 350,000 ha) : not yet adequately supervised.

2. Akure "Natural Forest Inviolate Plot " : no data available on size or supervision.

3. Five other reserves (no details) : Zamfara, Kogin Giri, Orle River, Gilli-Gilli and Old Oyo.

95. NORWAY

Listed Areas : three.

1. Börgefjell National Park.
2. Rondane National Park.
3. Fokstumyra Nature Reserve.

General Introduction :

The legal basis for Norwegian nature protection is a law enacted on 1 December 1954. The administration of the reserved areas is the responsibility of the State Forest Department, with which the Naturvernrådet (Nature Protection Council)

373

and the Statens naturverninspektor (Government Inspector for Nature Protection) are in consultative relationship. All the land is publicly owned. Nothing specific has been done in the way of organising scientific research, but there have been a considerable number of observations and studies.

None of the three Listed Areas was cited in the previous edition of the List, the first two of them having been established since its publication, though a number of other reserves, now excluded, were mentioned.

Details : application of criteria (II), general information (III) and description (IV)

1. BÖRGEFJELL NATIONAL PARK.

II.

a) Status : protected against all encroachments of a technical nature, including road and other building. But though the fauna and flora are generally

374

protected, hunting of certain animals is allowed (moose, wolf, glutton, lynx, fox, hare, willow grouse, ptarmigan and crow). However most of the shooting, especially of willow grouse, ptarmigan and moose is done on the periphery of the Park. People living in the vicinity retain certain grazing rights, but generally speaking these cannot be exercised in the interior of the Park, though there are some Lapp reindeer herds.

b) Area : 100,000 ha.

c) Staff : a forester, 3 rangers and, during summer only, 2 inspectors.

d) Budget : covers staff salaries.

Date established : 9 August 1963, by a decree under the law cited in the General Introduction.

Tourism : a remote area which has few visitors; there are two Lodges, but no roads or proper paths.

Altitude : about 450-1,700 m.

a) A fine landscape of hills, wild mountains, lakes and streams in the North Tröndelag and Northland region. The main elements of the vegetation are the birches *Betula pubescens odorata* and *B. nana* and willows *Salix* spp.; on the lower slopes Norway spruce *Picea abies* and Scots pines *Pinus sylvestris*.

b) Moose *A. alces*, glutton *G. gulo*, Arctic fox *Alopex lagopus*, wolf *Canis lupus* (occasional) lemming *L. lemmus*; willow grouse *Lagopus lagopus*, ptarmigan *L. mutus*, lesser white-fronted goose *Anser erythropus*, bean goose *A. fabalis*, long-tailed duck *Clangula hyemalis*, red-necked phalarope *Phalaropus lobatus*, Temminck's stint *Calidris temminckii*, long-tailed skua *Stercorarius longicaudatus*, snowy owl *Nyctea scandiaca* (occasional), rough-legged buzzard *Buteo lagopus*, snow bunting *Plectrophenax nivalis*, bluethroat *Luscinia svecica*, meadow pipit *Anthus pratensis*.

2. RONDANE NATIONAL PARK.

a) Status : comparable to that of No. 1 in the List except that there are no Lapp reindeer herds. Hunting of the same species is allowed, plus wild reindeer, the control of which is considered necessary throughout the area. Otherwise, in this Park also, shooting is largely localised on the periphery and mainly of willow grouse and ptarmigan. Some flocks of sheep and a few cattle are pastured in the Park.

b) Area : 57,500 ha.

c) Staff : 1 forester, 2 rangers and, in summer only, 1 inspector.

d) Budget : covers staff salaries.

Date established : on 21 December 1962, by decree.

Tourism : better situated for visitors than No. 1 on the List and therefore more frequented, with an estimated number of over 7,000 visitors in 1962; three lodges; no roads but some tourist footpaths.

Altitude : about 900-2,200 m.

a) A mountain massif in the Oppland and Hedmark districts, of great geological interest; the vegetation includes birches, least willow *Salix herbacea*, Scots pine, glacial crowfoot *Ranunculus glacialis*, mountain avens *Dryas octopetala* and *Saxifraga stellaris*.

375

b) Moose, reindeer *Rangifer tarandus*, otter *L. lutra*, arctic fox, red fox *V. vulpes*, lemming; the fine avifauna (124 species recorded) includes rough-legged buzzard, ptarmigan, snow bunting, meadow pipit and wheatear *Oe. oenanthe*, all of which are to be met with at about the 1,500 m level.

3. FOKSTUMYRA NATURE RESERVE.

II.   *a*) Status : fauna totally protected, flora partially; no human occupancy or exploitation. A railway passes through the Reserve.

b) Area : 900 ha, which is below the criterion level for a country averaging 11 inhabitants to the km², but the Reserve is "internationally known" and has a "rich bird fauna" so has been retained in the List on a recommendation of the Norwegian authorities dated 19 July 1964.

c) Staff : one; "a special inspector is engaged during the season when tourist traffic is forbidden".

d) Budget : salary of inspector.

III.   *Date established :* 9 November 1923, by decree, corroborated on 8 June 1962.

Tourism : no visitors allowed during the period 25 April to 8 July (bird breeding season).

IV.   *Altitude :* about 950 m.

a) Part of the Dovrefjell in the Oppland district; marshland, small lakes and torrents with some birch woods.

b) The rich avifauna includes crane *Grus grus*, hen harrier *Circus cyaneus*, rough-legged buzzard, long-eared owl *Asio otus*, willow grouse, common snipe, great snipe *Gallinago media*, ruff *Philomachus pugnax*, meadow pipit, bluethroat, Lapland bunting *Calcarius lapponicus* and grey-headed wagtail *Motacilla flava thunbergi*.

V.   **Areas excluded :**

A. — Five reserves for the protection of fauna and flora which are far below the size (2,000 ha) required by the criterion :

1. North Cape and Hornvika (Finnmark) ... ...   275 ha
2. Bekkenesholmen (Nordland) ... ...   52 ha

Both these enjoy official protection and the land is in public ownership.

3. Buvassdalen in Vassfaret (Buskerud) ... ...   150 ha
4. Jutulhugget (Hedmark) ... ...   100 ha
5. Övre Röd (Vestfold) . ...   36 ha

Though officially protected, these are private properties, the last-mentioned being run by the University of Oslo.

B. — One large reserve for fauna only :

6. Nordmarka ... ...   2,800 ha

C. — Two "National Botanical Parks" :

7. Helin (Oppland) . ...   3,500 ha
8. Nedalen (South Trondelag) ... ... 10,000 ha

D. — A number of Forest Department Reserves.

E. — Two new National Parks, created in 1968 :

    9. Ormtjernkampen (Oppland) ... ...   900 ha
   10. Gutulia (Hedmark) ... ...   1,900 ha

    Both of these are primeval forest areas.

96. PAKISTAN

Listed Areas : two.

A. — WEST PAKISTAN : nil.

B. — EAST PAKISTAN :

    1. Chittagong Hill Tracts National Park.
    2. Madhurpur National Park.

General Introduction :

The inclusion of No. 1 Chittagong Hill Tracts National Park in the List, almost entirely on the strength of the large staff allocated to it, is based, as will be seen below, on a report sent by the authorities in Karachi in 1961 : no more recent official information has been received. Similarly, omission from the List of two areas in West Pakistan, Chhanga Manga National Park and Kaghan Valley or Shogran National Park was decided only with some hesitation, due to the fact that no official information had been received to refute the somewhat pessimistic reports quoted in Section V below, where these areas are briefly described.

The Listed Areas and those now relegated to Section V were described in Part Two of the previous edition of the List. Since 1966 the reorganisation of the National Parks and Reserves system of Pakistan has been under active consideration by the Government, arising partly from the initiative of expeditions led by Mr. G. R. Mountfort under the aegis of the World Wildlife Fund.

The legislative basis for forest protection in Pakistan is the Forest Act of 1927 and for fauna protection the Wild Birds and Animals Protection Act dating from 1912. No special organisation for Tourism or Scientific Research in the National Parks has yet been officially confirmed, but the objectives have been described as " to create game sanctuaries, holiday resorts for the general people and to attract tourists from abroad " and to encourage the study of the fauna and flora in the field.

Details : application of criteria (II), general information (III) and description (IV) :

1. CHITTAGONG HILL TRACTS NATIONAL PARK.

    a) Status : protection seems to be generally assured by the allocation of staff, which is generous in relation to the size of the Park. However, the 1961 report spoke of " some scattered villages within and adjacent to the area; the tribal people collect timber, firewood, bamboo, etc. from the area and work in the forest" and, except for restriction on hunting, these activities "will not be disturbed in any way". It also stated that "a paper mill has been set up near Chandragona". Recent information suggests that these disturbances have greatly increased, so that it is now proposed that the whole Park should be moved to another nearby area where there is still some good primary forest.

b) Area : 25,900 ha.

c) Staff : 36 units, according to the 1961 programme.

d) Budget : U.S. $ 36,000 in local currency and U.S. $ 3,000 in foreign currency (1961 figures, based on the then official exchange rate for 1.8 and 0.15 lakhs of rupees).

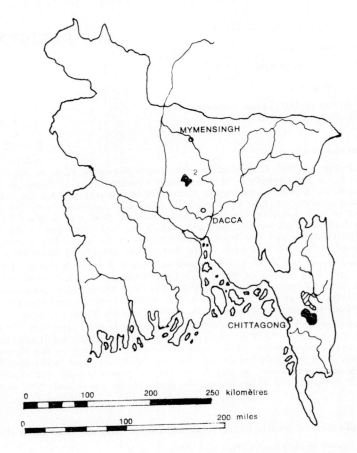

III.   *Date established :* establishment was not complete in 1961, and it seems that even by the end of 1965 the legal instrument creating the Park was not finally promulgated.

378

Tourism : the 1961 plans envisaged access to the public on a nominal fee and without limit, and the arrangement if necessary of guided tours and interpreters; there would also be provision for camp-sites and accommodation for tourists " with all possible amenities ".

Altitude : about 360 m.

a) Parallel ranges of hills on a north-south axis, with large river valleys between; the Karnafuli river, however, which runs from east to west, cuts deep gorges through the hills, though the general terrain is gently undulating; there are numerous crescent-shaped marshy depressions known as " dhepas "; dense bush and jungle or forest areas in which teak *Tectona grandis* predominates.

b) Tiger *Panthera tigris* and various species of deer.

2. MADHURPUR NATIONAL PARK.

a) Status : the 1961 programme envisaged general protection, particularly of all natural features, and in order to free the area from human occupancy the resettlement of some 3,000 people of the Garos tribe (which, however, has not even now been carried out); at present the general status remains more or less that of a forest reserve combined with that of a recreation/education area.

b) Area : 10,360 ha.

c) Staff : during the development stage, which was due to be completed by June 1965, one Senior Forest Ranger, 3 Forest Rangers and 16 other personnel were to be employed, more specialised staff being introduced when the Park was fully operational.

d) Budget : no recent information, but in 1961 an amount of U.S. $ 327,000 (Rs. 16.35 lakhs at the official rate) was estimated for development and a first annual budget (1961-1962) of about U.S. $ 30,000 (Rs. 1.5 lakhs).

Date established : previously a Forest Reserve, the development of the area into a National Park was launched in 1961. An alternative name for the area is the Mymensingh National Park.

Tourism : as for the Chittagong Hill Tracts N.P., the 1961 programme envisaged unlimited entry on a nominal fee basis, guided tours with interpreters, camping grounds and resthouses with catering facilities and a small zoo; in short facilities of a primarily recreational and educational nature.

Altitude : not quoted, but less than 200 m a.s.l.

a) A thickly forested plain traversed by rivers and canals.

b) Leopard *Panthera pardus* and various species of deer, of which chital or spotted deer *Axis axis* and muntjac or barking deer *Muntiacus muntjak* have been introduced; further introductions planned in 1965, of gayal *Bos frontalis,* nilgai *Boselaphus tragocamelus* and sambar *Cervus unicolor,* have not been implemented.

Areas excluded :

A. — WEST PAKISTAN.

1. Chhanga Manga National Park.

5,000 ha, established 1959 as an " artificial forest reserved area irrigated by a canal ". According to a report dated September 1965 " intensively managed plantation forest, producing sisham *Dalbergia sissoo* and mulberry *Morus* ", in which " game animals are to some extent in conflict with the cattle of the forest workers ". Clearly the standard of protection despite efficient supervision (" vigorous patrols against poaching ") does not satisfy the ICNP criterion, although this is a potentially good area from a recreational and educational standpoint.

2. Shogran or Kaghan Valley National Park.

2,880 ha, established 1961. According to the September 1965 report " grazed seasonally by domestic livestock ". and exploited " for a certain medicinal plant by a private business firm ", which has " hired a large number of local men to find this plant in the woods and propagate it from cuttings ". The report also states that the " local people cut a certain amount of wood " and that " some cultivation is being undertaken as high as 8,000 feet (2,438 m) either in or closely adjacent to the forest ".

3. Ayub National Park.

230 ha and therefore too small to satisfy the criterion, in the absence of any special reason for regarding it as worthy of inclusion on such grounds as that it affords protection to a scientifically interesting biotope; in fact it is said to contain " a big pond for swimming and angling " and to be a " tourist resort " etc.

4. Kalabagh Reserve.

In the Salt Range; it shelters the last 500 Punjab urial *Ovis orientalis punjabiensis* and has been given the status of a ' World Wildlife Fund reserve ' by its owner, the Nawab of Kalabagh.

B. — EAST PAKISTAN.

5. Sandarbans Game Sanctuary.

About 27,000 ha, established 1960; the 1961 report stated that " people visit the area for extraction of forest produce, hunting, shooting, fishing, honey collecting, etc., in large numbers throughout the whole year " and that there was no intention to restrict any of these activities except hunting and shooting. There are, therefore, no grounds for concluding that the status of the sanctuary corresponds at present to the fundamental ICNP criterion, but it has been reported unofficially that the area has a great potential and that plans for its development into a proper national park are well in hand.

97. PANAMA

I. **Listed Areas :** nil.

V. **Explanation :**

No mention was made of Panama in E/3436 or Part Two of the previous edition of the List, but subsequently several important projects for the creation of National Parks have been under consideration. Except for a recent report that one of these projects was actually implemented by Presidential Decree No. 155 of 28 June 1966 (see No. 7 below), none of them so far as is known have yet been completed. The names and some details of the proposed Parks are as follows :

1. Neighbourhood of the Baru or Chiriqui volcano and the Cerro Punta :

303,414 ha; altitude 1,600-3,475 m (the highest point in Panama); very varied topography, high rainfall, abundant forest, including pure stands of oak *Quercus* spp. and a plentiful montane fauna.

2. Extension of the Chepigara Forest Reserve : 262,640 ha; altitude sea level to 1,581 m; a rugged area with a wet cool climate, steep cliffs falling into the sea, heavy vegetation, rich fauna.

3. Tacarcuna area : 137,915 ha; altitude 200-1,875 m; steep ridges, wet to very wet climate; well wooded and with a good fauna, streams full of fish, a mountain lake at 900 m.

4. The mountain massif of Azuera peninsula on the south of the broader section of the isthmus : 134,965 ha; highest point 1,400 m; damp and cool mountain area with subtropical forest of frangipani *Plumeria* sp. and *Bombacopsis quinata*.

5. The Caimito river basin : 26,000 ha; low altitude, hot, high rainfall; humid tropical forest.

6. The Bayano river basin : area not fixed; humid tropical forest with more or less pure stands of cashew *Anacardium* sp. also sapucaia nut *Lecythis* sp. and red sandal-wood *Pterocarpus santalinus*.

7. Altos de Campana : 2,644 ha; altitude 250-1,034 m; rugged terrain, cool wet climate, volcanic activity; the meeting-place of several different ecological zones with a very varied vegetation, situated about 70 km S.W. of Panama City; demarcation and signposting of boundaries of this National Park and Biological Reserve reported to be in hand in 1969 and other facilities planned, but a full-time staff has not yet been appointed.

98. PARAGUAY

Listed Areas : nil.

Explanation :

There has been no official reply to enquiries, but the Law Number 854 enacted on 29 March 1963, which regulates the Agrarian System, contains the following passage, under section IV entitled " Concerning National Parks " :

" The Instituto de Bienestar Rural may set aside as National Parks, with the agreement of relevant organisations, such pieces of land as may be deemed necessary for their geographical, historical or touristic interest or for the preservation of fauna and flora. The aforesaid pieces of land may not be alienated and can be utilised solely for scientific, cultural or touristic purposes ". In addition, article 146 (*e*) of section XVIII of the same Law provides for expropriation for the setting up, in particular, of National Parks.

It is to be hoped therefore that measures for the implementation of these provisions are being undertaken, if not actually completed, and that Paraguay will soon be able to take its proper place in the U.N. List of National Parks.

I.   **Listed Areas :** nil.

V.   **Explanation :**

A. — It had originally been hoped that it would be possible to include in the List two National Parks :

1. San Andres de Cutervo National Park,
2. Cueva de las Lechuzas National Park,

(the latter of which, after a recent extension, was renamed the Tinga Maria National Park), but it has been decided that this should be deferred until success has been achieved in current efforts to provide the two areas with a firm juridical basis and to put a stop to serious deterioration arising from activities of the local populace, which has tended to continue despite all the authorities can do.

Both the Parks were briefly described in Part Two of the previous edition of the List.   Their details are as follows :

1. SAN ANDRES DE CUTERVO NATIONAL PARK.

II.   a) Status : theoretically total protection " of flora and fauna and natural scenic beauty ", but according to the latest reports (December 1965) the forest vegetation has been very heavily exploited and felling continues, while domestic stock are pastured in large numbers in the Park.   Human settlement is also reported and, moreover, a great part of the Park is still in private ownership.

b) Area : 2,500 ha.

c) Staff : the Park is supervised by a biologist.

d) Budget : an allocation was announced in January 1966, but had not yet been made to the Park authorities.

III.   *Date established :* 20 September 1961, under the general provisions of Legal Decree 14552 of 11 July 1963, which authorised the Forest Service to set aside National Parks in areas judged to be unsuitable for agriculture.   Responsibility for administering the parks rests with the Forest Service (Servicio Forestal y Caza) of the Ministry of Agriculture.

IV.   *Altitude :* 2,650 m.

a) A section of the Peruvian Andes, containing the San Andres caverns; the valleys between the ranges are forested with walnut *Juglans tropica,* alder *Alnus jorullensis,* yellow-wood *Podocarpus glomeratus,* cedar *Cedrela* sp. etc.

b) The oil-bird *Steatornis peruvianus (caripensis)* nests in the caverns; bear, puma, deer, wild pig and fox occur.

2. TINGA MARIA NATIONAL PARK.

II.   a) Status : again protection is in theory total, but although the land is nearly all in public ownership, one notes that there are some 70 agricultural enterprises, the tenants of which continue to provide themselves with timber and fuel cut within the Park.   Felling is moreover not forbidden (any more than is hunting or fishing), but merely regulated which unfortunately does not amount to anything very concrete.   Thus that very interesting species, the oil-bird, for the protection of which the first regulations were applied in 1950, continues to be taken every November and December for the sake of the rich fat content of the young birds.

b) Area : about 1,500 ha, but declaration and demarcation of boundaries have not yet been confirmed as completed.

c) Staff : no guards are attached to the Park, which is supervised on a part-time basis by the Forester of the local canton.

d) Budget : legal provision was made for an allocation of a million-and-a-half Sols (about U.S. $ 50,000) for the period 1965-1968.

Date established : 12 May 1965, under the same legal and administrative provisions as the San Andres de Cutervo Park, No. 1 above.

Altitude : 700-1,000 m.

a) A wooded hill shaped like a sleeping woman, hence its name 'La Bella Durmiente'. Hidden in the hill is a cavern (Cueva de las Lechuzas), the reservation of which, for the sake of the oil-birds which nest in it in great numbers, was the first protective measure undertaken and applied to only 31 ha. It is interesting to note, however, that the name ' Cueva de las Lechuzas ' arose from an error, since ' Lechuza ' really means owl, whereas the oil-bird is in no way connected with that family.

b) The oil-bird.

It is much to be hoped that both the above Parks will before long qualify for a place in the United Nationas List.

B. — In addition there are the following areas which for various reasons have had to be excluded :

1. Sixteen national forests set aside by the Forest Service, most of them in the Peruvian sector of the Amazon basin. The two biggest of these, Siabo-Cordillera Azul and Apurimac extend to no less than 2,084,000 and 2,071,700 hectares respectively.

2. Lomas de Lachay : a desert zone, with a very special vegetation of the greatest scientific interest, the reservation of which has been proposed.

3. A project initiated by the Pan-American Union concerning the Vilcabamba range, under the prospective name (1965) of Cutibireni National Park. A very fine brochure was published in support and description of this project. Unfortunately a recent investigation has made it clear that the site, which is of the greatest interest, is still too heavily occupied by Campa Indians to allow effective measures for its protection to be seriously considered.

4. The ' Vicuna Reserve ' (Pampa de Galeras), established in 1966 : 65,000 ha; situated in the Ayacucho region, rising to 4,000 m and with an estimated population of 1,000 vicuna *V. vicugna.*

5. Manu National Park : 1,223,000 ha; promulgated in March 1968, too late for consideration for this edition of the List, this Park comprises a fine unspoilt sample of the upper Amazonian biotope and promises to be one of the best and most valuable National Parks of the Continent.

100. PHILIPPINES

I. **Listed Areas:** twenty-three (two-thirds of them on Luzon island).

1. Mount Apo National Park (Mindanao).
2. Bataan National Park (Luzon).
3. Canlaon National Park (Negros).
4. Banahaw and San Cristobal Mountains National Park (Luzon).
5. Mount Isarog National Park (Luzon).
6. Tirad Pass National Park (Luzon).
7. Mayon Volcano National Park (Luzon).
8. Sohoton Natural Bridge National Park (Samar).
9. Bicol National Park (Luzon).
10. Aurora Memorial Park (Luzon).
11. Naujan Lake National Park (Mindoro).
12. Biak-na-bato National Park (Luzon).
13. Hundred Islands National Park (Luzon).
14. Mainit Hot Spring National Park (Mindanao).
15. Quezon National Park (Luzon).
16. Fuyot Spring National Park (Luzon).
17. Sudlon National Park (Cebu).
18. Mahagnao Volcano National Park (Leyte).
19. Kuapnit-Balinsasayao National Park (Leyte).
20. Bessang Pass National Park (Luzon).
21. Caramoan National Park (Luzon).
22. Callao Cave National Park (Luzon).
23. Pagsanjan Gorge National Park (Luzon).

General Introduction :

Officially there are 42 National Parks in the Philippines and the selection of about half of them for inclusion in the List, although undertaken with great care and in close consultation with the local authorities, could be open to certain criticism in that the particular circumstances of some areas make the application of the ICNP criteria a somewhat subjective exercise. For example, forest exploitation in many of the Parks makes one hesitate to retain some of them in the U.N. List and has led to the exclusion of others. According to the Parks and Wildlife Office at Manila :

II. 1. The legal status of the Philippines National Parks is due to be reviewed and strengthened (see the new programme published by the Parks and Wildlife Office in November 1966). Up till now it was based on a " Presidential Proclamation " made in the era of American administration under an American law enacted in 1932 (Act No. 3915), which was subsequently extended in scope by Republic Act No. 826 of 1953. Each Park established by " proclamation " was thus also " declared a game refuge and bird sanctuary ". Various proposals have since

384

been made in the Congress to amend this legislation and provide a legislative rather than executive basis for the creation — and for that matter modification or cancellation — of National Parks.

2. The population density of the archipelago (about 100 inhabitants per km^2), with a growing pressure of this population on natural resources throughout the islands, implies the application of the ICNP criteria of an average of one staff unit for every 4,000 ha and budgetary provision of $ 100 per 500 ha.

385

3. Taking the National Parks as a whole these criteria are fairly well satisfied as the following figures show :

a) Total area of the 42 Parks and 7 Wildlife Refuges administered by the Park and Wildlife Office : 450,000 ha.

N.B. — This figure does not include seven new National Parks which Congress in 1965 decided to establish and of which, as at January 1966, demarcation was incomplete and the precise areas not yet known.

b) Total staff establishment in 1965 was 266 units (with 45 still to be recruited as at the end of that year) or the equivalent of one per 1,700 ha.

c) The 1964-1965 budget was the equivalent of U.S. $ 225,000 or $ 250 per 500 ha.

Despite these generally satisfactory figures, however, there are still a number of National Parks — chiefly those now relegated to Section V below — to which according to a letter dated 11 August 1965, no staff had yet been allocated, though an increase of the establishment was being planned.

4. There are also unfortunately several National Parks in which considerable laxity has had to be allowed and it has not been feasible to enforce regulations properly, to such an extent that it is not yet possible to consider that the conditions for their inclusion in the U.N. List are adequately met. Hence, the exclusion further explained in Section V, of quite a number of reserves.

In view of what is said above, the details of the Listed Areas, below, cannot include figures of the individual budgetary provision, especially as account has to be taken of the fact that the total provision mentioned above covers other conservation areas besides national parks. Some additional information, under section heading (III), may also be conveniently summarised here, rather than repeated in the details of each Park :

III.   *Administration :* the Republic Act No. 826 of 1953, cited above, set up a Commission on Parks and Wildlife which was subsequently reorganised as a "Park and Wildlife Office". This administrative machinery is hampered by the fact that Congress, which had no part in establishing the National Parks, tends to show less interest than would be desirable both in any new measures affecting them and in voting supplementary funds to improve their management. The responsible organ of government is the Department of Agriculture and Natural Resources.

Land tenure : the land of all the reserves is State-owned.

Tourism : an organisation has been fairly recently (1964) set up to promote and develop tourism, including the use of national parks for attracting visitors from abroad and creating better opportunities for recreation for the people at home. It is to be hoped that it will be provided with adequate funds to enable it to develop the necessary facilities in the National Parks as quickly as possible.

Scientific research : there is no organisation as yet responsible for promoting and co-ordinating scientific work in the National Parks, but in January 1966 steps were being taken to set up a Research Division within the Parks and Wildlife Office. Co-ordination of research would be handled jointly by this Division and the Natural Resources Committee of the National Research Council.

All the Listed Areas were described, if sometimes rather briefly, in Part Two of the previous edition of the List.

386

Details : application of criteria (II), general information (III) and description (IV) :

1. MOUNT APO NATIONAL PARK (Mindanao).

a) Status : total protection; hunting is forbidden, as in all the Philippino National Parks (contrary to an incorrect report quoted in the previous edition of the List). Part of Mt. Apo is nevertheless under a temporary " timber licence ", though the Secretary of Agriculture and Natural Resources was in the process of trying to revoke it; however, above 500 m the vegetation is in fact undisturbed and unexploited and it is on this section that the conservation effort is concentrated, in keeping with the ' zoning ' principle.

b) Area : 72,936 ha, having been reduced by 3,946 ha in 1957.

c) Staff : " three stations now (August 1965) in operation for the protection of the Park ".

Date established : 1936, modified in 1957.

Administration : recently by a Regional Office based on Davao City, which is responsible for ten Parks and Wildlife sanctuaries.

Tourism : the Davao-Cotabato road passes near the Park, in which there are many motorable tracks and footpaths; no accommodation in the Park itself (though some is planned), but there are good hotels at Davao City, 30 km away.

Altitude : highest point 2,907 m.

a) A region of rugged relief, featuring numerous peaks and valleys, waterfalls, hot mineral springs, a lake and a volcano; Mt. Apo itself is the highest mountain in the Philippines, covered in dipterocarp forest and, higher up, forest festooned with lichens and mosses.

b) Monkey-eating eagle *Pithecophaga jefferyi.*

c) Monkey-eating eagle (subject of a specific Resolution, No. 17, of the Bangkok Conference, December 1965, in favour of its special protection).

2. BATAAN NATIONAL PARK (Luzon).

a) Status : general protection.

b) Area : 31,400 ha.

c) Staff : 6 units, stationed at three posts.

Date established : 1954.

Tourism : this historic site, scene of the 1942 battle, is a frequent objective of excursions from Manila, which is 105 km away, and reached by road or water; there is a network of tracks and footpaths and plenty of accommodation in the near vicinity.

Research : a good deal of scientific work has been centred on this Park.

Altitude : sea level to 300 m.

a) Bordering Manila Bay, with beaches of fine sand, rather rugged slopes and dipterocarp forest, with some bamboo and scrub.

b) Deer, monkeys, wild cats; megapodes, parrots and parakeets.

3. CANLAON NATIONAL PARK (Negros).

a) Status : general protection; few inhabitants in the surrounding region.

b) Area : 24,577 ha.

c) Staff : 4 units, at two posts.

III. *Date established :* 1934.

Tourism : access by water or air from Manila via Durnaguete and Bacolod City; tracks up the slopes of the volcano enter the Park, but there is no accommodation within its confines.

IV. *Altitude :* highest point 2,400 m (summit of Mt. Canlaon).

a) A mountainous area of sharp relief (ravines, gorges, rivers and water-falls), its volcanic features including craters and hot springs; dipterocarp forest.

b) Deer, monkeys; megapodes, quails, rails.

4. BANAHAW AND SAN CRISTOBAL MOUNTAINS NATIONAL PARK (Luzon).

II. *a)* Status : general protection.

b) Area : 11,133 ha, but see under III below.

c) Staff : 3 units, at two posts.

III. *Date established :* 1941, but apparently reduced in size to 9,056 ha in 1961 ?

Tourism : easy access by a network of roads from nearby Lucena and Santa Cruz and also Manila, 140 km away; no accommodation in the Park

Research : some scientific work undertaken.

IV. *Altitude :* highest point 2,100 m.

a) Embraces two mountains, Banahaw (1,800 m) and San Cristobal (2,100 m) rugged terrain with forest cover.

b) Deer, wild pig; rufous megapode *Megapodius nicobariensis* subsp., parrots parakeets, cockatoos, and many insectivorous song-birds.

5. MOUNT ISAROG NATIONAL PARK (Luzon).

II. *a)* Status : general protection; some Negrito tribesmen still, however, exercise their ancestral rights within the Park, building their huts in the crown of forest trees and hunting with bows and arrows.

b) Area : 10,112 ha.

c) Staff : two units stationed in the Park and another six at the regional office near Naga City.

III. *Date established :* 1938.

Tourism : access by rail to Naga City, thence by car, the nearest town (13 km) being Barrio Consocep; there is a resthouse in the Park, on the Napan taran plateau, well known as a summer resort for a country holiday.

IV. *Altitude :* not quoted.

a) Rugged country, with gorges, ravines, canyons, waterfalls and rapids dipterocarp forest.

b) Deer, wild pig, monkeys; rufous megapode, hornbills, pigeons and doves parrots, owls, falcons.

6. TIRAD PASS NATIONAL PARK (Luzon).

II. *a)* Status : total protection; no forest exploitation.

b) Area : 6,320 ha.

c) Staff : one unit (also responsible for area No. 20 Bessang Pass).

388

Date established : 1938.

Tourism : the historic scene of General del Pilar's resistance to the American forces; access either from the Concepcion-Angaki road or the Tagudin-Suyo road, which pass north and south of the Park respectively; tourist footpaths; no accommodation in the actual Park.

Altitude : about 1,400 m.

a) Area of sharp relief, the rather steep slopes covered by conifers and other species.

b) Deer; quail, doves and pigeons.

7. MAYON VOLCANO NATIONAL PARK (Luzon).

a) Status : general protection.
b) Area : variously quoted as 5,680 ha or 5,458 ha.
c) Staff : two units.

Date established : 1938 (formerly a Forest Reserve since 1930).

Tourism : a considerable attraction, due to the superb shape of the volcano; climbing and camping; access by road, the nearest town being Tabaco (22 km); there is a resthouse at 800 m, run by the Bureau of Public Works; guides are available to conduct tourist parties.

Research : some scientific work undertaken.

Altitude : highest point 2,400 m.

a) The region is deeply dissected by ravines and gorges, some with very precipitous sides, and contains one of the most beautiful volcanoes in the world; the greater part of the Park is grassland, but there are some stunted forests dominated by dipterocarp species of no commercial value.

b) Deer, wild pig; doves and pigeons.

8. SOHOTON NATURAL BRIDGE NATIONAL PARK (Samar).

a) Status : general protection.
b) Area : 5,650 ha, but n.b. Marcelo Buncio in a book published in November 1966, quotes an area of 840 ha only.
c) Staff : one full-time, plus a labourer.

Date established : 1935.

Tourism : access by road from Basey or water from Tacloban; the natural feature which gives the Park its name is a great tourist attraction, as are the grottoes and some very good excursions, especially by canoe down the rapids; no accommodation in the Park.

Altitude : not quoted.

a) A hilly region featuring, in addition to the natural bridge, caverns, cliffs, waterfalls and rapids; dipterocarp forest.

b) Deer, monkeys; many species of birds.

9. BICOL NATIONAL PARK (Luzon).

a) Status : general protection.
b) Area : 5,201 ha (originally 4,225 ha).
c) Staff : two full-time, plus four half-time, stationed at two posts.

389

III.   *Date established :* 1934, enlarged in 1940.

     Tourism : access by rail from Manila (210 km) and thence motor-bus from the neighbouring towns (Sinocot, etc.) to the heart of the Park; no accommodation in the Park.

     Research : some scientific work undertaken.

IV.   *Altitude :* not quoted.

     a) A region of hill and plateau, dissected by river valleys with sometimes gentle, sometimes precipitous slopes; virgin dipterocarp forest with many ferns, orchids and lichens.

     b) Deer, wild pig; megapodes, pigeons.

10. Aurora Memorial Park (Luzon).

II.   *a*) Status : general protection; exploitation was eliminated by August 1965, but various external pressures indicated that an effort was needed to demarcate the boundaries more precisely and this work was in hand; it was hoped also to establish some buffer zones for further protection.

     b) Area : 2,356 ha.

     c) Staff : 3 units, all at one station.

III.   *Date established :* 1937, under the name of Bongabon-Baler National Park, enlarged in 1941 and renamed in honour of the wife of President Manuel Quezon (after whom Area No. 15 is named).

     Tourism : access by the road from Bongabon and Baler which passes through the Park; a great tourist attraction, with its fine landscape, and rushing rivers; mountaineering, camping, bridle paths; no accommodation in the Park.

     Research : some scientific work undertaken.

IV.   *Altitude :* highest point 2,400 m.

     a) Rugged terrain, cut by rivers with both steep and gentle valleys; dipterocarp forest.

     b) Deer, wild buffalo, wild pig, monkeys; eagles, falcons, rufous megapode, pigeons, quail, rail, woodpeckers, parrots, parakeets, owls, etc.

11. Naujan Lake National Park (Mindoro).

II.   *a*) Status : general protection of the shores, waters and island of the Lake but the neighbouring towns have insisted on retaining certain fishing rights, as " the only source of livelihood of the people ", which in effect reduces the zone of proper protection to rather less than 2,000 ha.

     b) Area : 2,175 ha.

     c) Staff : 3 units, but only one of them full-time.

III.   *Date established :* 1956, modified in 1961.

     Administration : based on Naujan, where the officer in charge is stationed.

     Tourism : formerly a well-known hunting and sport-fishing area, though these activities, except for the localised fishing rights referred to above, have been suppressed within the Park; access is by air or water from Manila and by road from local centres, such as Naujan, where accommodation can be found.

     Research : some scientific work is undertaken.

Altitude : not known.

a) The Lake Naujan area; a hot spring; secondary forests.

b) Deer, wild pig, monkeys; a considerable concentration of water birds, such as Indian darter *Anhinga melanogaster,* herons, bitterns, ducks, rails; also doves, pigeons, owls, falcons and song-birds.

12. BIAK-NA-BATO NATIONAL PARK (Luzon).

a) Status : general protection.

b) Area : 2,117 ha.

c) Staff : one unit.

Date established : 1937, though the idea of giving the area a protected status goes back to 1925.

Tourism : the historic site of the 'Pact of Biak-na-bato', the treaty entered into by the Spaniards and the rebel Philippinos, with many caverns used by the rebels as refuges or redoubts; as such, a great tourist attraction and also of geological interest (see below); access is by a road, 117 km from Manila, to Sibul Springs, from which tracks branch off to various parts of the Park; no accommodation in the Park.

Altitude : not quoted.

a) Very rugged terrain, with sometimes very precipitous slopes; noted for its springs and caverns, such as Madlong Cave and Sibul Springs; forest dominated by dipterocarps.

b) Deer, monkeys; rufous megapode, doves and pigeons.

13. HUNDRED ISLANDS NATIONAL PARK (Luzon).

a) Status : general protection; some sport-fishing allowed, mostly along the shores.

b) Area : 1,844 ha.

c) Staff : 3 units, one of them full-time.

Date established : 1941.

Tourism : these very picturesque coral islands with their paradisiac climate command a considerable tourist following; rest-house and restaurant at Barrio Lucap; fishing; a historic cave once occupied by a famous Chinese pirate.

Research : some scientific work undertaken.

Altitude : sea level to 10 m.

a) Coral reef and its islands.

b) Geese, doves, pigeons, martins, warblers.

14. MAINIT HOT SPRING NATIONAL PARK (Mindanao).

a) Status : general protection.

b) Area : 1,380 ha.

c) Staff : one unit.

Date established : 1958, by President Magsaysay who was later killed in an air crash on Cebu Island, where there is a Commemorative Park — see Section V.

Administration : as for No. 1 Mount Apo National Park, by a Regional Office based at Davao City.

Tourism : access by road from Davao; a log-cabin lodge provides limited accommodation in the Park; the hot springs are renowned for their curative properties.

IV.   *Altitude :* not known.

a) A hilly area, with natural features of great beauty which only became well-known about 1955; hot springs.

b) Deer, wild pig, monkeys; rufous megapode, doves, pigeons, owls, falcons, song-birds.

15. Quezon National Park (Luzon).

II.   *a)* Status : general protection.

b) Area : 983 ha (originally 536 ha).

c) Staff : two in residence, with two men from the neighbouring Regional Office to assist.

III.   *Date established :* 1934, enlarged in 1940.

Tourism : access from Manila by rail and tarmac road; bus service; beautiful landscapes, with viewpoints and a network of tourist routes; no accommodation in the Park itself, but plenty in the neighbouring centres.

Research : some scientific work undertaken.

IV.   *Altitude :* 360 m.

a) Hills and plateau; dipterocarp forest.

b) Deer, wild pig, monkeys; hornbills, pigeons, parrots, megapodes.

16. Fuyot Spring National Park (Luzon).

II.   *a)* Status : general protection.

b) Area : 819 ha.

c) Staff : one in residence, with assistance from the neighbouring Regional Office.

III.   *Date established :* 1938.

Tourism : a scenic area accessible from Ilagan, the last part of the journey done on foot or horseback; no rest-house in the Park, but camping facilities.

IV.   *Altitude :* not known.

a) Undulating country, with hot springs and two grottoes.

b) Deer, monkeys; doves, pigeons, quail.

17. Sudlon National Park (Cebu).

II.   *a)* Status : general protection.

b) Area : 695 ha.

c) Staff : administered and supervised by the Regional Office at Cebu City.

III.   *Date established :* 1936.

Tourism : scene of the resistance to the Spaniards by the Philippinos, with remains of forts and trenches; this and the fine landscape ensures a steady

392

stream of visitors; the provincial highway from Cebu to Mabulo and Sudlon approaches the Park, entry to which is effected on foot or horseback.

Altitude : 720 m.

a) There are many waterfalls and some caverns, but the Park is essentially a plateau covered by dipterocarp forest.

b) No details.

18. MAHAGNAO VOLCANO NATIONAL PARK (Leyte).

a) Status : general protection, but sport-fishing is allowed.

b) Area : 635 ha.

c) Staff : one unit.

Date established : 1937.

Tourism : a great tourist attraction, access to which is from Burauen, 12 km away, by foot or horseback; no accommodation in the Park, but a night's lodging can be found at Burauen and camping facilities exist.

Research : some scientific work undertaken.

Altitude : not known.

a) The Mahagnao volcano region features hot springs, volcanic mud-baths and lakes; primitive dipterocarp forest.

b) Deer; falcons, ducks.

19. KUAPNIT BALINSASAYAO NATIONAL PARK (Leyte).

a) Status : total protection, including ban on shooting, but sport-fishing allowed locally.

b) Area : variously quoted as 564 ha or 364 ha.

c) Staff : one unit.

Date established : 1940.

General : the Park is named after two interesting animal species, a bat known as the 'Kuapnit' and a bird, the edible-nest swiftlet *Collocalia inexpectata* or 'balinsasayo'.

Tourism : access via the Baybay-Abuyog road; no accommodation in the Park.

Altitude : not known.

a) A rugged area, with rather steep precipices and primitive forest.

b) Bats; swiftlets.

20. BESSANG PASS NATIONAL PARK (Luzon).

a) Status : total protection; no exploitation.

b) Area : 464 ha.

c) Staff : the Park is administered and supervised by the officer responsible for No. 6 Tirad Pass N.P.

Date established : 1954.

General : the Park is adjacent to and formerly was part of the Tirad Pass National Park, but was separated to mark its historic importance as the scene of a great battle in the 1941-1945 war.

Tourism : access by road from Suyo; bus service; tourist footpaths; no accommodation in the Park.

IV.   *Altitude :* about 1,400 m.

a) Rugged terrain, with steep precipices and deep ravines, waterfalls and cataracts; secondary coniferous forest, some *Themeda* grassland.

b) Deer, monkeys; quail, doves, pigeons.

21. CARAMOAN NATIONAL PARK (Luzon).

II.   *a*) Status : total protection, but sport-fishing allowed locally.

b) Area : 347 ha, well below the criterion requirement, but the Park has been retained in the List at the request of the authorities on the ground that it is " one of the best preserved areas " and " undisturbed which is comparatively unusual in south-east Luzon ".

c) Staff : supervised and run by the staff of No. 5 Mount Isarag National Park, which is nearby, and of the Regional Office at Naga City.

III.   *Date established :* 1938.

Tourism : undeveloped; access from the Caramoan-Bicol road difficult and only possible by foot or horseback.

Research : an area of considerable scientific interest.

IV.   *Altitude :* sea level to 300 m.

a) Broken country, bounded by steep cliffs and a few beaches along the coast; the forest, though typically composed of coastal species, is mainly dominated by dipterocarps.

b) Parrots, parakeets, pigeons, owls, falcons and sea-birds.

22. CALLAO CAVE NATIONAL PARK (Luzon).

II.   a) Status : total protection except for sport-fishing; a forest nursery is maintained.

b) Area : 192 ha, also well below the criterion requirement, but inclusion requested by the authorities on the grounds of natural history interest and primary forest of considerable scientific importance.

c) Staff : one unit.

III.   *Date established :* 1935.

Tourism : rated as the most picturesque of the National Parks of the country, attracts many excursionists, mountaineers, speliologists, water sportsmen, fishermen as well as naturalists; access is by the road connecting Barrio Buyo with Iguig and Cagayan, on which accommodation is available at various places in the vicinity.

IV.   *Altitude :* not known.

a) Broken hill country, traversed by rivers and streams, with waterfalls, deep ravines, a canyon with 60-100 m walls and a long series of subterranean caverns; medium altitude mountain forest.

b) No details.

23. PAGSANJAN GORGE NATIONAL PARK (Luzon).

394

a) Status : total protection.

b) Area : 153 ha only, but included because the Park contains the finest waterfall in the country, caverns and other features of geological interest.

c) Staff : 3 units, all at one station.

Date established : 1939, but protected since 1904 and re-classified as a water supply protection area in 1913.

Tourism : only 87 km from Manila, the Park attracts crowds of visitors to see its famous falls, especially in the dry season; no accommodation in the Park itself.

Altitude : no information.

a) Many waterfalls, including the one rated as the most beautiful in the Philippines; caverns; secondary forest and scrub.

b) Ducks, doves, pigeons.

Areas excluded :

A. — The following Parks do not qualify for the List either because their protected status is not strict enough or is not effectively enforced or because they are of much too small a size to satisfy the criterion and there is no special reason, as in the case of Nos. 21, 22 and 23 above, to justify their inclusion :

1. Central Cebu National Park.

15,393 ha; memorial park at the scene of the air crash in which President Magsaysay was killed; described in a letter of 11 August 1965, as " no longer of any commercial value except for firewood and the construction of houses ".

2. Basilon National Park.

6,451 ha; " under commercial exploitation " (see the photographs published in ' Renewable Natural Resources of the Philippines ' by Lee and Martha Talbot, I.C.N.P., 1964, p. V - 13).

3. Mount Data National Park.

5,512 ha; " its retention in the List cannot be justified " (letter of 11 August 1965).

4. Makiling National Park.

3,767 ha; " no longer a national park " (ibid.).

5. Mount Arayat National Park.

3,714 ha; " only to be considered as a ' recreational park ' " (ibid.).

6. Bulusan Volcano National Park.

3,673 ha; " mostly covered with abaca (Manila hemp) plantations, coconuts and various plants like citrus, coffee, pili and others " (ibid.).

7. Roosevelt National Park.

1,385 ha; " should be ruled out from the List " (ibid.).

8. Tongonan Hot Spring National Park.

272 ha and, like all the following, too small for inclusion in the List, under the size criterion.

9. Mount Dajo National Park (213 ha).

10. Manleluag Spring National Park (91 ha).

11. Mado Hot Spring National Park (48 ha).

12. Tiwi Hot Spring National Park (47 ha).

13. Libmanan National Park (19 ha).

B. — The "Liguasan Game Refuge and Bird Sanctuary", a large marshland of 40,000 ha, where only the fauna is protected and which the letter of 11 August 1965 states "cannot be considered as an area to be included in the List".

Also, seven "Wildlife Refuges", totalling some 200,000 ha, managed by the Parks and Wildlife Office in Manila.

C. — Taal Volcano National Park.

The creation of this Park was the subject of a Resolution, No. 29, of the Conference on Conservation in Tropical South-East Asia, Bangkok, December 1965, but has not yet (1967) been reported as effective.

101. POLAND

I.   **Listed Areas :** thirty-five.

A. — NATIONAL PARKS :

1. Kampinos.
2. Tatras.
3. Slowinski.
4. Wielkopolski.
5. Swietokrzyski (Holy Cross).
6. Karkonosze.
7. Bialowieza.
8. Wolin.
9. Pieniny.
10. Babiagora.
11. Ojcow.

B. — RESERVES WHICH SATISFY THE SIZE CRITERION :

12. Czerwone Bagno.
13. Jezioro Karas.
14. Jezioro Lukniany.
15. Nart Czerkies.

C. — Twenty Reserves, which do not reach the standard minimum size but have been accepted because the Polish authorities have shown that they are of the highest scientific interest. They are listed in the detailed section below.

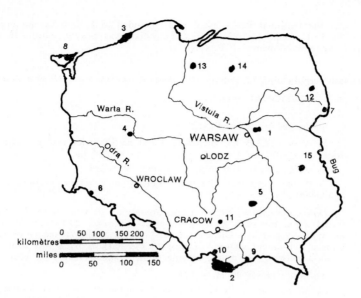

General Introduction to the Data :

Legislation : all the National Parks were established by the Council of Ministers by virtue of the powers given by the Nature Protection Law of 7 April 1949. In all of them the fundamental principle of total protection is observed, with the exceptions that in the Ojcow National Park (No. 11), situated in the valley of the river Pradnik, a village has been allowed to remain, and some easements persist elsewhere. Since the situation is therefore more or less uniform, Section II (*a*) is omitted from the detailed descriptions below.

Administration : general responsibility of the Nature Conservation Office of the Ministry of Forests and Timber Industry; local responsibility in each case rests with a Director serving under the aforesaid Office and a local Council. At the national level there is also a Consultative Council of Scientists.

Land tenure : usually the land of the national parks is in public ownership, but in some cases it forms part of the land held by a Commune or is privately owned.

Tourism : several of the National Parks, such as Wolin (No. 8) with its 17 km of beaches, constitute a great tourist attraction and are specially managed for the reception of visitors. Much attention is paid to the use of Parks for educational purposes, for example by the provision of a museum under a specially appointed director.

Research : scientific investigation of the national parks is undertaken by numerous institutions under the general supervision of the Academy of Sciences, which has a special Nature Protection Institute. Several parks have permanent research personnel, attached administratively to the State and scientifically directed by one or other of the institutions referred to. Laboratory and accommodation facilities for research workers are provided in these Parks.

POLAND

All the National Parks listed were included in E/3436 of the previous edition of the List, except for Wolin (No. 8), which was briefly mentioned in Part Two and the new Slowinski N.P. (No. 3).

Details : application of criteria (II), general information (III) and description (IV)

A. — NATIONAL PARKS.

1. KAMPINOS NATIONAL PARK.

II.   *b)* Area : 22,353 ha, including 1,890 ha of strict reserve; also a protective zone of 18,500 ha, bringing the total to 40,853 ha.

c) Staff : nearly 100 units including 50 guards.

d) Budget : criterion is largely met by staff salaries : about U.S. $ 176,000 (4,400,000 zl.).

Date established : 1959. There are about 30 villages in the 18,500 ha protected zone, the Park being quite near Warsaw. 22,184 ha of the main area are publicly owned. The Ecological Institute of the Academy of Sciences maintains a permanent station. Access to the Park is by a bus route and there is a good network of roads, serving some 100,000 visitors a year. A museum

IV.   *Altitude :* about 80 m.

a) Alluvial area, along the ancient course of the river Vistula, in which a forest of pines, hornbeam *Carpinus betulus,* and alder *Alnus glutinosa* has established itself; there is a dune zone with herbaceous flora and some peatland

b) Moose *A. alces*; common crane *Grus grus,* woodcat shrike *Lanius senator*

2. TATRAS NATIONAL PARK.

II.   *b)* Area : 22,075 ha, including 2,323 ha of strict reserve.

c) Staff : 10 units, including 30 guards.

d) Budget : U.S. $ 104,000 (2,600,000 zl.).

III.   *Date established :* 1954.

Land tenure : 14,300 ha out of the 22,075 ha are publicly owned and totally protected; the rest belongs to the commune or, the majority, to private owners There is still a grazing right for domestic stock in some 2,500 ha and there are also some easements for forest produce in favour of certain people living in the vicinity, so that to some extent the integrity of protection accorded to the Park is still compromised.

Tourism : access is by rail. There is a network of roads and paths ski-runs, a cable-way to the highest point and some twenty mountain huts serving more than 1,600,000 visitors a year. This Park is on the Czechoslovakian border and adjoins the National Park of the same name on the other side of the border. The Institute of the Academy of Sciences maintains a research station. There is also a general purposes museum at Zakopane.

IV.   *Altitude :* about 1,000-2,449 m.

a) Up to 1,250 m a lower forest belt of silver fir *Abies alba,* Norway spruce *Picea abies,* beech *Fagus sylvatica* and sycamore *Acer pseudoplatanus*; then from 1,250-1,650 m a zone of Norway spruce and some Arolla pine *Pinus cembra* and larch *Larix europaea*; and from 1,650-1,850 m mountain pine *Pinus mugo* giving way to alpine associations of such plants as mountain avens *Dryas octo-petala*, three-leaved rush *Juncus trifidus,* the endemic *Saxifraga perdurans,* etc.

b) Chamois *R. rupicapra*, common marmot *M. marmota,* occasional brown bear *Ursus arctos* and lynx *Felis lynx*; golden eagle *Aquila chrysaëtos,* eagle-owl *Bubo bubo* and wallcreeper *Tichodroma muraria.*

3. Slowinski National Park.

b) Area : 18,069 ha, of which 5,440 ha are strict nature reserve and 2,320 ha still privately owned.

c) Staff : ten units.

d) Budget : U.S. $ 80,000.

Date established : 23 September 1966.

Tourism : access by train or ' bus ' : no cars are allowed in the Park; there are some small built-up areas nearby, along the sea coast, with accommodation and camping-sites : 2-300,000 visitors a year.

Altitude : sea level to 115 m.

a) Coastal area with two saline lakes separated from the sea by a sandy strip of shifting dune, about 50 m high; inland from the lakes a zone of forest and marsh, with some signs of postglacial raised beaches; the plant associations range from the simple sea purslane *Honkenya peploides* of the dunes to coastal forest of Scots pine *Pinus sylvestris,* crowberry *Empetrum nigrum,* cross-leaved heath *Erica tetralix,* sea holly *Eryngium maritimum,* marsh clubmoss *Lycopo-dium inundatum* and bog myrtle *Myrica gale.*

b) Red deer *Cervus elaphus,* roe deer *C. capreolus,* wild pig *Sus scrofa*; badger *M. meles*; rich avifauna includes white-tailed sea-eagle *Haliaetus albi-cilla* and ruff *Philomachus pugnax.*

4. Wielkopolski National Park.

b) Area : 5,385 ha, including 132 ha of strict reserve; also a protective zone of 5,600 ha, making a total of 10,985 ha.

c) Staff : 30 units, including 8 guards.

d) Budget : U.S. $ 52,000 (1,300,000 zl.).

Date established : 1957.

Tenure : most of the fully protected parts of the Park are in public owner-ship — only 166 ha being otherwise.

Tourism : access is by rail or road. The numerous roads in the Park provide especially for the people of Poznan, for whom this is the main area for rest and recreation; nearly a million visitors a year. There is a resthouse for some 70 persons and three inns. A swimming pool. A botanical museum.

Research : the Institute of Forestry Research maintains an ecological station.

Altitude : 60-132 m.

a) A moraine-formed landscape typical of the neighbourhood of Poznan; numerous lakes; mixed forest of Scots pine, Norway spruce and broad-leaved species; some remnants of the original forest of pedunculate oak *Quercus robur,* wild service tree *Sorbus torminalis* and the water-loving *Najas marina.*

b) Red deer, roe deer; black stork *Ciconia nigra* and eagle-owl.

399

5. SWIETORKRZYSKI NATIONAL PARK.

II.
  b) Area : 6,044 ha, including 1,922 ha of strict reserve.
  c) Staff : 35 units, including 16 guards.
  d) Budget : U.S. $ 64,000 (1,600,000 zl.).

III.
  Date established : 1950 (protected since 1932).

  Tenure : the land is under public ownership throughout but there are some small enclaves in the middle of the Park. A management plan was drawn up in 1959.

  Tourism : access is by rail and bus. Accommodation for 120 persons. About half a million visitors a year. A museum.

IV.
  Altitude : highest point 611 m.

  a) The primitive Lysogory mountain range; heavily forested : silver fir, beech and Norway spruce, the oldest forest being composed of Polish larch *Larix polonica* RAC. and yew *Taxus baccata*.

  b) Roe deer, wild pig, badger; blackcock *Lyrurus tetrix*.

6. KARKONOSZE NATIONAL PARK.

II.
  b) Area : 5,562 ha, including 1,747 ha of strict reserve.
  c) Staff : 25 units, including 9 guards.
  d) Budget : U.S. $ 67,000 (1,680,000 zl.).

III.
  Date established : 1959.

  Tenure : all the land is in public ownership. The Park is on the Czechoslovakian frontier and adjacent to the Czech National Park of the same name (Krkonose).

  Tourism : Access is by rail and road. There are two cable-ways. About half a million visitors a year. Museum.

IV.
  Altitude : highest point 1,604 m.

  a) A granitic mountain region showing obvious traces of the effects of glaciation — cirques and lakes; the forest is partly plantation (spruce and beech), leading up to subalpine and alpine vegetation zones (linnaea *Linnaea borealis* and alpine saxifrage *Saxifraga nivalis*).

  b) Red deer, roe deer, wild pig; mouflon *Ovis mussimon* (introduced).

7. BIALOWIEZA NATIONAL PARK.

II.
  b) Area : 5,069 ha, including 4,747 ha of strict reserve.
  c) Staff : 20 units, including 10 guards.
  d) Budget : U.S. $ 111,000 (2,770,000 zl.).

III.
  Date established : 1947 (protected since 1919).

  Tenure : the most famous and valuable National Park of Poland, on the USSR border, entirely publicly owned and operated under a management plan.

  Tourism : visitors are not alowed to travel through the Park by car. There is a country hotel and accommodation for 300 people; about 70,000 visitors a year. Botanical garden. Museum.

  Research : the zoological and botanical investigation of the area has been especially thorough; there is a permanent station of the Primary Forest Research Department of the Academy of Sciences.

400

Altitude : averaging 160 m.

a) A sample of the primeval forest of the European plains; the plant associations vary from conifer forest through various kinds of mixed forest to marshland; the characteristic tree at lower levels is hornbeam *Carpinus betulus*; higher up are Scots pine, Norway spruce, pedunculate oak, aspen *Populus tremula,* silver birch *Betula verrucosa,* ash *Fraxinus excelsior* and alder *Alnus glutinosa*; the underwood is rich in species.

b) European bison *Bison bonasus,* moose or elk, tarpan *Equus caballus* and lynx; black stork, capercaillie *Tetrao urogallus,* spotted eagle *Aquila clanga* and collared flycatcher *Ficedula albicollis.*

c) European bison.

8. WOLIN NATIONAL PARK.

b) Area : 4,628 ha, including 137 ha of strict reserve.

c) Staff : 10 units.

d) Budget : U.S. $ 60,000 (1,500,000 zl.).

Date established : 1960.

Tenure : the island is entirely publicly owned.

Tourism : visited by very large numbers of tourists. Museum.

Altitude : sea level to 115 m.

a) The largest island in the Polish sector of the Baltic; steep cliffs border the sea; moraine-carved hills, many lakes; primitive forest of beech and pines with some oak; sea-holly.

b) White-tailed sea-eagle.

9. PIENINY NATIONAL PARK.

b) Area : 2,708 ha, including 500 ha of strict reserve.

c) Staff : 14 units, including 5 guards.

d) Budget : U.S. $ 32,000 (800,000 zl.).

Date established : 1954, protected since 1921.

Tenure : about half the land (1,459 ha) is publicly owned, the rest is in private hands. Adjoins the Czechoslovak protected area of the same name.

Tourism : in addition to tourist roads and paths, the Park is well-known for the trips by barge on the river Dunajec through the Pieniny gorges. Accommodation for 100 near the Park. About 400,000 visitors a year. Museum. Ruins of old castles.

Altitude : highest point 982 m.

a) Calcareous mountains cut by the gorges of the Dunajec; the steep slopes are densely forested with silver fir, beech, Norway spruce, sycamore, ash, aspen, savin *Juniperus sabina* and plantations of larch; also the chrysanthemum or tansy *Tanacetum zawadzkii* and other endemics.

b) The good variety of wildlife includes lynx, red deer and red fox *Vulpes vulpes*; eagle-owl and wallcreeper; and the Apollo butterfly *Parnassius apollo.*

10. BABIAGORA NATIONAL PARK.

II.

    b) Area : 1,709 ha, 1,049 being strict reserve.

    c) Staff : 11 units, including 4 guards.

    d) Budget : U.S. $ 43,000 (1,080,000 zl.).

III.

    Date established : 1954, protected since 1924.

    Tenure : some 1,585 ha of this Park, situated on the Czechoslovakian border, is publicly owned.

    Tourism : visitors are only allowed in on foot. Accommodation for 60 people. Camping sites. About 130,000-150,000 visitors a year. A botanical museum.

IV.

    Altitude : 600-1,725 m.

    a) A landscape of high sandstone mountains, with remnants of ancient Carpathian forests; up to 1,150 m beech-fir association, then up to 1,400 m spruce, then mountain pine to 1,650 m and above that alpine meadow flora.

    b) Red deer, lynx, wildcat *Felis silvestris*; eagle-owl.

11. OJCOW NATIONAL PARK.

    b) Area : 1,675 ha, including 216 ha strict nature reserve.

    c) Staff : 13 units, including 7 guards.

    d) Budget : U.S. $ 42,000 (1,060,000 zl.).

III.

    Date established : 1956, protected since 1924.

    Tenure : rather more than half the land in the Park is state-owned, but 703 ha are still in private hands.

    Tourism : the Park is traversed by a trunk road; about half a million visitors a year; accommodation for 80 persons. The grottoes are a tourist attraction. Museum.

IV.

    Altitude : 350-470 m.

    a) The Jurassic formations of this region have Karstic (limestone) characters, with gorges, grottoes and pinnacles; beech and maple forest; one notable endemic species *Betula oycoviensis*; xerothermic plant associations.

    b) There is an important cave-dwelling fauna, including horseshoe bat *Rhinolophus hipposideros* and the notch-eared bat *Myotis emarginatus*; roe deer, badger, red fox *V. vulpes*; many birds, such as rock thrush *Monticola saxatilis*, wheatear *Oe. oenanthe,* nightjar *Caprimulgus europaeus*, dipper *C. cinclus*, woodpeckers, thrushes, flycatchers.

B. — RESERVES.

    N o t e . — Assurances have been received from the Polish authorities, dated 12 August 1964, that in the case of these four Reserves accepted for the List, the criteria for staff and budget are satisfied. The same applies to the 20 smaller Reserves listed in Section C below. As previously stated, the latter have been accepted for the List because of their special scientific interest, as indicated under heading IV, although they are all theoretically too small.

    In keeping with this scientific value, the greater part of the land of the Reserves is state-owned and there is only quite incidental provision for the reception of visitors. On the other hand their use for scientific investigation is very well organised. The details which follow are therefore brief and largely confined to the description under heading IV.

12. CZERWONE BAGNO.

b) Area : 2,172 ha.

Altitude : about 110 m.

a) Forest associations of a marshland region, in which Scots pine is the dominant species; some peat-bog.

b) Moose, wild pig, beaver *Castor fiber*; blackcock, ruff.

13. JEZIORO KARAS.

b) Area : 689 ha.

Altitude : about 90 m.

a) Lake with aquatic vegetation, marsh, peatland and forest.

b) Plentiful bird life, especially waterbirds.

14. JEZIORO LUKNIANY.

b) Area : 623 ha.

Altitude : about 140 m.

a), *b*) Lake with plentiful birdlife; dominant species mute swan *Cygnus olor*; white-tailed sea-eagle.

15. NART CZERKIES.

b) Area : 481 ha.

Altitude : about 320 m.

a) Forest region dominated by silver fir, beech, sycamore, spruce and pedunculate oak — the typical woodland association of the Polish plains; in the lower mountain zone Carpathian beech/hornbeam association.

b) A varied fauna : black stork; Aesculapian snake *Elaphe longissima*.

16. U ZRÓDEL SOLINKI.

b) Area : 344 ha.

Altitude : about 700 m.

a) Part of the primitive forest of the eastern Carpathians (silver fir, beech and sycamore); endemic plants include the spurge *Euphorbia carpatica* and the cow-wheat *Melampyrium herbichii*.

b) Red deer, roe deer, wild pig.

17. MODRZEWINA.

b) Area : 337 ha.

Altitude : 173-193 m.

a) A fairly flat region near Warsaw, with a mixture of mainly Polish larch, pedunculate oak, sessile oak or durmast *Quercus petraea* and Scots pine.

b) Roe deer; plentiful birdlife.

18. JATA.

b) Area : 335 ha.

IV. *Altitude :* about 170 m.

a) Primitive forest in the Lublin region marking the northern edge of the natural range of silver fir in Poland : also small-leaved lime *Tilia cordata* sycamore and Norway maple *Acer platanoides,* elm *Ulmus procera,* hornbeam silver birch, alder, aspen, ash, Scots pine, pedunculate oak — altogether an area of great scientific interest.

b) Roe deer and wild pig.

19. WLADYSLAW ORKAN TURBACZ.

II. *b*) Area : 319 ha.

IV. *Altitude :* about 1,250 m.

a) Primitive Carpathian forest, which has however been partially exploited silver fir, beech, spruce, wych elm *Ulmus glabra,* sycamore, Norway maple honesty *Lunaria rediviva* and trifoliate bitter-cress *Cardamine trifolia.*

b) Pine marten *Martes martes,* badger, red and roe deer, wild pig; caper caillie, red-breasted flycatcher *Ficedula parva.*

20. BORKI.

II. *b*) Area : 232 ha.

IV. *Altitude :* about 130 m.

a) A sample of the original mixed forest of moraine soils : hornbeam Norway spruce, small-leaved lime, silver birch, aspen, elm, pedunculate oak alder, interrupted clubmoss *Lycopodium annotinum* and mezereon *Daphne mezereum.*

b) Red and roe deer, wild pig.

c) European bison.

21. STAROZYN.

II. *b*) Area : 183 ha.

IV. *Altitude :* about 120 m.

a) Fragment of primitive forest in the Bialystok region partially unde management for scientific and educational purposes; silver birch, spruce, alde aspen, lime, hornbeam, sycamore, ash, elm; Siberian iris *Iris sibirica* an mezereon.

b) Red and roe deer, badger.

22. TORFOWISKO POD ZIELENCEM.

II. *b*) Area : 157 ha.

IV. *Altitude :* about 750 m.

a) Elevated peat-bog, with its characteristic flora; dwarf birch *Betula nan* which is rare in the Wroclaw region; bottle sedge and mud sedge *Carex rostra* and *limosa.*

b) No information.

23. ZRÓDLISKOWA BUCZYNA.

II. *b*) Area : 120 ha.

Altitude : about 50 m.

a) Boreo-atlantic beech associations on soils of alluvial origin; pedunculate and sessile oak, elm, ash, aspen; along the rivers alder ash association; various species of orchid.

b) Red and roe deer, wild pig.

24. WETLINA.

b) Area : 111 ha.

Altitude : about 700 m.

a) Landscape of the western part of the Bieszczady mountains, with forest dominated by sycamore and beech.

b) Red deer, wild pig; occasional brown bear.

25. ROMANKA.

b) Area : 98 ha.

Altitude : about 1,366 m.

a) Primitive spruce forest covering the summit region of Mt. Romanka; another sample of the ancient Carpathian forest.

b) Mountain avifauna.

26. BIELINEK.

b) Area : 76 ha.

Altitude : about 40 m.

a) Woody steppe community on the slopes of the Odra river valley; white oak *Quercus pubescens,* also pedunculate and sessile oaks, sycamore, hornbeam, lime and Scots pine; steppe and xerothermic vegetation.

b) No information.

27. SWINIA GÓRA.

b) Area : 51 ha.

Altitude : about 400 m.

a) Forest associations of the Swietokrzyskie mountains; silver fir, silver birch, beech, hornbeam, spruce, pedunculate oak, Scots pine, alder, Polish larch and yew.

b) Roe and red deer, wild pig, red fox, badger; restricted avifauna, but the 56 species recorded include hazel hen *Tetrastes bonasia,* black grouse, black stork, woodcock *Scolopax rusticola,* a very few green sandpiper *Tringa ochropus,* plus passerines (especially tits Paridae) and a few raptors.

28. LEON WYCZOLKOWSKI (CISY STAROPOLSKIE).

b) Area : 37 ha.

Altitude : about 120 m.

a) As indicated by the alternative name, Cisy Staropolskie ('ancient Polish yew-trees '), this contains the biggest concentration of *Taxus baccata* in Poland, together with some Scots pine and various broad-leaved species.

b) No information.

29. CZARNE YEWS.

II.   *b)* Area : 25 ha.

IV.   *Altitude :* about 130 m.

a) Yew mixed with beech, sessile oak, Norway spruce and silver birch.

b) Red and roe deer.

30. SRUBITA.

II.   *b)* Area : 25 ha.

IV.   *Altitude :* about 900 m.

a) Primitive montane forest of the lower zone of the Beskidy mountains with silver fir, beech, sycamore, spruce.

b) Roe deer.

31. LIPOWKA.

II.   *b)* Area : 25 ha.

IV.   *Altitude :* about 180 m.

a) Ancient forest of pedunculate oak, small-leaved lime, hornbeam, alder elm and Scots pine.

b) Roe and red deer, wild pig; collared flycatcher.

32. MUSZ KOWICKI LAS BUKOWY.

II.   *b)* Area : 16 ha.

IV.   *Altitude :* about 260 m.

a) Forest, composed mainly of beech, but with an admixture of sessile oak spruce, lime and hornbeam; spring snowflake *Leucojum vernum,* summer snow flake *Galanthus nivalis* and lords-and-ladies *Arum maculatum.*

b) No information.

33. ZAMCZYSKA.

II.   *b)* Area : 12 ha.

IV.   *Altitude :* about 420 m.

a) Original mixed forest of beech, silver fir, sycamore, Norway maple, sessi oak and hornbeam.

b) Roe deer, wild pig.

34. SMOSZEW.

II.   *b)* Area : 10 ha.

IV.   *Altitude :* about 140 m.

a) Forest of hornbeam, sessile oak, Scots pine, alder, fluttering elm *Ulm laevis* and common maple *Acer campestre* : in the areas liable to flooding a typical Central European associations of oak, hornbeam and marsh-plants; prim rose *Primula vulgaris.*

b) No information.

35. Skorocice.

b) Area : 8 ha.

Altitude : about 200 m.

a) A ravine cut in an outcrop of gypseous rocks; caves; steep slopes covered with steppe vegetation — the saw-wort *Serratula lycopifolia*, the eyebright *Euphrasia tatarica*, the buttercup *Ranunculus illyricus*, erect speedwell *Veronica praecox*, the feather grass *Stipa capillata* and yellow adonis *Adonis vernalis*.

b) No information.

Excluded from the List :

A. — National Parks :

1. Bieszczady National Park. Area not yet fixed and, according to the latest information available, still not legally constituted.

B. — Reserves :

There are various protected areas which the Polish authorities in a letter dated 12 August 1964, could not recommend for inclusion in the List, e.g. :

Kúdypy Reserve : 3,150 ha (mainly for protection of the beaver);

The Lake Reserve : 1,000 ha, covering some 7 lakes;

some dozen other reserves which were listed in Part Two of the previous edition : Barania Gora, Bukowa Gora, Bytynskie Brzeki, Gora Chojna, Madohora, Osiedle Kormoranow, Puszcza Bukowa, Rseka Drweça, Wielki i Maly spekany Wierch, etc.

C. — Special Reserves (the figures given include the 24 areas listed as Nos. 11-34 above) :

251 Forest Reserves	(about 8,000 ha).
83 Flora Reserves	(about 500 ha).
50 Fauna Reserves	(about 13,000 ha).
30 Peat-bog Reserves	(about 1,800 ha).
8 Wetland Reserves.	
22 Steppe Reserves.	
3 Saltmarsh Reserves.	
22 Geological Reserves.	
56 Landscape Reserves.	

525 Reserves, of a total area of	48,576 ha.
Less the 24 Listed Areas	6,486 ha.
	42,090 ha.

I.

Listed Areas : five, in the following categories :

    A. — METROPOLITAN PORTUGAL : nil ([1]).

    B. — ANGOLA : four.
        1. Quiçama National Park.
        2. Iôna (formerly Porto Alexandre) National Park.
        3. Luando Strict Nature Reserve.
        4. Cangandala Strict Nature Reserve.

    C. — MOZAMBIQUE : one.
        5. Gorongosa National Park.

    D. — PORTUGUESE GUINEA : nil.

General Introduction :

Legislation : in Angola the Diploma Legislativo No. 2873 of 11 December 1957 is the legal basis for protected areas and provides for four categories — national parks, strict nature reserves, partial reserves and special reserves, each of which is defined. The one national park and a series of partial or special reserves in Mozambique are similarly provided for by a group of Diplomas Legislativos dated 23 July 1960. This legislation, like that in Angola, also included provision for strict nature reserves, but no use has yet been made of it.

Administration : in both overseas Provinces is the responsibility of the Provincial Department of Veterinary Service's Technical Division for Fauna Protection.

Land tenure : the land is State-owned, in the " plains and marshlands " category.

Portugal and its Provinces were not included in the previous edition of the List.

Details : application of criteria (II), general information (III) and description (IV) :

    B. — ANGOLA.

    1. QUIÇAMA NATIONAL PARK.

II.

    a) Status : total protection, except that a few habitations are allowed in the northern and eastern (Dernba Chio) part of the Park.

    b) Area : 996,000 ha.

    c) Staff : 16 guards and supervisor, plus 27 labourers; supervision is also periodically reinforced by patrols of administrative personnel, game officers, soldiers and even marines.

    d) Budget : U.S. $ 15,600 (450,000 escudos).

III.

    Date established : a Game Reserve since 1938, was upgraded to a National Park by the Diploma Legislativo No. 2873 of 1957, mentioned in the Introduction.

    Tourism : being only 60 km from the capital, Luanda, receives a regular influx of weekend visitors; an entrance fee is charged; organised excursions provided by tourist agencies and guides available; cross-country vehicles can be hired; the Park camp has rondavels, running water and electricity.

    Research : some zoological and geophysical work undertaken.

([1]) Gerês National Park (see Section V) is due to be officially inaugurated in October 1970.

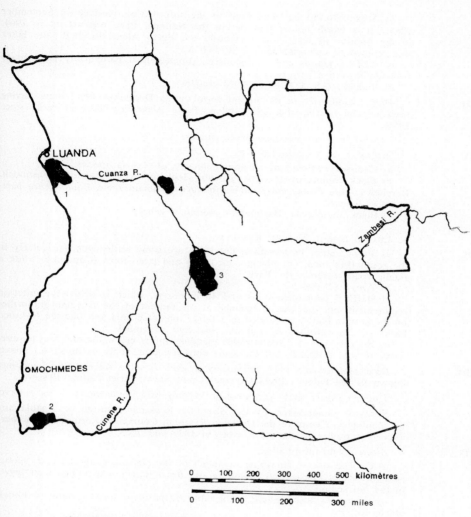

Altitude : sea level to 240 m.

a) Both cool-season and hot-season-flowering savannah species and herbaceous associations.

b) Hippopotamus *H. amphibius,* bushpig *Potamochoerus porcus,* elephant *Loxodonta africana,* roan *Hippotragus equinus,* eland *Taurotragus oryx,* reedbuck *Redunca* sp., bushbuck *Tragelaphus scriptus*; leopard *Panthera pardus,* jackal *Canis mesomelas.*

2. Iôna National Park.

a) Status : total protection.

409

b) Area : 270,750 ha, according to the information received in September 1965. It is worth noting that before the National Park was set up in 1964, in the interior of what was previously the Porto Alexandre N.P., the latter was reputed to comprise some 1,863,000 ha.

c) Staff : 6 guards and 18 labourers, supplemented periodically by military and administrative patrols.

d) Budget : U.S. $ 5,200 (150,000 escudos).

III.   *Date established :* in its present form on 26 December 1964 (there having been a game reserve since 1937 and a 'Porto Alexandre National Park' since 1957).

Tourism and research : no developments.

IV.   *Altitude :* sea level to 1,070 m.

a) Cool-season-flowering savannah, mostly of Acacia species.

b) Black rhinoceros *Diceros bicornis,* elephant, oryx *O. gazella,* bushbuck, Burchell's zebra *Equus burchelli* Hartmann's mountain zebra *Equus zebra hartmannae;* leopard.

c) Black rhinoceros, Hartmann's mountain zebra.

3. LUANDO STRICT NATURE RESERVE.

II.   *a)* Status : strict preservation, but there are some settlements particularly in the south (Melunda, Quimbango, etc.) and one large town (Capunda), while a public road traverses the Park.

b) Area : 828,000 ha.

c) Staff : 5 permanent units and 40 labourers, which is below the criterion requirement, but the area is retained at the request of the Angolan authorities on the ground that it is situated in a thinly inhabited area and like the National Parks is also patrolled by military and civil personnel.

d) Budget : U.S. $ 5,200 (150,000 escudos), much below the criterion requirement of U.S. $ 40,000, but the same considerations apply as under (c) above.

III.   *Date established :* 1957, previously a game reserve since 1938; sometimes known as the Palanca Preta Gigante (Giant Sable) Strict Nature Reserve.

Tourism : visits rarely permitted, in keeping with the category of the reserve.

Research : undertaken by the Scientific Research Institute of Angola and the Zoological Centre of the Overseas Research Council of Portugal; there were important studies of the giant sable in 1959 and 1965.

IV.   *Altitude :* no information.

a) Cool-season — flowering savannah of the plateau, including such species as *Combretum, Pterocarpus, Bauhinia* and *Brachystegia,* which shed their leaves in the hot season.

b) Hippopotamus, bushpig, giant sable *Hippotragus niger variani,* bushbuck, eland; leopard.

c) Giant sable.

4. CANGANDALA STRICT NATURE RESERVE.

II.   *a)* Status : strict preservation, but a public road crosses the north-east of the Reserve and there are occasional habitations.

b) Area : 60,000 ha.

c) Staff : 4 permanent units and 30 labourers, supplemented by patrols below the criterion requirement, but the same considerations apply as in the case of the Luando Reserve, No. 3 above; the Reserves are very close to one another.

410

d) Budget : U.S. $ 5,200 (150,000 escudos), as compared with a criterion requirement of $ 3,000.

II.

Date established : 1963.

Tourism : visits rarely permitted, as for No. 3.

Research : as for No. 3, the Luando Reserve.

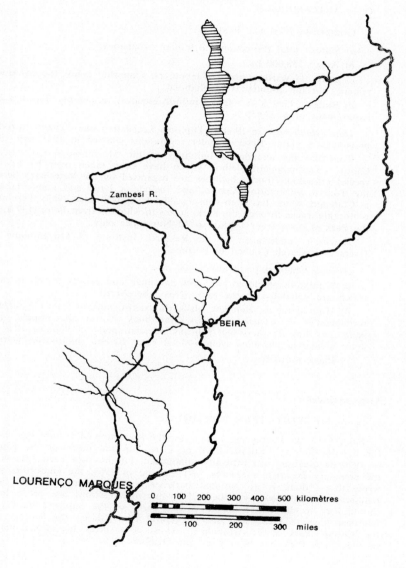

IV.   *Altitude :* no information.

a) Plateau savannah shedding its leaves in the hot season (*Combretum, Brachystegia, Pterocarpus*).

b) Hippopotamus, bushpig, giant sable, bushbuck, eland, leopard.

c) Giant sable.

C. — MOZAMBIQUE.

5. GORONGOSA NATIONAL PARK.

II.   *a*) Status : total protection; no human occupancy.

b) Area : 553,000 ha.

c) Staff : 12 wardens and 120 labourers, somewhat below the criterion requirement, but the country is uninhabited.

d) Budget : U.S. $ 48,500 (1.4 million escudos), as compared with a criterion requirement of $ 27,650.

III.   *Date established :* in 1960 by Diploma Legislativo (see General Introduction); previously a Game Reserve under regulations enacted in 1921 and 1935.

Tourism : the abandoned buildings of the Mozambique Company's 'Old Camp' (Acampamento Velho), which have been taken over by lions, are a special attraction; tourist facilities are organised by the Veterinary Service and the Tourist Information Centre, and include a large and comfortable Camp at Chitengo, which has been considerably developed since 1963; there are many motorable tracks through the Park, access to which is from Beira (137 km away); the Park is open from 1 May to 30 November only.

Research : undertaken by the Research Institute of Mozambique and the Overseas Research Council of Portugal.

IV.   *Altitude :* highest point about 600 m.

a) A mixture of closed and open savannah and gallery forest; marshy areas which are inundated in the rains (November-April).

b) Hippopotamus, elephant, black rhinoceros, buffalo *Syncerus caffer*, zebra, wildebeest *Connochaetes taurinus*, waterbuck *Kobus* sp., impala *Aepyceros melampus*, lion *Panthera leo*; pelicans, African spoonbill *Platalea alba*, crowned crane *Balearica pavonina*, yellow-billed egret *Egretta intermedia*; vultures.

c) Black rhinoceros.

V.   **Areas excluded :**

A. — METROPOLITAN PORTUGAL.

Since 1950, the Portuguese League for the Protection of Nature has campaigned for the 50,000 ha 'National Park of Gerês' in the north of the country and in 1954 its creation was officially announced, but has not been followed up by the necessary executive measures. At the end of 1964, the authorities in Lisbon wrote that " there is no national park or equivalent reserve which meets the requirements laid down by the ICNP, but investigations are proceeding which should lead to the establishment of two parks of the requisite standard — the National Park of Gerês and also in central Portugal, on the Setubal peninsula, the National Park of the Arrabida ". As we go to press, the official inauguration of the Gerês Park has been fixed for October 1970.

412

B. — ANGOLA.

1. Cameia National Park.

One million ha, very small staff, budget of the order of U.S. $ 5,000 and hence falling well short of the criteria. The authorities in a letter of 3 September 1965, indicated that inclusion in the U.N. List could not be justified. The Park area was first protected in 1940 and raised to its present status in 1957; it is situated near the Benguela railway, not far from the border of Katanga.

2. The Mupa or Girafa Strict Nature Reserve.

60,000 ha, first established as a game reserve in 1940. Neither the letter of 3 September 1965, mentioned above, nor an earlier official communication of 23 September 1964, which listed the Parks and Reserves of Angola and gave details of their budgets from 1960 to 1964, made any mention of the Mupa Reserve.

3. Various Partial Reserves, including :

Milando	1,212,000 ha.
Bikuar	812,000 ha.
Moçamedes	1,863,000 ha.

C. — MOZAMBIQUE.

4. Various Partial Reserves, including :

Niassa	1,500,000 ha.
Gile	210,000 ha.

5. Various Special Reserves, including :

The Buffalo Reserve, Manica and Sofala District (150,000 ha).
The Elephant Reserve, Lourenço Marques District (75,000 ha).

D. — PORTUGUESE GUINEA.

6. Three reserves established under the Provincial Game Law :
The Cantanhez Forest (Bedanda).
Cufada Lagoon (Fulacunda).
Varela (Varela beach).

103. RHODESIA

Listed Areas : sixteen.

A. — NATIONAL PARKS :

1. Wankie National Park Game Reserve.
2. Victoria Falls National Park.
3. Rhodes Matopos National Park.
4. Rhodes Inyanga National Park.
5. Chimanimani National Park.
6. Mushandike National Park.
7. Ngesi National Park.

    8. Robert McIlwaine National Park.
    9. Sebakwe National Park.
    10. Zimbabwe National Park.

    B. — GAME RESERVES :

    11. Chewore Game Reserve.
    12. Matusadona Game Reserve.
    13. Chizarira Game Reserve.
    14. Mana Pools Game Reserve.
    15. Chete Game Reserve.
    16. Kyle Dam Game Reserve.

General Introduction :

Legislation and administration : the legal basis for the National Parks derives from the National Park Act 1949 and the National Parks Designed Areas Act 1955. On 1 November 1963, what had up till then been " Federal National Parks " of the variously named " Central African Federation ", " Federation of Rhodesia and Nyasaland " (the title used in the previous edition, E/3436, of the List) or " Federation of the Rhodesias and Nyasaland " reverted as far as " Southern " Rhodesia was concerned to the control of the newly created Department of National Parks and Wildlife Management of Rhodesia. The Department is responsible to the Secretary for Mines and Lands of the Rhodesian Government and, with the partial exception of the Rhodes Matopos National Park, as detailed below, is charged with the management of all the National Parks of the country.

The legal status of the Game Reserves rests on the Wildlife Conservation Act 1961, but they are also the responsibility of the Department of National Parks and Wildlife Management.

Land tenure : all the land in the National Parks and Reserves is State-owned.

Scientific research : in 1958 a Fullbright team began a wideranging and important ecological study, to provide a rational basis for conservation policy both inside and outside the National Parks. It led in due course to the setting up of a Research Branch in the Department of National Parks and Wildlife Management, which is now responsible for the study of all aspects of the life, conservation management and utilisation of the wild fauna.

The ten National Parks included in the List were all rather fully described in the previous edition, E/3436, of the List.

Details : application of criteria (II), general information (III) and description (IV) :

    A. — NATIONAL PARKS.

    1. WANKIE NATIONAL PARK GAME RESERVE.

II.

    a) Status : total protection; the full official title of the Wankie National Park used above is rather unusual, but is explained by the desire to underline the greater importance attached to fauna conservation than to tourist facilities in the Park; in fact only a third of the area is open to visitors, the rest constituting a sanctuary which has practically the same status as a ' strict nature reserve '.

414

DA, Kagera N.P.

(photo : J.-P. Harroy)

SWEDEN, Muddus N.P.

SWEDEN, Sarek N.P.

N

(photo : Kai Curry-Lindahl)

(photo : Kai Curry-Lindahl)

FALKLAND Is., Cochon Is. R.

(photo : I.

ZERLAND, Derborence N.P.

ROMANIA, Pietrosul Mare R.   (photo : Val. F

H AFRICA, Kalahari Gemsbok N.P.

AFRICA, Hluhluwe R.

SWEDEN (photo : Kai Curry

SWEDEN (photo : Kai Curry

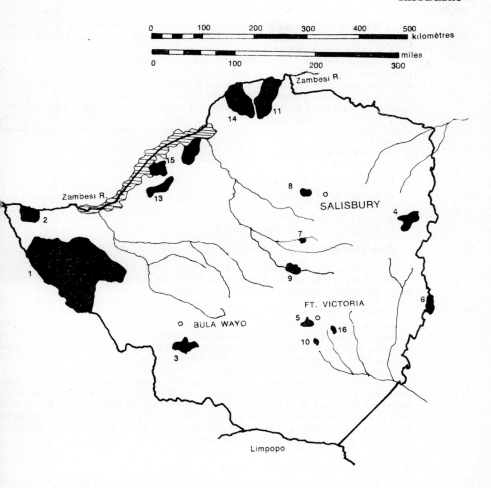

b) Area : 1,439,080 ha (including the so-called Robins sector).

c) Staff : 211 units (1964-1965).

d) Budget : U.S. $ 86,000.

Date established : 1949, previously a game reserve since 1927.

Tourism : as already mentioned, only a third of the Park is organised to receive visitors, though in the remaining two-thirds of 'undeveloped' area water-points have been established, where interesting concentrations of wild animals can be expected; access is by road and rail and there is plenty of accommodation; observation platforms have been built overlooking several 'water pans', notably Nyamandhlovu pan; the Park is open all the year round.

Altitude : 900 m.

415

14

a) A great expanse of Kalahari sands, covered by woodlands of *Baikiaea plurijuga* (Rhodesian ' teak '), *Guibourtia coleosperma* (sand mopani or ' umt-shibi ') and *Pterocarpus angolensis* (' mukwa ').

b) Many elephant *Loxodonta africana* and buffalo *Syncerus caffer,* black rhinoceros *Diceros bicornis,* a few hippopotamus *H. amphibius,* eland *Tauro-tragus oryx,* giraffe *Girafa camelopardalis,* sable and roan antelope *Hippotragus niger* and *equinus,* tsessebe *Damaliscus lunatus,* occasional gemsbok *Oryx g. gazella,* zebra *Equus burchelli,* wildebeest *Connochaetes taurinus*; lion and leopard *Panthera leo* and *pardus,* cheetah *Acinonyx jubatus,* hyaena *C. crocuta,* jackal *Canis mesomelas*; crocodile; ostrich *Struthio camelus* and a very large avifauna.

c) Black rhinoceros.

2. VICTORIA FALLS NATIONAL PARK.

II.   *a*) Status : total protection.
b) Area : 58,440 ha.
c) Staff : 70 units (1964-1965).
d) Budget : U.S. $ 32,000 (1964-1965).

III.   *Date established :* 1952, previously game reserve from 1939.

Tourism : access by road, rail or air; a 56 km road along the Zambesi and 26 km of roads through the game areas, which are open from May to December only; plentiful accommodation; caravan sites.

IV.   *Altitude :* 1,000 m.

a) The region is essentially composed of Kalahari sands, surrounding the famous Victoria Falls; the forest along the Zambesi is mainly *Colophospermum mopane,* and on the Kalahari sands *Baikiaea plurijuga, Burkea africana* and *Afzelia quanzensis*; the luxuriant rain forest facing the Falls contains ebony *Diospyros mespiliformis* and the figs *Ficus mallotocarpa* and *ingens.*

b) Elephant, hippopotamus, buffalo, giraffe, kudu *Tragelaphus strepsiceros,* bushbuck *Tragelaphus scriptus,* waterbuck *Kobus ellipsiprymnus,* roan and sable antelopes (the later in one of the largest concentrations anywhere in the world); lion and leopard; crocodile; innumerable baboons *Papio* sp. and vervet monkeys *Cercopithecus aethiops*; plentiful birdlife, especially along the Zambesi, including herons of many species and cormorants.

3. RHODES MATOPOS NATIONAL PARK.

II.   *a*) Status : total protection, but in severe droughts the neighbouring people are occasionally permitted to pasture their stock for a limited period " as a special drought relief measure ". Usually no one lives in the Park, though there are five large and many small dams or reservoirs in which sport-fishing is allowed; about 2,600 ha of the Park are fenced to make a ' game park '

b) Area : 43,320 ha; up till 1963 the Park was much larger (the figure given in the previous edition of the List is 383 sq. miles or 98,050 ha), but was reduced by three-fifths when areas in human occupation were excluded, although somewhat increased again in 1966, when part of the Rhodes Matopos Estate owned by Cecil Rhodes and in which he is buried, was bequeathed by him to the Rhodesian people.

c) Staff : 69 units (1964-1965).
d) Budget : U.S. $ 33,600 (1964-1965).

III.   *Date established :* 1953.

416

Administration : under the Rhodes Estates, Inyanga and Rhodes Estates, Matopos, Act of 1965, by which part of the Matopos estate was incorporated in the Park, the latter is run by a Special Committee, although its members and financial resources are provided for by the Department of National Parks and Wildlife Management.

Tourism : access by road, only 48 km from Bulawayo; accommodation and camp-sites provided and sport-fishing allowed in the dams; Cecil Rhodes's grave is in the Park, which is also much visited for its interesting rock paintings.

Altitude : 1,350 m.

a) Granite hills, in which many other geological intrusions can be seen and caves, some with prehistoric cave paintings, are found; the area is generally covered by woody savannah, dominated by *Brachystegia spicaeiformis, Isoberlinia globiflora, Parinari mobola, Euphorbia ingens* and *Cyathea dregei*; flame trees *Erythrina caffra* and Cape chestnut *Calodendron capense* also occur.

b) Impala *Aepyccros melampus,* kudu, bushbuck and sable antelope; numerous baboons; leopards; a wealth of birds, including Verreaux's eagle *Aquila verreauxi*; the animals to be seen have been much augmented by species translocated from Wankie National Park to the fenced Game Park, notably giraffe, buffalo, ' white ' and black rhinoceros, eland, sable, wildebeest, reedbuck *Redunca arundinum* and ostrich.

c) Square-lipped or white rhinoceros *Ceratotherium simum* and black rhinoceros (both introduced).

4. RHODES INYANGA NATIONAL PARK.

a) Status : total protection, except in respect of sport-fishing ("modern trout hatcheries have been constructed and fishing research is carried out ").

b) Area : 34,609 ha; this includes the 2,943 ha of the Mtazari Falls National Park, a contiguous area formerly treated as distinct but now " considered to be a part " of the Rhodes Inyanga.

c) Staff : 70 units (1964-1965).

d) Budget : U.S. $ 13,3000 (1964-1965).

Date established : 1950, the Mtarazi Falls N.P., now incorporated, being founded in 1953.

Tourism : access by road and a good road network in the Park; accommodation in the Inyanga but not Mtarazi Falls sector; much effort expended on tourist promotion and development of trout-fishing and water-sports (" a programme of dam construction is under way to provide recreational facilities "); open all the year round.

Altitude : 1,200-2,550 m.

a) The west and south-west of the Park is a plateau averaging 1,700 m, which rises gradually towards the east; many waterfalls; extensive grasslands cover the hills, but there is some Mlanje cedar *Widdringtonia whytei* forest on the slopes of Inyanga mountain; the Mtarazi Falls sector is a high plateau, its shoulders covered in evergreen forest and with many cliffs, from one of which the Falls drop nearly 600 m.

b) Kudu, waterbuck, bushbuck, klipspringer *O. oreotragus,* reedbuck, blue duiker *Cephalophus monticola*; hyaena, jackal, bushpig *Potamochoerus porcus*; leopard; secretary-bird *Sagittarius serpentarius,* various francolins.

5. CHIMANIMANI NATIONAL PARK.

a) Status : total protection, but sport-fishing allowed.

b) Area : 13,680 ha.

417

c) Staff : 16 units (1964-1965).

d) Budget : U.S. $ 1,260, plus salaries of staff.

III. *Date established :* 1950.

Tourism : not accessible by car due to the very rugged country; there is a mountain ' chalet '; mountaineering and trout-fishing.

IV. *Altitude :* 1,800 m.

a) A good sample of the Chimanimani mountain range, the stony lower slopes clothed in montane species of acacia, dense *Philippia* heath or more open *Protea* scrub; along the rocky shores of the streams *Lobelia cobaltica,* the pin-cushion protea *Leucospermum saxorum,* tree ferns and *Strelitzia* occur; in the moss-hags and marshes many *Xyris* species and numbers of orchids in the open grasslands.

b) Large herds of eland; sable, bushbuck, klipspringer, kudu, duiker; leopard; baboon and various monkeys as well as many small animals and a good avifauna.

6. MUSHANDIKE NATIONAL PARK.

a) Status : total protection; however the Park is established around and for the protection of the Mushandike Reservoir, in which sport-fishing is allowed.

b) Area : 12,888 ha.

c) Staff : 21 units (1964-1965).

d) Budget : U.S. $ 14,000 (1964-1965).

III. *Date established :* 1954.

Tourism : " under development as a fishing and yachting area " and open all the year round; access by road; accommodation and camp-sites available.

IV. *Altitude :* 1,200 m.

a) Thickly wooded hills (*Brachystegia spicaeiformis, Batesanthus speciosus, Afzelia quanzensis, Colophospermum mopane* and acacias) surrounding the man-made lake.

b) Sable, kudu, waterbuck, reedbuck, steinbok *Raphiceros campestris,* klip-springer, common duiker *Sylvicapra grimmia*; the plentiful birdlife includes terns, egrets, herons and flamingoes.

7. NGESI NATIONAL PARK.

II. *a*) Status : total protection, but the lake from which the Park takes its name is open for fishing.

b) Area : 5,818 ha.

c) Staff : 27 units (1964-1965).

d) Budget : U.S. $ 11,200 (1964-1965).

III. *Date established :* 1956.

Tourism : access by road; only a rather limited amount of accommodation; sport-fishing, camping.

IV. *Altitude :* 1,200 m.

a) The area surrounding the Ngesi dam constructed on the eastern slope of the Great Dyke, a gigantic igneous intrusion which extends north and south

418

for over 530 km in the middle of Rhodesia; whereas the western slopes of the Dyke are thickly wooded with *Brachystegia boehmii* ("mfuti"), the crest and eastern slopes are much more open, with such trees as *Faurea saligna* and some *Kirkia acuminata, Sterculia quinqueloba* and baobab *Adansonia digitata* on the hills and tall grass in the hollows.

b) Sable, impala, zebra, bushbuck, duiker; leopard; hippopotamus, crocodile; many birds including the only known breeding population of pygmy goose *Nettapus auritus* in Rhodesia.

8. ROBERT MCILWAINE NATIONAL PARK.

a) Status : total protection, but about half the Park is given over to a large lake, greatly developed for yachting and other water-sports for the people of Salisbury and in which even commercial fishing is permitted; hence the rather large staff and budget; an arboretum with some 200 labelled species has been established by the 'Tree Society of Rhodesia'.

b) Area : 5,736 ha.

c) Staff : 69 units (1964-1965).

d) Budget : U.S. $ 42,000 (1964-1965).

Date established : 1952.

Tourism : not far from Salisbury and actively exploited, with boating, "entertainment facilities", accommodation; open all the year round.

Altitude : 1,380 m.

a) Lake surrounded by woods; the characteristic trees of the granitic soils are *Brachystegia spicaeiformis, Julbernardia globiflora* and *Combretum* spp.; along the watercourses *Rhus lancea, Salix subserrata* and *Syzygium*; also found *Burkea africana, Pterocarpus angolensis* and *P. rotundifolius*.

b) 250 species of birds including ostrich; a number of species from Wankie N.P. have been introduced into a fenced enclosure, including giraffe, zebra, wildebeest, buffalo, eland, impala, oribi, kudu, waterbuck, reedbuck, steinbok, duiker, tsessebe and sable; leopard; wart-hog *Phacochoerus aethiopicus*, monkeys, baboon; crocodile.

9. SEBAKWE NATIONAL PARK.

a) Status : total protection, but like the last-named Park, half the area is a reservoir lake devoted to yachting and fishing.

b) Area : 2,654 ha.

c) Staff : 6 units (1964-1965).

d) Budget : U.S. $ 840 (1964-1965), plus staff salaries.

Date established : 1959.

Tourism : the Park is primarily a yachting and fishing resort, open throughout the year; access by road; accommodation available.

Altitude : 1,350 m.

a) Another area traversed by the Great Dyke (cf. No. 7 Ngesi), which affects the topography as well as vegetation; artificial lake; springs; the hills on the west of the lake covered with *Brachystegia boehmii,* the vegetation to the east more open and dominated by *Faurea saligna,* with tall grass in the hollows;

the granitic sands are wooded with *Julbernardia globiflora, Terminalia sericea* and *Burkea africana.*

b) Zebra, impala, reedbuck, duiker, kudu; leopard, jackal; baboon; many birds, including passage migrants.

10. ZIMBABWE NATIONAL PARK.

II.
a) Status : total protection; but the main objectives are archaeological rather than biological.

b) Area : 729 ha, well below the criterion requirement, but the Park is retained in the List at the suggestion of the Rhodesian authorities, because of the world renown of the Zimbabwe ruins which it contains and taking account of the fact that, as in the case of Angkor (Cambodia), the protection given also benefits natural associations which are undoubtedly of the greatest interest, both from the point of view of animals and plants.

c) Staff : 27 units (1964-1965).

d) Budget : U.S. $ 12,600 (1964-1965).

III.
Date established : 1957.

Tourism : very active and centred on the Zimbabwe ruins; access by road, Fort Victoria being only 32 km away and Lake Kyle also quite close; plentiful accommodation; open throughout the year; a golf course.

Research : much archaeological work is undertaken and there is an archaeological museum.

IV.
Altitude : 1,200 m.

a) A rather flat area with luxuriant vegetation, including *Senecio* spp. and *Albizzia adianthifolia.*

b) Kudu, duiker, steinbok, bushbuck, klipspringer; leopard; baboon; the abundant birdlife includes hornbills, green pigeon, freckled nightjar *Capri mulgus tristigma,* purple-crested lourie *Tauraco porphyriolophus.*

B. — GAME RESERVES.

11. CHEWORE GAME RESERVE.

II.
a) Status : remote, uninhabited area; no hunting, fishing, woodcutting, grazing or occupancy allowed; restrictions on movement through the reserve (no roads), but sport-fishing allowed in the Zambesi.

b) Area : 282,800 ha.

c) Staff : no information, except statement that " policing is effective, but there is no resident ranger ".

d) Budget : combined with that of the Mana Pools Game Reserve (No. 14 q.v.) and neighbouring " controlled hunting areas ".

III.
Date established : 1963.

Tourism : a motorable road to the borders of the Reserve is open from May to October, but movement inside this " wilderness area " is by foot only; no accommodation, but camping allowed; sport-fishing.

IV.
Altitude : 600 m.

a) Part of the Zambesi valley, mainly mopani bush *Colophospermum mopane* with *Acacia* spp. on the hills.

420

b) Contains the largest concentration of black rhinoceros in Central and Southern Africa; also many buffalo and elephant, sable and roan antelope, kudu, waterbuck, nyala *Tragelaphus angasi*, bushbuck, impala, wart-hog and bushpig, baboon, several kinds of monkey; crocodile, hippopotamus; interesting avifauna.

c) Black rhinoceros.

12. MATUSADOMA GAME RESERVE.

a) Status : an uninhabited area near the Kariba dam, in which a good number of the animals rescued from the floodwaters were released; hunting, wood-cutting and grazing prohibited.

b) Area : 210,080 ha.

c) Staff : 21 units, exactly corresponding to the criterion.

d) Budget : U.S. $ 4,620 (1964-1965).

Date established : 1963.

Tourism : access mainly by boat (Kariba dam) and by road only in the dry season; there is a network of motorable tracks in the Reserve for game-viewing.

Altitude : 540 m.

a) Situated on the shores of the dam, near Kariba itself; *Brachystegia boehmii, Colophospermum mopane* and *Julbernardia globiflora* woods in the hilly areas.

b) Black rhinoceros, elephant, buffalo, sable and roan antelope, kudu, bush-buck, waterbuck, hippopotamus, crocodile, lion, leopard, hyaena and bushpig; plentiful birdlife.

c) Black rhinoceros.

13. CHIZARIRA GAME RESERVE.

a) Status : classified as a ' wilderness area ' and therefore fully protected; no hunting, fishing or grazing.

b) Area : 145,440 ha.

c) Staff : 21 units (1964-1965), shared with No. 15 Chete Reserve.

d) Budget : U.S. $ 5,000, plus salaries and transport costs.

Date established : 1963.

Tourism : has a good potential for development as a tourist area with its fine landscapes and abundant fauna, though it is intended to keep circulation restricted in keeping with the ' wilderness area ' status; access by road in the dry season only.

Altitude : 1,110 m.

a) Comprises the Chizarira range of hills, south of the Kariba dam; *Colophospermum mopane, Brachystegia tamarindoides* and other species of *Brachystegia* are the main features of the woody plateau, interspersed with open grasslands; fast-running streams.

b) A good number of black rhinoceros; elephant, lion, leopard, sable, roan, kudu, bushbuck, tsessebe, impala, buffalo, zebra, warthog, bushpig, hyaena, jackal; many species of birds.

c) Black rhinoceros.

14. MANA POOLS GAME RESERVE.

II. *a*) Status : uninhabited region in the Zambesi valley, in which hunting and pasturing of livestock are forbidden, but sport-fishing is allowed in the river.

b) Area : 121,200 ha.

c) Staff : 9 units (1964-1965).

d) Budget : U.S. $ 5,600 plus salaries and transport costs, shared with No. 11 Chewore Reserve.

III. *Date established :* 1963.

Tourism : not yet organised, but the area already attracts many visitors; access by road in the dry season; camping-site; fishing in the Zambesi.

IV. *Altitude :* 360 m.

a) Situated on an ancient arm of the Zambesi, grassy plains with relict pools of the old river bed; fine gallery forest (*Acacia* spp.) in these alluvial sectors, with thick mopane *Colophospermum* and *Dichrostachys* thorn bush on the higher ground to the south.

b) Elephant, buffalo, black rhinoceros, sable, eland, zebra, waterbuck, impala; lion, leopard, hyaena; crocodile; hippopotamus, bushpig; no giraffe; many species of birds.

c) Black rhinoceros.

15. CHETE GAME RESERVE.

II. *a*) Status : remote, uninhabited area near the Kariba dam and with the status of a 'wilderness area' as other Reserves mentioned above.

b) Area : 64,640 ha.

c) Staff : 21 units shared with No. 13 Chizarira Reserve, conforming with the criterion for the total combined area of 210,080 ha.

d) Budget : no information, presumably shared with No. 13.

III. *Date established :* 1963.

Tourism : only accessible by water; like No. 12 Matusadona Reserve the area was used for the release of animals rescued in the famous Operation Noah, completed in 1963, when many animals stranded on islands in the rising waters of the Kariba dam and fated to die from starvation were removed to carefully selected refuges.

IV. *Altitude :* 600 m.

a) On the shores of the Kariba lake, the higher ground being covered with *Colophospermum mopane, Brachystegia boehmii* and other woodland species.

b) Hippopotamus, for which the Reserve affords the main breeding sanctuary on Lake Kariba, elephant, buffalo, kudu, waterbuck, impala, lion, leopard, hyaena, jackal, crocodile and many birds.

16. KYLE DAM GAME RESERVE.

II. *a*) Status : total protection in a fenced area in which animals from Wankie National Park and the Zambesi valley have been introduced; there is a fisheries research station.

b) Area : 4,040 ha.

c) Staff : 21 units (1964-1965).

d) Budget : U.S. $ 20,000.

422

III. *Date established :* 1963 (recently upgraded to National Park status).

Tourism : large numbers of visitors are attracted by the bigger animals, notably white rhinoceros, introduced into this Fenced Reserve; Fort Victoria is only 48 km away; a start was made with construction of accommodation in December 1965.

V. *Altitude :* 1,200 m.

a) A large expanse of "high veldt" grassland bordering Lake Kyle, interspersed with clumps of *Brachystegia* and thickly wooded ravines.

b) White rhinoceros (reintroduced from South Africa), giraffe, buffalo, kudu, Lichtenstein's hartebeest *Alcelaphus lichtensteini,* wildebeest, nyala, reedbuck, bushbuck, impala, sable, eland, oribi *Ourebia ourebi,* zebra, duiker, steinbok, hippopotamus, warthog, crocodile — many of these species also reintroduced; plentiful birdlife.

c) White rhinoceros (introduced).

Areas excluded :

A. — Three national parks too small in size to satisfy the ICNP criterion :

Sinoia Caves National Park	290 ha.
Ewanrigg National Park	286 ha.
Manchester National Park	183 ha.

These three have been excluded with the concurrence of the Rhodesian authorities and despite the fact that for many other countries an exception would have been made in view of the particular interest and well-protected status of the areas. Thus Ewanrigg could be regarded as having "one of the best collections of aloes in the world".

B. — Various game reserves, including :

Dandanda Pan Game Reserve.
Lake Allis Game Reserve.
Kariba Game Reserve.
Mbaze Pan Game Reserve.

C. — Numerous "no hunting" or "controlled hunting" areas.

D. — Numerous private reserves.

104. ROMANIA

Listed Areas : sixteen.

1. Retezat National Park.
2. Danube Delta Reserve.
3. Bucegi Reserve.
4. Pietrosul Mare or Rodnei Reserve.
5. Ceahlau Reserve.
6. Snagov Forest and Lake Reserve.
7. Mount Domogled Reserve.
8. Letea Forest Reserve.

ROMANIA

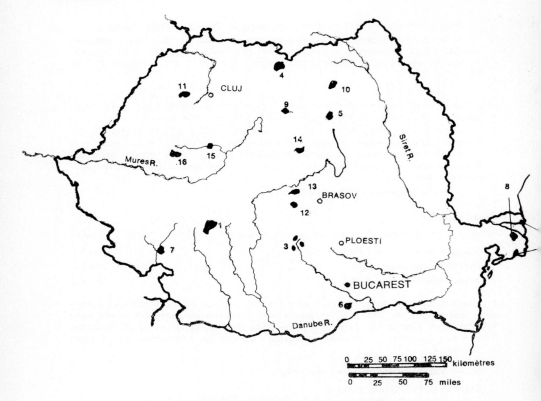

9. Tinovul Mare Peatland Reserve of Poïana Stampei.
10. Slatioara Old Forest Reserve.
11. Cetatile Ponorului Reserve.
12. Piatra Craiului Mare Reserve.
13. The Reserve of the Poienile cu Narcisse of Dumbrava Vadului.
14. Tinovul Lucs Peatland Reserve.
15. Turda Gorges Reserve.
16. Scàrisoara Karstic Complex Reserve.

General Introduction :

II.   According to a letter dated 19 September 1964, from the Natural Monuments Commission of the Academy of the Romanian Socialist Republic, the status of the fifteen listed Reserves (Nos. 2-16) is generally identical — total protection, except for certain privileges extended to visitors, though even for them entry to most of the areas is subject to special authorisation. Several reserves also include a ' strict nature reserve ' or ' scientific zone ' (which has an equivalent status), where the standard of protection and management is the same as that in the ' strict nature reserve ' sector of the Retezat National Park.

All the listed Reserves, except the last four, are larger than 500 ha, the criterion requirement for a country of 77 inhabitants per km^2, and the brief explanation,

424

supplied as requested, of the particular scientific interest justifying the inclusion in the List of the four exceptions is given in the letter referred to above and quoted in the details below.

The letter also explains that it is difficult to provide separate details of the staff and budget for each of the Reserves, but gives an assurance that the requirements of the relevant criteria are in fact satisfied in each case.

Legal basis: Decree No. 237, 1950, on the Protection of Natural Monuments.

Administration: the responsible authorities are the Natural Monuments Commission and the Regional, Cantonal and Communal Peoples' Councils, as the case may be, in collaboration with the Department of Forest Economy for Hunting and Fishing.

Tourism and Research: scientific investigation and assessment, together with the publication of results, and the regulation of tourism are all the responsibility of the Natural Monuments Commission set up under the Praesidium of the Academy and consisting of a Chairman and eight Members.

The National Park and the fifteen Reserves, as well as a number of small reserves now relegated to Section V, were included in Part Two of the previous edition of the List.

Details : application of criteria (II), general information (III) and description (IV) :

1. RETEZAT NATIONAL PARK.

a) Status : the Park is divided into two quite distinct zones, a strict reserve of 1,840 ha and a less strictly protected zone of 11,160 ha. The former is completely protected, although with the authority of the Natural Monuments Commission there is provision for the control of insect pests in dead trees and for some visitors to enter but not to camp in the area. In the generally protected sector, hunting is forbidden, but fishing allowed in some of the lakes subject to a limit on numbers; the grazing of domestic stock is also permitted in July and August, though sheep may not be taken into the central part of the mountain massif.

b) Area : 13,000 ha.

c) Staff : 15 units permanently resident.

d) Budget : the criterion requirement is met by the staff salaries.

Date established: 1935, the strict reserve sector being later demarcated in 1959.

Land tenure: state ownership (Ministry of Forest Economy).

Tourism: encouraged in the generally protected zone; four mountain refuges, with a capacity of 150 beds.

Research: undertaken by the Institute of Biology of Bucarest, the Institute of General and Applied Biology of Tassy, the Academy's Biology Centre of Cluj and the University Biology Faculties at Bucarest and Cluj; a biological station and laboratory, with accommodation for 15 research workers, were opened at Gemencle in August 1964.

Altitude: 784-2,484 m.

a) An alpine region of mountain and lake, with some 40 peaks of over 2,200 m; the slopes are covered with forest of beech *Fagus,* spruce *Picea excelsa* and silver fir *Abies alba*; the alpine zone features *Rhododendron kotschyi*; other characteristic plants are the whitlow-grass *Draba stylosa,* hawkweed *Hieracium* spp., the monkshood *Aconitum hunyadense,* the lousewort *Pedicularis baumgarteni* and the knapweed *Centaurea ratezatensis.*

425

b) The rich avifauna includes lammergeier *Gypaetus barbatus* (apparently only on passage), griffon *Gyps fulvus* and golden eagle *Aquila chrysaetos*; trout *Salmo fario* (= *trutta*).

2. DANUBE DELTA RESERVE.

II.
a) Status : see General Introduction.
b) Area : 40,000 ha.
c) and *d*) Staff and Budget : see General Introduction.

III.
Date established : 1962.

General : comprises three sections :
    i) The Rosca-Buhaiova-Hrecisca reserves.
    ii) The Perisor-Zàtoane reserve.
    iii) Periteasca-Leahova.

IV.
Altitude : 0.8 m below sea level to 2.5 m a.s.l.

a) A vast freshwater area, with a network of waterways, islands and great *Phragmites* beds; the characteristic floating " plaur " vegetation consists typically of the waterlilies *Nymphaea alba* and *Nuphar lutea* and water soldier *Stratiotes aloides*.

b) Important as the main breeding ground in Europe of the two pelicans *Pelecanus onocrotalus* and *P. crispus*; also nesting are the cormorants *Phalacrocorax carbo* and *P. pygmaeus,* white stork *C. ciconia,* glossy ibis *Plegadis falcinellus,* spoonbill *Platalea leucorodia,* many species of heron including the great white heron *Egretta alba* and little egret *Egretta garzetta,* swans, ducks, grebes, gulls, waders, including stilt *H. himantopus* and avocet *Recurvirostra avosetta,* stone curlew *Burhinus oedicnemus,* and birds of prey such as white-tailed sea-eagle *Haliaetus albicilla,* and the spotted eagles *Aquila clanga* and *A. pomarina.* Important passage and wintering area, especially for geese, duck, cranes and waders, particularly round the brackish Razelm and Sinoe lakes.

3. BUCEGI RESERVE.

II.
a) Status : see General Introduction.
b) Area : 4,775 ha, including a 260 ha strict reserve.
c) and *d*) Staff and Budget : see General Introduction.

III.
Date established : 1943 and 1958.

General : divided into various separate sections, the Prahova-Bucegi valley, Caraiman-Omu, the Ialomita Valley.

Land tenure : state ownership (Ministry of Forest Economy).

Tourism : there are several ' chalets ' and mountain huts,

IV.
Altitude : 845-2,509 m.

a) The Bucegi massif, traversed by the Prahova valley; fir and pitch-pine *Pinus palustris* forests; alpine meadows; rare plants include the mezereon *Daphne blagayana,* the bastard toadflax *Thesium kernerianum,* the fescue *Festuca apennina, Iris dacica* and mountain rye *Secale montanum.*

b) Chamois *R. rupicapra.*

4. PIETROSUL MARE or RODNEI RESERVE.

II.
a) Status : see General Introduction.
b) Area : 2,700 ha.
c) and *d*) Staff and Budget : see General Introduction.

Date established : 1932 and 1964.

Tourism : mountain hut under construction (1966).

Altitude : 800-2,303 m.

a) Mountain area with lakes and other relicts of past glaciations; typical alpine flora.

b) Chamois (introduced).

5. CEAHLAU RESERVE.

a) Status : see General Introduction; this Reserve is pastured by sheep.

b) Area : 1,836 ha.

c) and *d)* Staff and Budget : see General Introduction.

Date established : 1941 and 1962; surrounds the Polita cu Crini ('Lily Terrace ') Reserve, of 141 ha, established in 1941 and cited in the last edition of the List (see Section V below).

Tourism : a chalet, two mountain refuges; several hostels at the foot of the mountain.

Altitude : 600-1,904 m.

a) A botanical reserve designed to protect a special subspecies of larch *Larix europaea* var. *polonica,* with an otherwise typical montane flora.

b) No information.

6. SMAGOV FOREST AND LAKE RESERVE.

a) Status : see General Introduction.

b) Area : 1,767 ha, including a 159 ha strict reserve.

c) and *d)* Staff and Budget : see General Introduction.

Date established : 1952.

Land tenure : owned by the People's Council of Bucarest.

Tourism : being close to the capital (40 km to the south), the reserve is much visited and there are restaurants, jetties and water-sports facilities around its 109 ha lake.

Altitude : 80-100 m.

a) Lake and forest in the Danube plain; the southern limit in Romania of the beech *Fagus sylvatica*; other species are pedunculate oak *Quercus robur,* hornbeam *Carpinus betulus,* hazel *Corylus avellana,* water lilies *Nymphaea alba* and *Nuphar luteum* and the rootless aquatic ' fly-trap ' *Aldrovanda vesiculosa.*

b) Molluscs and other aquatic species such as *Dreissena* (= *Dreissensia*), *Calcaburnus* and *Proterorhynchus.*

7. MOUNT DOMOGLED RESERVE.

a) Status : see General Introduction.

b) Area : 810 ha.

c) and *d)* Staff and Budget : see General Introduction.

Date established : 1932, 1943.

Land tenure : state ownership (Ministry of Forest Economy).

427

Tourism : a mountain resort, Baile Herculare, is situated in the Reserve and receives 5,000 holidaymakers a year and there are also large numbers of day-trippers.

IV.
Altitude : 168-1,110 m.

a) A valley dominated by a 1,000 m massif, with a flora of varied origin, including among its less usual species the hazel or filbert *Corylus colurna* and the soapwort *Saponaria bellidifolia.*

b) No information.

8. LETEA FOREST RESERVE.

II.
a) Status : see General Introduction; the village of Rosetti is situated in the Reserve, which is under some external pressure from cultivation.

b) Area : 701 ha.

c) and *d)* Staff and Budget : see General Introduction.

III.
Date established : 1938, 1954.

Land tenure : state ownership (Ministry of Forest Economy).

IV.
Altitude : 1-3 m.

a) The most important forest in the Danube delta, with many Mediterranean elements (e.g. wild vine *Vitis vinifera sylvestris* and the silk-vine *Periploca graeca),* grasses and, on the mudbanks, sclerophytic species; the forest occupies the greater part of the bar off shore of Letea and is composed of oaks, ash *Fraxinus* sp., white poplar *Populus alba,* aspen *Populus tremula,* alder *Alnus* sp., elm *Ulmus* sp., hornbeam and hazel.

b) Woodcock *Scolopax rusticola,* especially in autumn; a viper *Vipera renardi.*

9. TINOVUL MARE PEATLAND RESERVE OF POÏANA STAMPEI.

II.
a) Status : see General Introduction.

b) Area : 675 ha.

c) and *d)* Staff and Budget : see General Introduction.

III.
Date established : 1955.

Land tenure : state ownership (Ministry of Forest Economy).

IV.
Altitude : 898-969 m.

a) A large area of peatbog forming part of the Stampei ' poïana ' or glades, dominated by a dense association of *Sphagnum,* whortleberry *Vaccinium,* Scots pine *Pinus sylvestris* and birch *Betula*; rare mosses include *Sphagnum wulfianum* and *Schistostega osmundacea.*

b) The fauna includes some rare protozoa and water-spiders.

10. SLATIOARA OLD FOREST RESERVE.

II.
a) Status : see General Introduction.

b) Area : 609 ha.

c) and *d)* Staff and Budget : see General Introduction.

428

Date established : 1941.

Altitude : 900-1,400 m.

a) 180 to 300 year-old forest of spruce and silver fir on the north-east shoulder of Mt. Todirescu, plus an alpine zone above it in which noteworthy plants are garland flower *Daphne cneorum*, the hawkweed *Hieracium pojoritense* and the meadow-grass *Poa anceps*.

b) No information.

11. CETATILE PONORULUI RESERVE.

a) Status : see General Introduction.

b) Area : 462 ha.

c) and *d)* Staff and Budget : see General Introduction.

Date established : 1955.

Land tenure : state ownership (Ministry of Forest Economy).

Tourism : there are two mountain refuges at Padis, in the vicinity of the Reserve, with accommodation for 40.

Altitude : 800-1,400 m.

a) The name " Citadels of Ponor " derives from the extraordinary Karstic landscape of this comparatively isolated area — towering peaks, grottoes through which subterranean rivers flow and swallow-holes; the forests are of beech.

b) No information.

12. PIATRA CRAIULUI MARE RESERVE.

a) Status : see General Introduction.

b) Area : 457 ha.

c) and *d)* Staff and Budget : see General Introduction.

Date established : 1938.

Tourism : a popular area frequented in the summer by people from Brasov.

Altitude : 1,600-2,239 m.

a) The mountain massif which gives its name to the Reserve dominates the neighbouring massifs; the flora is rich in endemic and uncommon plants such as the pink *Dianthus callizonus*.

b) Chamois.

13. THE RESERVE OF THE POIENILE CU NARCISSE OF DUMBRAVA VADULUI.

a) Status : see General Introduction.

b) Area : 390 ha, below the criterion requirement, but the Reserve is retained in the List because of its scientific interest and the fact that 88 ha are a specially protected ' scientific zone '.

c) and *d)* Staff and Budget : see General Introduction.

Date established : 1957, 1964.

Land tenure : state ownership (Ministry of Forest Economy).

Tourism : the narcissus flowering season (10-30 May) attracts tens of thousands of visitors.

IV.   *Altitude :* 450 m.

a) Broad glades, in which *Narcissus stellaris* flowers abundantly (hence the name of the Reserve, which means " the narcissus glades of the oak-grove "); situated in oak forest on the lower slopes of the Fagaras mountains.

b) No information.

14. Tinovul Lucs Peatland Reserve.

II.   *a*) Status : see General Introduction; a very remote area.

b) Area : 120 ha, well below criterion requirement, but Reserve retained in the List because of its botanical interest.

c) and *d*) Staff and Budget : see General Introduction.

III.   *Date established :* 1955.

Land tenure : state ownership (Ministry of Forest Economy).

IV.   *Altitude :* 1,080-1,231 m.

a) Peat bogs, with Scots pine, marsh andromeda *Andromeda polifolia* and common sundew *Drosera rotundifolia,* and a number of more unusual species such as the wild black-currant *Ribes nigrum,* grey alder *Alnus incana* and *Ligularia sibirica*; of special interest is the most southerly occurrence of the dwarf birch *Betula nana.*

15. Turda Gorges Reserve.

II.   *a*) Status : see General Introduction.

b) Area : 104 ha, well below the criterion requirement, but Reserve retained in the List because of its geological interest and endemic plants.

c) and *d*) Staff and Budget : see General Introduction.

III.   *Date established :* 1938.

Tourism : there is a chalet for tourist accommodation, but access to the gorges is difficult.

IV.   *Altitude :* 420-794 m.

a) Gorges 2.9 km in length and 800 m in depth in a limestone massif; the flora is a mixture of southern, steppe and forest elements, typical species being the garlic *Allium obliquum,* the feather-grass *Stipa pulcherrima,* Dacian service tree *Sorbus dacica,* the pink *Dianthus speculifolius,* and endemic species of monkshood *Aconitum fissure* and thistle *Carduus fissure* and an endemic sub-species of pink *Dianthus simon kaianus.*

b) No information.

16. Scărisoara Karstic Complex Reserve.

II.   *a*) Status : see General Introduction; there are some scattered dwellings of ' Motzi ', who make a living out of the woods.

b) Area : 80 ha, well below the criterion requirement, but Reserve retained in the List because of its remarkable geological interest.

c) and *d*) Staff and Budget : see General Introduction.

III.   *Date established :* 1938, 1960.

Tourism : very active during the summer; there is a hostel near the Scări-soara Glacier.

430

Research : many of the main geological features, such as the Little Glacier, the Great Concretionary Chamber of the Scǎrisoara Glacier and the two Grottoes mentioned below, are only open to research workers.

Altitude : 1,000-1,100 m.

a) The karstic complex of Scǎrisoara comprises :

i) the Scǎrisoara Glacier with its remarkable diversity of ice formations — stalagmites, huge blocks, concretionary chambers and glistening caverns;

ii) the Peşterǎ (Grotto) din Sesuri and Peşterǎ of the Pojarul Politei — very peculiar formations featuring pure crystallised calcium.

b) Characteristic cave-dwelling fauna; interesting beetles, centipedes and millipedes, Coleoptera and Myriapoda.

Areas excluded :

A. — Seven Reserves of very small size :

1. Crişul Repede Defile and Vadul Crişului Grotto		247 ha.
2. Luncaviţa Forest		146 ha.
3. Poliţa cu Crini (see No. 5 in List)		142 ha.
4. Lake Bîlea		115 ha.
5. Beuşniţa Forest		100 ha.
6. Bejan Forest		70 ha.
7. Miociar Forest		48 ha.

B. — About a hundred other Reserves of still smaller size or less strict protection.

C. — A proposed new ' National Park of the Apuseni Mountains ', which would surround Reserve No. 11 in the List, Cetatile Ponorului; scheduled to be established in 1967, but before qualifying for inclusion would need measures to be taken to restrict the grazing of domestic stock, which at present goes on in many sectors.

105. RWANDA

Listed Areas : two.

1. The Kagera National Park.
2. The Volcanoes National Park.

General Introduction :

Administration : since 1962, when Rwanda became independent, the Parks have been administered by the Ministry of Agriculture at Kigali. Before that the Kagera National Park was the responsibility of the independent Institut des Parcs Nationaux du Congo Belge based on Brussels, while the Volcanoes National Park, at that time a sector of the Albert National Park, was administered from Rumangato in the Kivu province.

431

RWANDA

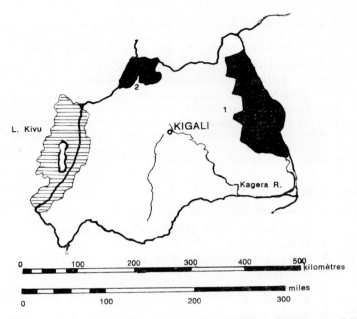

Research : included in the work of the Institut des Parcs Nationaux of Brussels; about 300 volumes covering 500 studies having been published since 1933.

The Kagera National Park, only, was included in Part Two of the previous edition of the List.

Details : application of criteria (II), general information (III) and description (IV) :

1. KAGERA NATIONAL PARK.

II. *a*) Status : nearly three-quarters of the Park has 'strict nature reserve' status and is uninhabited (the last Banyambo occupants having been resettled elsewhere in 1957); entry into this sector is not normally allowed; the remaining 72,000 ha is treated as an "appended area", in which although no hunting, fishing or wood-cutting are permitted, about 1,500 families live and grow their food-crops but are mainly pastoralists, their livestock and wild animals often mingling in the same pastures. In 1966 at the request of the Rwanda Government, the European Economic Community thought fit to finance a mineral prospecting programme in the area, but steps were taken to minimise the harmful effects on the Park of the presence of prospectors and their equipment.

b) Area : 251,000 ha.

c) Staff : 110 units.

d) Budget : about U.S. $ 20,000.

III. *Date established :* 1934.

Land tenure : State ownership.

Tourism : there are established circuits by motorable tracks through the Park, entry to which is by permit for which a fee is charged; guest-house hotel at Gabiro.

432

Altitude : 1,250-1,825 m.

a) From west to east a succession of large valleys, with level floors and gentle slopes, most of them lacking any permanent flow of water; the eastern-most of them, however, is occupied by the lakes and marshes of the Kagera river; the vegetation comprises various grassland associations — *Hyparrhenia collina/Loudetia arundinacea, Hyparrhenia lecomtei/Themeda triandra, Themeda triandra/Bothriochla insculpta* and woody *Acacia nefasia* savannahs, with patches of xerophile *Croton dichogamus/Euphorbia dawei* forest, thickets of other xero-phytes and marshes dominated by *Cyperus papyrus.*

b) Baboon *Papio* sp.; lion *Panthera leo massaicus,* leopard *Panthera pardus,* African wild cat *Felis lybica ugandae,* zebra *Equus burchelli,* hippopotamus *H. amphibius,* warthog *Phacochoerus aethiopicus,* buffalo *Syncerus caffer* and various antelopes, notably sitatunga *Tragelaphus spekei.*

c) Black rhinoceros *Diceros bicornis,* of which some were reintroduced in 1958 from the neighbouring Karagwe district of Tanzania and seem to be doing well (a birth recorded in 1961).

2. VOLCANOES NATIONAL PARK.

a) Status : that of a strict nature reserve, but since the Rwanda troubles in 1959 — and to a lesser extent before that — the Tutsi pastoralists have started surreptitiously taking their herds into the forests, clearings and even alpine-moorland zones of the Virunga volcanoes; at the same time the lower margin of the Park has been nibbled into by cultivators and also two pyrethrum concerns.

b) Area : 23,000 ha.

c) Staff : 8 guards, supervised from Kigali and Gabiro.

d) Budget : about U.S. $ 2,000.

Date established : 1925, when what subsequently became the Rwanda sector of the Albert National Park already had Park status as the ' Gorilla Sanc-tuary '; the Albert National Park came into existence in 1929 and the Institut des Parcs Nationaux du Congo Belge in 1934, while the Albert National Park on the Congo side was enlarged in 1929, 1934 and finally 1935. The Rwanda sector was renamed recently after the volcanoes which are its principal feature.

Land tenure : state ownership.

Tourism : the Park is closed to tourists as a general rule, but there are plans for opening certain routes which would give access to the summits of the volcanoes.

Altitude : 2,000-4,507 m.

a) The eastern group of the Virunga volcanoes, along the slopes of which the vegetational stages comprise : mountain rain forest (around 2,000 m), bamboo forest (2,300-2,600 m), *Hagenia* woods (2,600-3,100 m), tree-heath associations (3,100-3,700 m) and finally alpine moorland associations (above 3,600 m).

b) Mountain gorilla *Gorilla g. beringei,* chimpanzee *Pan troglodytes,* golden monkey *Cercopithecus mitis kandti;* leopard and lion.

c) Mountain gorilla.

Areas excluded : nil.

106. SALVADOR

I.   **Listed Areas :** nil.

V.   **Explanation :**

No reply received to official requests for information, but cross-checking through private channels indicates that no areas yet qualify.

107. SAUDI ARABIA

I.   **Listed Areas :** nil.

V.   **Explanation :**

There has been no response to enquiries from the Government at Riyadh, but information from foreign sources indicates that no areas qualify.

108. SENEGAL

I.   **Listed Areas :** two.

1. Niokolo Koba National Park.
2. The Djovol Strict Nature Reserve.

General Introduction :

National Parks and equivalent reserves in the Senegal Republic are administered by a National Park Bureau, located at Tambacounda, under the President's authority.

Part Two of the previous edition of the List gave an account of the original 250,000 ha section of the Niokolo Koba N.P. which dates from 1954.

Details : application of criteria (II), general information (III) and description (IV) :

1. NIOKOLO KOBA NATIONAL PARK.

II.   *a)* Status : total protection.

b) Area : 813,000 ha (to be extended to 1 million ha).

c) Staff : a Conservator, a sub-Director, 37 armed and uniformed wildlife guards and over 40 auxiliaries; a labour force of 200 for the upkeep of park roads. The Park is divided into several zones for the purposes of surveillance; the excellent equipment includes two-way radios, 15 cross-country vehicles, lorries, bicycles and a motor-boat. The Army regularly puts a Piper aircraft or a helicopter at the disposal of the Conservator.

d) Budget : U.S. $ 200,000 (Frs. C.F.A. 50,000,000).

III.   *Date established :* 1962, though rather more than half the area (250,000 ha) was under protection since 1954.

Land tenure : state ownership.

434

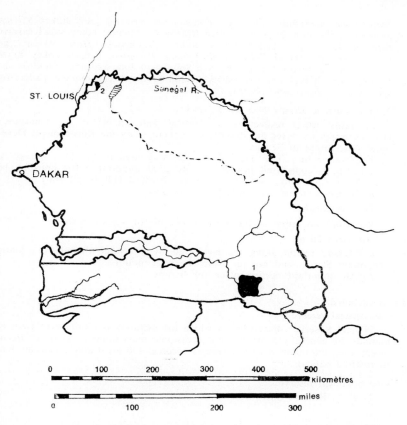

Administration : comes directly under the authority of the President of the Republic.

Tourism : 600 km of motorable track; a hotel at Simenti in the west of the Park, a holiday camp in the east at Niokolo; about 4,000 visitors in 1968/1969; two airstrips.

Research : the Park has an important role in scientific studies, especially of the University of Dakar (I.F.A.N.); there is a laboratory and other facilities.

Altitude : highest point 500 m.

a) Part of the Pre-Cambrian shield of the Upper Gambia watershed over-layed with a lateritic intrusion; Soudanian type savannah with tall grasses, shea-butter tree *Butyrospermum, Parkia,* the bastard mahogany *Khaya senega-lensis* and some beautiful bamboos; the lower marshy areas are interspersed with ranges of dry sandstone hills (" bovals ") and gallery forests.

b) Elephant *Loxodonta africana,* hippopotamus *H. amphibius,* warthog *Phacochoerus aethiopicus,* bushpig *Potamochoerus porcus,* roan antelope *Hippo-tragus equinus,* reedbuck *Redunca arundinum,* Buffon's kob *Kobus kob,* water-buck *Kobus ellipsiprymnus,* hartebeest *Alcelaphus buselaphus,* Derby eland

435

Taurotragus derbianus, bushbuck *Tragelaphus scriptus,* grey duiker *Sylvicapra grimmia,* oribi, lion, leopard, spotted hyaena *C. crocuta*; many small carnivores such as side-striped jackal *Canis adustus,* mongoose *Herpestes* sp., genet *Genetta* sp. and serval *Felis serval*; baboon *P. papio,* patas monkey *Erythrocebus patas,* bushbaby *Galago* sp.; rich Soudanian zone avifauna; monitor lizards *Varanus* sp., snakes and crocodiles, including the broad-snouted gallery-forest species *Crocodilus cataphractus.*

2. THE DJOVOL STRICT NATURE RESERVE.

II.   *a)* Status : strict protection; a plentiful water-supply in the 'marigot' or channel which traverses the Reserve is maintained by the Rice-growers Development Association of Senegal.

b) Area : 3 ha. The inclusion of this tiny area in the List, though quite exceptional, is considered justified by its great importance for breeding birds.

c) Staff : one unit, seconded from the Richard-Toll forest staff.

d) Budget : covers staff salary and expenses.

III.   *Date established :* 1962.

Tourism : no entry to the Reserve except for scientific staff.

IV.   *Altitude :* 20 m.

a) Marshy region along the river, fed by a special channel or 'marigot' (see under Status) and not far from the river-mouth.

b) An important nesting place for herons.

V.   **Areas excluded :**

One special reserve :

N'diaël Reserve : 46,550 ha, in which the avifauna is totally protected; other animals are generally protected, but occasional mass hunts of warthog are organised, when the numbers of this species becomes too great and is causing damage to riverine habitats.

One botanical reserve :

Noflaye Reserve (near Dakar).

109. SIERRA LEONE

I.   **Listed Areas :** nil.

V.   *a)* **Explanation :**

" There are no national parks and equivalent reserves in Sierra Leone, but their establishment is under active consideration... " (letter from the Permanent Secretary for External Affairs dated August 1963). Since then " the Government of Sierra Leone has now approved a national policy on Game and Nature Conservation which makes provision for the establishment of National Parks. The Loma Mountains Forest Reserve will be one of the first areas to be so declared once the necessary legislation has been enacted " (letter from the Chief Conservator of Forests dated November 1964).

b) **Areas excluded :**

1. The proposed Konsilica National Park of about 52,000 ha (200 sq.m.) on the Guinée boundary, which will involve the resettlement of about 10 small villages totalling 250 people (a third of them in one of the villages).

2. The proposed Loma Mountains National Park, now Forest Reserve (see quotation above), the establishment of which was strongly recommended by the General Assembly of IUCN meeting at Nairobi in September 1963 (Resolution No. 22).

3. An area between the Greater and Lower Scarcies Rivers in Port Loko and Kambia Districts.

4. The Colony Forest Reserve near Freetown.

110. SINGAPORE

Listed Areas : four.

1. Water Catchment Area.
2. Pandan Reserve.
3. Bukit Timah Reserve.
4. Kranji Reserve.

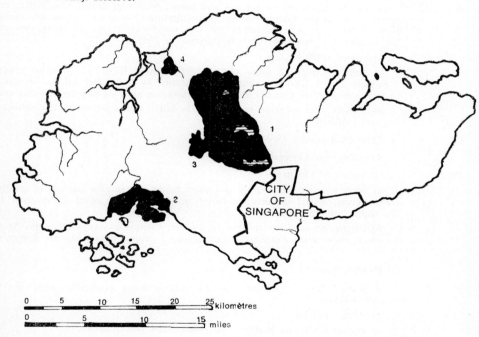

General Introduction :

The administration of the four Reserves is the responsibility of a Board of Trustees under the chairmanship of the Director of the Singapore Botanic Gardens. The land of all the Reserves is in public ownership.

The Water Catchment Area, the main object of which is to protect the watershed immediately to the north of the city of Singapore, is not particularly planned for the reception of visitors, unlike the other three Reserves; Bukit Timah, for

437

example, " is well supplied with paths, which are named and signposted, and with sheltered seats at vantage points ".

The Reserves are systematically used both for research and public education. The research is mainly botanical, taking into account the situation of the Reserves which explains why they have very few animals of any size. This emphasis on botany is of course in keeping with their history, Bukit Timah having been visitied in 1882 by Sir Stamford Raffles who brought with him Nathaniel Wallich, a botanist from Calcutta, for the first survey of the flora of the then quite new colony of Singapore.

The previous edition of the List, E/3436, contained a description of the Reserves and one other now relegated to Section V.

Details : application of criteria (II), general information (III) and description (IV) :

1. WATER CATCHMENT AREA.

II.   *a*) Status : uninhabited wetland and forest, totally protected since 1951; previously was under various forms of occupation, including cultivation, though part of the area was set aside for the water-supply of Singapore city and the whole of it reserved for that purpose in 1941.

b) Area : 1,620 ha.

c) Staff : at least 2 units out of the total staff of 13, a head ranger, 3 rangers and 9 labourers, employed full-time to look after all the Reserves; in addition the City Council maintains a separate staff of rangers for this area.

d) Budget : the criterion requirement is fairly well covered by the provision for staff salaries.

III.   *Date established :* 1951.

Tourism : see General Introduction.

IV.   *Altitude :* 20-130 m.

a) Some primary but mainly secondary forest and smaller patches of groundwater forest; mixed dipterocarp forest at lower levels; sweet water used for the supply of Singapore city.

b) Flying lemur *Cynocephalus variegatus*; various monkeys; pangolin *Manis javanica*; chevrotains *Tragulus javanicus* and *T. napu*; otter *Lutra* or *Aonyx* sp.

2. PANDAN RESERVE.

II.   *a*) Status : total protection, but the area is being gradually eaten into by industrialisation.

b) Area : 549 ha.

c) and *d*) Staff and Budget : see under Area No. 1 above.

III.   *Date established :* 1883.

IV.   *Altitude :* sea level.

a) Situated on the south-west coast of the island; flora typical of the zone colonised by mangrove but with variations governed by the depth and frequency of the tide.

b) Many species of waders visit the marginal mudflats.

438

3. BUKIT TIMAH RESERVE.

a) Status : total protection, but the area is endangered by external pressures such as a large granite quarry.

b) Area : 74 ha, below the criterion requirement but the Reserve retained in the List because " on a density area basis more new species have been found there than anywhere else in the world ".

c) and *d*) Staff and Budget : see under Area No. 1 above.

Date established : 1883.

Tourism and research : see General Introduction.

Altitude : 60-235 m.

a) The granitic Bukit Timah hill is covered with regenerating lowland dipte-rocarp forest with a particularly rich associated flora.

b) Identical with Area No. 1, flying lemur, various monkeys, pangolin, chevrotains, otter.

4. KRANJI RESERVE.

a) Status : total protection, but like other Reserves under considerable pressure.

b) Area : 21 ha, but Reserve retained in List as being " typical of the larger mangrove areas of the west coast of Malaya ".

c) and *d*) Staff and Budget : see under Area No. 1 above.

Date established : 1883.

Altitude : sea level.

a) Mangrove climax typical of the Malayan coast, showing the gradation from the tidal zone to the vegetation of the drier inland soils, which features the last undisturbed stand of low level dipterocarp forest; this is very similar to that of Reserve No. 2 Pandan, except that the process of capture by drier vegetation has been more rapid.

Areas excluded :

The Labrador Nature Reserve, which was cited in the previous edition of the List, has been alienated for industrial development.

111. SOLOMON ISLANDS

Listed Areas : one.

1. Queen Elizabeth Park.

General Introduction :

The legal basis for National Parks in the Solomons is provided by a Queen's Regulation of 19 March 1954.

439

SOLOMON ISLANDS

According to a letter dated 10 April 1965, there are no forest reserves or hunting rserves in the archipelago, although the creation of forest reserves is contemplated.

The Queen Elizabeth Park was cited in the previous edition, E/3436, of the List.

Details : application of criteria (II), general information (III) and description (IV) :

1. QUEEN ELIZABETH PARK.

II.   *a*) Status : total protection, but there are four enclaves each containing a village of some half-dozen families who retain the right to move freely in the Park, continue with their rural pursuits and in particular engage in their traditional fishing. According to the letter mentioned in the Introduction, the Park is nevertheless reasonably well protected.

b) Area : 6,080 ha.

c) Staff : more than ten forest guards of the Forestry Department are allotted to the supervision of the Park on a part-time basis.

d) Budget : U.S. $ 2,250 ($ A. 2,000).

III.   *Date established :* 9 June 1954, the relevant proclamation by the High Commissioner stipulating a ' Queen Elizabeth Park ' rather than a ' Queen Elizabeth National Park '.

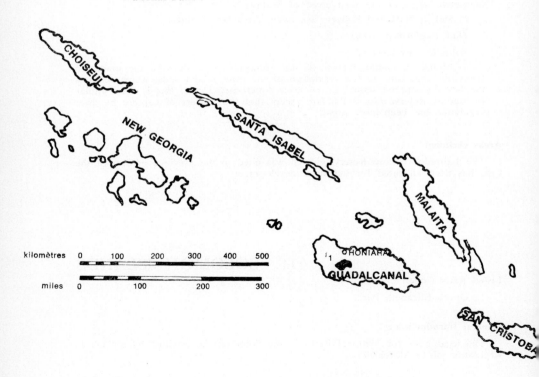

440

Land tenure : public ownership, but subject to the maintenance of traditional rights by the inhabitants of the four enclaves described above.

Tourism : the Park is very close to the capital Honiara and access is by rather rough motorable tracks and footpaths, though many sectors are inaccessible.

Research : no special organisation.

V.   *Altitude :* no information.

a) A mountainous area of numerous peaks and valleys, with a tropical vegetation.

b) Not much in the way of animals except for birds.

Areas excluded :

Seven Bird Sanctuaries situated on small islands or groups of small islands.

112. SOMALI REPUBLIC

Listed Areas : one.

1. Bubasci Strict Reserve.

General Introduction :

Somalia was not included in the previous edition of the List.

Details : application of criteria (II), general information (III) and description (IV) :

1. BUBASCI STRICT RESERVE.

a) Status : the title ' strict reserve ' (' riserva assoluta ') is encouraging, although the upgrading of the whole area to ' National Park ' status might be desirable; the country as a whole is lightly inhabited and the Reserve itself apparently quite uninhabited.

b) Area : 625,000 ha, in which a section of 10×10 km (10,000 ha) constitutes ' National Park ' (the Parco Nazionale Faunistico di Uar-Ghersei).

c) Staff : a Director (an Italian expert supplied under a technical aid programme, but not in fact in office as at February 1967) plus 15 Somali Assistants; well below the criterion requirement but stated to be providing active and efficient supervision.

d) Budget : no information.

Date established : 1926 (by the Italian authorities), with modifications on 16 February 1939 and 6 December 1951.

Tourism : access to this area is very difficult, although there are motorable tracks from Kismayu to Lake Colbio and Kismayu 100 km south-westwards to Lake Badana, on the shores of which the administrative centre for the Reserve is situated; aaccommodation may be had at the latter by special invitation, otherwise it is a case of camping as there are no tourist lodges.

Altitude : from sea level up to less than 200 m.

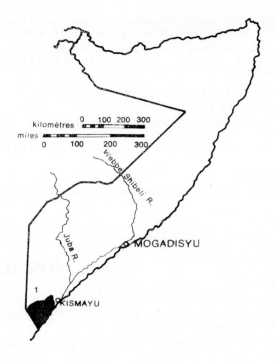

a) The Reserve is bordered by the Indian Ocean and subject to a long dry season, but rain when it comes can be extremely heavy; acacia bush.

b) Population of elephants *Loxodonta africana* estimated at 2,000, black rhinoceros *Diceros bicornis* 100, buffalo *Syncerus caffer* 100, lion *Panthera leo* 300, leopard *Panthera pardus* 8, the rare Hunter's hartebeest or hirola *Damaliscus hunteri* 150; also kudu and lesser kudu *Tragelaphus strepsiceros* and *imberbis*, zebra *Equus grevyi*, kob *Kobus kob*, oribi *Ourebia ourebi*, oryx *Oryx gazella*, klipspringer *O. oreotragus*, Beira antelope *Dorcotragus megalotis*, dik-dik *Madoqua* sp. and many other antelopes; feral camel *Camelus dromedarius* and hippopotamus *H. amphibius*.

c) Black rhinoceros, Beira antelope.

V.   **Areas excluded :**

A. — The proposed Lower Juba National Park.

B. — The following former reserves of which the status is uncertain :

a) In what was previously the Italian sector :

A partial reserve for elephant, rhinoceros and giraffe on the Ethiopian frontier. A partial reserve for rhinoceros and dibatag *Ammodorcas clarkei* on the left bank of the Wadi Shebeli.

A partial reserve for ostriches on the right bank of the Wadi Shebeli.

442

A hunting reserve north of the present Bubasci Reserve.

A hunting reserve west of the Juba, no doubt in the same area as the proposed National Park.

b) In what was previously the British sector :

A partial reserve in the Borama district, where, however, bird shooting was still permitted.

113. SOUTH AFRICA
AND SOUTH-WEST AFRICA

Listed Areas : thirty-one.

REPUBLIC OF SOUTH AFRICA

A. — NATIONAL PARKS : six to which should doubtless be added a seventh, the Aughrabies Falls National Park (about 4,600 ha), established in 1966, as soon as details are available :

1. Kruger National Park.
2. Kalahari Gemsbok National Park.
3. Addo Elephant National Park.
4. Mountain Zebra National Park.
5. Golden Gate Highlands National Park.
6. Bontebok National Park.

B. — PROTECTED AREAS IN THE CAPE PROVINCE :

7. Cape of Good Hope Nature Reserve.
8. De Hoop Wildlife Farm.
9. Goukama Nature Reserve.
10. Jonkershoek Nature Reserve.

C. — RESERVES :

a) Natal (as in all other cases throughout the List these are placed in order of size, not of importance or interest) :

11. Umfolozi Game Reserve.
12. St. Lucia Game Reserve.
13. Mkuzi Game Reserve.
14. Giant's Castle Game Reserve.
15. Hluhluwe Game Reserve.
16. St. Lucia Park.
17. Ndumu Game Reserve.
18. Royal Natal National Park.
19. False Bay Park.
20. Kamberg Nature Reserve.
21. Loteni Nature Reserve.
22. Oribi Gorge Nature Reserve.
23. Coleford Nature Reserve.
24. Umlalazi Nature Reserve.

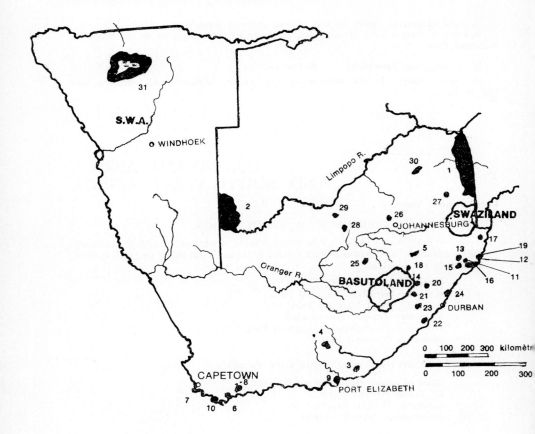

b) Orange Free State :

25. Willem Pretorius Game Reserve.

c) Transvaal (also in order of size not importance) :

26. Loskop Dam Nature Reserve and Public Resort.
27. Hans Merensky Nature Reserve.
28. S.A. Lombard Nature Reserve.
29. Barberspan Nature Reserve.
30. Percy Fyfe Nature Reserve.

SOUTH-WEST AFRICA

31. Etosha National Park.

444

SOUTH AFRICA AND SOUTH-WEST AFRICA

General Introduction :

Since the situation varies from category to category and province to province, general information on the legal basis, administration, etc., of these 31 areas is given in an introduction under each sub-heading. The information available on the South African Parks and Reserves is very extensive and those wishing to have additional details are recommended to refer to the Koedoe publication " The position of Nature Conservation in South Africa ".

Under the heading ' Union of South Africa ' full coverage was given in the previous edition, E/3436, of the List, which also included a section on South-west Africa.

Details : application of criteria (II), general information (III) and description (IV) :

REPUBLIC OF SOUTH AFRICA

A. — NATIONAL PARKS.

Introduction :

The legal basis of the National Parks is the National Parks Act 1962.

Administration : comprehensive powers for the maintenance of the National Parks are exercised by a National Parks Board of Trustees appointed by the President of the Republic. The total strength of the supervisory staff is 1,072 and the over-all budget amounts to U.S. $ 2,240,000 (1.6 million rands).

Land tenure : entirely State ownership, since under the National Parks Act only State-owned land can be designated as National Park.

Tourism : there is a powerful organisation, especially for the Kruger National Park, producing large numbers of informative publications; educational programmes; museums.

Research : well-co-ordinated and partly undertaken by National Parks Board of Trustees staff, which includes five biologists based on the Kruger National Park and two others operating in the National Parks of the Cape Province. The Administration publishes a journal " Koedoe ". Research by independent naturalists is systematically encouraged and aided.

1. KRUGER NATIONAL PARK.

a) Status : total protection; nearly 800 km of fencing separates the wildlife of the Park from the domestic stock of neighbouring farms; various ' game management ' practices include grass burning, maintenance of watering-points and occasional control of predators.

b) Area : 1,817,146 ha.

c) Staff : of the 301 units in 1962, about 200 were working on a permanent and 100 on a temporary basis for the conservation Department; an additional (approx.) 30 permanent staff were responsible for looking after tourists, reinforced by a further 250 auxiliaries during the height of the season, and there is also the technical scientific staff mentioned in the Introduction.

d) Budget : expenditure on salaries covers criterion.

Date established : 1926, replacing the Sabie Game Reserve created by President Kruger's signature of an Ordinance in 1898.

445

Tourism : over 1,900 km of motor roads serve the Park which is divided into three districts because of its great size; the principal rest-camps are Skukuza Pretorius Kop, Lower Sabie Olifants and Letaba; the growth of tourism can be assessed from the following figures :

1927 : 10 visitors, 3 vehicles.
1939 : 32,603 visitors, 8,533 vehicles.
1959 : 135,740 visitors, 34,501 vehicles.
1963 : 184,044 visitors, 46,681 vehicles.
1968 : 258,936 visitors, 68,852 vehicles.

IV.   *Altitude :* 210-800 m.

a) Gently undulating region of hills and doleritic dykes; grassy plains, park savannah, dry deciduous forest, thornbush.

b) Elephant *Loxodonta africana,* hippopotamus *H. amphibius,* white rhinoceros *Ceratotherium simum*; giraffe *Girafa camelopardalis*; seventeen species of antelope including sable and roan *Hippotragus niger* and *equinus,* kudu *Tragelaphus strepsiceros,* impala *Aepyceros melampus* and waterbuck *Kobus ellipsiprymnus*; lion and leopard *Panthera leo* and *pardus,* hyaena *C. crocuta,* jackal *Canis mesomelas.*

c) White or square-lipped rhinoceros.

2. KALAHARI GEMSBOK NATIONAL PARK.

II.   *a)* Status : total protection, but one family group of Bushmen still lives and hunts freely in the Park.

b) Area : 895,316 ha.

c) Staff : only 10 units, but due to the desert country of the Kalahari supervision is only necessary round the borders of the Park and can in any case be justified at a lower level than usual in the absence of human pressure in this very sparsely inhabited region.

d) Budget : expenditure is also below the criterion requirement, but this can be excused for the same reasons as apply to the staff position.

III.   *Date established :* 1931.

Administration : the Park authorities also undertake the supervision of the neighbouring Game Reserve in Botswana (q.v.).

Tourism : only about 320 km of motorable track, which restricts the circulation of tourists; rest-camps at Twee Rivieren (34 beds) and Mata Mata (12 beds).

Research : there is a research centre at the Park headquarters.

IV.   *Altitude :* about 1,200 m.

a) A vast expanse of dunes of red sand, supporting a meagre vegetation adapted to sub-desert or even full-desert conditions, consisting mainly of grasses such as *Aristida* spp., and bush of *Acacia* spp.

b) Eight species of antelope, including springbok *Antidorcas marsupialis* * eland *Taurotragus oryx,* red hartebeest *Alcelaphus buselaphus caama* and gemsbok *Oryx g. gazella* *; lion *, leopard, hyaena, jackal; secretary-bird, *Sagittarius serpentarius,* bustards, ostrich *Struthio camelus*; the numbers in this area of those marked * are declining dangerously.

446

3. ADDO ELEPHANT NATIONAL PARK.

a) Status : total protection; it has been necessary at great expense to erect a strong fence, 18 km in length, to prevent the herd of 40 elephants from doing damage on neighbouring properties.

b) Area : 6,397 ha.

c) Staff : 10 permanent, 7 temporary; includes a " tourist officer ".

d) Budget : expenditure on salaries covers criterion.

Date established : 1931; also known as the Addo Bush Elephant National Park.

Tourism : a watchtower has been built from which tourists can view the elephants at night; there is no accommodation in the Park, but light refreshments can be obtained at a cafe.

Altitude : 60-180 m.

a) Broken country covered with dense bush which is difficult to penetrate; the main species is *Portulacaria afra,* interspersed with acacias, many herbaceous plants and succulents, such as *Crassula* spp. and *Aloe* spp.

b) Elephant (considered by some to be a distinct subspecies), Cape buffalo (also a subspecies), hartebeest; advantage taken of protected status to reintroduce black rhinoceros *Diceros bicornis,* hippopotamus and a dozen species of antelope, including eland and kudu.

c) Black rhinoceros (reintroduced).

4. MOUNTAIN ZEBRA NATIONAL PARK.

a) Status : total protection.

b) Area : 5,020 ha (before the recent acquisition of four farms was only 1,418 ha).

c) Staff : 5 permanent, 2 temporary.

d) Budget : expenditure on salaries covers criterion.

Date established : 1937.

Tourism : strictly controlled, but there is some accommodation in the Park.

Altitude : about 900 m.

a) Karroo veld, a great expanse of flat country sprinkled with hills, on which the grasses, bush and trees are well adapted to the xerophytic conditions (e.g. *Acacia karroo* and succulents *Crassula* spp. and *Aloe* spp.).

b) Mountain zebra *Equus z. zebra*; various species of antelope have been reintroduced including eland, white-tailed gnu *Connochaetes gnou,* gemsbok, blesbok *Damaliscus dorcas albifrons*; ostrich.

c) Mountain zebra.

5. GOLDEN GATE HIGHLANDS NATIONAL PARK.

a) Status : total protection.

b) Area : 4,010 ha.

c) Staff : 13 units.

d) Budget : expenditure on salaries covers criterion.

15

III.   *Date established :* 1963.

Tourism : access only by road; one rest camp; this Park is mainly visited for its remarkable scenery, but also as the scene of a successful experiment in the reintroduction of large mammals, carried out in 1963 (see under **IV** *b*) below).

IV.   *Altitude :* 1,810-2,700 m.

a) Landscape of great beauty, with numerous rocky outcrops or kopjes and a distinctive high altitude flora.

b) Mammals introduced in 1963 were 12 blesbok, 23 white-tailed gnu, 6 eland, 7 red hartebeest, 9 springbok, plus zebra, buffalo and brindled gnu *Connochaetes taurinus*; mountain reedbuck *Redunca fulvorufula* and klipspringer *O. oreotragus* also reported.

6. BONTEBOK NATIONAL PARK.

II.   *a*) Status : total protection.

b) Area : 1,330 ha, below the criterion requirement, but the Park retained in the List because " it harbours one of the rarest antelopes in the world ".

c) Staff : 3 units.

d) Budget : expenditure on salaries covers criterion.

III.   *Date established :* 1959.

Tourism : access only by road; no accommodation in the Park.

IV.   *Altitude :* 90-100 m.

a) A sandy depression in a rocky plateau; scrub-veld (*Protea* spp.) and grassland, the only indigenous trees being *Acacia karroo* and *Podocarpus falcatus.*

b) Bontebok *Damaliscus d. dorcas*; the Cape buffalo and eight species of antelope have been introduced.

c) Bontebok.

B. — PROTECTED AREAS IN THE CAPE PROVINCE.

Introduction :

The legal basis for the Reserve numbered No. 7 in the Nature Reserves Ordinance No. 18 of 1939 and for the other three Reserves, the Financial Relations Consolidation and Amendment Act No. 38 of 1945.

Administration : No. 7 Cape of Good Hope Nature Reserve was the creation of and administered by the local Divisional Council of the Cape of Good Hope County, which in 1961 appointed a Director of Nature Reserves. This category of a Divisional Council Nature Reserve is not found in any other Province of the Republic and, even in the Cape, the three other Reserves, Nos. 8-10, have provincial origin and status; an Advisory Committee on Nature Conservation was set up for them in 1952. The Province also has provision for the appointment as a special privilege of carefully chosen unpaid ' Honorary Nature Conservation Officers ', of whom there are some 500 altogether.

Land tenure : the land is publicly owned, on a regional (County) or provincial basis as the case may be.

448

Tourism : fully organised reception, accommodation and information service, much effort being devoted to the latter educational function, with the publication of books and pamphlets, establishment of museum, etc.

Research : mainly directed and undertaken under the sponsorship of the de Hoop Provincial Wildlife Farm, which has concentrated on animal ecology, particularly in connection with problems of capture, transport, reintroduction, breeding, etc., of wild species. Research work is also sponsored by the Divisional Councils.

7. CAPE OF GOOD HOPE NATURE RESERVE.

a) Status : total protection.

b) Area : 6,700 ha.

c) Staff : a supervisor and 10 others, in the service of the Cape of Good Hope Divisional Council.

d) Budget : expenditure on salaries covers criterion.

Date established : 1939.

Tourism : open throughout the year.

Research : a special study is being undertaken of a baboon community.

Altitude : sea level to 380 m.

a) The extreme southern tip of the Cape peninsula, with a varied and abundant flora, including several endemic species; the trees include *Acacia* spp. and *Pinus* spp.

b) Eland, steinbok *Raphiceros campestris,* grysbok *Raphiceros melanotis,* red hartebeest, bontebok, common zebra *Equus burchelli.*

c) Bontebok.

8. DE HOOP WILDLIFE FARM.

a) Status : total protection, but since the main object is wildlife management the treatment of many species amounts to domesticated rearing in free conditions.

b) Area : 5,536 ha.

c) Staff : 41 units, including 35 labourers.

d) Budget : expenditure on salaries covers criterion.

Date established : 1956.

Altitude : sea level to about 90 m.

a) Poor grassland, to a large extent under such management practices as cutting and burning.

b) Eland, white-tailed gnu, springbok, grysbok, steinbok.

9. GOUKAMA NATURE RESERVE.

a) Status : total protection.

b) Area : 1,640 ha, somewhat below the criterion requirement but retained at the particular request of the South African authorities because of the biological interest of the protected zone.

c) Staff : one guard, 8 labourers.

d) Budget : expenditure on salaries covers criterion.

III.   *Date established :* 1960.

IV.   *Altitude :* sea level.

a) An area of coastal dunes and estuaries, bordered by rolling veld land with some indigenous 'milkwood' *Calvaria inermo* forest; the dunes have been planted with marram and acacias.

b) Various small antelopes such as common or grey duiker *Sylvicapra grimmia* and grysbok; the intertidal and estuarine fauna is specially varied and interesting.

10. JONKERSHOEK NATURE RESERVE.

II.   *a)* Status : total protection, but like No. 8 above, or even more so, is in effect a study centre specially concerned with the breeding of game animals in semi-domesticated conditions.

b) Area : 11 ha, and therefore could not be considered for the List, but the South African authorities have represented that it is " a most important establishment as far as wild fowl is concerned ", which it would be a pity to miss out.

c) Staff : 4 units, assisted by a staff of several dozen attached to the nearby Jonkershoek Fish Hatchery.

d) Budget : expenditure on salaries covers criterion.

III.   *Date established :* 1952.

IV.   *Altitude :* about 240 m.

a) Man-made lagoons; meadows.

b) Some small antelopes including springbok, but above all birds : black duck *Anas sparsa,* hottentot teal *Anas punctata,* Cape shoveler *Anas smithi* and others; several species are hand-reared.

C. — RESERVES.

a) **Natal.**

Introduction :

The legal authority for each Province to establish Nature Reserves is the Financial Relations Consolidation and Amendment Act No. 38 of 1945. Natal has one peculiarity which may cause confusion, in that one of its reserves, No. 18 below, having been established on State-owned land but transferred to Provincial control, still bears the title of a 'national park'; the 25 other reserves (13 of which find a place in the List) go by a variety of names — " nature reserve " (13), " park " (4), " game reserve " (7) and even " park nature reserve " (1).

Administration : entirely a provincial responsibility; the Natal Parks, Game and Fish Preservation Board, set up in 1950, is charged with implementing the various regulations including those dealing with the establishment of Parks and Reserves; it is assisted by a consultative committee called the Zululand Reserves Committee.

Land tenure : the land is owned by the Province but in one or two instances by the State.

Tourism : there is a special organisation for looking after visitors, with the usual information services, including films and booklets. It is worth noting that the nine Natal Reserves classified by the South African authorities as most typical of the Province, in order of importance and interest rather than size (as listed here) are : 1. Hluhluwe, 2. Umfolozi, 3. St. Lucia Game Reserve and Park, 4. Giants Castle, 5. Ndumu, 6. Mkuzi, 7. Royal Natal National Park, 8. Coteni and 9. Kamberg.

Research : co-ordinated and undertaken by the Natal Parks, Game and Fish Preservation Board; the Council for Scientific and Industrial Research has been associated with a particular hydrobiological study.

11. UMFOLOZI GAME RESERVE.

a) Status : total protection.

b) Area : about 48,000 ha.

c) Staff : 60 units, including a Warden and 7 Rangers.

d) Budget : U.S. $ 150,000 (1962-1963).

Date established : 1897.

Tourism : hutted camp (24 beds) for accommodation of visitors; 51 km from Mtubatuba; travel in Reserve by car or foot, but in latter case accompaniment by Game Guide compulsory; 3-day ' wilderness-trail ' walks are organised.

Altitude : 450 m.

a) Zululand thornveld, with acacias the dominant species; *Ficus* spp. are found along the rivers.

b) White rhinoceros, black rhinoceros, kudu, waterbuck, reedbuck *Redunca arundinum,* nyala *Tragelaphus angasi* and many other ungulates; leopard; plentiful birdlife including martial eagle *Polemaetus bellicosus.*

c) Both the rhinoceroses.

12. ST. LUCIA GAME RESERVE.

a) Status : total protection, but sport-fishing permitted; the scientific value of the Reserve and particularly its birdlife are threatened by a process of salinisation due to upstream irrigation works (see also special note under No. 15 below).

b) Area : 36,500 ha.

c) Staff : 7 units, including a Senior Ranger and 2 Rangers.

d) Budget : U.S. $ 16,000 (1962-1963).

Date established : 1897.

Tourism : camping sites; hutted camps at Charter's Creek (30 beds) and Fanies Island (24 beds); boats for hire, launch tours; ' wilderness trails ' by boat and foot under supervision of a Ranger.

General : this Reserve forms a complex with Nos. 15 and 16; see special note under No. 15.

Altitude : sea level.

a) Coastal forest and stretches of grassland; reed-beds along the lake shores; mangrove.

b) Hippopotamus, crocodile *C. nilotica*; plentiful birdlife, especially pelicans, herons, avocets and other waterfowl.

451

13. MKUZI GAME RESERVE.

II.   *a)* Status : total protection.

b) Area : 24,600 ha.

c) Staff : 34 units, including a Senior Ranger and 3 Rangers.

d) Budget : U.S. $ 39,000 (1962-1963).

III.   *Date established :* 1912.

Tourism : hutted camp (including 6 new "squaredavels "); observation hide at Bube Pan; 110 km from Mtubatuba.

IV.   *Altitude :* about 800 m.

a) More or less low-lying thornveld, with acacias the dominant species; gallery forest of *Ficus* spp.

b) Black rhinoceros, Burchell's zebra, ten species of antelope including kudu and impala; leopard; seasonal wealth of waterfowl in Nsumu pan and many other bird species.

c) Black rhinoceros.

14. GIANT'S CASTLE GAME RESERVE.

II.   *a)* Status : total protection; trout-fishing under permit.

b) Area : 23,850 ha.

c) Staff : 22 units, including a Warden and 3 Rangers.

d) Budget : U.S. $ 40,600 (1962-1963).

III.   *Date established :* 1903.

Tourism : hutted camp (40 beds); only one road through Reserve, but walking and climbing are allowed and excellent; 73 km from Estcourt.

IV.   *Altitude :* 1,500-3,240 m.

a) A rugged area forming part of the Drakensberg range; high altitude meadows with many flowers (orchids, lilies), tree ferns, bamboos.

b) Eland, oribi *Ourebia ourebi,* vaal or grey rhebok *Pelea capreolus,* mountain reedbuck; leopard; black stork *Ciconia nigra,* martial eagle, black eagle *Aquila verreauxi,* African lammergeier *Gypaëtus barbatus meridionalis.*

c) African lammergeier.

15. HLUHLUWE GAME RESERVE.

II.   *a)* Status : total protection.

b) Area : 22,800 ha.

c) Staff : 37 units, including a Conservator, 3 Wardens and 2 Ecologists.

d) Budget : U.S. $ 144,800 (1962-1963).

III.   *Date established :* 1897.

Tourism : hutted camp (74 beds), with electricity; maps and other literature on sale; visitors leaving their cars must be accompanied by Game Guide; 51 km from Mtubatuba.

Special Note : there is a plan for building a barrage on the Hluhluwe river, which gives grounds for fearing undesirable changes in the natural biome, affecting both this Reserve and also the neighbouring St. Lucia Game Reserve

452

(No. 12) and the St. Lucia Park (No. 16). At its General Assembly in Nairobi, 1963, IUCN asked that a full scientific enquiry be undertaken before irreversible changes are allowed to be made in this area, and this enquiry has been completed although its findings are not yet known.

Altitude : 80-580 m.

a) Hilly thornveld, with clumps of trees and thicker forest along the rivers, on higher ground and in the north of the Reserve (*Acacia* spp., Cape chestnut *Calodendron*).

b) Black rhinoceros, white rhinoceros; various antelopes including nyala, impala, waterbuck, kudu, white-tailed and brindled gnu and many others; plentiful birdlife including marabou stork *Leptoptilos crumeniferus,* vultures and ground hornbill *Bucorvus cafer.*

c) Both the rhinoceroses.

16. St. Lucia Park.

a) Status : total protection, identical with that of the adjoining Game Reserve (No. 12 above), from which it only differs in providing more systematic arrangements for tourism. For threat to the scientific status of this area due to water development work see under Nos. 12 and 15 above.

b) Area : 12,400 ha.

c) Staff : 17 units, including 3 Rangers and 2 Camp Superintendents, the latter for the tourist organisation.

d) Budget : U.S. $ 33,000 (1962-1963).

Date established : 1939.

Tourism : camping sites, only, at St. Lucia estuary; boats for hire; launch tours.

Altitude : sea level.

a) Coastal forest and stretches of grassland; reed-beds along the lake shores; mangrove.

b) Hippopotamus, crocodile; many birds, especially waterfowl.

17. Ndumu Game Reserve.

a) Status : total protection.

b) Area : 10,000 ha.

c) Staff : 18 units, including a Senior Ranger and 2 Rangers.

d) Budget : U.S. $ 23,800 (1962-1963).

Date established : 1924.

Tourism : rondavels for accommodation of visitors.

Altitude : about 800 m.

a) Subtropical bush-savannah, with gallery forest of *Ficus* spp. along rivers and around lakes; reed-beds also border the lakes and the alluvial Pongola plains.

b) Elephant, hippopotamus, crocodile; plentiful birdlife, including black heron *Melanophoyx ardesiaca,* fish eagle *Cuncuma vocifer* and fishing owl *Scotopelia peli.*

453

18. Royal Natal National Park.

II.
    a) Status : total protection, but limited trout-fishing facilities.

    b) Area : 8,000 ha (the 750 ha Rugged Glen Nature Reserve adjoins the Park).

    c) Staff : 14 units, including a Warden, Ranger and Camp Superintendent.

    d) Budget : U.S. $ 21,000 (1962-1963).

III.
    Date established : 1916 (the neighbouring Rugged Glen Nature Reserve in 1950).

    Tourism : modern hotel and Park headquarters at Mont-aux-Sources, 88 km from Ladysmith; hutted camp (26 beds), Tendele, and a large well-equipped camp site; map and literature on sale; good walks and climbs.

IV.
    Altitude : 1,400-3,300 m.

    a) Montane area with forest patches.

    b) Brindled gnu or wildebeest, bushbuck, mountain reedbuck.

19. False Bay Park.

II.
    a) Status : total protection, sport-fishing permitted.

    b) Area : 2,225 ha.

    c) Staff : 8 units, including a Senior Ranger and a Ranger.

    d) Budget : U.S. $ 16,000 (1962-1963).

III.
    Date established : 1944.

    Tourism : camping-sites only; boats for hire; Hluhluwe Station is 11 km away.

IV.
    Altitude : sea level.

    a) A peninsula covered with coastal vegetation, the more inland areas having some woody bush (notably *Newtonia hildebrandti*).

    b) Hippopotamus, bushpig *Potamochoerus porcus,* suni *Nesotragus moschatus,* red duiker *Cephalophus natalensis,* nyala, bushbuck *Tragelaphus scriptus,* impala, reedbuck; crocodile; birds include white pelican *Pelecanus onocrotalus,* goliath heron *Ardea goliath* and African spoonbill *Platalea alba.*

20. Kamberg Nature Reserve.

II.
    a) Status : total protection; trout-fishing under licence.

    b) Area : 2,200 ha.

    c) Staff : 5 units, including a Senior Ranger, 2 Rangers and a Camp Superintendent.

    d) Budget : U.S. $ 19,000 (1962-1963).

III.
    Date established : 1951.

    Tourism : hutted camp (5 'squaredavels'); also accommodation for 12 at Stillerust farmhouse; 40 km from Rosetta.

IV.
    Altitude : about 1,200 m.

    a) Grassland at the foot of the Drakensberg mountains, with trout streams.

    b) Eland, oribi, mountain reedbuck, grey rhebok, common or grey duiker; a herd of Zulu Royal Cattle is maintained.

21. LOTENI NATURE RESERVE.

   a) Status : total protection; trout-fishing permitted.

   b) Area : 2,120 ha.

   c) Staff : 11 units, including a Senior Ranger and a Ranger.

   d) Budget : U.S. $ 13,000 (1962-1963).

   Date established : 1953.

   Tourism : hutted camp (12 ' squaredavels '); 120 km from Pietermaritzburg.

   Altitude : about 1,400 m.

   a) Grassland in a very rugged section of the Drakensberg.

   b) Eland, oribi, mountain reedbuck, grey rhebok, grey duiker, reedbuck and bushbuck.

22. ORIBI GORGE NATURE RESERVE.

   a) Status : total protection.

   b) Area : 1,765 ha, rather below the criterion requirement, but in view of the importance of these smaller reserves it has been decided to include this and the next two in the List, while relegating to Section V the other 12 out of the total of 26 Reserves in Natal.

   c) Staff : 10 units, including a Senior Ranger.

   d) Budget : U.S. $ 7,800 (1962-1963).

   Date established : 1950.

   Tourism : hutted camps (12 beds); 21 km from Port Shepstone.

   Altitude : about 500 m.

   a) On the flank of the gorge; forest-covered.

   b) Leopard; oribi, bushbuck, blue duiker *Cephalophus monticola,* grey duiker; vervet and diadem monkeys *Cercopithecus aethiops* and *mitis.*

23. COLEFORD NATURE RESERVE.

   a) Status : total protection; trout fishing permitted.

   b) Area : 1,265 ha; see note under No. 22, head II (*b*).

   c) Staff : 12 units, including a Ranger.

   d) Budget : U.S. $ 13,500 (1962-1963).

   Date established : 1959.

   Tourism : hutted camp (about 20 beds) and a ' fisherman's cottage ' (6 beds); horses for hire; tennis court; 33 km from Underberg.

   Altitude : about 300 m.

   a) Fairly level grassy plains.

   b) Various small antelopes; white-tailed gnu and blesbok have been re-introduced.

24. UMLALAZI NATURE RESERVE.

   a) Status : total protection.

   b) Area : 900 ha, but combined for maintenance purposes with the neighbouring Dhlinza Forest Nature Reserve of 185 ha; see note under No. 22, head II (*b*).

   c) Staff : 3 units, including a Ranger.

   d) Budget : U.S. $ 9,500 (1962-1963).

III.   *Date established :* 1948.

   Tourism : camping-sites only; 130 km from Durban.

IV.   *Altitude :* about 50 m.

   a) Mangrove and other coastal forest, with reed-beds surrounding part of the lagoon.

   b) Bushpig, reedbuck, bushbuck, blue duiker, grey duiker; crocodile; birds of dense coastal vegetation.

b) **Orange Free State.**

Introduction :

   Legal authority for the creation of Provincial Reserves is given by the Financial Relations Consolidation and Amendment Act No. 38 of 1945.

   Administration : there is an Administrator assisted by a Nature Conservation and Public Resorts Control Board, meeting five times a year in the Willem Pretorius Game Reserve. A 'Division of Nature Conservation' was also set up in 1965.

   Land tenure : the land is owned by the Province.

   Tourism : concentrated in the Willem Pretorius Reserve; little has yet been done on the educational side.

   Research : the Province has no biologist on its staff as yet and research is undertaken by the Bloemfontein Museum.

25. WILLEM PRETORIUS GAME RESERVE.

II.   *a*) Status : total protection; 1,500 ha of the Reserve consists of the reservoir lake created by the construction of the Allemanskraal dam; the boundaries are still in dispute, so the status is rather uncertain; there is a 'Dog breeding and training Centre' in the vicinity.

   b) Area : 9,000 ha.

   c) Staff : for conservation duties, 5 units, including a Conservator; for the supervision of visitors, 53 units including a Director.

   d) Budget : expenditure on salaries covers criterion.

III.   *Date established :* 1955.

   Tourism : the Director and his staff of 52 control facilities, which include 40 rondavels, a camp-site and a restaurant.

IV.   *Altitude :* about 300 m.

   a) Situated in the Doornberg mountains and surrounding plains; the principal trees are *Olea africana, Rhus lancea* and the kiepersol *Cussonia spicata.*

   b) Eland, blesbok, white-tailed gnu, springbok.

c) **Transvaal.**

456

Introduction :

As with the other Provinces, the legal basis is the 1945 Act No. 38.

Administration : by a Director of Nature Conservation, assisted by 17 biologists and other scientists and a Fauna and Flora Advisory Board established in 1949; there is also a Game and Fisheries Research department.

Land tenure : the land is owned by the Province.

Tourism : the organisation for the reception of visitors is based on Loskop; there is a full educational programme, with conferences, films and publications.

Research : based on the Hans Merensky, S.A. Lombard and Barberspan Reserves (q.v.).

26. LOSKOP DAM NATURE RESERVE AND PUBLIC RESORT.

a) Status : total protection, but this area is rated as " a public and angling resort ", with consequential permission for sport-fishing, although there is no game ranching.

b) Area : 12,400 ha.

c) Staff : 71 permanent, 60 part-time units, including a Manager, two clerks, a farm foreman and some labourers.

d) Budget : provision for the Transvaal Reserves is covered by the over-all budget of the Nature Conservation Branch.

Date established : 1940; enlarged in 1954.

Altitude : about 1,000 m.

a) Alluvial plains bordering the dam and hemmed in by hills and mountains with very steep slopes; reed-beds, grassland, woody savannah, bush and forest; a rare species of *Encephalarctos* (Cycadaceae) occurs.

b) Sable antelope; many species have been reintroduced including white (square-lipped) and black rhinoceroses, kudu, impala, oribi, eland, zebra (the local Damaraland or Chapman's zebra, a race of Burchell's, *Equus burchelli antiquorum*), giraffe and wildebeest.

c) Both rhinoceroses.

27. HANS MERENSKY NATURE RESERVE.

a) Status : total protection, but this Reserve, like Nos. 28 and 30 below, is to a certain extent devoted to game-ranching.

b) Area : 4,100 ha.

c) Staff : a Nature Conservation Officer and 10 handymen.

d) Budget : see under No. 26, head II (*d*).

Date established : 1954.

Research : this Reserve is set aside for botanical research.

Altitude : about 500 m.

a) A hilly region, containing a hot mineralised spring; the trees typical of the bush are *Acacia* spp. and *Combretum* spp.

b) Sable, tsessebe *Damaliscus lunatus*, eland, kudu, waterbuck, duiker, giraffe (all except duiker managed on a ranching basis); leopard, lynx *Felis lynx*, spotted hyaena.

457

28. S.A. LOMBARD NATURE RESERVE.

II.   *a*) Status : total protection; used for game-ranching, research (see below) and training of dogs for jackal extermination work, but, despite these activities, the greater part of the Reserve can be considered as kept in a sufficiently natural state to allow it to qualify for the List.

b) Area : 3,730 ha.

c) Staff : a Senior Research Officer, 3 Biologists, 1 Farm Manager, 1 Clerk, 2 Dog Masters, 2 Vermin Control Officers and 26 Handymen.

d) Budget : see note under No. 26, head II (*d*).

III.   *Date established :* 1949, enlarged in 1953.

Research : the centre for research on High Veld ungulates and on control of carnivorous predators; there is a laboratory, herbarium and library.

IV.   *Altitude :* about 1,220 m.

a) Typical grassy plains of the western Transvaal.

b) Eland, blesbok, springbok, impala, red hartebeest, white-tailed gnu, buffalo.

29. BARBERSPAN NATURE RESERVE.

II.   *a*) Status : total protection; mainly a bird sanctuary.

b) Area : 3,575 ha.

c) Staff : an Ornithologist, with a technical assistant and 7 handymen.

d) Budget : see note under No. 26, head II (*d*).

III.   *Date established :* 1949, enlarged in 1954.

Research : a centre for waterfowl research and bird-ringing.

IV.   *Altitude :* about 1,340 m.

a) A lake surrounded by grassland.

b) Birds include both the greater and lesser flamingo *Phoenicopterus ruber roseus* and *Phoeniconaias minor,* African spoonbill, goliath heron, black korhaan or bustaard *Afrotis afra* and many palaearctic migrants.

30. PERCY FYFE NATURE RESERVE.

II.   *a*) Status : total protection; emphasis on game-ranching.

b) Area : 2,475 ha.

c) Staff : a Farm Foreman and 9 handymen.

d) Budget : see note under No. 26, head II (*d*).

III.   *Date established :* 1954.

IV.   *Altitude :* about 1,370 m.

a) An area of very rugged hills.

b) Ranch-rearing of blesbok for distribution to farmers, also nucleus herds of steinbok, kudu, impala, white-tailed gnu, zebra.

V.   **Areas excluded** (Republic of South Africa) :

A. — Two National Parks in process of full establishment :

1. Tsitsikama Forest and Coastal National Park.

458

Partly proclaimed in 1964, this covers a strip of coastline (58 km long and 9,400 ha in area) in Cape Province, near Knysna; it will include a marine park, as recommended by the First World Conference on National Parks, Seattle, 1962 (Recommendation No. 15).

2. The Blyde River Canyon Recreational Area and Nature Reserve, Transvaal : about 21,500 ha.

B. — Various Provincial Reserves, which do not satisfy the criteria requirements, particularly in regard to size :

a) Cape Province : nil.

b) Natal : twelve, of which two have received previous mentions as being adjuncts of Listed Areas Nos. 18 and 24 :

1. Richards Bay Game Reserve	800 ha.
2. Rugged Glen Nature Reserve (adjoins No. 18 Royal Natal N.P.).	750 ha.
3. Krantz Kloof Nature Reserve	442 ha.
4. Sordwana Bay Park	408 ha.
5. Richards Bay Park	390 ha.
6. Enseleni Nature Reserve	290 ha.
7. Dhlinza Forest Nature Reserve (adjoins No. 24 Umlalazi N.R.).	185 ha.
8. Queen Elizabeth Park Nature Reserve	92 ha.
9. Stainbank or Coedmore Nature Reserve	79 ha.
10. Himeville Nature Reserve	48 ha.
11. Kosi Bay Nature Reserve	20 ha.
12. Paradise Valley Nature Reserve	20 ha.

N.B. — It is in order not to overburden the List and data and with the agreement of the South African authorities that these twelve sanctuaries have been omitted, because they are all of considerable biological interest and all are very well supervised, most of them with at least one Ranger and a budget of over U.S. $ 3,000; in fact a pair of them, No. 1 and No. 5 Richards Bay Game Reserve and Richards Bay Park, share an annual budget of nearly U.S. $ 24,000.

c) Orange Free State : nil.

d) Transvaal : two reserves of sufficient size sited around dams and reservoirs, but which the South African authorities themselves (letter of 4 February 1964) did not consider to be sufficiently well protected to qualify for the List :

1. Vaaldam Nature Reserve : 25,312 ha, mainly a ' pleasure resort ' cum ' angling resort '.

2. Ohrigstad Dam Nature Reserve : 2,568 ha, also classified as a 'pleasure resort '.

Also five areas smaller than 2,000 ha in size of which the two largest are also considered not to have a sufficiently strict protected status :

1. Honnet Nature Reserve	1,876 ha.

Mainly a ' pleasure resort '.

2. Langjan Nature Reserve	1,652 ha.

Of special interest as being the only Reserve in the Transvaal where the gemsbok is indigenous and still survives.

3. Berghoek Nature Reserve	700 ha.
4. Vertroosting Nature Reserve	24 ha.
5. N'Jelele Nature Reserve	20 ha.

C. — Twenty-one Municipal Reserves of which the South African authorities have advised the omission :

a) Cape Province : 10 (the largest 240 ha).
b) Natal : nil.
c) Orange Free State : 2 (the largest 196 ha).
d) Transvaal : 9, of which the two largest are :

1. Lydenburg	7,470 ha.
2. Fountains Valley	6,850 ha.

The last-named is the oldest Nature Reserve in South Africa, dating from 1895, but its protected status is not up to standard.

D. — A number of Divisional Council Reserves.

As explained under No. 7 in the List, the Cape of Good Hope Nature Reserve, this category only exists in the Cape Province, where there are in fact five others, three in the Port Elizabeth Divisional Council area, one in that of Knysna and one in that of Cape Town. The authorities have, however, advised their omission from the List.

E. — A number of private reserves :

These pertain either to industrial companies or to land-owners with large farms, although responsibility for their protected status is entrusted to the Provincial authorities.

a) Cape Province : De Beers Consolidated Mining Company has established two such Reserves on its Kimberley concessions for the protection of the Veld fauna, at Rooipoort (39,850 ha) and Benaauwheidsfontein (10,950 ha).

b) Transvaal : no less than 245 farmers have declared their concessions or properties to be game reserves, covering a total area of 560,230 ha — a form of protection not found either in Orange Free State or Natal. Since, however, they are protected from hunting rather than totally reserved areas, it has been decided that they can be left out of the List, though they certainly merit a mention.

F. — Finally, a number of important special category reserves :

67 Forest Nature Reserves of the Department of Forestry, covering a total of about 12,000 ha.

5 Rock Lobster Reserves.

33 State Guano Islands, where all web-footed species of bird as well as sea-birds are protected.

SOUTH-WEST AFRICA

Introduction :

The Game Parks, Nature Parks and Private Game Reserves Ordinance No. 18 of 1958, is the legal basis for the reserves of South-west Africa.

Administration : by the Nature Conservation and Tourism Branch, Windhoek.

Land tenure : State ownership.

31. ETOSHA NATIONAL PARK.

II.

a) Status : total protection; an uninhabited region.

460

b) Area : about 6,500,000 ha; a buffer zone known as Game Reserve No. 2 and some 9,250,000 ha in size surrounds the Park.

c) Staff : 310 units.

d) Budget : U.S. $ 200,000, plus staff salaries.

II. *Date of establishment :* 1958, under the Ordinance referred to in the Introductory section; the surrounding buffer zone, Game Reserve No. 2, dates from 1907.

Tourism : the Park is now fully open to tourists, with accommodation available at several rest camps; motorable tracks have been cut and are maintained to permit free movement through the Park.

V. *Altitude :* no information.

a) The range of this great Park extends from the coastal Namib sand desert to the semi-arid interior, with its typical Karstveld, Mopaniveld and Kaokoveld vegetation of bush, thornbush, grassy plains and mopane *Colophospermum mopane* forest.

b) Elephant, black rhinoceros, giraffe, Hartmann's mountain zebra *Equus zebra hartmannae,* eland, impala, kudu, red hartebeest, wildebeest; ostrich.

c) Black rhinoceros, Hartmann's mountain zebra.

Areas excluded (South-West Africa) :

1. Game Reserve No. 2, which as its name indicates is less strictly supervised than the Game (now National) Park it surrounds.

2. The Game Reserves formerly numbered 1 and 4, which have ceased to be maintained since 1962 and 1947, respectively.

3. Game Reserve No. 3, 1,150,000 ha, in the Walfisch Bay area, which has very little supervision.

4. The Dean Viljoen Game Reserve, 4,000 ha, established in 1962 near Windhoek.

5. Some thirty private Reserves, covering a total of 303,539 ha.

The omission of these areas is supported by a letter from the local authorities dated 9 July 1964, which states that " only the Etosha Game Park justifies a reference in the United Nations List. More than 90 % of the total budget, the staff and the activities (of the Nature Conservation and Tourist Branch) is centred around this national park ".

114. SOUTH YEMEN

Listed Areas : nil.

Explanation :

In a letter dated 13 August 1964, the Department of Technical Co-operation, London, stated that " the Aden Government has confirmed that there are no National Parks or Reserves in Aden ". No information has been received to suggest that the situation has altered since the establishment of the People's Republic of South Yemen.

METROPOLITAN SPAIN INCLUDING THE CANARIES

I. **Listed Areas** : three.

A. — NATIONAL PARKS :

1. La Montaña de Covadonga or de Peña Santa National Park.
2. Valle de Ordesa or del Rio Ara National Park.

B. — NATURE RESERVES :

3. Coto Doñana Nature Reserve.

General Introduction :

The administration of the National Parks is the responsibility of the National Parks Commission of the Direccion General de Montes, Caza y Pesca Fluvial of the Ministry of Agriculture. That of the existing and future Reserves in the Coto Doñana and Guadalquivir Marismas region is entrusted to the Consejo Superior de Investigaciones Scientificas.

The two listed National Parks were also described in Part Two of the previous edition of the List, as well as three other National Parks now placed in Section V.

Details : application of criteria (II), general information (III) and description (IV) :

A. — NATIONAL PARKS.

1. LA MONTAÑA DE COVADONGA/DE PEÑA SANTA NATIONAL PARK.

II.   *a*) Status : full protection but pasturing of stock still allowed in some sectors, though this concession is being gradually eliminated; culling of excess numbers of game species occasionally necessary.

b) Area : 16,925 ha.

c) Staff : 5 units.

d) Budget : U.S. $ 3,200.

III.   *Date established :* 1918.

Land tenure : municipal land, but there are still scattered private properties, totalling 510 ha, in this Park.

Tourism : unrestricted entry; hostelries, with a considerable amount of accommodation, and also mountain huts in the Park.

IV.   *Altitude :* 140-2,595 m.

a) A section of the mountain range of the Asturias and León, clothed, except for the highest snow-covered summits, with forests of beech *Fagus,* ash *Fraxinus,* birch *Betula* and oak *Quercus* and with meadows in which many alpine species of plant are found.

b) The montane fauna includes chamois, described by Cabrera as a distinct race *R. rupicapra parva,* roe deer *C. capreolus,* bear *Ursus arctos pyrenaicus*

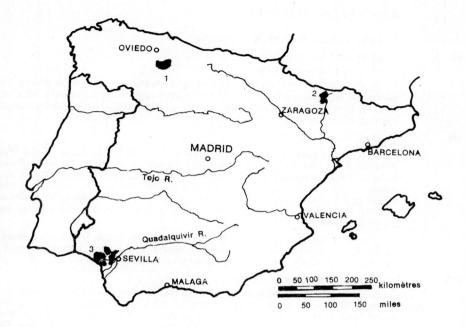

FISCHER, wolf *Canis lupus,* wild pig *Sus scrofa,* fox *V. vulpes,* badger *M. meles* and squirrel *Sciurus* sp.

2. VALLE DE ORDESA OR DEL RIO ARA NATIONAL PARK.

a) Status : full protection.

b) Area : 2,046 ha.

c) Staff : 3 units.

d) Budget : U.S. $ 500.

Date established : 1918.

Tourism : 25,000 visitors a year; accommodation in hostelries and mountain huts; entry unrestricted.

Altitude : 1,064-2,460 m.

a) A valley in the Pyrenees of Aragon; the most important elements in the vegetation are silver fir *Abies alba,* ash *Fraxinus angustifolia,* beech *Fagus sylvatica,* pedunculate oak *Quercus robur,* juniper *Juniperus communis* and, especially, the Scots pine *Pinus sylvestris* and mountain pine *P. mugo*; azaleas, violets and edelweis *Leontopodium* are features of the flora.

b) Notable items in the fauna are chamois, ibex (*Capra pyrenaica victoriae* and *Capra p. hispanica,* from the Gredos and Cazorla hills, respectively, have been released in the area), fox, squirrel and, among birds, the lammergeier *Gypaëtus barbatus.*

463

B. — NATURE RESERVES.

3. COTO DOÑANA NATURE RESERVE (*).

II.
    a) Status : full protection.

    b) Area : about 6,500 ha.

    c) and *d*) Staff and Budget : according to estimates published in March 1967, an annual expenditure of U.S. $ 15,500 is envisaged, covering salaries of a staff of 9 (including an Administrator and 6 guards) and other maintenance and running expenses.

III.
    Date established : 1963, 1965.

    General : originating with the purchase of land on the initiative of the World Wildlife Fund, the Reserve was formally handed over to the Spanish Government in 1965, responsibility for it and for its Biological Research Station being vested in the C.S.I.C. (see General Introduction). Efforts to secure the reservation and a similar status for important sections of the neighbouring *marismas,* notably those of Las Nuevas, Hinojos and Guadiamar, have continued and been partly achieved.

    Tourism : the organisation of facilities for visitors to the Reserve (on permit), including the construction of a road of access and limited accommodation at the Palacio Doñana, has made considerable progress.

IV.
    Altitude : sea level to 30 m.

    a) Delta of the Guadalquivir; a great expanse of marshland separated on the west from the sea by the sand-dunes of the Coto Doñana proper; the flora is rich and varied, that of the Coto characterised by stone pines *Pinus pinea,* cork oak *Quercus suber* woods and sandy heath dominated by rock-roses *Halimium* (= *Helianthemum*), and that of the Marismas by bulrush and sedge *Scirpus* and *Carex,* and the glassworts *Arthrocnemum fruticosum* and *macrostachyum.*

    b) Wild pig, red deer *Cervus elaphus,* fallow deer *D. dama,* Spanish lynx *Felis lynx pardina*; many reptiles; a large avifauna including herons, egrets, bitterns, storks, glossy ibis *Plegadis falcinellus,* flamingo *Phoenicopterus ruber,* swans, geese and ducks, plovers, curlews and other waders, cranes and many birds of prey, notably the Spanish imperial eagle *Aquila heliaca adalberti,* other eagles, vultures, kites and falcons.

    c) Spanish lynx, Spanish imperial eagle.

V.
    Areas excluded (Metropolitan Spain, including the Canaries) :

El Teide National Park (Canaries) ... ... 11,000 ha.
La Caldera de Taburiente National Park (Canaries) ... ... 3,500 ha.

In the case of these two Parks the criteria of effective management are not satisfied, since neither staff nor maintenance funds have been made available.

Aigues Tortes y Lago de San Mauricio National Park . ... 10,500 ha.

(*) Coto Doñana was declared as national park by Decree of 15 August 1969. The new national park comprises the two nature reserves of Coto Doñana and Guadiamar and is now 35,000 ha in extent.

Although for this Park, situated in the Province of Lerida, the appointment of two wardens goes some way to satisfying the 'effective management' criteria, from the angle of the 'protected status' criterion a factor intervenes which must result in the omission of the Park from the List; this rests on the fact that not only is there very extensive forest exploitation but also the presence of huge hydroelectric installations has resulted in serious disturbance of the natural balance of the ecosystem.

The exclusion from the List of these three areas has been agreed in consultation with the Direccion General de Montes, Caza y Pesca Fluvial of the Ministry of Agriculture in Madrid (letter of 18 October 1963).

EQUATORIAL GUINEA (including Rio Muni and Fernando Po)

N.B. — Formerly Spanish Guinea : became independent in October 1968.

Listed Areas : two.

1. Monte Raices Territorial Park (Rio Muni).
2. Pico de Santa Isabel Strict Faunal and Botanical Reserve (Fernando Po).

General Introduction :

At the request of the Spanish authorities these two areas have been included in the List, although at the time of going to press of this edition sufficiently detailed information had only been received about the first of them. The Equatorial Region was not cited in the previous edition of the List.

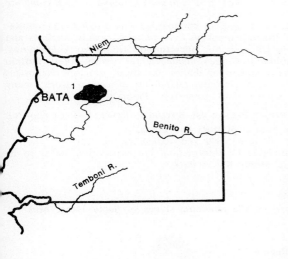

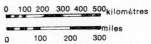

SPAIN

The legal basis for the establishment of these two reserves was a Ministerial Decree of 29 April 1953. As for Metropolitan Spain responsibility for administration was formerly vested in the Montes, Caza y Pesca Fluvial division of the Ministry of Agriculture.

Land tenure : State ownership.

Tourism : not yet developed, the few people who have visited the areas having done so solely for scientific work, though no organised research programme has been set up.

Details : application of criteria (II), general information (III) and description (IV) :

1. MONTE RAICES TERRITORIAL PARK (Rio Muni).

II.
    a) Status : total protection both for the fauna and flora except for a 2 km wide strip on the east, south and west of the Park, where the people living in the vicinity retain a right to gather and harvest forest produce.

    b) Area : 26,000 ha.

    c) Staff : two guards.

    d) Budget : salary and allowances for the staff should cover the criterion requirement.

III.
    Date established : 1953.

IV.
    Altitude : no information.

    a) Country of rather sharp relief in a region of metamorphic rocks; thick primary forest characteristic of a high rainfall, with secondary forest where shifting agriculture and burning have taken place; in the central, western and more mountainous sectors ' okoumé ' *Aucoumea klaiheana* is the dominant tree, while in the north-east the nutmeg tree *Pycnanthus angolensis,* the combretum *Terminalia superba* and *Pterocarpus soyausii* and in the south-east mahogany *Khaya ivorensis, Eribroma oblonga* and *Entandrophragma cylindricum* are characteristic.

    b) The lowland gorilla *G. g. gorilla,* chimpanzee *Pan troglodytes,* moustached, white-nosed and De Brazza's monkeys *Cercopithecus cephus, nictitans* and *neglectus,* the potto *Perodicticus potto,* angwantibo *Arctocebus calabarensis,* Demidoff's or dwarf bushbaby *Galago demidovi,* the dwarf forest buffalo *Syncerus caffer nanus,* many species of duiker, the dwarf antelope *Neotragus batesi,* pygmy or forest race of elephant *Loxodonta africana cyclotis*; many birds including the little known black guineafowl *Phasidus niger.*

2. PICO DE SANTA ISABEL STRICT FAUNAL AND BOTANICAL RESERVE (Fernando Po).

II.
    a) Status : complete protection of flora and fauna.

    b) Area : estimated at between 5,000 and 10,000 ha.

    c) and *d)* Staff and Budget : no information, but supervision stated to be of the same standard as in Monte Raices Park.

III.
    Date established : 1953.

IV.
    Altitude : 1,500-2,850 m.

    a) The summit and part of the adjoining slopes of Santa Isabel peak.

    b) No information.

V.
Areas excluded (Equatorial Region) :

1. Rio Ekuku Hunting Reserve.

7,500 ha, designed chiefly for the protection of a race of the sitatunga *Tragelaphus spekei gratus.*

466

2. Mount Alen Partial Reserve.

95,000 ha; containing gorilla, elephant, a race of the black and white colobus monkey *Colobus polykomos satanas* and fresh-water turtles of the genus *Trionyx*.

Listed Areas : nine.

1. Southern National Park.
2. Dinder National Park.
3. Nimule National Park.
4. Sabaloka Game Reserve.
5. Mbarizunga Game Reserve.
6. Bire Kpatua Game Reserve.
7. Tokar Game Reserve.
8. Rahad Game Reserve.
9. Mongalla Game Reserve.

General Introduction :

The legal basis of the Parks and Reserves of the Sudan is provided by the Preservation of Wild Animals Ordinance and Regulations, 1935 and the National Parks, Sanctuaries and Reserves Regulations 1939 L.R.O. No. 23.

In addition to the three National Parks, some fifteen game reserves in all play an important part in assuring the protection of the country's wildlife assets, which include many interesting and some very rare species. With the concurrence of the authorities in Khartoum, a perhaps somewhat arbitrary choice has had to be made of the six of these for inclusion in the List, as generally satisfying the criteria of effective management laid down by the I.C.N.P. It has nevertheless been deemed appropriate to give a fair amount of detail about the nine other Reserves, when listing them in Section V.

Administration : responsibility of the Ministry of Animal Resources (Game and Fisheries). It is noted with regret that at the time when basic work on the present edition of the List was approaching completion (January 1966) political troubles were hampering effective administration of the five areas situated in the southern Provinces, namely Nos. 1, 3, 5, 6 and 9 on the List.

Land tenure : all the land is State-owned.

Research : largely sponsored by the University of Khartoum; in 1962, the protected areas were visited by a qualified ecologist.

Details : application of criteria (II), general information (III) and description (IV) :

1. SOUTHERN NATIONAL PARK.

a) Status : total protection; a generally uninhabited area, but occasionally at the beginning of the rains a few nomadic herdsmen with their stock find their way into the Park; no cultivation.

b) Area : 1,600,000 ha.

467

c) Staff : 15 units, which is far below the criterion requirement. But th
Park deserves a place in the List in the light of the total absence of permanen
inhabitants and the known intention of the Government to reinforce the staf
(60 men have been requested), as soon as the political troubles of the regio
permit.

d) Budget : U.S. $ 12,000 (as against a criterion requirement of $ 80,00(
but the same consideration as above apply). The actual allowance for staf
salaries is $ 6,000, compared with $ 20,000 for the Dinder and $ 6,000 fo
the Nimule National Parks, but a further provision of about $ 28,000 unde
4 budgetary heads is made available for the general running of the three Park

Date established : 1939.

Tourism : when political conditions allow, a great deal will have to be done to attract and welcome tourists to this remote area, where roads and hotel accommodation are scarce. The intention is to develop such facilities as soon as those for the Dinder National Park are completed.

Altitude : 600 m.

a) Fairly flat country, covered by bush and with some gallery forest.

b) Elephant *Loxodonta africana,* white rhinoceros *Ceratotherium simum,* giraffe *Giraffa camelopardalis,* giant eland *Taurotragus derbianus,* hartebeest *Alcelaphus buselaphus,* kob *Kobus kob,* roan antelope *Hippotragus equinus,* hippopotamus *H. amphibius,* giant forest hog *Hylochoerus meinertzhageni,* leopard and lion *Panthera pardus* and *leo,* colobus monkey *Colobus polykomos,* crocodile *Crocodylus niloticus.*

c) White rhinoceros.

2. DINDER NATIONAL PARK.

a) Status : total protection; exploitation of gum arabic is allowed in the western sector, but under strict control; measures to suppress poaching have been taken, but the biggest threat to the area stems from an agricultural development programme which was being put into effect in January 1966, and involves an irrigation canal liable to cut an important annual migration route of various wild ungulates, which are already slaughtered in large numbers when they venture outside the Park.

b) Area : 650,000 ha.

c) Staff : 42 units, including a game warden and assistant game warden; it was intended to raise the staff to 70 units as soon as possible.

d) Budget : about U.S. $ 35,000 (criterion requirement $ 32,500).

Date established : 1935.

Tourism : a motor road crosses the Park from north-west to south-east and a dozen branch roads lead to the good game areas; a rest-camp with 50 beds at Galegu in the west of the Park, and three other camps; look-out posts (hides); an airstrip is planned (1965).

Altitude : 700-800 m.

a) Acacia seyal/Balanites aegyptiaca thornbush savannah in the north, and *Combretum hartmannnianum* woodland in the south; clayey flood plain of the Dinder and Rahad rivers, with dom palm *Hyphaene thebaica* or gallery forest of *Acacia sieberiana, Tamarindus indica* and *Ficus* spp. along the banks and swampy areas (reeds, *Nymphaea* spp. and *Ipomoea* spp.).

b) Giraffe, hartebeest, reedbuck *Redunca arundinum,* roan antelope, bushbuck *Tragelaphus scriptus,* oribi *Ourebia oribi,* waterbuck *Kobus ellipsiprymnus,* greater kudu *Tragelaphus strepsiceros,* several species of gazelle, dik-dik *Madoqua* sp.; buffalo *Syncerus caffer;* lion; ostrich *Struthio camelus.* Black rhinoceros *Diceros bicornis,* leopard, cheetah *Acinonyx jubatus,* elephant (during rains), hyaenas *H. hyaena* and *C. crocuta* and jackal *Canis mesomelas* also recorded.

c) Black rhinoceros (?).

3. NIMULE NATIONAL PARK.

a) Status : full protection, entry by permit only; there are no inhabitants or domestic livestock; a little fishing is allowed in the Fula Rapids; the Park is of course in an areas which is at present in a disturbed state politically.

b) Area : 25,600 ha.

c) Staff : 10 units, including a game ranger, responsible to the Senior Inspector of Game Preservation at Juba; this more than satisfies the criterion but, due to the proximity of the Uganda frontier, the area needs close supervision.

d) Budget : U.S. $ 12,000 (criterion $ 1,250).

III.   *Date established :* 1954, previously a Reserve since 1946.

Tourism : not yet developed, but this Park could be a great attraction as the animals are not shy; easy access could be provided from Uganda by railway and river steamer to Nimule and there is a ferry across the Nile.

IV.   *Altitude :* 500-800 m.

a) Plains bordering the Nile, with the Illingua mountain chain on the west cut by " khors " or valleys, through which small streams flow; Fula Rapids; bush and savannah with a sprinkling of *Tamarindus indica.*

b) White rhinoceros, elephant, buffalo, waterbuck, reedbuck, hartebeest, oribi, kob, hippopotamus, warthog *Phacochoerus aethiopicus.*

c) White rhinoceros.

4. SABALOKA GAME RESERVE.

II.   *a*) Status : full protection of fauna and flora, though there is a very small human population on the western border and a narrow strip of cultivation along the Nile; also some risk of poaching because of the proximity of Khartoum.

b) Area : 115,000 ha.

c) Staff : only two guards, but frequent assistance given by a neighbouring Game Warden and his 5 scouts.

d) Budget : no details, but criterion should be covered by staff salaries and allowances.

III.   *Date established :* 1939.

Tourism : no special organisation but a number of visitors come from Khartoum.

IV.   *Altitude :* 800 m.

a) Rolling hilly country for the most part, on the left bank of the Nile; valleys with scattered *Acacia* bush and *Panicum turgidum* grassland; suitable habitat and an assured water supply in the nearby river for the wild sheep and ibex which the Reserve is specially designed to protect.

b) Aoudad or Barbary sheep *Ammotragus lervia,* ibex *Capra ibex* (reintroduced in 1948, after having vanished at the end of the last War).

5. MBARIZUNGA GAME RESERVE.

II.   *a*) Status : protection of fauna and flora; uninhabited region, with no poaching, but situated in the zone which is unfortunately at present in a disturbed state.

b) Area : 15,000 ha.

c) Staff : one game guard under the supervision of the Game Preservation Officer at Yambio and assisted by Forest Department staff.

d) Budget : provision for salaries covers criterion.

470

Date established : 1939.

Tourism : not yet developed.

Altitude : 800 m.

a) A rather flat area, though near the Congo-Nile watershed; woodland derived from equatorial rain forest; gallery forest; papyrus.

b) Bongo *Taurotragus eurycerus,* yellow-backed duiker *Cephalophus silvicultor,* giant forest hog, chimpanzee, colobus monkey.

6. BIRE KPATUA GAME RESERVE.

a) Status : protection of flora and fauna; no human occupancy; the Reserve is in the presently disturbed zone.

b) Area : 12,500 ha.

c) Staff : 2 game guards.

d) Budget : provision for salaries covers criterion.

Date established : 1939.

Altitude : 800 m.

a) Like No. 5 above is fairly flat country, though near the Congo-Nile watershed; rain forest with dense undergrowth.

b) Bongo (it is of interest that this animal is left alone by the local Zande people, who believe it carries leprosy !); yellow-backed duiker, elephant, buffalo.

7. TOKAR GAME RESERVE.

a) Status : total protection of flora and fauna, but a few people live in the area, which is free from political troubles and not far from the Red Sea; used for grazing domestic camels.

b) Area : about 12,500 ha, but another contradictory report gives the much larger figure of 650,000 ha.

c) Staff : a Game Officer and five game scouts are stationed not far away at Sinkat and devote more than half their time to this Reserve.

d) Budget : salary provision covers criterion.

Date established : 1939.

Altitude : 200 m.

a) Desert salt-marsh area near the Red Sea, including the periodically flooded Tokar delta, with some *Acacia tortilis* scrub and part of the less arid Karora hills with relicts of dense *Olea* sp., *Juniperus procera* and many interesting plants.

b) Ibex, a few gazelles including *Gazella rufifrons* and *G. soemmeringi,* roan antelope, greater kudu, leopard.

8. RAHAD GAME RESERVE.

a) Status : total protection; an uninhabited region adjacent to the Dinder National Park and near the Ethiopian frontier.

b) Area : about 12,500 ha, but again there are contradictory reports giving a much larger figure.

c) Staff : benefits from the proximity of the Dinder National Park and the fact that a Game Officer and five game scouts are based not far away and devote about 3 weeks per month to supervising this Reserve.

d) Budget : salary provision covers criterion.

III.　　　　*Date established :* 1939.

Tourism : a few people come to this Reserve when they are visiting the Dinder National Park.

IV.　　　　*Altitude :* 700 m.

a) Savannah; *Terminalia laxiflora, Sclerocarya birrea, Combretum harmannianum.*

b) Giraffe, hartebeest, reedbuck, oribi, ibex, roan antelope, bushbuck, Soemmering's gazelle, waterbuck, greater kudu, lion; ostrich.　Black rhinoceros also reported.

c) Black rhinoceros (?).

9. MONGALLA GAME RESERVE.

II.　　　　*a*) Status : free from human occupancy and exploitation, although situated in a strip of country 40 km long and 2 km wide between the Juba-Mongalla road and the Nile; the only disturbance comes from footpaths leading from villages on the other side of the road down to the river, but the Reserve is of course in the zone which is at present politically troubled and extensive seasonal poaching has been reported.

b) Area : 7,500 ha.

c) Staff : one Game Scout and two game guards responsible to the Game Protection Officer at Juba.

d) Budget : salaries of staff would cover criterion.

III.　　　　*Date established :* 1939.

IV.　　　　*Altitude :* 500 m.

a) The Nile riverine plain; well-scattered large trees, including dom palm *Hyphaene,* with no undergrowth, open grasslands in seasonally flooded areas; no obstruction to game-viewing; a favourite watering-place for wild animals during the dry season.

b) Elephant, buffalo, black rhinoceros; giraffe, zebra *Equus burchelli böhmi,* eland *Taurotragus oryx,* roan antelope, kob, reedbuck, waterbuck, bushbuck, lion, leopard, cheetah, hyaena; ostrich.

c) Black rhinoceros.

V.　　　**Areas excluded :**

As indicated in the General Introduction, it is probable that some of the nine Reserves detailed below deserve to be in the List as much as some of the six chosen, but the reasons for their exclusion are briefly mentioned.

1. Zeraf Game Reserve (1939).

675,000 ha; no permanent staff, but an annual patrol is undertaken by the Senior Game Officer at Malakal; designed for the protection of the Nile lechwe *Kobus megaceros* population between the Bahr el Jebel and Bahr el Zeraf and of the sitatunga *Tragelaphus spekei.*

472

2. Numatina Game Reserve (1939).

250,000 ha, but only 2 wardens; lies to the north-west of the Southern National Park and has a similarly good selection of large animals.

3. Bengaigai Game Reserve (1939).

150,000 ha, but only 2 wardens; thick forest with fauna similar to that of No. 6 Bire Kpatua, e.g. bongo.

4. Buma Game Reserve (1960).

135,000 ha, but only 2 wardens; a mountainous area on the Ethiopian frontier, north-west of Lake Rudolf, with exceptional concentrations of game animals tending to migrate into Ethiopia; there is a village on the plateau and grazing of domestic livestock; inaccessible by road during nine months of the year.

5. Shambe Game Reserve (1935).

100,000 ha, but only 2 wardens; near Lake Shambe, papyrus marshlands with some *Hyparrhenia/Setaria* grassland and savannah woodland; habitat of the Nile lechwe (now scarce); other large animals including a few black rhinoceros, giraffe, elephant, buffalo, etc.

6. Badigeru or Bandingilu Game Reserve (1935).

50,000 ha, but only one warden; marshland near the Nile, with poor *Acacia seyal* thorn savannah; situated north of the Mbarizunga Reserve, No. 4, and south of Bor; black rhinoceros, elephant, giraffe, buffalo, zebra, eland and lion.

7. Juba Game Reserve (1939).

30,000 ha, but lacking proper supervision except for visits of inspection from the Juba headquarters of the Game Department (Southern Region); remnants of deciduous woodland bordering the Nile, now mainly grassland with many water channels; also many villages in the Reserve; white rhinoceros, elephant, buffalo.

8. Ashana Game Reserve (1939).

30,000 ha, two guards, but the Dinka tribesmen use the Reserve to pasture their cattle; grassy plains, with some gallery forest and woodland savannah; designed specially for the protection of the giant eland.

9. Fanyikang Game Reserve (1939).

13,000 ha, but without proper supervision; situated on an island in the Nile sudd region, a little to the east of Lake No; lechwe, sitatunga.

117. SURINAM

Listed Areas : six.

1. Kaysergebergte Natural Reserve.
2. Coppename River (Raleigh Rapids) and the Voltzberg Natural Reserve.
3. Tafelberg Natural Reserve.
4. Wia-Wia Natural Reserve.
5. Coppename River-Mouth Natural Reserve.
6. Brinckheuvel Natural Reserve.

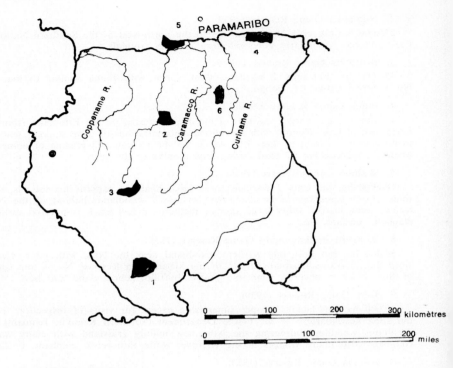

General Introduction :

Status : the legal basis is provided by the Natural Reserves Protection Ordinance of 3rd April 1954 (G.B. No. 26), applied by a Resolution of 22nd April 1966, under which all the six Reserves were established in their present form. Total protection is accorded and facilitated by the fact that the first three of the Parks listed were entirely uninhabited and the remaining three had very few people in them. There is still some poaching, shooting and fishing and some danger from outside pressure for mineral, forest and agricultural exploitation. The Coppename River-Mouth Reserve (No. 5) is perhaps the most threatened, because of its proximity to Paramaribo.

Staff and Budget : responsibility for supervision and maintenance lies with the Forest Service. It has not been possible to provide a break-down, but the total staff employed full-time on the Reserves amounts to one Forester and seven Assistants, and additional personnel of the Service are reported to be assigned to duties in the Reserves on a part-time basis. This situation can perhaps be accepted as sufficiently satisfying the criteria laid down for effective management on the grounds that the areas in which the Reserves are situated are largely unpopulated. The annual budget is quoted as being of the order of U.S. $ 10,000 plus irregular funds (part time salaries).

Administration : the Forest Service, which is responsible, belongs to the Ministry of Development. For this particular matter the Chief Conservator is assisted by a Foundation for Nature Preservation (" Stinasu "), replacing a former committee in 1969.

474

Tourism : undergoing development. The Wia-Wia reserve is not far from Paramaribo and accessible by boat.

Research : the Committee for Nature Protection based on the Surinam Museum at Paramaribo plays a part in co-ordinating studies undertaken in the various Reserves.

Surinam was not included in E/3436 or Part Two of the previous edition of the List.

Details : application of criteria (II), general information (III) and description (IV) :

1. KAYSERGEBERGTE NATURAL RESERVE (Eilerts de Haan gebergte).

   a), *c)* and *d)* Status, staff, budget : see general introduction.
   b) Area : 160,000 ha.

   Date established : 1966; see introduction for other details.

   Altitude : highest point about 1,000 m.

   a) and *b)* The flora and fauna are said to be a representative sample of those of southern Surinam; no other information.

2. COPPENAME R. (RALEIGH RAPIDS) AND VOLTZBERG NATURAL RESERVE.

   a), *c)* and *d)* Status, staff, budget : see general introduction.
   b) Area : 56,000 ha.

   Date established : 1961; see introduction for other details.

   Altitude : 50-360 m (the Voltzberg is 240 m and the Stockumberg 360 m).

   Tourism : guesthouses at Raleighvallen.

   a) Numerous falls and rapids; mesophile forest with granite outcrops, stony savannah, a peculiar flora including *Melocactus* sp. and other endemics.

   b) Smaller forest animals, the status of which has not noticeably improved since the area was put under protection; breeding colonies of herons, scarlet ibis *Eudocimus ruber*, roseate spoonbill *Ajaia ajaja*; the magnificent frigate-bird *Fregata magnificens* and black skimmer *Rynchops nigra* visit the area.

3. TAFELBERG NATURAL RESERVE.

   a), *c)* and *d)* Status, staff, budget : see general introduction.
   b) Area : 40,000 ha.

   Date established : 1966; see introduction for other details.

   Altitude : 500-1,026 m.

   a) Sandstone formations. More or less flat sparsely forested plateau, surrounded by a forest-covered pediment below a scarp; a few creeks feed a number of waterfalls; several endemic plant species.

   b) No information.

475

4. WIA-WIA NATURAL RESERVE.

II. *a), c)* and *d)* Status, staff, budget : see general introduction.

b) Area : 36,000 ha.

III. *Date established :* 1966; see introduction for other details.

IV. *Altitude :* near sea-level.

a) A sea-coast reserve with alluvial shelves, sand beaches, fresh and brackish water lagoons, swamp forest.

b) Breeding sea-turtles (*Chelonia mydas, Dermochelys coriacea, Lepidochelys olivacea*); sea-bird colonies, also scarlet ibis and flamingo *Phoenicopterus ruber).*

c) All the turtles.

5. COPPENAME RIVER-MOUTH NATURAL RESERVE.

II. *a), c)* and *d)* Status, staff, budget : see general introduction.

b) Area : 10,000 ha.

III. *Date established :* 1966; see introduction for other details; this reserve replaces an old one named the Bormoffo-Tonihollokreek reserve.

IV. *Altitude :* near sea-level.

a) Coastal area, similar to No. 4.

b) Scarlet ibis, brown pelican *Pelecanus occidentalis,* herons.

6. BRINCKHEUVEL NATURAL RESERVE.

II. *a), c)* and *d)* Status, staff, budget : see general introduction.

b) Area : 6,000 ha.

III. *Date established :* 1966; see introduction for other details.

IV. *Altitude :* 70 m.

a) Savannah on white clay (kaolin) soils; some low hills; the main interest of the reserve is geological and pedological.

b) There is nothing specially noteworthy about its fauna.

V. **Excluded from the List :**

1. Galibi Nature Reserve : 4,000 ha.

This reserve is reported to have been legally established in 1969 and may well justify inclusion in the next edition of the List. Its main purpose is to protect the nesting-ground of the endangered olive ridley turtle *Lepidochelys olivacea.*

2. Brownberg Nature Reserve : 11,200 ha.

Established in January 1970. May as well justify inclusion in the next edition of the List.

3. Sipaliwini Nature Reserve : 100,000 ha.

News of the enactment of legislation to establish the reserve and other details still awaited.

476

Listed Areas : one.

    1. Mlilwane Game Sanctuary.

General Introduction :

    According to an official leter dated 17 September 1964, there were at that time no statutory game reserves in the territory, nor was Swaziland mentioned in the previous edition of the U.N. List.

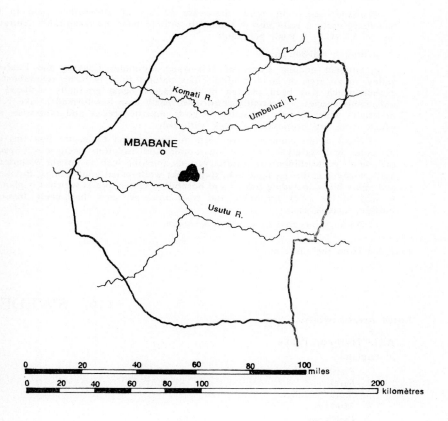

Details : application of criteria (II), general information (III) and description (IV) :

    1. MLILWANE GAME SANCTUARY.

    a) Status : private property, on which total protection is assured, but legislation is being prepared to back this protection with legal sanctions.

b) Area : 480 ha; this does not satisfy the criterion, but there is a plan to increase the size to 2,180 ha and it is felt that the private initiative shown in the creation of this sanctuary deserves official encouragement.

c) Staff : the proprietor, Mr. T. E. Reilly, who has been accorded by the Government the status of an Honorary Game Ranger and Forest Officer, employs two Game Rangers, a Gate Attendant and four Game Catchers, whose job is to capture animals for introduction into the Sanctuary.

d) Budget : U.S. $ 10,000.

III.   *Date established :* 1963.

Land tenure : private ownership; the land is fenced.

Tourism : access by road; there are 32 km of all-weather road in the Sanctuary itself, a rest-camp (6 rondavels with 18 beds, no restaurant) : entrance fee — 5/- (U.S. $ 0.60) per adult.

IV.   *Altitude :* 600-840 m.

a) Situated on the slopes of Nyonyane mountain flanking the Ezulwini valley, in an area of good rainfall. The natural flora is being re-established, exotics which had been planted in the reserve being gradually replaced by indigenous species. A recently constructed earth dam has formed a lake 1 km in length, which is very attractive to birds, aquatic species and otherwise, and which there are proposals to stock with fish.

b) Most of the animals have been introduced and to ensure that this can be done with safety there are quarantine and isolation enclosures : species include — white rhinoceros, giraffe, various antelope such as impala, waterbuck, kudu, bushbuck, duiker, reedbuck, springbok; white-tailed gnu; jackals; monkeys; and many birds, including ostrich and hornbills. Other species which it is planned to add to the stock are sable and roan antelope, oryx, hartebeest, tsessebe, buffalo, hyaena, etc.

c) White rhinoceros *Ceratotherium simum*.

V.   **Excluded from the List :** nil.

119. SWEDEN

I.   **Listed Areas :** twenty.

A. — NATIONAL PARKS :

a) Lapland :

1. Padjelanta.
2. Sarek.
3. Stora Sjöfallet.
4. Muddus.
5. Peljekajse.
6. Abisko.
7. Vadvetjåkko.

b) Central Sweden :

8. Sonfjället.
9. Töfsingdalen.

NIA

(photo : F. Vollmar/WWF)

TURKEY, Karatepe N.P.   (photo :

EY, Uludag N.P.   (photo : Z. Bayer)

AUSTRALIA (Tasmania), Cradle Mt.-Lake St. Clair N.P.

(photo : S. C. Hurley)

UGANDA, Queen Elizabeth N.P.   (photo : N. Myers

.., Oka R.

(photo : I. Koustantinov)

U.S.S.R., Oka R.

(photo : I. Koust▪

c) Southern Sweden :
  10. Gotska Sandön.

B. — STATE RESERVES :
  11. Reivo.
  12. Buberget.
  13. Tjuoltavuobme.

C. — NATURAL MONUMENT :
  14. Luletjarve.

D. — ZOOLOGICAL AND FOREST RESERVES :
  15. Sjaunja.
  16. Mittådalen.
  17. Svaipa.

479

E. — Private Reserves :
18. Komosse.
19. Haparanda Sandskär.
20. Lilla Karlsö.

General Introduction :

Administration : under the Nature Conservation Law of 1952, the Swedish National Parks are administered by the Council for Crown Domains in co-operation with the Royal Academy of Sciences.

Land tenure : the land in all the areas listed is state-owned with the exception of the three private reserves, which are the property of the Svenska Naturskydds-föreningen.

Scientific research : organised by the Royal Academy of Sciences in co-operation with the Universities and Museums. In most cases and notably in the reserves north of the Arctic Circle, research is undertaken on annual expeditions : these may be authorised in any of the National Parks, but are given special facilities in some of them, by way of accommodation and/or well-equipped research laboratories, the scientific station at Abisko (No. 6) being certainly the most noteworthy example. Research results are published in specialist journals and papers issued by the Academy of Sciences, Museums, Universities and learned Societies, etc.

Tourism : the administering authority makes arrangements for the reception and in some cases accommodation of visitors, of which details are given below.

Most of the listed areas and also those now placed in Section V were included in the previous edition, E/3436, of the List.

Details : application of criteria (II), general information (III) and description (IV) :
A. — NATIONAL PARKS.

a) **Lapland.**
1. Padjelanta.

II.
    a) Status : general protection, with certain rights still reserved for the Lapps.
    b) Area : 204,000 ha.
    c) Staff : one Superintendent is in charge of this Park, together with Sarek, Stora Sjöfallet and Muddus National Parks and Tjuoltavuobme State Reserve; there are four permanent Guards, occasionally reinforced by Forest Guards from the Pärlälven Range.
    d) Budget : U.S. $ 116,000, exclusive of staff salaries (1965 figure, which included provision for a large building programme).

III.
    Date established : 1962.

    Tourism : there is no road to the Park, but a track leading from Kvikkjokk, near which it is situated, to Vaisaluokta, serves a series of Lapp huts and encampments (Kåta) : there are seven tourist lodges, three of them with accommodation for 20 and the other four for four persons each.
    This Park was awarded the Council of Europe's 'European Diploma' on 27 October 1967.

IV.
    Altitude : 531-1,592 m.

    a) Mountainous area of Swedish Lapland, with valleys, lakes and glaciers; an interesting alpine flora, especially on the calcareous soils, which include three species not found elsewhere in Sweden — the sandwort *Arenaria humifusa*, *Potentilla hypartica* and the felwort *Gentianella aurea*.

480

b) Wolverine *G. gulo,* arctic fox *Alopex lagopus,* brown bear *Ursus arctos*; golden eagle *Aquila chrysaetos,* merlin *Falco columbarius,* rough-legged buzzard *Buteo lagopus,* lesser white-fronted goose *Anser erythropus.*

2. SAREK.

a) Status : as for No. 1 Padjelanta, which it adjoins : there is a Lapp encampment during summer in the south of the Park, for which certain hunting and fishing rights are reserved. Much destruction of habitat has been caused by building of dams for hydroelectric installations.

b) Area : 195,000 ha.

c) Staff : see under No. 1 Padjelanta.

d) Budget : about U.S. $ 8,500, exclusive of staff salaries.

Date established : 1909.

Tourism : access from Kvikkjokk (20 km away) but no motorable road; no accommodation in the Park, in which the going is rough.

The "European Diploma" was awarded jointly to this Park and No. 1 Padjelanta by the Council of Europe in 1967.

Altitude : 477-2,150 m.

a) A typical sample of the high altitude (above the coniferous forest zone) alpine region of Swedish Lapland — high plateaux, peaks, glaciers, rivers and lakes, meadows, marshes, heaths, glacial deposits; three vegetational zones of birch forest (subalpine), dwarf willow (lower alpine) and, on the high plateaux from 1,200-1,400 m, the upper alpine zone, dominated by lichens, above which snow prevails.

b) All the large Scandinavian carnivores, including lynx *Felis lynx* and wolf *Canis lupus,* as well as wolverine and brown bear, together with several herbivores such as moose *A. alces* and reindeer *Rangifer tarandus* (domesticated).

3. STORA SJÖFALLET.

a) Status : general protection, but certain Lapp rights persist, though kept to a minimum (reindeer husbandry, hunting, fishing); there is also much disturbance arising from a hydroelectric installation built in 1920, when some 12,000 hectares were excised for the purpose, and a further excision is being made for a second plant now under construction.

b) Area : 150,000 ha.

c) Staff : see under No. 1 Padjelanta.

d) Budget : U.S. $ 12,000, exclusive of staff salaries.

Date established : 1909.

Tourism : access by boat, but a road has been built : the tourist lodges are at Saltoluokta (76 beds), Stora Sjöfallet itself (40 beds), Suorva (28 beds), Vietas and Ritsemjokk (30 beds, plus tents).

Altitude : 375-2,013 m.

a) Mountains of Swedish Lapland, with a series of arctic and sub-arctic lakes and the cascades and great waterfall of Stora Sjöfallet; primeval Scots pine *Pinus sylvestris* and Norway spruce *Picea abies* forest at the lower levels, then birch *Betula tortuosa* in the subalpine zone and, dominating all, the high fjells.

b) Bear, wolf, wolverine, lynx, arctic fox; golden eagle, whooper swan *Cygnus cygnus.*

4. MUDDUS.

II.
a) Status : general protection, but some drainage works have been carried out in the Muddus river catchment and certain rights (reindeer husbandry, cutting of mature timber in the southern sector) are retained by the Lapps, although 9,700 ha are strictly if only seasonally protected from disturbance.

b) Area : 49,200 ha.

c) Staff : see under No. 1 Padjelanta.

d) Budget : U.S. $ 9,200, exclusive of staff salaries.

III.
Date established : 1941.

Tourism : access by road to the south-west border of the Park, thence only by footpaths; there are five cabin, hut and ' Kåta ' sites, with accommodation for 20 visitors in all. No access (except for special scientific purposes) to the protected zone of 9,700 ha, established as sanctuary for breeding birds, is allowed during the period 1 May-31 October.

The Park was awarded the Council of Europe's " European Diploma " on 27 October 1967.

IV.
Altitude : 160-661 m.

a) A plateau transected by a broad shallow valley of not more than 100-200 m in depth, but more sharply cleft to the south, where there are gorges and waterfalls; moraine action has formed the landscape and soils, leaving behind in some places 10-15 m high eskers; the whole Park is within the coniferous zone (*Picea abies* and *Pinus sylvestris*), though there is a frequent admixture of broad-leaved species, especially of *Betula* and *Salix,* and the forest area occupies 53 % of the surface; 45 % of the surface consists of the peatlands and marshes of the level areas and the remaining 2 % high fjell.

b) Nearly 100 species of birds, including the whooper swan (rare in Sweden); the brown bear occurs and most of the typical species of the *taiga,* peatlands and marshes, including wolverine, pine marten *M. martes,* weasel *Mustela nivalis,* otter *L. lutra,* lemming *L. lemmus* (occasional), water vole *Arvicola terrestris,* rat-headed vole *Microtus oeconomus,* field vole *Microtus agrestis,* red-backed vole *Clethrionomys glareolus,* shrews *Sorex* spp., water shrew *Neomys fodiens*; common lizard *Lacerta vivipara;* and adder *Vipera berus.*

5. PELJEKAJSE.

II.
a) Status : general protection, but a small Lapp encampment (13 families) is occupied in the summer and carries the usual reindeer grazing, hunting and fishing rights, which however have little effect.

b) Area : 14,600 ha.

c) Staff : one Forest Guard is especially posted to the Park and assisted by others from the Arjeplog Range.

d) Budget : U.S. $ 360, exclusive of staff salaries.

III.
Date established : 1909, but greatly enlarged (from only 200 ha) in 1913.

Tourism : no motorable roads, access by foot 5 km from the road at Jäkkvik village (where there is accommodation) to the Park border.

482

Altitude : 470-1,133 m.

a) A mountain massif with slopes covered by birch woods and lakes, marshes and alpine moorland on the plateaux.

b) Fauna typical of the zone surrounding the main Scandinavian mountain chain and still quite undisturbed.

6. ABISKO.

a) Status : general protection, with only minimal disturbance from Lapp reindeer husbandry, hunting and fishing rights; however, at the north end of the Park, near Lake Torneträsk, where electricity power lines and a railway traverse the area and there is a railway station, the large numbers of visiting tourists constitute some threat to the integrity of the Park.

b) Area : 7,500 ha.

c) Staff : one superintendent looks after the Abisko and Vadvetjåkko National Parks, assisted by one full-time Guard from the Jukkasjärvi Range.

d) Budget : U.S. $ 6,200, exclusive of staff salaries, shared with Vadvetjåkko.

Date established : 1909.

Tourism : active, with 8-10,000 visitors a year; accommodation for 200 people near the station on the railway line which crosses the Park and a special 9 ha tourist centre, developed by the Swedish Tourist Association; no motorable road.

Research : a scientific station, see General Introduction.

Altitude : 342-1,174 m.

a) A subalpine birch zone, succeeded by an alpine zone of dwarf willow and birch-scrub, meadows and boulder-fields; some orchids, which occur rarely in this northern region, are to be found.

b) Wolf, otter, weasel, varying hare *Lepus timidus*; plentiful birdlife.

7. VADVETJÅKKO.

a) Status : general protection, very occasional visits only by Lapp herdsmen who retain their reindeer grazing, shooting and fishing rights.

b) Area : 2,450 ha.

c) Staff : see No. 6 Abisko.

d) Budget : shared with No. 6 Abisko (q.v.).

Date established : 1920.

Tourism : access by water, no road; one mountain-hut.

Altitude : 420-1,109 m.

a) There is a subalpine birch forest zone, but the alpine meadow zone covers 80 % of the surface area : some traces have been found in one area of ancient human occupation.

b) The lake in this Park with its delta provides a refuge for large numbers of birds.

b) **Central Sweden.**

8. SONFJÄLLET.

II.   *a)* Status : general protection, domestic animals are occasionally brought in to graze.

b) Area : 2,700 ha.

c) Staff : one superintendent, also a full-time Guard shared between this National Park and Luletjarve Natural Monument.

d) Budget : U.S. $ 200, exclusive of staff salaries.

III.   *Date established :* 1909.

Tourism : access by road to Hede (12 km away), but no roads in the Park itself : accommodation can be found in neighbouring farms.

IV.   *Altitude :* 430-1,277 m.

a) An isolated massif separated from the Scandinavian mountain chain, hence its special biogeographical interest; coniferous forest, alpine grasslands.

b) A population of brown bear isolated from those of Swedish Lapland and of Jämtland Province.

9. TÖFSINGDALEN.

II.   *a)* Status : total protection, but occasional pasturage of reindeer, hunting and fishing by nomadic Lapps.

b) Area : 1,365 ha, which is below the criterion requirement for a sparsely inhabited country (Sweden has 17 inhabitants to the km^2); but as this Park is in the central part of the country and not in the unpopulated north, an exception seems justified.

c) Staff : a superintendent and a full-time Forest Guard from the Idre Range.

d) Budget : U.S. $ 200, exclusive of staff salaries.

III.   *Date established :* 1930.

Tourism : no roads in the Park, but access via Grövelsjön (15 km away), where there is accommodation for up to 100 persons.

IV.   *Altitude :* 670-900 m.

a) Morainic deposits, subdivided by fault blocks, and covered in primeval vegetation in three zones, the coniferous forest-zone of pine and spruce, the subalpine birch scrub and the alpine grasslands.

b) Brown bear, wolverine.

c) **Southern Sweden.**

10. GOTSKA SANDÖN.

II.   *a)* Status : total protection, except for a hundred hectares on the east where the lighthouse is situated and the lighthouse staff are allowed to cut wood.

b) Area : 3,535 ha; proposal afoot for an increase.

c) Staff : two special Forest Guards from the Gotland establishment, plus the lighthouse keeper.

d) Budget : U.S. $ 100, exclusive of staff salaries.

1.

Date established : starting with a 368 ha reserve in 1909, 3,167 ha were added in 1950, and the two units were given National Park status in 1963.

Tourism : access by boat (55 km from Fårösund); accommodation can occasionally be provided at the lighthouse.

Altitude : sea level.

a) A Baltic island off the north of Gotland, with evidence of phyto- and zoogeographical isolation; sand dunes tending to invade the primeval pine forest; among the 400 vascular plants, a few orchids.

b) Invertebrate fauna is of special interest, because of the favourable climate and abundance of old, decayed and dead timber in the virgin forest.

B. — STATE RESERVES.

11. REIVO.

a) Status : total protection, except for one sector where the Lapps concentrate their reindeer for culling; their encampments retain the traditional rights, but the adverse effects on the forested areas are reported to be small.

b) Area : 8,700 ha.

c) Staff : one superintendent and one Forest Guard.

d) Budget : no special allocation, but staff salaries are covered in the general departmental budget.

Date established : 1958.

Tourism : two roads give access; accommodation at Arvidsjaur (20 km away).

Altitude : 360-640 m.

a) Part of the Lapland plateau, covered in pine and spruce forest.

b) Typical *taiga* fauna.

12. BUBERGET.

a) Status : general protection; an uninhabited area and no apparent disturbance from people living in the neighbourhood.

b) Area : 2,270 ha.

c) Staff : a superintendent and a Forest Guard.

d) Budget : as for No. 11 Reivo.

Date established : 1958.

Tourism : one road traverses the reserve, the nearest village being Stensele, 40 km away.

Altitude : 500-600 m.

a) Hilly region in which the original forest was devastated by fire in the 19th Century, leaving only a few remnants; secondary growth of pines, firs and birch.

b) Typical *taiga* fauna.

13. TJUOLTAVUOBME.

a) Status : general protection, though the Lapps retain rights, seldom exercised, to pasture reindeer, hunt and fish.

485

b) Area : 1,500 ha, which is below the criterion requirement, this reserve being in Lapland a short distance from the Sarek National Park. Admitted as an adjunct thereto and because of its special biological interest.

c) Staff : see under No. 1 Padjelanta.

d) Budget : see under No. 1 Padjelanta.

III. *Date established :* 1952.

Tourism : access via Kvikkjokk (20 km away); no road in the reserve itself.

IV. *Altitude :* 500-1,440 m.

a) The southern flank of the Tjuolta fjell : primeval birch forest in the valleys, the largest subalpine sample in Europe, above which is a vast expanse of fjell.

b) Brown bear, lynx; a rich avifauna.

C. — NATURAL MONUMENT.

14. LULETJARVE.

II. *a*) Status : general protection; undisturbed forest, the residual Lapp rights or grazing, hunting and fishing being seldom exercised.

b) Area : 600 ha, but as this area is situated in central Sweden a criterion level of 500 ha has been accepted.

c) Staff : see under No. 8 Sonfjället.

d) Budget : as for No. 8 Sonfjället.

III. *Date established :* 1946.

Tourism : access from a road situated 30 km away; no roads within the area itself.

IV. *Altitude :* 544-792 m.

a) An area of pine and fir forest on the slopes dropping down to the Stora Mjölkvattnet.

b) Typical *taiga* fauna.

D. — ZOOLOGICAL AND FOREST RESERVES.

15. SJAUNJA.

II. *a*) Status : still not fixed, but birds are protected and total protection is planned.

b) Area : 290,000 ha.

c) Staff : not yet appointed.

d) Budget : none as yet. This and the two following Reserves have only been included in the List at the express wish of the Swedish authorities.

III. *Date established :* 1937.

Tourism : not yet developed; a new road passes along the south-east of the Reserve.

IV. *Altitude :* 441-1,720 m.

a) The biggest expanse of peatland in Europe outside Russia, but also many shallow lakes (the area is included in the MAR List of internationally important wetlands); some coniferous forest.

b) Ornithologically very rich, notably in respect of whooper swans, geese, duck and waders : golden eagle and white-tailed eagle *Haliaetus albicilla*; brown bear, lynx, wolverine, wolf.

16. MITTÅDALEN.

a) Status : total protection, except for hunting rights still retained by Lapps.

b) Area : 100,000 ha.

c) and *d*) Staff and Budget : none at present, see under No. 15 Sjaunja.

Date established : 1937.

Tourism : not yet developed; no roads.

Altitude : no information.

a) A complex of mountains, birch and conifer forest, lakes and rivers.

b) The fauna is typical of that of alpine, subalpine and boreal regions of Sweden.

17. SVAIPA.

a) Status : not yet settled.

b) Area : 49,400 ha.

c) and *d*) Staff and Budget : none at present, see under No. 15 Sjaunja.

Date established : 1937.

Tourism : not yet developed; no roads.

Altitude : 470-1,427 m.

a) In the subalpine and alpine zones, with birch forests, peatbogs, marshes and lakes surrounded by dense willow *Salix* thicket : the Tjålmejaure lake is notable for its numerous small islands, forming a subarctic archipelago.

b) Plentiful birdlife, notably lesser white-fronted goose, ducks and waders (including the Great Snipe *Gallinago media*).

E. — PRIVATE RESERVES.

18. KOMOSSE.

a) Status : total protection accorded by the proprietors, the Swedish Nature Conservation Society (Svenska Naturskyddsföreningen).

b) Area : 2,300 ha, well above the appropriate 500 ha criterion level for southern Sweden.

c) Staff : supervision given by the Forester at Jönköping.

d) Budget : U.S. $ 200 (1963).

Date established : 1949.

Tourism : there were 4,500 visitors in 1963.

Altitude : no information.

a) Peatland.

b) Many birds, including cranes *Grus grus* and golden plover *Pluvialis apricaria*.

487

19. Haparanda Sandskär.

II.   *a*) Status : total protection accorded by the Svenska Naturskyddsföreningen.

b) Area : 200 ha only, well below the criterion, but included at the request of the Swedish authorities because of the Reserve's special interest.

c) Staff : none specially appointed, but supervision undertaken by the Nature Conservation Society.

d) Budget : included in the general budget of the Society.

III.   *Date established :* 1961.

Administration : undertaken by the State Forest Department.

IV.   *Altitude :* sea level to 20 m.

a) An isolated islet in the extreme north of the Gulf of Bothnia; dunes, lagoons, various types of forest including an undisturbed sample of aspen *Populus tremula* forest.

b) Very interesting and varied flora and fauna (especially birds).

20. Lilla Karlsö.

II.   *a*) Status : total protection, under the Svenska Naturkyddsföreningen, which owns this uninhabited island.

b) Area : 150 ha, well below the criterion even for an area situated in a well-populated region (off Gotland), but admitted to the List as one of the most important bird sanctuaries in the Baltic.

c) Staff : a representative of the Society at Klintehamn, assisted by a Superintendent and a Guide stationed on the island from 1 June to 31 August.

d) Budget : U.S. $ 660 (1963).

III.   *Date established :* 1954.

Tourism : 2,000 visitors in 1963.

IV.   *Altitude :* sea level.

a) This Baltic island was an ancient pasturage for sheep.

b) An important bird sanctuary, especially for auks and gulls.

V.   **Excluded from the List :**

A. — Six National Parks, which even in a populous region are too small to satisfy the criterion :

Garphyttan	108 ha.
Ängsö	75 ha.
Blå Jungfrun	66 ha.
Dalby Soderskog	36 ha.
Hamra	27 ha.
Norra Kvill	27 ha.

B. — About 750 State Reserves of equally small dimensions, though totalling 50,000 ha altogether.

C. — About 320 Natural Monuments, averaging less than 10 ha in size and totalling some 3,000 ha.

488

120. SWITZERLAND

Listed Areas : three.

1. The Swiss National Park.
2. The Forest of Aletsch.
3. The Virgin Forest of Derborence.

General Introduction :

It is probable that some other areas, owned and managed by the Ligue Suisse pour la Protection de la Nature ought also to be included in the List, but is has not yet been possible to obtain the necessary information and reference should be made to the further remarks on the subject in Section V below. The Ligue Suisse does in fact also play a major role in respect of the three Listed areas, making a large contribution to the cost of maintaining the Swiss National Park, holding a long lease for the Forêt d'Aletsch and owning the Forêt Vierge de Derborence.

All three areas were briefly described in the previous edition, E/3436, of the List.

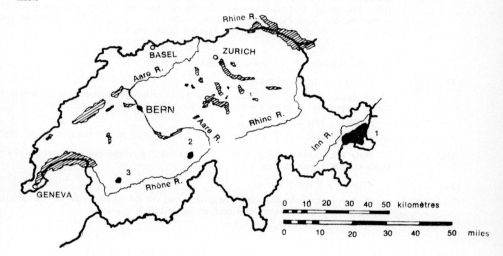

Details : application of criteria (II), general information (III) and description (IV) :

1. THE SWISS NATIONAL PARK.

a) Status : total protection.
b) Area : 16,887 ha.
c) Staff : 10 full-time, with several part-time assistants.
d) Budget : about U.S. $ 30,000 (Swiss francs 118,000) in 1962.

Date established : 1914.

Administration : by a 'Federal Commission for the Swiss National Park', responsible to the Inspectorate for Forests, Hunting and Fishing of the Federal Department of the Interior.

Land tenure : the land is leased from the Communes at an annual rental of 78,200 Swiss francs paid by the Confederation.

489

Tourism : entry free; there is a hostel ' Il Fuorn ' in the centre of the Park and hotels on the periphery, also a number of chalets (cluozza). About 10,000 visitors a years. Museum at Coire.

The Park was awarded the Council of Europe's 'European Diploma' on 27 October 1967.

Research : directed by a 'Commission for Scientific Studies in the National Park' and very active; more than thirty publications have been issued including a special Park handbook. The Swiss Society for Natural Sciences also plays an important role.

IV. *Altitude :* 1,500-3,173 m.

a) Part of the Grisons (Basse-Engadine) Alps, with a dry and continental climate; the vegetational zones are — subalpine to 2,300 m, alpine to 2,800 m and snow-zone above 2,800 m.

b) Ibex *Capra ibex,* red and roe deer *Cervus elaphus* and *Capreolus capreolus,* chamois *R. rupicapra*; marmot *M. marmota*; golden eagle *Aquila chrysaetus,* five species of Tetraonidae and the black and three-toed woodpeckers *Dryocopus martius* and *Picoides tridactylus* (rare) are among the 100 resident species of birds; a further 150 migrant species have been recorded.

2. The Forest of Aletsch (Valais).

II. *a*) Status : total protection.

b) Area : 256 ha; retained in the List, although below the criterion level for a populous country (Switzerland has 130 inhabitants per km^2).

c) Staff : one unit.

d) Budget : covered by the Ligue Suisse pour la Protection de la Nature.

III. *Date established :* 1933, when the Cantonal government approved a 99 year lease to the Ligue Suisse.

IV. *Altitude :* 2,100-2,300 m.

a) A forest of Arolla pine *Pinus cembra,* on the shady side of the mountain slopes closely overlooking the end of the Aletsch glacier.

b) Typical forest fauna.

3. The Virgin Forest of Derborence.

II. *a*) Status : total protection.

b) Area : 51 ha only, but retained in the List because of its special interest as the last remnant of virgin forest in Switzerland.

c) Staff : one unit.

d) Budget : covered by the Ligue Suisse pour la Protection de la Nature.

III. *Date established :* 1959, when acquired by the Ligue Suisse.

Research : undertaken by the Sylviculture Institute of the Federal Polytechnic College at Zurich.

IV. *Altitude :* 2,100-2,300 m.

a) Only remaining primeval forest in the Swiss Confederation.

b) Typical forest fauna.

490

V. **Excluded from the List :**

There are 466 other strict or partial reserves in Switzerland, 92 of them owned by the Ligue Suisse, which occupy a total area of 550 km². All the larger ones are only partial reserves and so do not satisfy the fundamental criterion of 'total protection'. The reserves which are in fact strictly protected are generally so small that one cannot very well overlook in their favour the criterion requirement of 500 ha, though it has been decided to make an exception in the case of the Aletsch (256 ha) and Derborence (51 ha) reserves, as noted above. It is arguable, that on grounds of outstanding scientific interest, an exception should have been made also in favour of the Combe Grède reserve (No. 10 below), which is situated in the Jura.

A sample of some of the more important of the areas omitted from the List can be enumerated as follows :

A. — Owned by the Ligue Suisse pour la Protection de la Nature :

1. Baldeggersee (Lucerne) . ... 529 ha.
This is one which, if the details were known, might qualify for the List.

2. Untersteiniberg or Breitlauenen (Berne) ... ...
3. Les Morteys (Vaud) ... ... 137 ha.
4. Hagleren-Seewenalp (Lucerne) ... ... 115 ha.
                                            45 ha.

B. — Areas partially protected by decree of the Cantonal Government of Berne :

5. Grimsel (alpine flora) ... ... 10,000 ha.
6. Lauterbrunnen Valley ... ... 2,630 ha.
This Reserve surrounds No. 2 above : Untersteiniberg.

7. Hohgant (prealpine forest and flora) . ... 1,504 ha.
8. Celtental (alpine flora) . ... 1,371 ha.
9. Fisi-Biberg-Fründe . ... 1,250 ha.
10. Combe Grède (see remarks above) ... ... 1,202 ha.
11. Heidenweg and Ile de Saint-Pierre on the Lac de Bienne ... 758 ha.
12. Engstigenfälle (waterfalls and forest) . ... 458 ha.
13. Etang de Gruyère . ... 124 ha.

C. — Areas partially protected by decree of the Cantonal Government of Neuchâtel :

14. Gorges de L'Areuse ... ... 950 ha.
15. Combe Biosse . ... 213 ha.

Listed Areas : nil.

121. SYRIA

Explanation :

Situation confirmed by private sources, no official reply having been received from the authorities in Damascus.

I. **Listed Areas :** eight.

A. — NATIONAL PARKS :
1. Serengeti National Park.
2. Ruaha National Park.
3. Tarangire National Park.
4. Mikumi National Park.
5. Gombe Stream National Park.
6. Arusha National Park.
7. Lake Manyara National Park.

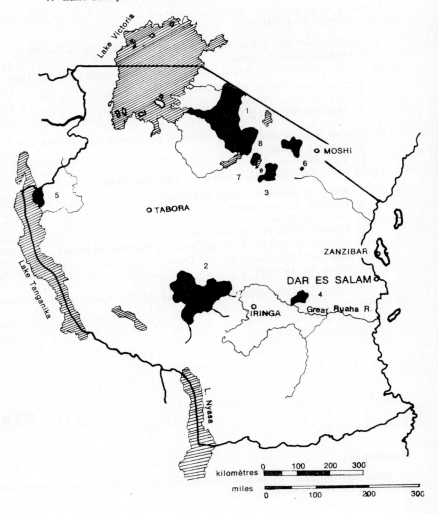

B. — CONSERVATION AREA :

    8. Ngorongoro Conservation Area.

General Introduction :

Legislation and administration : the legal basis of the National Parks is the National Parks Ordinance (Cap. 412 of the Laws), enacted on 24 June 1959, under which administration of the Parks is entrusted to a National Board of Trustees.

The Ngorongoro Conservation Area has hitherto been administered as a ' Unit ' by a Conservator, responsible to the Ministry of Lands, Forests and Wildlife, Dar es Salaam, and there is an Advisory Board composed of distinguished scientists with a knowledge of the area. The creation of this unusual type of protected area involved extensive legislation : the Ngorongoro Conservation Areas Ordinance of 1959 (Cap. 413 of the Laws), with an amending Ordinance in 1963, the Ngorongoro Conservation Rules of 1960, amended in 1962, and various Orders. A report has, however, been received at the time of going to press (1969) that a totally new status, placing the emphasis on ranching development, may shortly be promulgated.

The Game Reserves referred to in section V are constituted under the provisions of the Fauna Conservation Ordinance (Cap. 302 of the Laws).

Land tenure : state ownership.

Tourism : the main governmental body concerned is the Tanzania Tourist Corporation.

Research : in recent years the main effort has meen concentrated on the Serengeti area, where a big research programme is based on the Serengeti Research Institute, now established at Seronera under a Director with a staff of about 14 scientists. Financial support for this has been derived from many sources and since 1965 has amounted to several hundred thousand dollars annually, to cover capital and recurrent expenditure. Scientific Officers are also posted to the Arusha, Manyara and Tarangire National Parks.

Most of the listed areas were described in the previous edition, E/3436, of the List, although some of them at that time were Game Reserves and only later given National Park status. E/3436 also included the areas now placed, for various reasons indicated therein, in Section V below.

Details : application of criteria (II), general information (III) and description (IV) :
A. — NATIONAL PARKS.

1. SERENGETI NATIONAL PARK.

    a) Status : protection is total; Masai rights were annulled with compensation some years ago and, more recently, certain mineral rights (e.g. involving a small gold mine now closed down) have also been terminated; there are ' controlled hunting areas ' on the periphery, but outside the Park borders, which act as an effective buffer-zone.

    b) Area : 1,295,000 ha (about 5,000 sq.m.).

    c) Staff : about 50 units, well below the criterion, but 2 patrol aircraft are operated and, in present circumstances, the strength of the staff can be regarded as sufficient.

    d) Budget : U.S. $ 200,000 recurrent and over $ 250,000 capital (1969).

III.   *Date established :* the area was first protected in 1940, and became a National Park in 1951; completely reorganised in 1959, when a large section on the south-east was excised and incorporated in the Ngorongoro Conservation Area, but the Park was extended northwards, by a broad corridor, to the Kenya border, joining up with the important Kenya Masai-Mara Reserve.

Tourism : access is provided by roads crossing the Park from east to west and north to south; there is a 100-bed Safari Lodge at Seronera, a camp-site and a students' hostel; a landing-ground for aircraft near Seronera and several airstrips. About twelve thousand visitors a year; a museum, guides and brochures. A 100-bed hotel is now under construction at Lobo in the northern corridor and due to be completed in 1970 and further extensive accommodation is to be provided at Seronera and at Mara and Kirawira.

Research : see General Introduction.

IV.   *Altitude :* 1,100-2,200 m.

a) Vast grassland steppe, interspersed with areas of bushy and woodland savannah (especially *Acacia* spp.), gallery forest and hilly ranges, isolated hills and rocky ' kopjes '.

b) Astonishing concentrations of many more or less migratory herbivorous species, especially wildebeest *Connochaetes taurinus,* zebra *Equus burchelli,* and Grant's and Thomson's gazelle *Gazella granti* and *thomsoni*; hence the concomitant of exceptional numbers of lion, leopard, cheetah, hunting-dog and hyaena, *Panthera leo, P. pardus, Acinonyx jubatus, Lycaon pictus* and *C. crocuta*; also, notably, giraffe *Giraffa camelopardalis,* black rhinoceros *Diceros bicornis,* eland *Taurotragus oryx,* hartebeest *Alcelaphus buselaphus cokei,* topi *Damaliscus korrigum,* buffalo *Syncerus caffer* (48,000 at a recent census) and, in increasing numbers, elephant *Loxodonta africana.*

c) Black rhinoceros.

2. RUAHA NATIONAL PARK.

II.   *a*) Status : total protection (official letter of 18 December 1965).

b) Area : 1,150,000 ha (about 4,400 sq.m).

c) Staff : 30 units, including a warden and 20 rangers; supported by a patrol aircraft and judged, in the present circumstances, to be sufficient.

d) Budget : U.S. $ 36,000 recurrent, plus $ 24,000 capital (1969).

III.   *Date established :* 27 July 1964.

Tourism : still under development; access by road from Iringa (liable to be difficult during the rains from February to May), with a ferry over the Ruaha river at the Park entrance; Park headquarters at Msembe on the Ruaha, camping-sites near the Park entrance, self-help rondavels; airstrip.

IV.   *Altitude :* 750-1,250 m.

a) A region of plateaux, in which wooded areas of miombo (*Brachystegia/ Isoberlinia*) and acacia (especially *Acacia albida*) alternate with rocky ridges and open grassy depressions, which turn into swamps during the rains. Baobabs *Adansonia digitata* are common, but rather subject to damage by elephants.

b) Elephant, black rhinoceros, hippopotamus *H. amphibius,* buffalo, lion, sable and roan antelope *Hippotragus niger* and *equinus,* lesser and greater kudu *Tragelaphus imberbis* and *strepsiceros.*

c) Black rhinoceros.

494

3. TARANGIRE NATIONAL PARK.

a) Status : total protection; the proposal announced in an official letter of 7 September 1964 to upgrade the area to National Park status was implemented in 1969; it is uninhabited and situated in an area with a very small population.
b) Area : 261,440 ha (1,010 sq.m.).
c) Staff : 30 units including a warden and 20 rangers, with the use of an aircraft.
d) Budget : U.S. $ 24,000, plus $ 36,000 for capital expenditure (1969).

Date established : 1969, having been a Game Reserve since 1957.

Tourism : in the process of organisation; Arusha is only about 125 km away; a tented camp with 100 beds is open from June to December annually.

Research : the Game Department used to maintain a station for research into ecology, game census methods, etc., but this is not at present maintained, except by visits from the Serengeti Research Team and by the Park's own Scientific Officer.

Altitude : 1,000-1,800 m.

a) The ruling level of the plateau in which the Reserve is situated is not more than 1,200 m but there are scattered hills and the plateau is also dissected by the drainage line of the Tarangire river, which dries back to a series of pools during the dry season; most of the area is covered in acacia bush, and tsetse fly is prevalent.
b) Elephant, buffalo, black rhinoceros, wildebeest, zebra, eland, oryx *O. gazella*, impala *Aepyceros melampus,* lesser kudu, gerenuk *Litocranius walleri :* the Park is a dry season concentration area for migratory animals from the Masai steppe.
c) Black rhinoceros.

4. MIKUMI NATIONAL PARK.

a) Status : total protection (letter of 18 December 1965).
b) Area : 116,500 ha.
c) Staff : 2 wardens and 30 rangers, supported by a light aircraft.
d) Budget : U.S. $ 55,500 recurrent and $ 96,000 capital (1969).

Date established : 1965.

Tourism : still under development; access by tarmac road (the capital Dar es Salaam is only 256 km away), also an airstrip; new hotel (100 beds); tented camp with 16 beds, run by private enterprise; a well-stocked store.

Altitude : 540 m.

a) Part of the alluvial plain of the Mkata river, and part of the surrounding hills, with typical East African woodland savannah vegetation.
b) Elephant, hippopotamus, buffalo, lion, leopard, hyaena, wild dog, zebra, impala, eland, waterbuck, wildebeest, giraffe, hippopotamus.

5. GOMBE STREAM NATIONAL PARK.

a) Status : even prior to upgrading to National Park status, protection stated to be sufficient to meet requirements (letter of September 1964), although the right of fishermen from Lake Tanganyika to use the lake shore of the Reserve and cut firewood for drying their catch then continued. The upgrading implemented a Resolution, No. 11, adopted at IUCN's General Assembly in Nairobi in September 1963, which included a recommendation that entry should be strictly controlled.

    b) Area : 14,800 ha (61 sq.m.).

    c) Staff : 5 rangers.

    d) Budget : covered by National Parks budget, but amount not yet known.

III.   *Date established :* 1943, small extension in 1956; National Park 1968.

    Tourism : in process of organisation; access is by motor-boat, 1 ½ hours from Kigoma, and footpaths lead into the Reserve from the Lake Tanganyika shore.

    Research : highly important work on the chimpanzee population has been conducted for some years by Baroness van Lawick-Goodall and is continuing.

IV.   *Altitude :* 750-1,500 m.

    a) Part of the eastern escarpment dominating Lake Tanganyika, with *Brachystegia* forest on the lower slopes and thick gallery-forest along the watercourses and crest of the escarpment, in which the oil-palm *Elaeis guineensis* is an important constituent.

    b) Chimpanzee *Pan troglodytes* and red colobus *Colobus badius*; buffalo, waterbuck, bushbuck, leopard.

6. ARUSHA NATIONAL PARK.

II.   *a*) Status : total protection.

    b) Area : 12,940 ha (50 sq.m.).

    c) Staff : 40 units.

    d) Budget : U.S. $ 25,000.

III.   *Date established :* 1962, as the Ngurdoto Crater National Park (1,280 ha), enlarged by the incorporation of the Momela Lakes sector (with the assistance of international funds) in 1964 (6,480 ha) and now further enlarged by the inclusion of Mount Meru crater and summit and the purchase of two former farms, to its present status and size.

    Tourism : easy access from Arusha (40 km away) by tarmac and branch road; Momela Game Lodge, run by private enterprise, near the entrance, also rondavels, camp-site and stores; picnic-sites in the Park itself. From July 1963 to June 1964, the Park was visited by 7,000 people, 2,000 of them from abroad, increasing to 10,000 in 1968.

IV.   *Altitude :* 1,430-4,464 m.

    a) Rugged terrain, including summit of the fourth highest mountain in Africa, its crater, ash-cone and caldera, the subsidiary crater of Ngurdoto to the south-east and the swarm of lahar hillocks and dells blocking the drainage at Momela and creating a series of beautiful lakes; the latter are surrounded by grassland and there are some swampy areas, while the greater part of the Park is covered by mountain rainforest, including a bamboo zone, with moorland towards the rocky summit : much of the forest is degraded by former exploitation, but is regenerating.

    b) Elephant, black rhinoceros, hippopotamus, buffalo, eland, bushbuck *Tragelaphus scriptus*, waterbuck *Kobus ellipsiprymnus,* reedbuck *Redunca arundinum*; leopard; black and white colobus *Colobus polykomos*; rich bird life especially in the vicinity of lakes, over 350 species recorded.

    c) Black rhinoceros.

496

7. LAKE MANYARA NATIONAL PARK.

II.

a) Status : total protection.

b) Area : 8,550 ha (33 sq.m., which does not include the lake itself, approximately three times that area).

c) Staff : 2 wardens and 20 rangers and other staff.

d) Budget : U.S. $ 36,000 recurrent plus $ 20,400 capital (1969).

III.

Date established : 1960.

Tourism : access by motorable tracks along the lake shore; airstrip; a modern hotel is situated near but outside the Park, at the edge of the Great Rift wall overlooking the lake (200 beds, swimming bath); also a students' hostel and camping-sites; a museum. About 30,000 visitors a year.

IV.

Altitude : 950-1,800 m.

a) A salt-lake of the Great Rift, dominated on the west by the fault-scarp of the Rift wall, gallery-forest, acacia woodland, grassland and marshy areas at the mouth of inflowing streams.

b) Elephant, buffalo, black rhinoceros, zebra, impala, wildebeest, lion, leopard, hippopotamus; vast numbers of water birds, including two species of pelican *Pelecanus onocrotalus* and *rufescens* and two species of flamingo *Phoenicopterus ruber* and *Phoeniconaias minor*.

c) Black rhinoceros.

B. — CONSERVATION AREA.

8. NGORONGORO CONSERVATION AREA.

I.

a) Status : until 1966 the Area was divided into two sections, the Ngorongoro Controlled Area, where hunting and cultivation were prohibited and the movements of Masai pastoralists strictly controlled, especially in the ' crater '; and the Endulen Controlled Area, where local inhabitants were allowed to hunt and cultivate and pastoral activities were unrestricted. The former area was deemed to satisfy the criterion, according to an official letter of 19 October 1964, while the latter area did not qualify for inclusion. There is now a proposal for a complete reorganisation (see General Introduction) which unfortunately might make it impossible to retain this famous area in future editions of the U.N. List, with the possible exception of the crater floor, which may become more fully protected.

b) Area : 828,800 ha (3,200 sq.m.), of which perhaps about three-quarters can be regarded as reasonably undisturbed and effectively protected from a wildlife point of view, though hunting is as previously stated prohibited everywhere.

c) Staff : the large Conservation Area staff works as an integrated unit, but falls into three main groups under the over-all direction of the Conservator, concerned respectively with management (under a Chief Management Officer with a staff of about 100), research (the establishment is five officers) and general administration.

d) Budget : now about U.S. $ 150,000 for the whole organisation.

I.

Date established : 1959.

Tourism : adjoining the Serengeti National Park (No. 1) on the east, with access by three roads, plus a rough track from the south, the main road from

497

the Great North Road and Arusha having been reconstructed in 1962; Ngorongoro Crater Lodge (run by private enterprise) accommodates 105 people, Dillon's Lodge 42 and Kimba Lodge 60; also a Youth Hostel (40 beds) and camping on permit (about 200 permits issued annually). There is an airstrip in the crater. The number of visitors has risen from 7,394 in 1962, to about 10,000 in 1965 and 26,000 in 1967; a large staff of Masai guides and vehicles are available for hire.

IV. *Altitude :* about 1,220 to 3,648 m; 'crater' floor 1,500 m.

a) Ranging from dry plains, through bush, tropical rain forest and bamboos to high altitude moorland; there is a large salt-lake and smaller fresh-water lakes in the floor of the 'crater', which is in fact a vast caldera 24 km in diameter; several subsidiary craters and crater-lakes in the higher summits to the north of the area and considerable expanses of tussock *Eleusine jaegeri* and *Artemisia* thicket.

b) Black rhinoceros, buffalo, elephant, lion, leopard, wildebeest, zebra, Grant's and Thomson's gazelle, mountain reedbuck *Redunca fulvorufula*; bushpig *Potamochoerus porcus* and perhaps giant forest hog *Hylochoerus meinertzhageni*.

c) Black rhinoceros.

V. **Areas excluded :**

Six Game Reserves (exclusion based on official letters from Tanzania dated 7 September and 19 October 1964) :

1. Selous : 3,970,000 ha (15,332 sq.m.).

" Opened to very strictly controlled hunting via the Tanzania Wildlife Development Company and therefore cannot qualify for inclusion. Part of the north may become a National Park, but no action is being taken at present on the upgrading of this area. "

2. Rungwa River : 905,000 ha (3,500 sq.m.).

Formerly much more extensive (7,882 sq.m.), but the southern section has been excised to become the Ruaha National Park (No. 2 in the List) and the status of what remains does not justify inclusion.

3. Mkomazi Game Reserve : 350,000 ha (1,350 sq.m.).

" Presence of a large number of pastoralists... rules it out for consideration. "

4. Kilimanjaro Game Reserve : 186,000 ha (720 sq.m.).

" At present, in view of the necessity to shoot occasional animals, it probably does not qualify ", but " part of this Reserve will become National Park. "

5. Katavi Plain Game Reserve : 167,500 ha (650 sq.m.).

" There is a dispute over its boundaries and until this is settled... it should not be considered. "

6. Biharamulo Game Reserve : 116,000 ha (450 sq.m.).

Originally scheduled for inclusion, but the advice was later given to " delete this Reserve : limited hunting has been permitted... which will automatically disqualify it from consideration. "

Mention may also be made of the Sanctuary on Rubondo Island in Lake Victoria, which is in the process of becoming a full Reserve; fishermen who lived in it have been removed with compensation and a programme has been started to introduce endangered species from neighbouring areas and ensure their protection. There is also another small island sanctuary in the Lake, near Mwanza, known as the " Saa Nane Game Sanctuary ".

*
* *

Zanzibar island, with Pemba, does not at present contain any reserve which can be included in the List. One may mention, however, that

a) there are a number of forest reserves, some of them formerly exploited but now regenerating : Jozani, Masingini, Kichweli and, on Pemba, Ngezi;

b) there was formerly a rather strict reserve (no form of exploitation) on Pemba, but it was of small size (240 ha) and has since (May 1964) been affected by " pressure for more agricultural land ".

The IUCN General Assembly at Nairobi in September 1964, called on Zanzibar to give protection, by the preservation of some samples of their habitat, to the endangered endemic races of the red colobus and Livingstone's antelope or suni *Nesotragus moschatus.*

123. THAILAND

Listed Areas : nine.

A. — DECLARED NATIONAL PARKS :

1. Khao Yai.
2. Tung Slang Luang.
3. Pu Kradeung.

B. — NATIONAL PARKS WHICH HAVE BEEN CREATED AND WHICH ARE SUPERVISED, BUT HAD NOT (AS AT DECEMBER 1965) BEEN FORMALLY DECLARED :

4. Khao Salob.
5. Khao Luang.
6. Khao Phu Phan.
7. Doi Pui.
8. Larn Sang.
9. Khao Samroiyod.

General Introduction :

The legal basis for National Parks is the National Park Act of 1961, under which a Park only becomes finally established when it has been 'declared' as such, but its constitution has to be previously approved by a resolution of the Council of Ministers.

This explains why the first three National Parks are listed under 'A' above as officially declared, while the remaining six under 'B' had still, by the end of 1965, only reached the stage of a proposal approved by Resolution of the Council of Ministers on 7 October 1959. The status of one of them, however, No. 4 Khao Salob, unlike the other five in group 'B', derives from Land Code legislation of 1954. It should be noted that the October 1959 Resolution also proposed a number of other Parks not admitted to the List (for reasons explained below in Section V).

Administration of all Parks is undertaken by the Royal Forest Department and the land is held in public ownership. Tourist facilities are in the course of development, as indicated below, including in some areas permission to fish for sport. There is no particular provision at present for the promotion, co-ordination or implementation of scientific research programmes in the National Parks.

The previous edition of the List gave a brief description of five areas, three of them corresponding to the three in group 'A' (with minor variations in respect of size and shape), the fourth being Khao Salob (then given as 204,796 ha in size as opposed to the 400,000 ha now quoted) and the fifth being the Doi Intanon National Park, which is not yet as far advanced towards full establishment as the six Parks admitted under group 'B' (see Section V below).

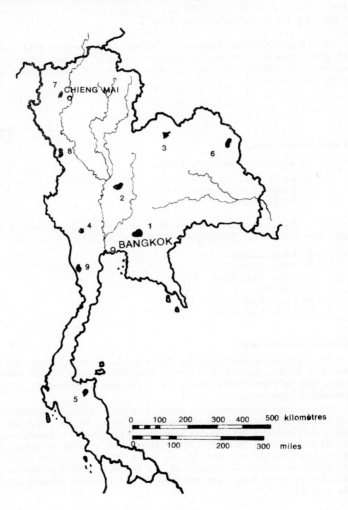

Details : application of criteria (II), general information (III) and description (IV) :

A. 1. KHAO YAI NATIONAL PARK.

a) Status : total protection accorded by regulations enacted in 1961, which forbid all settlement, cultivation, wood-cutting, etc., but nevertheless allow certain local user-rights to continue. It is expected that some 50,000 ha of the higher levels of the Park will, however, be given " total sanctuary " status.

b) Area : 216,875 ha.

c) Staff : 60 units.

d) Budget : U.S. $ 16,000 per annum.

Date established : 18 September 1962.

Tourism : situated in a heavily populated region, access to the Park is by road, a special 40 km branch road known as the Dhanarajata having been constructed to link its centre with the 'Friendship Highway'. There is also a helicopter-pad. A local 'Khao Yai National Park Development Committee' has been set up. Bungalows and camping facilities are provided and the Tourist Organisation of Thailand (T.O.T.) plays an important role, e.g. in running a large restaurant. There is also a golf course, the construction of which has led to some serious soil erosion.

Altitude : 800-1,328 m.

a) A mountainous area with streams and waterfalls. Vegetation includes *Dipterocarpus, Calamus* palms, the Australasian conifer *Dacrydium,* bamboos and ferns. Orchids and other epiphytes abound.

b) Elephant *Elephas maximus,* sun bear *Helarctus malayanus,* deer (including sambar *Cervus unicolor* and barking deer *Muntiacus* sp.), wild boar *Sus scrofa,* gaur *Bos gaurus,* langur *Presbytis* sp., gibbon *Hylobates* spp., tiger *Panthera tigris*; many colourful birds, including three species of hornbills, woodpeckers and the emerald dove *Chalcophaps indica.*

2. TUNG SLANG LUANG NATIONAL PARK.

a) Status : total protection, under 1961 regulations; no pressure from human activities.

b) Area : 128,000 ha.

c) Staff : 65 units.

d) Budget : U.S. $ 15,000 per annum.

Date established : 29 January 1963 (the name being also sometimes quoted as Tung Salang Luang.

Tourism : access is by road or rail : there is a guest-house and some 'cabins', with hotels 64 km away at Pitsanulok.

Altitude : 800 m.

a) Tropical forest, mainly coniferous, with *Dipterocarpus, Quercus,* rhododendrons and orchids; some open meadows.

b) Elephant, gaur, sambar, mouse-deer *Tragulus javanicus,* wild boar, gibbon; many birds.

3. PU KRADEUNG NATIONAL PARK.

a) Status : total protection, under 1961 regulations.

b) Area : 34,813 ha.

c) Staff : 20 units.

d) Budget : U.S. $ 13,000 per annum.

III.   *Date established :* 23 November 1962, having been a forest reserve since 1947.

Tourism : access by road or rail; guest-house and cabins.

IV.   *Altitude :* about 1,350 m.

a) Subtropical conifer forest (*Pinus khasya* and *Pinus merkusii*), meadows, rhododendrons dominating one fairly level plateau area; some waterfalls, caves and sandstone cliffs.

b) Sambar, mouse-deer, wild boar, langur, gibbon; the birds include pheasants.

B. 4. KHAO SALOB NATIONAL PARK.

II.   *a*) Status : it is proposed to accord total protection but to allow sport-fishing.

b) Area : 400,000 ha.

c) Staff : 29 units.

d) Budget : U.S. $ 7,500.

III.   *Date established :* proposed as a National Park in 1959, and organised as such in 1961, under various names — Khao Salorp, Erawan (= elephant) and Sai Yoke.

Tourism : access by road and rail from Bangkok; open during hours of daylight only. There are some small hotels at Kanburi, 60 km away, with only camping facilities in the Park itself (although accommodation is to be constructed).

IV.   *Altitude :* 160-950 m.

a) Mountainous area, with waterfalls, picturesque grottoes and evergreen forest, mainly *Dipterocarpus,* but also many medicinal and ornamental plants, including orchids and bamboos.

b) Rhinoceros, elephant, bear, deer, gaur, tiger, leopard *Panthera pardus* and wild boar; birds include pheasant, jungle-fowl *G. gallus* and peacock *Pavo cristatus.*

c) Sumatran rhinoceros *Didermoceros sumatrensis,* is reported to be still found in this area.

5. KHAO LUANG NATIONAL PARK.

II.   *a*) Status : it is proposed to give total protection under the regulations enacted in 1961.

b) Area : 205,600 ha.

c) Staff : 11 units.

d) Budget : U.S. $ 5,000 per annum.

III.   *Date established :* proposed as a National Park in 1959 and organised as such in 1965.

Tourism : access is by rail; only camping facilities available.

IV.   *Altitude :* 150-1,550 m.

a) A mountainous landscape, with fine waterfalls and tropical evergreen forest; tin deposits occur.

b) Rhinoceros, elephant, sambar, mouse-deer, bear, gaur, banteng *Bos banteng*; plentiful birdlife.

c) Sumatran rhinoceros.

6. KHAO PHU PHAN NATIONAL PARK.

   a) Status : total protection is proposed.

   b) Area : 131,500 ha.

   c) Staff : 33 units.

   d) Budget : U.S. $ 8,500 per annum.

Date established : proposed for Park status in 1959 and organised as such in 1961.

Tourism : access by road and rail : the Sakol Nakorn to Kalsin road traverses the Park. There are some inns at Sakol Nakorn, but at present (1968) this is a 'disturbed area' and a visit is out of the question.

Altitude : 180-630 m.

a) Mountainous area, with both evergreens and deciduous forest species, including dipterocarps, epiphytes, bamboos and ferns.

b) Elephant, gaur, sambar, swamp-deer, wild boar, bear, langur and other species of monkey; plentiful birdlife.

7. DOI PUI NATIONAL PARK (Doi Suthep).

   a) Status : total protection is proposed.

   b) Area : 16,000 ha.

   c) Staff : 27 units.

   d) Budget : U.S. $ 4,650.

Date established : more often referred to as Doi Suthep (the mountain on which it is situated, the second highest in Thailand) this area was proposed for Park status in 1959 and organised as such in 1962.

Tourism : access by train or air, the Park being in the vicinity of the economically flourishing centre of Chiengmai, where there are several good hotels.

Altitude : 1,450 m.

a) Hills and small mountains, forest covered with species of *Pinus, Quercus,* rhododendrons, epiphytes, ferns and flowering plants.

b) Wild boar, gibbon, several kinds of monkey including langur, sambar, mouse-deer; plentiful birdlife.

8. LARN SANG NATIONAL PARK.

   a) Status : total protection is proposed.

   b) Area : 14,200 ha.

   c) Staff : 35 units.

   d) Budget : U.S. $ 5,500 per annum.

Date established : proposed for National Park status in 1959 and organised as such in 1964.

Tourism : access is by road and the Park is about 15 km from a well-developed area of Tak Province and in the immediate vicinity of a " hill-tribe development region ", four hill-tribe settlements being established nearby. There is a guest-house and camping facilities, with inns at Tak provincial headquarters.

IV.   *Altitude :* 140-1,230 m.

a) Mountainous region, with waterfalls, mixed deciduous forest and pure stands of deciduous dipterocarps; also some evergreen forest, medicinal plants and orchids.

b) A race of the Sumatran serow *Capricornis sumatraensis,* gaur, elephant, mouse-deer, sambar; the birdlife is probably specially interesting, but as yet has hardly been studied.

9. KHAO SAMROIYOD NATIONAL PARK.

II.   *a)* Status : general protection afforded by the National Reservation Act of 1963.

b) Area : 6,128 ha.

c) Staff : 30 units.

d) Budget : U.S. $ 4,650.

III.   *Date established :* proposed for National Park status in 1959 and organised as such in 1963, in which year it was also declared as a reserve under The National Forest Reservation Act; formally established 1966.

Tourism : access is by road and rail; only camping facilities are available, but accommodation is still to be constructed.

IV.   *Altitude :* 150-460 m.

a) A mountainous region, with evergreen forest, some well-known grottoes, limestone scarps and very picturesque waterside areas.

b) Sambar, mouse-deer, langur and other species of monkey, bear, wild boar; the very interesting avifauna includes several seabirds; the rare Malay sand-plover *Charadrius peroni* has been recorded.

V.   **Areas excluded :**

1. Khao Sabarp : 10,000 ha with 7 staff units and an annual budget of U.S. $ 1,650. This area almost merits inclusion in the List, since supervision is adequate, but it still needs legislative action to give it a proper measure of protection.

2. Nam Nao : 58,800 ha; no details available.

3. Doi Intanon : 13,200 ha, which is close to the figure quoted in the previous edition of the List, E/3436. But the definition of the boundaries is still causing difficulty and the Park is under threat from a proposal for large installations on the summit of this mountain, which is the highest in Thailand.

4. Khoon Tarn : 11,700 ha; was scheduled for establishment as a Park in 1966, but it is not known if this was implemented.

5. Khao Kitchagoot : 10,400 ha.

None of these last four had (as at October 1965) been given the staff and budget which would be appropriate, merely receiving some supervision from local Forest Department personnel.

Other areas excluded from the List which deserve brief mention are :

Pukae Botanic Gardens (listed in the previous edition, E/3436).

Eleven arboretums.

Sundry game reserves or game sanctuaries set up under the Wild Animals Reservation and Protection Act, 1960.

Eighteen "forest-parks" developed for touristic purposes in the vicinity of towns.

124. TOGO

Listed Areas : three.

1. The Koué strict faunal reserve (part of the Fazao-Malfacassa forest reserve).
2. The Kamassi hunting reserve (also in the Fazao-Malfacassa forest reserve).
3. The Kéran hunting reserve.

General Introduction :

The protection of the Fazao-Malfacassa area, in which two other reserves are situated, was secured in the case of the Fazao sector (162,000 ha) by a Decree of 15 April 1954 and, for the Malfacassa sector (30,000 ha) by a Decree of 19 June 1951. Hunting in a protected forest had already been prohibited by General Decree No. 1214 of 24 March 1943. However, still stricter protection of the fauna was provided, when the two special reserves of Koué and Kamassi were created.

Administration : by the Service des Eaux, Forêts et Chasses of the Ministry of Rural Economy.

Land tenure : state ownership.

Tourism : in the process of being organised; the National Development Plan includes an item for this purpose.

Research : the faunal wealth of the country was first analysed and described by Dr. Brinn in 1945 and, twenty years later, a sum of U.S. $ 2,800 was allocated for technical studies and other purposes (see under Koué Reserve below), while at the request of the Togo Government a U.N. expert on fauna and nature reserves was made available for a period of twelve months.

Both the listed areas were included in Part Two of the previous edition of the List.

Details : application of criteria (II), general information (III) and description (IV) :

1. KOUÉ RESERVE.

a) Status : uninhabited zone, where human occupancy and exploitation, including hunting, are prohibited, but limited rights to collect dead wood still exist, although this is a protected forest area.

b) Area : 40,000 ha (out of the 192,000 ha of the protected Fazao-Malfacassa forest as a whole).

c) Staff : 4 units, plus 4 others at the Fazao forest station.

d) Budget : staff salaries would satisfy the criterion requirement, but it may be noted that of the U.S. $ 2,800 allocated in 1965 to finance technical studies in the reserves and to rehabilitate the forest generally, a proportion was allocated to Koué Reserve, as was an additional sum for capital equipment.

III. *Date established :* no information.

IV. *Altitude :* 250-730 m.

a) Part of the Fazao-Malfacassa Protected Forest, taking in a large section of the Fazao massif, which dominates the Bassari plain, to the west, by a line of cliffs some 500 m high and is distinguished generally by its very steep slopes; the massif is covered by more or less thickly wooded savannah and penetrated by narrow strips of gallery forest; at its foot there are beautiful savannah woodlands. This chance assemblage of natural geographical features combines to produce a very attractive area from the tourist point of view.

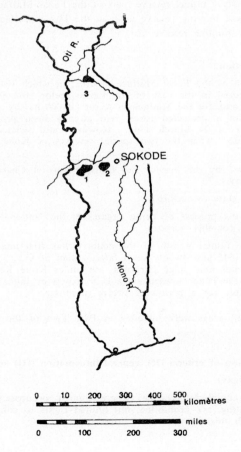

b) A large and varied fauna : elephant *Loxodonta africana,* buffalo *Syncerus caffer* (300-400), many antelopes including Buffon's kob *Kobus kob,* Defassa waterbuck *Kobus defassa,* Bohor reedbuck *Kobus redunca,* hartebeest *Alcelaphus buselaphus,* bongo *Taurotragus eurycerus,* sitatunga *Tragelaphus spekei,* roan *Hippotragus equinus* and yellow-backed duiker *Cephalophus sylvicultor;* forest genet *Genetta maculata;* warthog *Phacochoerus aethiopicus,* lion and leopard *Panthera leo* and *pardus;* gorilla *G. gorilla,* chimpanzee *Pan troglodytes,* various colobus monkeys, baboon *Papio papio* and many other monkeys *Cercopithecus* spp., *Erythrocebus patas,* etc.; hippopotamus *H. amphibius;* birds include the saddle-bill and marabou storks *Ephippiorhynchus senegalensis* and *Leptoptilus crumeniferus,* herons, little and cattle egrets *Egretta garzetta* and *Bubulcus ibis,* secretary-bird *Sagittarius serpentarius* and vultures.

2. KAMASSI HUNTING RESERVE.

a) Status : as for No. 1 Koué Reserve (q.v.).

b) Area : 17,000 ha (included in Fazao-Malfacassa Protected Forest).

c) Staff : 11 units, stationed at the Malfacassa, Baghan and d'Ayengré forest stations.

d) Budget : as for No. 1 Koué Reserve (q.v.).

Date established : no information.

Altitude : 200-840 m.

a) General features identical with those of the neighbouring Koué Reserve (see No. 1 above).

b) As for No. 1 Koué Reserve.

3. KÉRAN HUNTING RESERVE.

a) Status : classified by Decree as a Forest and Faunal Reserve; no human occupancy.

b) Area : 6,700 ha.

c) Staff : three full-time guards, posted respectively to Kéran, Naboulgou and Péssidé.

d) Budget : staff salaries satisfy criterion.

Date established : no information.

Altitude : about 150 m.

a) A fairly flat area at the confluence of the Kéran and Koumoungou rivers; gallery forest and more or less woody savannah.

b) Roan, Buffon's kob, Defassa waterbuck, buffalo.

Areas excluded :

Two reserves which are planned but not yet properly established :

1. The Oti Reserve (Borghou-Mandouri Forest).
2. Dongh Reserve (said to be at an advanced stage of planning).

125. TRINIDAD AND TOBAGO

I.   **Listed Areas :** nil.

V.   **Explanation :**

The exclusion from the List of the following areas is based on an official reply from Trinidad dated February 1966 :

A. — Nature Reserves, which are too small in size to meet the 500 ha criterion (Trinidad has 170 inhabitants to the km²) :

Caroni Swamp Reserve	283 ha.

This is part of the Caroni Swamp Forest Reserve, strictly protected for its breeding water-birds, especially scarlet ibis; it is planned to enlarge the sanctuary to 2,800 ha, in which case it would probably qualify for the List.

Mora Forest Nature Reserve (Melayo)	235 ha.
Tumana Hill Nature Reserve	131 ha.
Mount Harris Nature Reserve	17 ha.
Brickfield Nature Reserve	16 ha.
Blue Basin	1 ha.

B. — Game Sanctuaries, in which only the fauna is protected. The total list is eleven, of which one (Morne L'Enfer) has ceased to be of interest following the discovery and exploitation of oil; the four which are over 1,000 ha in area are :

Trinity Hills Game Sanctuary	6,672 ha.
Valencia Game Sanctuary	2,784 ha.
Central Range Game Sanctuary	2,064 ha.
Southern Watershed Game Sanctuary	2,023 ha.

C. — Forest reserves, totalling 153,800 ha or 30 % of the surface of the islands (530,000 ha). The largest of them, the Victoria-Mayaro Forest Reserve, is 53,263 ha.

The duty of looking after the fauna in these three classes of reserves is vested in a corps of 10 guards under a Senior Game Warden, who is responsible in turn to the Conservator of Forests *ex officio* Chief Game Warden.

126. TUNISIA

I.   **Listed Areas :** one.

1. Bou-Hedma State Park.

General Introduction :

Administration of Parks and Reserves is vested in the Forest Service of the State Secretariat for agriculture. The land is State Forest land. The title of 'State Park' is elsewhere in official correspondence replaced by the more usual term 'National Park', the latter also being used in the official 1 : 200,000 map of the country.

508

There is no special provision yet for tourists, but access is easy. A research programme is likely to be launched as a result of a recent initiative of the Section on Conservation of Terrestrial Communities of the International Biological Programme.

The Bou-Hedma National Park, as well as the two Forest Reserves now placed in Section V, were described in the previous edition, E/3436, of the List.

Details : application of criteria (II), general information (III) and description (IV) :

1. BOU-HEDMA STATE PARK.

a) Status : total protection, but the vegetational cover has been seriously degraded (for example gum-trees *Acacia tortilis* reduced to 10 ha) by the illegal grazing of sheep and goats. Success has been achieved in removing the people who used to live in the Park, but the removal of their flocks and herds has run into great difficulties. There is a proposal to fence the southern boundary and in fact the Administration seem to be doing all in their power to rehabilitate the area by replanting the acacias and introducing eucalypts and then protecting them sternly against invading domestic animals.

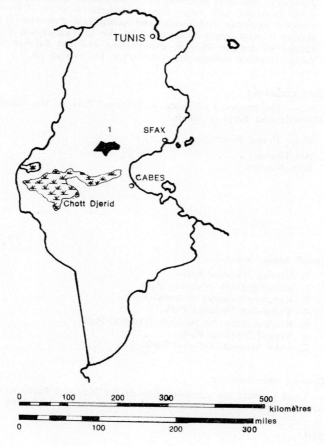

b) Area : 11,625 ha, but in fact only 10,300 ha if remaining inhabited enclaves on the boundary are excluded.

c) Staff : one Officer stationed at Bou-Hedma and a Warden.

d) Budget : staff salaries covered and an annual allocation made under the heading of " game ".

III. *Date established :* 1936, but the actual boundaries could not be fixed until the Sfax Land Court pronounced judgment in 1961.

IV. *Altitude :* 90-821 m.

a) Relict population of gum-acacias (*Acacia tortilis* Forssk.), of particular botanical interest because they combine characters of both *A. spirocarpa* and *A. raddiana*); they constitute a sample of forest-steppe on a plateau sheltered from northerly winds by the Jebel Bou-Hedma range; the flora is rich and varied, with steppe associations dominating the foothills and remnants or juniper forest.

b) Gazelles *Gazella dorcas* survive on the plains and Barbary sheep *Ammotragus lervia,* of the typical race, on the mountains; various rodents, including porcupine *Hystrix* sp., gundi *Ctenodactylus gundi,* gerbils *Gerbillus* sp., jerboas *Jaculus* sp. and jirds *Meriones* sp.; birds include a few houbara bustards *Chlamydotis undulata* and many cream-coloured coursers *Cursorius cursor,* stone curlews *Burhinus oedicnemus* and sandgrouse *Pterocles* spp.; two species of special interest which occur nowhere else in Tunisia are the Mauritanian subspecies of magpie *Pica p. mauretanica* and the fulvous chatterer *Turdoides fulvus*; reptiles include the dabb-lizard *Uromastyx* sp.

V. **Areas excluded :**

A. — The proposed Ghardimaou National Park on the Algerian border, with its oakwoods and Barbary sheep.

B. — Forest Reserves :

Aïn Draham	1,300 ha
Bou Kornine	900 ha

127. TURKEY

I. **Listed Areas :** seven.

1. Uludag National Park.
2. Kuşadasi-Dilek National Park.
3. Karatepe-Aslantaş National Park.
4. Yedigöller National Park.
5. Kizilçahamam or Sogüksu National Park.
6. Yozgat National Park.
7. Lake Manyas National Park.

General Introduction :

Until recently the administration of the National Parks was vested in the sixth department of the Forest Service, but since the end of 1966 is reported to hav been given greater autonomy. The legal basis for the Parks is a law enacted in 1956. All the land contained in them is in State ownership, with the exception of a few pieces of private property.

Research : mainly sponsored by the Universities of Istanbul, Ege (Izmir) and Ankara.

Tourism : now being promoted jointly by the Forest Service, Ministry of Tourism and private organisations; the section of the National Five-Year Plan dealing with National Parks in general emphasises the tourist aspect.

With regard to the criteria it should be noted that although Turkey as a whole has only 33 inhabitants per km², the figure for the western part of the country where all the Listed Areas are situated is well above 50, so that a minimum size criterion of 500 ha has been accepted.

Four of the Listed Areas only (Nos. 3, 5, 6 and 7) were described in the previous edition, E/3436, of the List.

Details : application of criteria (II), general information (III) and description (IV) :

1. ULUDAG NATIONAL PARK.

a) Status : protection is in theory total, with no hunting or extraction of timber, but about half the Park area is still grazed by domestic cattle and goats, the removal of which is being attempted but proving difficult; there is also a sanatorium and a wolfram mine within its boundaries.

b) Area : 27,300 ha, of which it is proposed to fence off 14,875 ha as a strict nature reserve.

c) Staff : a director, two Parks officers, 8 guards and a driver.

d) Budget : apart from salaries the following expenditure has been reported — U.S. $ 14,000 (1963), 41,000 (1964) and 22,000 (1965) : there is an allocation of $ 300,000 in the Five-Year Plan.

Date established : 1961.

Tourism : considerable development effort; a wide tarmac road gives access from Bursa, as does a cable-car which takes visitors up to the reception centre where there are several hotels; from here there are roads and footpaths, ski-lifts and ski-runs; many well-managed camp-sites, picnic places and parking-places. Entry is free. Some sectors are fenced in, notably an 80 ha strongly netted enclosure where game animals are fed and reared.

Altitude : highest point 2,543 m.

a) Situated to the south of Bursa on the slopes of Mt. Uludag, a mainly granitic massif of considerable geological interest : traces of former glaciations; the ecosystems comprise a series of vegetational zones from the Meditterranean littoral type to the snow-zone, dominant species in order of altitude being laurel, chestnut, beech, pine (mainly *Pinus nigra*) and silver fir *Abies alba,* and Norway spruce *Picea abies.*

b) Brown bear *Ursus arctos,* wolf *Canis lupus,* fox *V. vulpes,* wild pig *Sus scrofa,* jackal *Canis aureus*; a good avifauna.

2. KUŞADASI-DILEK NATIONAL PARK.

a) Status : total protection.

b) Area : variously quoted as 10,700 ha and 16,000 ha.

511

c) Staff : a Ranger and four guards.

d) Budget : staff salaries, to which it was proposed to add a sum for other expenditure with effect from 1966; allocation in the Five-Year Plan U.S. $ 27,500.

III.   *Date established :* 1966.

Tourism : the ancient ruins and fine landscape are the principal attractions, but there are facilities for swimming, boating and fishing in the Mediterranean and camping is allowed, although there is no other accommodation inside the Park.

Research : sponsored by Istanbul University.

IV.   *Altitude :* sea level to 1,237 m.

a) An outstanding area, containing a good sample of Mediterranean coastal flora.

b) Fox, jackal, wild pig, marten *M. martes,* porcupine *Hystrix,* badger *M. meles,* hare *Lepus* sp., hyaena *H. hyaena* and leopard *Panthera pardus* have been recorded; there is a great variety of birds.

3. KARATEPE-ASLANTAŞ NATIONAL PARK.

II.   *a*) Status : protection in theory total, hunting prohibited, but, as in the case of No. 1 Uludag, a considerable area, amounting to about a third of the total, is still grazed, though efforts are being made to remove the stock; there are also a couple of villages, comprising some 80 homesteads, at the entrance to the Park.

b) Area : 7,715 ha.

c) Staff : 5 units, a ranger and 4 guards.

d) Budget : covers staff salaries plus, in 1965, U.S. $ 4,400 for other expenditure; allocation in the Five-Year Plan is U.S. $ 93,000.

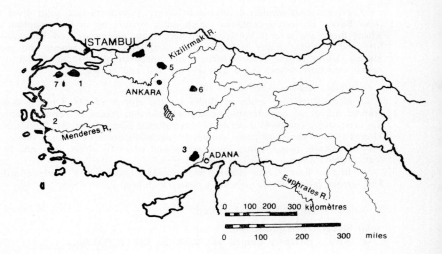

Date established : 1958.

Tourism : the important historical remains of the Hittite, Phoenician and Roman civilisations attract great numbers (c. 10,000) of visitors annually; the main hotel accommodation is at Adana, but there is a motel in the Park itself, which is also known by the name ' Aslantaş National Park '.

Altitude : 80-630 m.

a) A plateau dissected by valleys and partly covered in forest of pines, oaks, olive-trees; *Cistus* sp.

b) Roe deer *C. capreolus,* wild pig, wolf, jackal; birds include eagles, falcons and partridges.

4. YEDIGÖLLER NATIONAL PARK.

a) Status : general protection, with no qualifications.

b) Area : 2,019 ha.

c) Staff : 5 units, a ranger and 4 guards.

d) Budget : covers staff salaries plus, in 1965, U.S. $ 6,600 for other expenses; allocation in the Five-Year Plan $ 53,000.

Date established : 1965.

Tourism : Yedigöller, which means Seven Lakes, National Park offers camping and picnic facilities, trout fishing in the lakes, but no accommodation in the Park itself; access is by a 66 km branch road from the main Istanbul-Ankara highway.

Research : hydrological studies undertaken by Istanbul University.

Altitude : 700-1,600 m.

a) Western slopes of a mountain range which runs parallel with the Black Sea; forest ranging from beech/oak and beech/silver fir at lower altitudes, to pine (*P. nigra* and *P. sylvestris*)/silver fir, mainly above 1,100 m level.

b) Red deer, roe deer, wild pig, wolf, fox; brown bear recorded; many species of birds nest; trout in the lakes.

5. KIZILÇAHAMAM or SOGÜKSU NATIONAL PARK.

a) Status : total protection; no qualifications.

b) Area : 1,025 ha, of which 500 ha is strict nature reserve.

c) Staff : apparently one ranger only.

d) Budget : covers staff salaries plus, in 1965, U.S. $ 10,000 for other expenses; allocation in Five-Year Plan $ 70,000.

Date established : 1959.

Tourism : mainly visited by excursionists from Ankara; youth camps; reception centre; small zoo containing bears, foxes and wolves. The objective of this unexpected woodland oasis in the arid Anatolian landscape is to provide a demonstration of what can be achieved by protective measures, in contrast to the more and more overgrazed neighbouring regions. There is a plan to put a barbed-wire fence round the 500 ha strict nature reserve in which some twenty bears are believed still to survive.

Research : being undertaken by Istanbul and Ankara Universities.

513

IV.   *Altitude :* 1,020-1,303 m.

a) Elevated plateau covered in forest which has been partly destroyed by cutting and grazing; snow-covered in winter; hot springs in the vicinity.

b) Brown bear, wild pig, wolf, fox.

6. YOZGAT NATIONAL PARK.

II.   *a*) Status : total protection.

b) Area : 294 ha, less than criterion requirement but inclusion deemed to be justifiable.

c) Staff : 3 units.

d) Budget : covers staff salaries plus, in 1964, U.S. $ 4,100 for other expenses; $ 60,000 allocation under the Five-Year Plan.

III.   *Date established :* 1958.

Administration : the objective of this Park, known also as the Yozgat Pine Forest, is similar to the previous one, namely to underline the contrast between the former condition of Anatolia, four of five centuries ago, when it was covered with oakwoods and pines, and what it has become through having to sustain over thirty million head of sheep and goats; reafforestation is being undertaken.

IV.   *Altitude :* 1,304-1,647 m.

a) The shoulder of a high plateau, covered with pine and oak forest and bordered by deforested country with at most some bush cover.

b) No information available.

7. LAKE MANYAS NATIONAL PARK.

II.   *a*) Status : strict nature reserve.

b) Area : 52 ha only, but further extensions are planned and the Park is retained in the List because of its very special interest for bird study.

c) Staff : 4 units, including a biologist.

d) Budget : covers staff salaries plus, in 1965, U.S. $ 5,200 for other expenses; Five-Year Plan allocation of $ 44,000.

III.   *Date established :* 1959 (in its present form).

Administration : often known as the Kuş Cenneti (Bird Paradise), the Park has been the subject of special protective measures, starting from a private initiative in 1950, sponsored by the Turkish Biological Society (which was founded the previous year) and recently stimulated by the interest taken by the Council of Europe's Conservation Committee, at the request of its Turkish member, and by the IUCN Technical Meeting on wetland conservation held at Ankara in 1967.

Tourism : no accommodation in the Park, but a reception centre is planned for the considerable number of visitors (about 5,000 a year), whose movements in the area are carefully controlled.

Research : a research station, with a laboratory, museum and accommodation for research workers, has been built; research has been undertaken under the auspices of Istanbul University, originally in co-operation with the University of Hamburg and recently with experts appointed by the Council of Europe and international conservation organisations (ICBP, etc.).

514

V.   *Altitude :* 8-12 m.

a) Lake shore with reedbeds, reeds and water plants (*Phragmites* interspersed with *Typha, Scirpus, Juncus* and *Nymphaea alba* waterlily) and mature willow forest *Salix nigra,* usually inundated from March to May; forming a sanctuary and breeding place for many waterbirds; the sea of Marmara into which the lake drains is a few kilometres to the north.

b) The most numerous breeding waterbirds are cormorants *Phalacrocorax carbo* and *pygmaeus,* grey and purple heron *Ardea cinerea* and *purpurea,* night heron *N. nycticorax,* squacco heron *Ardeola ralloides,* little egret *Egretta garzetta,* little bittern *Ixobrychus minutus* and spoonbill *Platalea leucorodia*; the area is also visited by Dalmatian and white pelican *P. crispus* (which bred for the first time in 1968) and *P. onocrotalus,* and by glossy ibis *Plegadis falcinellus.* Crayfish *Potamobius fluviatilis* and amphibia *Bufo* spp. and *Rana agilis* abound and there are more than 8 species of fish; the common reptile is the grass-snake *Tropidonotus natrix.*

Excluded from the List :

Parks not yet confirmed as fully established or for which details are lacking :

1. Cilo Dag (Mt. Cilo)-Hakkari ... ...   67,000 ha.
2. Munzur-Tunceli ... ...   31,000 ha.
3. Beşkonak-Manavgat ... ...   13,000 ha.
4. Göreme ... ...   9,795 ha.
5. Spil Dagi (Mt. Spilos) . ...   8,000 ha.
6. Termosos . ...   7,000 ha.
7. Kovada Gölü (Lake Kovada) ... ...   6,000 ha.
8. Pamukkale (Hierapolis) . ...   800 ha.

128. UGANDA

Listed Areas : seven.

1. Murchison Falls National Park.
2. Queen Elizabeth National Park.
3. Kidepo Valley National Park.
4. Toro Game Reserve.
5. Kigezi Game Reserve.
6. Aswa-Lolim Game Reserve.
7. Lumunga Game Reserve.

General Introduction :

Administration : for the National Parks, vested in Trustees appointed under the Uganda National Parks Act of 1952; for the Reserves, the responsibility of the Ministry of Animal Industry, Game and Fisheries under the Game Act of 1959.

Land tenure : state ownership throughout.

Scientific research : no special organisation, except as noted under No. 2 Queen Elizabeth National Park, but visits by research workers to other areas are encouraged and frequent.

515

Tourism : organised for the National Parks only, by the Parks administration.

All the National Parks, with the exception of No. 3 Kidepo, and the Reserves, with the exception of No. 7 Lumunga, were briefly described in the previous edition, E/3436, of the List.

Details : application of criteria (II), general information (III) and description (IV) :

1. MURCHISON FALLS NATIONAL PARK.

II.
a) Status : total protection, but some game control measures have had to be carried out since 1967, in order to reduce the number of elephant.
b) Area : 384,000 ha.
c) Staff : 300 units.
d) Budget : about U.S. $ 103,000.

III.
Date established : 1952.

Tourism : accommodation : two lodges at Paraa (100 beds, to be increased to 150 by 1969); one lodge at Chobe (70 beds); 21,000 visitors in 1963, entrance fee; 240 km of motorable tracks.

IV.
Altitude : 500-1,500 m.
a) The greater part of the Park is savannah, well-wooded in places, and bush; but there are also areas of forest and papyrus-beds, especially along the river Nile.
b) Elephant *Loxodonta africana,* buffalo *Syncerus caffer,* giraffe *Giraffa camelopardalis rothschildi,* many antelopes, hippopotamus *H. amphibius,* black rhinoceros *Diceros bicornis,* white rhinoceros *Ceratotherium simum cottoni* (twelve introduced successfully from the west bank of the Albert Nile in 1962); lion and leopard *Panthera leo* and *pardus,* chimpanzee *Pan troglodytes*; a great concentration of crocodiles *C. nilotica* on the river.
c) Black rhinoceros, white rhinoceros.

2. QUEEN ELIZABETH NATIONAL PARK.

II.
a) Status : total protection, but measures have had to be carried out since 1958 to control the number of hippopotamus; there are also still some fishermen living in the Park.
b) Area : 220,000 ha.
c) Staff : 150 units.
d) Budget : about U.S. $ 69,000.

III.
Date established : 1952.

Tourism : accommodation for 100 persons at Mweya Lodge; 8,000 visitors in 1963; entrance fee; 480 km of motorable tracks.

Research : undertaken by the Nuffield Unit of Tropical Animal Ecology, based at Mweya.

IV.
Altitude : 912-1,350 m.
a) Tropical forest in the south-east, a volcanic zone pockmarked with no less than 78 craters in the north-west; otherwise savannah and swamps, with attractive scenery along the shores of Lake Edward and the Kazinga Channel which links it with Lake George.
b) Elephant, buffalo, hippopotamus, kob *Kobus kob,* topi *Damaliscus korrigum,* chimpanzee, lion and leopard.

516

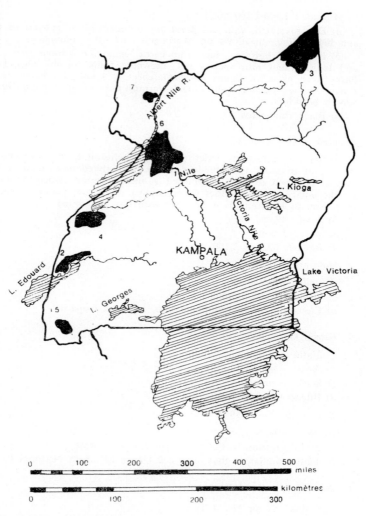

3. KIDEPO VALLEY NATIONAL PARK.

a) Status : total protection, but difficulties still occur over tribal hunting rights and access to water.

b) Area : 125,000 ha.

c) Staff : 80 units.

d) Budget : about U.S. $ 41,000.

Date established : 1962.

Tourism : recently developed, with accommodation for 30 people; motorable tracks; airstrip.

517

IV.   *Altitude :* 1,300-2,250 m.

a) **Dry savannah, with tall grass and wooded areas; patches of rain forest and high-altitude meadows on Morongole and other mountains.

b) Elephant, buffalo, black rhinoceros, eland *Taurotragus oryx,* kob, lion and leopard and also species not elsewhere found in the Uganda National Parks, such as zebra *Equus burchelli,* cheetah *Acinonyx jubatus,* roan *Hippotragus equinus,* greater kudu *Tragelaphus strepsiceros*; ostrich *Struthio camelus*; superb birdlife.

c) Black rhinoceros.

4. Toro Game Reserve.

II.   *a*) Status : sufficiently strict to justify inclusion in the List, but although grazing of livestock is forbidden in this uninhabited area, hunting is allowed, though confined to persons granted a special permit issued by the Ministry on the advice of the District Commissioner and Chief Game Warden; the use of poison to kill animals is however expressly prohibited.

b) Area : 49,000 ha.

c) Staff : 5 units.

d) Budget : U.S. $ 2,100.

III.   *Date established :* 1946.

IV.   *Altitude :* 690-750 m.

a) Savannah and swamps.

b) Elephant, buffalo, hippopotamus, lion and leopard.

5. Kigezi Game Reserve.

II.   *a*) Status : as for No. 4 Toro.

b) Area : 33,000 ha.

c) Staff : 3 units.

d) Budget : U.S. $ 1,260.

III.   *Date established :* 1952.

IV.   *Altitude :* about 1,050 m.

a) Mainly savannah, but some tropical rain forest.

b) Fauna similar to that of No. 2 Queen Elizabeth National Park.

6. Aswa-Lolim Game Reserve.

II.   *a*) Status : as for No. 4 Toro.

b) Area : 8,000 ha.

c) Staff : 3 units.

d) Budget : U.S. $ 1,260.

III.   *Date established :* 1959.

IV.   *Altitude :* averaging 1,200 m.

a) Dry savannah.

b) Elephant, buffalo, antelopes especially kob which come from the Murchison Falls National Park (No. 1) and make much use of this reserve for grazing.

518

7. LUMUNGA GAME RESERVE.

    a) Status : as for No. 4 Toro.
    b) Area : 6,500 ha.
    c) Staff : 2 units.
    d) Budget : U.S. $ 840.

Date established : not reported, but believed recent.

Altitude : 500-600 m.

    a) Dry scrubland on the western side of the valley of the Albert Nile.
    b) Typical plains species, but including some white rhinoceros.
    c) White rhinoceros.

Excluded from the List :

    A. — Nine Reserves with a similar status to those listed, but of which insufficient information was available at the date when the present edition of the List was ready for press :

    Gorilla Game Reserve, Kikagati, Lake Mburo, Katonga, Kibale Forest-corridor, Karuma, Matheniko, Pian-Upe and Bokora Corridor (all of these established on 26 August 1964).

    B. — Twelve 'Sanctuaries' totalling 345,900 ha. Eighteen "controlled hunting areas" totalling 3,630,400 ha. Two "close season areas" totalling 51,450 ha.

    The protected status of all of these is insufficient to justify their inclusion in the List, but three deserve special mention :

Mount Kei White Rhino Sanctuary ... ...   44,000 ha.
Mount Otze White Rhino Sanctuary . ...   20,700 ha.
Gorilla Sanctuary (Rwanda border) ... ...   4,660 ha.

129. UKRAINIAN SOVIET SOCIALIST REPUBLIC

See under Union of Soviet Socialist Republics immediately below.

I.   **Listed Areas :** fifty-one.

A. — RUSSIAN SOCIALIŞT FEDERATED SOVIET REPUBLICS :

1. Pechora-Ilych.
2. Sikhote-Alin.
3. Kavkaz (Caucasus).
4. Barguzin.
5. Kandalakshska/Lapland.
6. Darvin.
7. Teberda.
8. Zeya.
9. Bashkiri.
10. Astrakhan.
11. Khingan.
12. Stolby (" Pillars ").
13. Bolshe-Khekhtsir.
14. Komsomol.
15. Ilmen.
16. Voronezh.
17. Oka.
18. Kedrovaya Pad.
19. Suputinsk.
20. Kivach.
21. Volga-Kama.
22. Prioksko-Terrasny.
23. Tsentralno-Chernozyomny.

B. — AZERBAIJAN :

24. Kyzyl-Agach.
25. Zakataly.
26. Turianchai.
27. Gek Gel.

C. — KAZAKHSTAN :

28. Aksu-Dzhabagli.
29. Barsa-Kelmes.

D. — LATVIA :

30. Slitere.
31. Engure.
32. Moritsala.
33. Grini.

E. — LITHUANIA :

34. Zhuvintas.

F. — BYELORUSSIA :

35. Berezina.
36. Belovezha Pushcha.

G. — GEORGIA :

37. Borzhom.
38. Ritsa-Avadkhar.
39. Lagodekhi.
40. Kintrish.
41. Vashlovan.
42. Saguram.
43. Adzhamet.
44. Batsara.
45. Satapli.

H. — TURKMENIA :

46. Badkhyz.
47. Repetek.

I. — UKRAINE :

48. Askania Nova.
49. Chernomora (' Black Sea ').
50. Ukrainski Stepni (" Ukraine Steppes ").

J. — UZBEKISTAN :

51. Zaaminski Gorno Lesnoe (Zaamin ' mountain forest ').

520

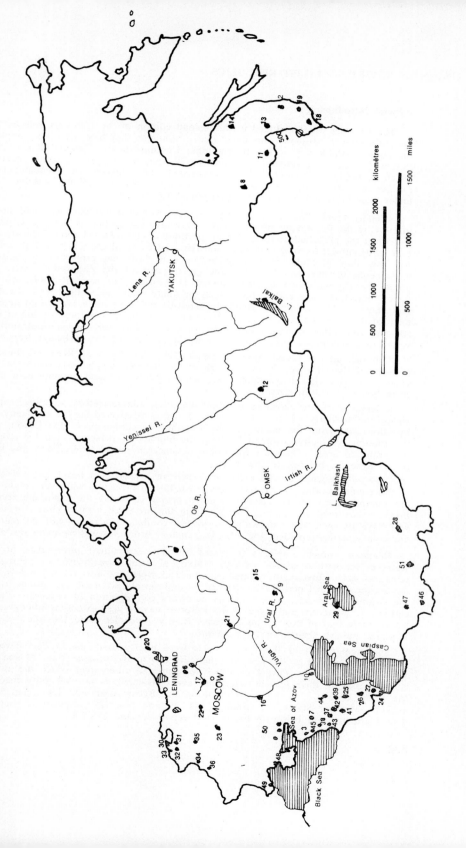

UNION OF SOVIET SOCIALIST REPUBLICS

General Introduction :

The fifty-one areas included in this second edition of the List were selected by the authorities in Moscow, who stated that in doing so they have rigorously applied the criteria established by the International Commission on National Parks. On this basis it can be assumed that the Reserves enjoy a status of general protection which is sufficiently strict and are supervised and managed by adequate staff. Figures of staff strength and budget of each area are not available and the data under Section II below is generally confined to the size.

Administration : the legal basis of the Reserves (Zapovedniki) was laid down in 1924 by the Praesidium of the Central Executive Committee of the USSR, when it defined the protected areas as " those portions of the national soil which are for ever made subject to total protection and removed from all economic exploitation ". The law thus promulgated was entitled a Law " for the protection of natural monuments, gardens and parks ". The greater part of the Zapovedniki were set up at the regional level by the Council of Ministers of each Republic of the Union, but there are still a few which originate from decisions by the Central Government. Most Reserves are administered by the responsible Ministerial department of the Republic concerned, the Minister relying for this purpose on an *ad hoc* advisory committee or organisation. In some cases, however, the administration is vested in a special section of the Academy of Sciences of the particular Republic.

Although all the Listed Areas at present have the status of Reserves, there is a proposal that the first National Park of the USSR may be established in the vicinity of Lake Baikal, extending over some 1,300,000 ha and possibly at a later stage being tripled in size.

Reserves staff are classified in four categories, administrative, scientific, supervisory and auxiliary. Expenditure on the Reserves is covered, as the case may be, by allocations from the budget of the Republic concerned or of the Union, and the amount is usually governed by both the number of personnel and the size of the protected area. There are no problems concerning land tenure, since the land of all Reserves belongs to the State.

Tourism : depends on the extent to which an organisation has been developed in the region in which a Reserve is situated, but in principle, wherever conditions are suitable, every effort is made to allow people to derive the maximum recreational, educational and cultural benefit from the protected areas. Thus a Reserve will have its own Museum with informative exhibits, itineraries will be marked and commentaries provided, and other explanatory brochures will be made available.

Research : much emphasis is placed on the exceptional importance of the Reserves for natural science students. Many of them have a virtually permanent scientific staff. Investigations and experimental work are also carried out, sometimes over extended periods, by universities and various scientific institutions, while the Academies of Science provide the necessary co-ordination of research. Publications are numerous and some of the Reserves have a very extensive bibliography, for example that of No. 3, the Caucasus Reserve, includes some 150 titles. Some Reserves publish their own *Acta Scientifica*.

The greater part of the Listed Areas were briefly described in Part Two of the previous edition of the List, although the two in Byelorussia (Nos. 35 and 36) were cited in E/3436. Part Two also listed some 52 other areas which the authorities in making their present selection have considered as not yet fully meeting the ICNP criteria. In the present edition the Byelorussian and Ukrainian SSR, as U.N. Member States, are listed as No. 17 and No. 129, respectively, but all details are included below in the general report for the U.S.S.R.

UNION OF SOVIET SOCIALIST REPUBLICS

Details : application of criteria (II), general information (III) and description (IV) :

A. — RUSSIAN SOCIALIST FEDERATED SOVIET REPUBLICS.

1. PECHORA-ILYCH (Komi ASSR).

II.
a) Status : total protection.

b) Area : 721,322 ha.

III.
Date established : 1930.

Research : experimental station for breeding domesticated moose *Alces alces.*

IV.
Altitude : 250-1,200 m.

a) Mountainous area of the North Ural and including upper reaches of the Pechora river; pine forests, coniferous *taiga* with *Pinus sibirica,* stunted mountain forest and tundra; caves along the Pechora contain Palaeolithic deposits and there are remarkable rock formations in the mountains.

b) Moose, reindeer *Rangifer tarandus,* brown bear *Ursus arctos,* sable *Martes zibellina,* beaver *Castor fiber* (introduced); salmon *Salmo salar* (large spawning grounds, wthich the Reserve was specially designed to protect).

2. SIKHOTE-ALIN (Primorski Territory).

I.
b) Area : 310,100 ha.

II.
Date established : 1935.

V.
Altitude : sea level to 1,600 m.

a) Eastern slope of Sikhote-Alin mountains bordering the Sea of Japan; broad-leaved and coniferous forest, the later dominant at higher levels, typical of the Manchurian region and northern *taiga.*

b) Siberian tiger *Panthera tigris altaica,* sika deer *Cervus nippon,* goral *Naemorhedus goral,* brown bear, Asiatic black bear *Selenarctos thibetanus,* yellow-throated marten *Martes flavigula.*

c) Siberian tiger.

3. KAVKAZ (Caucasus) (Krasnodarski Territory).

I.
b) Area : 262,500 ha.

II.
Date established : 1924.

Tourism : camping outside the Reserve; no hotels or roads within its borders.

V.
Altitude : 1,200-3,300 m.

a) Western part of the main Caucasian ridge and the Peredovye ridges; all high altitude vegetational zones represented, from forest of oak *Quercus* and other broad-leaved species to alpine meadows; rich flora with many endemics.

b) Chamois *R. rupicapra,* Caucasian tur *Capra caucasica,* European bison *Bison bonasus* (re-introduced), red deer *Cervus elaphus,* brown bear, leopard *Panthera pardus;* Caucasian blackcock *Lyrurus mlokosiewiczi.*

c) Bison.

4. BARGUZIN (Buryat ASSR).

b) Area : 248,200 ha.

523

III.   *Date established :* 1916.

IV.   *Altitude :* 400-4,000 m.

a) North-east shores of Lake Baikal and western slopes of the Barguzin range; mountain larch *Larix* sp., coniferous *taiga,* especially Siberian ' cedar ' *Pinus cembra,* and high altitude tundra.

b) Sable (for which the Reserve is specially designed; numerous), stoat *Mustela erminea,* brown bear (common), red deer, moose, musk deer *Moschus moschiferus;* Baikal seal *Pusa sibirica* abound along the lake shore.

5. KANDALAKSHSKA/LAPLAND (Murmansk Region).

II.   *b)* Area : 22,000 ha and 158,400 ha respectively.

III.   *Date established :* 1930.

Research : centre for animal (mammals and birds) and forest ecology; many publications.

IV.   *Altitude :* sea level to 1,000 m.

a) These twin reserves comprise four sections :

(i) Archipelago of Kandalakshska Bay in the White Sea, covered with northern type *taiga* (pines, firs and birch);
(ii) The Seven Islands, Barents Sea;
(iii) The Ainor Islands, Barents Sea; both tundra;
(iv) The Lapland Reserve, on the Kola peninsula and including Lake Imandra; pine forests, with *Cladonia rangiferina* moss, high altitude tundra.

b) Kandalakshska : seals *Phoca vitulina;* many seabirds including guillemot *Uria aalge,* puffin *Fratercula arctica,* black guillemot *Cepphus grylle,* kittiwake *Rissa tridactyla,* eiders of several species. Lapland : reindeer, moose, brown bear, mink *Mustela* sp., otter *L. lutra,* red squirrel *Sciurus* sp.; many Tetraonidae including blackcock *Lyrurus tetrix,* hazel hen *Tetrastes bonasia,* capercaillie *Tetrao urogallus* and willow-grouse *L. lagopus.*

6. DARVIN (Kalinin Region).

II.   *b)* Area : 112,600 ha (about half under water).

III.   *Date established :* 1945.

Tourism : not developed.

Research : experimental farm for the breeding of capercaillie.

IV.   *Altitude :* 450 m.

a) Mologo-Sheksninski lowlands in the north eastern part of the Rybinski reservoir; pine and birch *Betula* forest, sphagnum bogs.

b) Especially rich in waterfowl, mainly migratory, e.g. wild geese and swans; also moose, brown bear, wolf *Canis lupus.*

7. TEBERDA (Stavropol Territory, Caucasus).

II.   *b)* Area : 83,400 ha.

III.   *Date established :* 1936.

Tourism : hotels and roads within the Reserve boundaries; winter-sports centre.

524

Altitude : 2,000-4,500 m.

a) North slope of Bolshoi Caucasus, comprising the upper reaches of the Teberda river and of the Arkhyz and Zelenchuk rivers, high mountain areas with forest and alpine meadows.

b) Caucasian tur, chamois, brown bear, sika deer (introduced).

8. ZEYA (Amur Region).

b) Area : 82,300 ha.

Date established : 1963.

Research : protection and propagation of Far East flora and fauna.

Altitude : about 300-500 m.

a) On the right bank of the Zeya river, along the Tukuringa mountain chain, between the Gilyuya and Gulska rivers which flow into the Zeya; mixture of East Siberian pine/larch forest and elements of the Manchurian flora, with scanty vegetation at the foot of the mountains, but mostly mixed conifers and broad-leaved species, with some tundra at the highest altitudes.

b) Roe deer *C. capreolus,* musk deer, moose, brown bear, sable, squirrel, Amur dormouse (*Glis glis* subsp ?); blackcock, Siberian horned owl (*Bubo* sp.), pied harrier *Circus melanoleucos,* little cuckoo *Cuculus poliocephalus*; flycatchers.

9. BASHKIRI (Bashkir ASSR, Ural region).

b) Area : 72,049 ha.

Date established : 1930.

Tourism : visited for the remarkable Bolshaya Kapskaya cave with its Upper Palaeolithic wall carvings.

Altitude : 500-800 m.

a) Typical sample of the south Urals, with a landscape characterising the transition from Europe to Asia; one section of the reserve is situated in the south Kraka massif, with mountain forests of Scots pine *Pinus sylvestris,* larch and birch, and in the second section, in a curve of the Belaya river, with forest-steppe of typical Siberian birch " kolki ".

b) Moose, roe deer, Siberian deer *Cervus elaphus sibiricus,* squirrel, flying-squirrel *Pteromys* sp., mink, bear; capercaillie, hazel hen, blackcock.

10. ASTRAKHAN.

b) Area : 72,500 ha.

Date established : 1919.

Tourism : no hotel accommodation in vicinity and no roads in this wetland area.

Altitude : sea level.

a) Three sections of the Volga delta, including many large and small islands, channels and shallow bays; the islands are covered with willow thicket and reed-beds and there are large areas of aquatic plants, including the lotus *Nelumbium caspicum,* which is specially protected.

525

b) Herons, egrets, spoonbill *Platalea leucorodia,* glossy ibis *Plegadis falci-nellus* and geese breed; cormorant, flamingo and pelican also recorded; great concentrations of migrant wildfowl visit the islands to moult; spawning and wintering grounds of commercial fish.

11. KHINGAN (Amur Region).

II. *b*) Area : 58,300 ha.

III. *Date established :* 1963.

IV. *Altitude :* 300-500 m.

a) Spurs of the Little Khingan on the right bank of the Amur and between the Uril and Khingan tributaries; the southern part consists of the terraces bordering the Amur, more or less marshy grassland; the north of the mode-rately high plateau, dissected by steep valleys and covered by *taiga* of mixed conifer and broad-leaved species, including some birch, willow *Salix* and a good many shrubby species.

b) Bear, squirrel, Manchurian hare *Lepus* sp.; capercaillie, blackcock, hazel hen, pheasant *Phasianus colchicus pallasi.*

12. STOLBY or 'PILLARS' (Krasnoyarsk, Yenisei).

II. *b*) Area : 47,200 ha.

III. *Date established :* 1925.

Tourism : a centre for Siberian tourism; mountaineering school.

Research : productivity studies of *taiga,* especially of the Siberian 'cedar' or Arolla pine *Pinus cembra.*

IV. *Altitude :* 600-800 m.

a) Spurs of the Kuisunski ridge of the East Sayan Mountains, near the confluence of the Yenisei and Mana; the 'Stolby' or Pillars are granito-sienite rocks up to 100 m high; larch and larch-pine *taiga,* with some pure stands of *Pinus siberica* and other pines, as well as Siberian cedar.

b) Siberian musk and roe deer, sable, glutton *G. gulo,* bear; blackcock, capercaillie.

13. BOLSHE-KHEKHTSIR (Khabarovsk Territory, Ussuri).

II. *b*) Area : 46,000 ha.

III. *Date established :* no information.

Tourism : no development.

Research : forestry, Cervidae.

IV. *Altitude :* 300-800 m.

a) Steep and jagged ridge overlooking the right bank of the Ussuri river, with rich coniferous and broad-leaved forests.

b) Bear, squirrels, Manchurian hare; capercaillie, blackcock, and other typical Manchurian species.

14. KOMSOMOL (Khabarovsk Region, Amur).

II. *b*) Area : 32,200 ha.

526

Date established : 1963.

Research : programme started within the last few years.

Altitude : 20-100 m.

a) Right bank of river opposite the city of Komsomolsk-on-Amur; vegetation comprises the various forest associations of the Ussuri-Amur floristic region, the Okhotsk *taiga* sandwiched between belts of conifer/broad-leaf forest, in which the main species are Korean ' cedar ' *Pinus cembra* subsp., birch, Manchurian ash *Fraxinus* sp., alder *Alnus* sp., willow, linden *Tilia* sp. and oak.

b) Interesting subspecies of brown bear and moose; glutton; hazel hen; spawning grounds of chum and humpback salmon *Oncorhynchus teta* and *gorbuscha,* as well as of fresh-water species.

15. ILMEN (Chelyabinsk Region, Urals).

b) Area : 32,100 ha.

Date established : 1920, dedicated to V. I. Lenin.

Tourism : guided tours are provided.

Administration and research : by Academy of Sciences; over 400 scientific papers have been published.

Altitude : 500-1,000 m.

a) The Ilmen mountain range and the western slope of the Ural massif, separated by the broad valley of the Miass river; gentle and steep-sloping mountain-sides, with many gorges; very rich in minerals, the 150 kinds recorded including topaz, garnet and other precious and semi-precious stones; mixture of pine and broad-leaved forest, mainly larch/pine and birch, but often pure stands of pine.

b) Roe deer, moose, fox *V. vulpes,* lynx *Felis lynx,* dormouse, varying hare *Lepus timidus,* squirrel; fallow deer *D. dama,* sika deer and beaver have been introduced; blackcock, hazel hen, capercaillie.

16. VORONEZH.

b) Area : 30,800 ha.

Date established : 1927, specifically for protection of beaver *Castor fiber.*

Tourism : accommodation at Voronezh, none in Reserve.

Research : centre for study and breeding of pedigree beavers, which are distributed from here all over the country.

Altitude : 150 m.

a) Comprises the Usmanski pine forest on the Usman and Voronezh rivers; interspersed with the pines are oak groves and much boggy flood-plain overgrown with aspen *Populus tremula.*

b) Red deer, moose, wild pig, beaver, desman *Desmana moschata.*

17. OKA (Ryazan Region).

b) Area : 22,900 ha.

Date established : 1935.

Research : ornithological experimental station; breeding paddocks for *Bison bonasus.*

IV.   *Altitude :* 200-300 m.

a) Southern part of Meshcherskaya lowlands, near confluence of Oka and Pra rivers, covered with pine, oak and mixed birchwoods, and studded with flood-plain lakes.

b) European bison, moose, red deer; beaver re-introduced and sika deer introduced.

c) European bison.

18. KEDROVAYA PAD (Primorski Territory).

II.   *b*) Area : 17,900 ha.

III.   *Date established :* 1916.

Administration and research : by the Academy of Sciences of the USSR; like Nos. 8 and 10 above, Zeya and Khingan, a centre for Far East studies, in this case particularly entomological.

IV.   *Altitude :* 100-750 m.

a) Mountainous part of Khasan district between the North Korea border and the southern extremity of the Ussuri region; relief deeply dissected by numerous rivers; mixed conifer/broad-leaf forests or forest of broad-leaved species only and a good sample of the most southern variant of the forests of the USSR Far East; notable species include the ' iron birch ' *Betula schmidtii* and the creeper *Aralia continentalis,* near the northern extremity of their range, Schippenlach's rhododendron and the maple *Acer komarovi.*

b) Leopard, sika deer, wild pig *Sus scrofa,* bear, giant shrew *Sorex pacificus* (northern limit of range); Jankowski's bunting *Emberiza jankowskii* (also at northern limit).

19. SUPUTINSK (Primorski Territory).

II.   *b*) Area : 16,500 ha, not far from No. 18.

III.   *Date established :* 1932.

Research : another Far East research centre, administered by the USSR Academy of Sciences and specialising in studies of forest ecology and of medicinal plants.

IV.   *Altitude :* 450-660 m.

a) South-west spurs of the Sikhote Alin mountain range, with typical south Ussuri *taiga* along the banks of the Upper Suputina river which rises in the Dadian Shan; primeval conifer (fir and spruce *Picea*) forest and broad-leaved forest.

b) Wild pig fallow deer, Siberian tiger *Panthera tigris altaica.*

c) Siberian tiger.

20. KIVACH (Karelian ASSR).

II.   *b*) Area : 10,315 ha.

III.   *Date established :* 1931.

Tourism : visited especially for the well-known waterfall after which the Reserve is named.

Research : studies of the middle *taiga* complex; bird migration observatory linked with an international programme.

IV.   *Altitude :* towards 500 or 600 m.

a) Typical landscape of the middle *taiga,* with firs, pines, Karelian birch, elm *Ulmus* sp., linden, alder; areas of marshland.

b) Moose, brown bear, marten *Martes* sp., stoat, fox, dormouse, varying hare, otter, mink, squirrel; muskrat *Ondatra zibethica* (introduced); blackcock, hazel hen.

21. VOLGA-KAMA (Tatar ASSR).

II.   *b)* Area : 7,538 ha, in two sections.

III.   *Date established :* 1960.

Research : studies of southern *taiga* productivity; arboretum.

IV.   *Altitude :* 200-400 m.

a) Near the confluence of the two rivers after which it is named; the Raifski section contains samples of pine, linden/oak and mixed conifer/broad-leaved forest; the Saralovski section occupies the shores and islands of the Kuibyshev reservoir, covered by woodland.

b) Moose, stoat, marten, hare; muskrat (introduced); capercaillie, blackcock, hazel hen, partridge; plentiful fish.

22. PRIOKSKO-TERRASNY (Moscow region).

II.   *b)* Area : 4,800 ha.

III.   *Date established :* 1945.

Tourism : easy access, large numbers of visitors.

Research : centre for studies of the European bison, which is bred in enclosures.

IV.   *Altitude :* 300-400 m.

a) Terraces of the left bank of the Oka river, covered by pine and broad-leaved forest with clearings of relic steppe flora.

b) European bison, moose, roe deer, wild pig.

c) European bison.

23. TSENTRALNO-CHERNOZYOMNY (Kursk Region).

II.   *b)* Area : 4,200 ha, in three sections.

III.   *Date established :* 1930, dedicated to V. V. Alekhin.

IV.   *Altitude :* 300 m.

a) The three sections — Streletski, Kasatski and Yamskoi — protect samples of virgin herbaceous steppe, in which clumps of oak are established on the rich black soil; some of the grassland contains alpine elements, such as bistort *Polygonum* sp. and tutsan *Hypericum androsaemum.*

b) Marmot *Marmota* sp., ground squirrel (*Cynomys* sp. ?); great bustard *Otis tarda.*

B. — AZERBAIJAN SSR.

24. KYZYL-AGACH.

II.   *b*) Area : 88,000 ha.

III.   *Date established :* 1926, dedicated to S. M. Kirov.

           Tourism : no development.

IV.   *Altitude :* Caspian sea level (—30 m).

           a) South-west coast of Caspian near Iranian frontier, including Kirov Bay, the coastal strip of reeds and saltmarsh, raised peatbog and a group of islands.

           b) Major resting-place of migrant waterfowl, swans, geese, ducks, flamingoes, pelicans, herons and egrets.

25. ZAKATALY.

II.   *b*) Area : 25,300 ha.

III.   *Date established :* 1929.

           Tourism : no development.

IV.   *Altitude :* 650-3,668 m.

           a) Southern slopes of the eastern end of the Caucasus range; all the altitudinal vegetation zones, from subalpine forest of oak, beech, hornbeam *Carpinus,* ash, birch,maple, dwarf Siberian elm and linden up to alpine meadows.

           b) Chamois, roe deer, red deer (local race of *Cervus elaphus*), Caucasian tur, bear, wolf, lynx, wildcat *Felis silvestris*; otter, pine and stone marten *Martes martes* and *foina*; Caucasian blackcock, Caucasian snowcock *Tetraogallus caucasicus* and chukar *Alectoris chukar.*

26. TURIANCHAI.

II.   *b*) Area : 12,700 ha, plus a small annexe of 390 ha.

III.   *Date established :* 1958.

IV.   *Altitude :* 500-700 m.

           a) Foothills of main Caucasian range in vicinity of the Bozdag ridge; south-facing slopes of the plateau are heavily eroded, the northern comparatively sheer, the more level parts of the ridge being sparsely covered by *Juniperus* and mastic *Pistacia* sp., with some *Quercus iberica* and Georgian hornbeam; honeysuckle *Lonicera* sp., common jasmine *Jasminum officinale,* buckthorn *Rhamnus* sp.; the small annexe, situated on the Eilyarugu ridge, protects a relic patch of drought-resistant *Pinus eldaricata.*

           b) Small fauna of wild pig, dormouse, marten, wolf, jackal *Canis mesomelas,* fox; noted for migratory birds.

27. GEK GEL.

II.   *b*) Area : 7,500 ha.

III.   *Date established :* 1925.

IV.   *Altitude :* 200-1,570 m.

530

a) A lake caused by the blocking of a valley by a landslide in 1139; surrounded by sub-alpine grassland and mountain forest.

b) Brown bear, marten, roe deer; wintering area for waterfowl.

C. — KAZAKH SSR.

28. AKSU-DZHABAGLI.

b) Area : 75,000 ha.

Date established : 1926.

Altitude : 500-4,000 m.

a) Mountainous region with the characteristic landscape and flora of the northern part of the West Tien Shan range, from dry tall-grass steppe, with clumps of deciduous shrub and juniper, to high-altitude moorland and meadow; the rich flora (some 1,200 species of tree, shrub and flowering plant) includes the poplar *Populus talassi,* apple *Malus* sp., yew *Taxus* and birch; permanent snow and glaciers on the Ala-Tau summit ridge.

b) Siberian ibex *Capra ibex sibirica,* Asiatic black bear, wolf, fox, wild cat, marten, snow leopard *Panthera uncia;* roe deer.

c) Snow leopard.

29. BARSA-KELMES.

b) Area : 18,500 ha.

Date established : 1939.

Altitude : below sea level.

a) Named after the island on which it is situated, in the Aral Sea; rather flat, sand-dunes and mainly saline soil, surrounded by a string of salt lakes; poor desertic flora (goose-foot *Chenopodium* and saltwort *Salsola*), often forming areas of low bush.

b) Saiga antelope *Saiga tatarica,* Persian wild ass *Equus hemionus onager* and Persian gazelle *Gazella subgutturosa* have been re-introduced; wolf, fox, jerboa (Dipodidae); 200 species of resident and migratory birds, including pelicans.

c) Persian wild ass or onager.

D. — LATVIAN SSR.

30. SLITERE.

a) Status : game management on a scientific basis.

b) Area : 7,848 ha.

Date established : 1957.

Research : experimental work on yew cultivation; geobotanical, ichthyological and entomological studies.

Altitude : sea level.

a) Sandy plain on Baltic coast surrounded by the Zilie-Kalni hills; pine and birch forests with some relic Atlantic elements such as the yew and ivy *Hedera helix.*

b) Roe deer, wild pig, European hare, fox.

31. ENGURE.

II.   *b)* Area : 1,340 ha (below criterion).

III.   *Date established :* 1957.

       Research : ornithological studies.

IV.   *Altitude :* sea level to 10 m.

       a) Situated on the island after which it is named in the Gulf of Riga.

       b) Waterfowl; breeding-place of numerous duck, geese and swans.

32. MORITSALA.

II.   *a)* Status : scientific control of the fauna.

       b) Area : 835 ha (below criterion).

III.   *Date established :* 1911.

       Research : ichthyological studies.

IV.   *Altitude :* sea level.

       a) Situated on Morits Island on Lake Usma and including the Luzikerte Bay of that Lake; the flat sandy island is covered with deciduous woods of oak, ash, birch, small-leaved lime *Tilia cordata* and conifers.

       b) Roe deer, hare, fox; great numbers of waterfowl; fish spawning grounds.

33. GRINI.

II.   *b)* Area : 600 ha (below the criterion).

III.   *Date established :* 1957.

IV.   *Altitude :* sea level to 10 m.

       a) Clayey-sandy plain on the Baltic coast, covered with mixed forest of Scots pine, Norway spruce *Picea abies,* oak and birch; only Reserve in the USSR which contains some *Erica* heathland, hence inclusion in the List despite its small size.

       b) Red deer, roe deer, wild pig, European hare *Lepus europaeus,* fox.

E. — LITHUANIAN SSR.

34. ZHUVINTAS.

II.   *b)* Area : 5,421 ha, of which 1,039 ha are occupied by the lake after which the Reserve is named.

III.   *Date established :* 1937.

IV.   *Altitude :* sea level.

       a) Lake Zhuvintas and its surroundings, with on the western side sphagnum bog partly covered by coniferous and broad-leaved forest.

       b) Numerous waterfowl and waders and the biggest breeding colony of mute swan *Cygnus olor* in the USSR.

F. — BYELORUSSIAN SSR.

35. BEREZINA.

b) Area : 76,500 ha.

Date established : 1925.

Altitude : about 300 m.

a) Part of the fairly flat plain along the upper reaches of the Berezina river in the western Dvina region, covered by coniferous and conifer/birch forest and with large areas of boggy alder thicket and sphagnum marshland; the Reserve is traversed by the Serguchevsky Canal completed early in the 19th Century.

b) Beaver (for the protection and study of which the Reserve was originally created); moose, roe deer, wild pig, bear, marten, otter, fox; blackcock, capercaillie, hazel hen, willow-grouse, mallard and teal *Anas platyrhynchos* and *crecca*; rivers and lakes are full of fish.

36. BELOVEZHA PUSHCHA.

a) Status : on the international boundary with Poland; breeding enclosures for European bison.

b) Area : 74,200 ha.

Date established : 1939, but under protection since the 13th-14th Century and, as such, one of the oldest reserves in the world.

Altitude : 150-205 m.

a) Ancient forest on the watershed of the Neman, Bug and Pripet rivers, pine, spruce, oak, hornbeam, alder, etc.

b) European bison, red and roe deer, wild pig.

c) European bison.

G. — GEORGIAN SSR.

37. BORZHOM.

b) Area : 18,082 ha.

Date established : 1935.

Research : forest research; breeding up of the Caucasian race of the red deer.

Altitude : 600-2,000 m.

a) Mountainous sector of eastern Georgia, comprising the Trialetski ridge, which is forested with mixed forests of oak, beech and conifers; hot springs.

b) Caucasian red deer, wild pig, brown bear.

38. RITSA-AVADKHAR.

b) Area : 15,923 ha, plus the Pitzunda annexe of 200 ha.

Date established : 1947, annexe in 1962.

533

IV.   *Altitude :* 500-2,200 m, the Pitzunda annexe being at sea level.

a) The main Ritsa sector borders the lake of that name and is mainly Norway spruce forest of the southern slopes of the western Caucasus; also some yew and laurel *Laurus nobilis.* The Pitzunda annexe on the Black Sea coast protects the only stand of the endemic *Pinus pithynsa* left in the Caucasian area.

b) Brown bear, red and roe deer, mink.

39. LAGODEKHI.

II.   *b*) Area : 13,283 ha.

III.   *Date established :* 1912.

Tourism : slightly developed.

IV.   *Altitude :* 600-3,500 m.

a) Southern spurs of the main Caucasus range along the Alazan river; many lakes and waterfalls; vegetation zones include beech and oak forest, conifers and subalpine and alpine meadows.

b) Red deer, chamois, ibex *Capra ibex cylindricornis,* the Persian squirrel *Sciurus persicus*; Caucasian snowcock.

40. KINTRISH.

II.   *b*) Area : 6,943 ha.

III.   *Date established :* 1959.

Research : mountain forest ecology.

IV.   *Altitude :* 400-2,000 m.

a) West Georgian mountains, forested with oak, laurel, Medviediev's birch.

b) Red deer, wild pig; pheasant.

41. VASHLOVAN.

II.   *b*) Area : 5,952 ha.

III.   *Date established :* 1946.

IV.   *Altitude :* 300-1,000 m.

a) Semi-desertic area in extreme eastern Georgia, south of the Alazan river, distinguished for its groves of *Pistacia vera* and juniper thickets.

b) Brown bear, wild pig, hare; chukar.

42. SAGURAM.

II.   *b*) Area : 5,083 ha.

III.   *Date established :* 1946.

Research : the reserve is not far from the Georgian capital Tbilisi and is used for forestry studies.

IV.   *Altitude :* 600-1,250 m.

a) Forested area, dominated by yew, box *Buxus colchicus*, cherry-laurel *Prunus laurocerasus* and holly *Ilex colchica.*

b) Caucasian red deer, roe deer; chukar.

43. ADZHAMET.

II.　　*b*) Area : 4,848 ha.

III.　　*Date established :* 1946.

IV.　　*Altitude :* 300-600 m.

a) Flat country, covered by the only tracts of *Quercus iberica* and *Zelkova colchica* (Ulmaceae) forest to be found in western Georgia.

b) Plains animals; mink; many species of birds.

44. BATSARA.

II.　　*b*) Area : 3,052 ha.

III.　　*Date established :* 1957.

IV.　　*Altitude :* 500-1,200 m.

a) Typical montane forest of eastern Georgia with relic yew (now being replanted) and some beechwoods.

b) Forest fauna of mainly ornithological interest.

45. SATAPLI.

II.　　*b*) Area : 300 ha, well below the criterion requirement, but the outstanding palaeontological interest of the Reserve justifies retention.

II.　　*Date established :* 1957.

Tourism : intensive, the main attraction being the cavern dating back to the Lower Cretaceous in which fossil traces of dinosaurs have been found.

V.　　*Altitude :* 300-850 m.

a) Karstic cave with stalactites and Lower Cretaceous deposits.

b) Cave fauna.

H. — TURKMEN SSR.

46. BADKHYZ.

I.　　*a*) Status : part of the Reserve is used for Pistacia plantations and the breeding up of mouflon *Ovis* sp.

b) Area : 133,000 ha, of which 87,500 ha constitutes strict reserve, the remainder being made up of three protected buffer zones.

II.　　*Date established :* 1941.

V.　　*Altitude :* 800-1,200 m.

a) At the confluence of the Tedzhen and Murgat rivers in the extreme south of the USSR, the Reserve comprises — (1) a plateau of desert steppe with shallow valleys, seasonally covered with ephemeral vegetation; (2) the Namak-Sarskaya, Er-Oilan-Duz salt lake and Kizyl-Dzhar depressions, the second of which is dominated to the north by the 300 m cliffs of an escarpment; (3) a deeply dissected plateau with mountain ridges and broad valleys. The vegetation at lower levels is of a savannah type with Pistacia groves, oleander *Nerium* and *Haloxylon* in the hollows; the mountains are covered by grassy steppe with numerous flowers (tulip, iris, milk-vetch *Astragalus,* sainfoin *Onobrychis viciifolia.*)

b) Onager (Persian wild ass), mouflon, Persian gazelle, leopard, caracal lynx *Felis caracal,* Asiatic cheetah *Acinonyx jubatus venaticus,* hyaena *H. hyaena,* wolf, ratel *Mellivora capensis*; vultures and falcons.

c) Persian wild ass, Asiatic cheetah.

47. REPETEK.

II.   *b*) Area : 34,600 ha.

III.   *Date established :* 1928.

Research : there is a biological station.

IV.   *Altitude :* 400-600 m.

a) In the eastern part of the Kara Kum sand desert; the desertic flora includes saltwort *Salsola* sp. (black and white), the curious steppe-plant *Haloxylon* and joint-pine *Ephedra strobilacea.*

b) Sand cat *Felis margarita,* the hare *Lepus tolai,* long-clawed ground squirrel *Spermophilopsis leptodactylus,* comb-toed jerboa *Paradipus ctenodactylus*; skink *Teratoscincus scincus,* the monitor lizard *Varanus griseus,* the tortoise *Testudo horsfieldi*; and the beetles *Sternodes caspicus* and *Podoces panderi* of the Tenebrionid family.

I. — UKRAINIAN SSR.

48. ASKANIA NOVA.

II.   *a*) Status : domestic stock pastured in some sectors; the Reserve is also used as a centre for experimental introductions and breeding of endangered and other species of very varied origin, which has been done on a large scale and with a considerable degree of success.

b) Area : 10,500 ha.

III.   *Date established :* 1921, but under protection since 1874.

Administration : by Ukrainian Academy of Agriculture.

IV.   *Altitude :* sea level to 8 m.

a) Sample of virgin arid steppe, in which, in addition to the characteristic fescue *Festuca sulcata,* the dominant grasses are the three species of feather grass *Stipa lessingiana, ucranica* and *capillata.*

b) Hare, ground squirrel, fox, wolf (rare); eagles, bustards, black stork *Ciconia nigra*; some 40 introduced mammals include onager, Przewalski's horse, zebra, gnu, American and European bison, nilgai and eland; among the many birds introduced are ostriches.

c) Persian wild ass or onager, Przewalski's horse (both introduced).

49. CHERNOMORA (" Black Sea ").

II.   *b*) Area : 9,695 ha, with about another 35,000 ha of the adjacent sea.

III.   *Date established :* 1927.

Administration : by the Zoological Institute of the Ukrainian Academy of Sciences.

536

Tourism : intensive; guided visits; museum.

Altitude : sea level to 10 m.

a) Steppe zone along Black Sea coast, with sandy saline soils, stretching from the Dnieper-Bug estuary to Karkinitski Bay, with many sandspits, fresh and saltwater lakes or lagoons; frequent patches of virgin oak, birch, willow and alder woods.

b) Large numbers of waterfowl, breed, rest on migration and winter; only breeding place in USSR of the Mediterranean gull *Larus melanocephalus.*

50. UKRAINSKI STEPNI (" Ukraine Steppes ").

a) and *b)* Status and Area : consists of four separate sections situated in three different Regions :

  (i) Mihailovsk : 202.4 ha (Sumskaya Region);
  (ii) Streletskaya Steppe : 480.6 ha (Luganskaya);
  (iii) Khomutovskaya Steppe : 1,028 ha (Donetskaya);
  (iv) Kamennye Mogily (" Stone tombs ") : 404 ha ((Donetskaya).

Date established : Sector (i) 1937; (ii) 1936; (iii) 1926; (iv) 1925.

Administration : by the Botanical Institute of the Ukrainian Academy of Sciences.

Tourism : developed; guided visits.

Altitude : 300-400 m.

a) Sector (i) Mihailovsk : only section of virgin meadow steppe left in the Ukraine.

Sector (ii) Streletskaya : virgin fescue and feather-grass *Stipa* steppe of the eastern type.

Sector (iii) Khomutovskaya : rich chernozem or black soil steppe bordering the Sea of Azov, with fescue and feather-grass.

Sector (iv) Kamennye Mogily : stony steppe with granite hills up to 100 m high and specialised vegetation.

b) The marmot *Marmota bobak* occurs in sector (ii).

J. — UZBEK SSR.

51. ZAAMINSKI GORNO-LESNOE (' Zaamin mountain forest ').

b) Area : 10,500 ha.

Date established : 1960.

Altitude : 600-3,500 m.

a) Northern slope of the western end of the Turkestan mountain range, where the juniper belt is especially well defined; mainly shrubby vegetation tending to form thicket, including such species as dog-rose *Rosa* sp., honeysuckle, barberry *Berberis,* currant *Ribes* sp., service tree *Sorbus torminalis,* mint *Mentha* sp. and deadly nightshade *Atropa belladonna.*

b) Siberian ibex, wild pig; the marmot *Marmota caudata,* the porcupine *Hystrix hirsutirostris,* brown bear of the local race *Ursus arctos leucomyx,* fox, wolf, marten, lynx, snow leopard; quail *C. coturnix,* chukar, vultures, falcons.

c) Snow leopard.

537

V.   Areas excluded :

Reference has already been made in the General Introduction to the 52 other Reserves included in Part Two of the previous edition of the List. The most recent review received from the authorities suggests that there are about 32 Reserves which have a status comparable to the 51 now selected and which should be considered for inclusion in the next edition. Consultations with the experts tend, however, to support the view that at present the network of reserves in the USSR, although extremely extensive, is at the same time very variable in the strictness with which protected status is defined and applied.

131. UNITED ARAB REPUBLIC

I.   Listed Areas : nil.

V.   Explanation :

The U.A.R. was not cited in E/3436 or Part Two of the previous edition of the List and requests for information to the governmental authorities have so far elicited no reply. However, information from various sources confirms that at present no area in the country corresponds with the criteria of status and effectiveness (supervisory staff and budget) laid down for admission to the present List.

In the deserts adjoining the Nile valley, the surviving wildlife does of course enjoy the natural protection afforded by these vast uninhabited areas. Thus various gazelles (*Gazella gazella, dorcas* and *leptoceros*), ibex, Barbary stag, leopard, cheetah, striped hyaena, wild asses, may still exist, especially in the south. In the valley itself it is much to be hoped that one or more refuges will be established for the migratory birds, for which the Nile constitutes a main route to their winter quarters and of which at present the shooting is subject to no restriction.

It is worth remarking that the bas-reliefs of the tombs of the Pharaohs, as well as the remarkable collection of mummies of wild animals in the Cairo Museum, throw much light on the differences between the fauna of today and that of 4,000 years ago, when for instance the range of hippopotamus, crocodile, monkeys and sacred ibis extended into Egypt. No doubt, however, the desert fauna has undergone less change than that of the valley.

Excluded from the List :

The hunting Reserve of Wadi Rishrash. This was the old royal hunting ground, 80 km south of Cairo, where some ibex of the desert race used to survive, but it appears that despite the interest of the relatively unchanged biological associations of the area, it is no longer protected.

132. UNITED KINGDOM OF GREAT BRITAIN AND NORTHERN IRELAND

METROPOLITAN

Listed Areas : seventy-four, comprising :

A. — NATIONAL NATURE RESERVES :

a) 22 of over 500 ha;
b) 34 of between 100 and 500 ha;

B. — LOCAL NATURE RESERVES : 7.

C. — FOREST NATURE RESERVES : 3.

D. — PRIVATE RESERVES : 8.

For names see under Details below.

General Introduction :

Due to the comparatively large number of listed areas and the wealth of published information on them, it has been decided that it would be impractical in the present edition of the List to present the administrative, ecological and other details of each of the 74 areas in turn, as has been done in the reports on most other countries. However, for the 22 National Nature Reserves of over 500 ha, which, having a high conservation status and fully satisfying the ICNP criteria, properly head the list, it has seemde desirable to amplify the information included in the original French text by providing at least a brief summary of their geophysical characteristics, flora and fauna. The procedure adopted, therefore, has been to limit Sections II and III to a general review of the relevant situation and then, in Section IV, to list the selected reserves in their various categories and order of size, ending with a short description under sub-heads (a) and (b) of the 22 largest NNR.

It is worth noting that the previous edition of the List, E/3436, described at some length nine of these 22 reserves (Nos. 1, 3-6, 16-18 and 20, as now listed) and also half a dozen of the others (Nos. 32, 41, 42, 47, 50 and 55). Included with the latter was Old Winchester Hill NNR, the small size of which (56 ha) has debarred it from a place in the present edition. This is of some significance, since it points to one not altogether satisfactory effect of applying a size criterion. The 1962 edition, in selecting for fuller treatment a broadly representative sample, was in the position to draw attention to an area as small as the one mentioned, simply because it was judged to have specially interesting and unusual features. By excluding such areas, the present selection, despite its more objective approach, does in fact remain very arbitrary.

Details : application of criteria (II), general information (III) and description (IV) :

a) Status : total protection; in a few cases a very small part of an area may

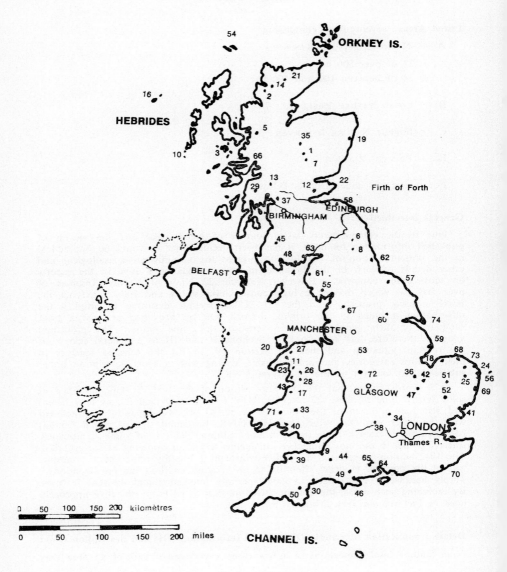

15

SHETLAND IS.

31

54

ORKNEY IS.

21

14
2

16

HEBRIDES

5

10   3   66

13
29   12   22
37
BIRMINGHAM

35
1
7

19

Firth of Forth

58
EDINBURGH

45

48   63
4   61
55

BELFAST

6
8
62

57

67
60   74

MANCHESTER   59

20   27
11
23   26
43   28
17
71   33
40

53   72
36   42   51   25
GLASGOW   47   52

18   68   73
24
56
69

41

34
38   LONDON
Thames R.

9
39   44   65   64
49
50   30   46

70

50   100   150   200   kilomètres

0   50   100   150   200   miles

CHANNEL IS.

540

still be open to human exploitation and, even more rarely, as in the case of the Forest Nature Reserves, forest produce continues to be exploited although under very strict control.

b) Area : because of the great scientific interest of the protected biotopes in the U.K., application of the size criterion is often particularly arbitrary, as already mentioned in the General Introduction. Nevertheless, in order to maintain the consistency of the U.N. List, it has seemed necessary to accept the criterion, subject to certain qualifications indicated below under sections III and IV. But the reader would do well to keep the matter in mind, to refer to section V in order to form a clear idea of the large number of Reserves which have had to be discarded and, above all, to consult the extensive documentation which exists on the subject of these small but valuable areas.

c) Staff : under the criterion, the strength of the personnel employed full-time to control and supervise the 108 National Nature Reserves administered by the Nature Conservancy as at May 1964, should have been not less than 23 persons for the 90,000 ha involved : in fact the scientific staff alone already exceeded 100. For the other Listed Areas, it is clear that the supervisory staff is also considerably greater than demanded by a criterion of one full-time unit per 4,000 ha.

d) Budget : the same considerations apply as to staff. For the areas controlled by the Nature Conservancy, the criterion would demand a minimum annual expenditure of U.S. $ 18,000, whereas its budget in 1961-1962 was £ 552,000, at that time equivalent to over 1 ½ million dollars. The same situation applies to the Reserves maintained by other organisations.

A. — NATIONAL NATURE RESERVES.

II.

Since 23 March 1949, responsibility in the United Kingdom for conservation in general and for " national parks and equivalent reserves " as defined in the present List, has been vested in the Nature Conservancy, the status of which since 1 June 1965 has been that of a component body of the Natural Environment Research Council established by Royal Charter at that date.

The terms of reference of the Conservancy have not altered under its new status and are set out as follows :

" To provide scientific advice on the conservation and control of the natural flora and fauna of Great Britain, to establish, maintain and manage Nature Reserves in Great Britain, including the maintenance of physical features of scientific interest; and to organise and develop the research and scientific services related thereto. "

By virtue of the National Parks and Access to the Countryside Act, 1949, the Nature Conservancy is empowered to declare an area a " National Nature Reserve " (NNR), either under a " Nature Reserve Agreement " or upon purchase — in exceptional cases, expropriation — or by taking up a lease, whichever method may be deemed appropriate, the land in question thereupon acquiring the status of Crown Land.

At the end of April 1968, these powers had been exercised to create 124 NNRs, of which 37 were in Scotland, the rest in England or Wales (the Nature Conservancy not having extended its activities to Northern Ireland). As might be expected in the light of the distribution of industrialisation and population, the largest NNRs are situated in Scotland, for example Nos. 1-5 in the List, or in the extreme north of England (No. 6). The NNRs totalled 104,105 ha in area.

Entry of visitors is unrestricted in some of the Reserves, but it is only allowed in others under special permit.

541

Perhaps the most remarkable feature of the NNRs is the scientific thoroughness with which (*a*) the areas have been chosen following a comprehensive national survey, (*b*) are directed and managed on sound ecological lines and (*c*) are subjected to a co-ordinated programme of investigation and research.

For these purposes a second very comprehensive national survey is shortly due to be completed (1969).

Mention has already been made of the fact that the Conservancy has over a hundred scientific officers, of whom the greater part are posted to six research stations and the remainder constitute the " Conservation Branch ".

B. — LOCAL NATURE RESERVES.

The LNR set up by a County authority, also under powers given by the 1949 Act and in agreement with the Nature Conservancy. The standard of protection enjoyed by them is comparable to that of the NNR and by May 1968, fifteen LNRs, with a total area of 3,602 ha, had been established.

C. — FOREST NATURE RESERVES.

The FNR are forest areas managed " in the interests of nature conservation and of ecological research concurrently with the interests of forest production ". These areas have not been constituted as NNRs on the grounds that to do so would have been superfluous, since their protection is sufficiently assured by a tacit understanding between the Public Authority responsible for them (normally of course the Forestry Commission) and the Nature Conservancy. As at May 1968, the number of FNRs was thirteen, covering a total area of 1,733 ha.

D. — PRIVATE RESERVES.

This Non-Statutory Nature Reserves, established by independent organisations, some 150 in all, of which the eight Listed cover a total area of 4,542 ha. They pertain chiefly to three organisations :

(i) The National Trust (NT), which originated in 1895;

(ii) The Royal Society for the Protection of Birds (RSPB);

(iii) The Society for the Promotion of Nature Reserves and its associated County Naturalists' Trusts (CNT).

None of these areas is subject to specific legal sanctions, although in many of them special protection of birds and their eggs is assured by the Protection of Birds Act 1954. However, all of them are subject to the constraints which derive from the free exercise of the rights of private property under the Common Law.

The 74 Listed Areas which, in the light of the previous discussion, can only be desinted as an arbitrary selection, are as follows :

A. — NATIONAL NATURE RESERVES.

a) 22 exceeding the criterion minimum of 500 ha (1,235 acres) :

1. Cairngorms (Inverness)	25,949 ha
2. Inverpolly (Ross and Cromarty)	10,857 ha
3. Rhum (Inverness)	10,684 ha
4. Caerlaverock (Dumfries and Kirkcudbright)	5,406 ha
5. Beinn Eighe (Ross and Cromarty)	4,203 ha

R., Oka R.

(photo : I. Koustantinov)

U.S.S.R., Caucasus R.

(photo : Aleks

NDA, Queen Elizabeth N.P.

U.S.A., Olympic N.P.

(photo : National Park Service)

U.S.A., Glacier Bay N.M.

Yellowstone N.P.

U.S.A., Great Smoky Mountain N.S.

(photo : National Park

 6. Moor House (Westmorland) ... ... 4,047 ha.
 7. Caenlochan (Aberdeen, Angus, Perth) ... ... 3,596 ha.
 8. Upper Teesdale (Yorkshire) ... ... 2,630 ha.
 9. Bridgwater Bay (Somerset) ... ... 2,430 ha.
10. Loch Druidibeg (Inverness) ... ... 1,658 ha.
11. Snowdon (Y Wyddfa) (Caernavon) ... ... 1,658 ha.
12. Loch Leven (Kinross) ... ... 1,578 ha.
13. Rannoch Moor (Perth) ... ... 1,482 ha.
14. Inchnadamph (Sutherland) ... ... 1,295 ha.
15. Hermaness (Shetland) ... ... 953 ha.
16. St. Kilda (Inverness) . ... 850 ha.
17. Cors Tregaron (Cardigan) . ... 759 ha.
18. Scolt Head (Norfolk) ... ... 728 ha.
19. Sands of Forvie (Aberdeen) ... ... 710 ha.
20. Newborough Warren — Ynys Llanddwyn (Anglesey) ... ... 628 ha.
21. Invernaver (Sutherland) ... ... 545 ha.
22. Tentsmuir Point (Fife) ... ... 506 ha.

b) Although less than 500 ha and therefore below the criterion requirement, the following 34 NNR of over 100 ha in size are deemed to merit inclusion :

23. Morfa Harlech ... ... 486 ha.
24. Hickling Broad ... ... 482 ha.
25. Bure Marshes ... ... 408 ha.
26. Rhinog . ... 376 ha.
27. Cwm Idwal . ... 394 ha.
28. Cader Idris ... ... 388 ha.
29. Ben Lui . ... 370 ha.
30. Axmouth-Lyme Regis Undercliffs . ... 320 ha.
31. Noss ... ... 310 ha.
32. Skomer Island ... ... 304 ha.
33. Craig Cerrig Gleisiad . ... 279 ha.
34. Wychwood ... ... 259 ha.
35. Craigellachie . ... 257 ha.
36. Holme Fen ... ... 256 ha.
37. Loch Lomond ... ... 250 ha.
38. Fyfield Down ... ... 245 ha.
39. Braunton Burrows ... ... 224 ha.
40. Oxwich . ... 217 ha.
41. Orfordness-Havergate . ... 206 ha.
42. Woodwalton Fen . ... 206 ha.
43. Morfa Dyffryn ... ... 200 ha.
44. Shapwick Heath . ... 194 ha.
45. Silver Flowe . ... 189 ha.
46. Studland Heath ... ... 172 ha.
47. Monks Wood ... ... 155 ha.
48. Kirkconnell Flow ... ... 153 ha.
49. Morden Bog ... ... 147 ha.
50. Yarner Wood ... ... 144 ha.
51. Weeting Heath ... ... 135 ha.
52. Cavenham Heath . ... 135 ha.
53. Rostherne Mere . ... 131 ha.
54. North Rona and Sula Sgeir ... ... 128 ha.
55. Roudsea Wood ... ... 115 ha.
56. Winterton Dunes . ... 104 ha.

B. — LOCAL NATURE RESERVES.

Seven LNR exceeding 100 ha in size, two of them being over 500 ha :

57. Farndale (Yorkshire)	1,000 ha.
58. Aberlady Bay (East Lothian)	576 ha.

followed by :

59. Gibraltar Point	405 ha.
60. Fairburn Ings	247 ha.
61. Drigg Dunes and Gullery	233 ha.
62. Castle Eden Denes	207 ha.
63. Castle and Hightae Lochs	136 ha.

C. — FOREST NATURE RESERVES.

Three FNR exceeding 100 ha in size, one of them being over 500 ha :

64. Matley and Denny (New Forest, Hampshire)	1,031 ha.
65. Bramshaw (New Forest, Hampshire)	210 ha.
66. Arriundle Oakwood (Argyll)	115 ha.

D. — PRIVATE RESERVES.

Finally, the eight largest Private Reserves, which although there is no agreement between their owners and the Nature Conservancy conferring on them the status of NNR, are in some cases governed by such an agreement to the extent of being officially recognised as partial Reserves (for example as a Wildfowl Refuge, etc.) :

67. Malham Tarn (Yorkshire) : NT	920 ha.
68. Horsey Mere (Norfolk) : NT	694 ha.
69. Minsmere (Suffolk) : RSPB	611 ha.
70. Dungeness (Kent) : RSPB	493 ha.
71. Gwenffrwd (Carmarthenshire) : RSPB	486 ha.
72. Sutton Park (Warwickshire) : CNT	465 ha.
73. Blakeney Point (Norfolk) : NT	440 ha.
74. Spurn Head (Yorkshire) : CNT	433 ha.

⋆
⋆

Description of the 22 National Nature Reserves exceeding the criterion minimum of 500 ha (for the sake of brevity scientific names are only quoted for a few rarities) :

1. CAIRNGORMS.

a) Mountain area, with vegetation ranging from Scots pine, juniper and birch forest to the arctic-alpine associations of the screes and exposed summits (over 1,200 m). More than 200 species of flowering plants.

b) Wild cat, red and roe deer, mountain hare; golden eagle, ptarmigan, blackcock, dotterel, greenshank, crested tit, snow bunting, crossbill.

2. INVERPOLLY.

a) Includes the whole of Loch Sionascaig and several Torridon sandstone peaks, together with small lochs, rivers, sea-coast and off-shore islands.

b) Pine marten, red and roe deer, wild cat; golden eagle.

3. RHUM.

a) Island, with mountain ridge, rising to over 750 m, of geologically interesting ultra-basic rocks of volcanic origin. Rare plants including alpine pennycress *Thlaspi alpestre,* fungus flora of over 700 species.

b) Rhum mouse *Apodemus hebridensis hamiltoni,* hebridean vole *Microtus agrestis exsul,* red deer, grey seal; Manx shearwater, golden eagle.

4. CAERLAVEROCK.

a) Mixture of salt-marsh and of sand and mud banks between the river Nith and the Lochar water.

b) Large numbers of barnacle, pink-footed and grey-lag geese winter in the reserve; shelduck, gulls, terns and several waders nest in the saltings.

5. BEINN EIGHE.

a) Mountain of Cambrian quartzite and pre-Cambrian Torridon sandstone, containing important remnant of Caledonian pine forest, with an admixture of oak, holly, rowan, birch and *Sphagnum* moss.

b) Wild cat, pine marten, red deer, mountain hare; golden eagle, ptarmigan, redstart, whinchat, wood warbler, redpoll, crossbill and bullfinch.

6. MOOR HOUSE.

a) Ridge of the Pennines, with carboniferous limestone beds, its poor eroded peat moorland a legacy of former mine workings and overgrazing.

b) Typical upland avifauna; invertebrate fauna includes 180 species of Diptera.

7. CAENLOCHAN.

a) Limestone area rising from 250 to over 1,000 m, with rather dry continental climate, resulting in a varied montane flora.

b) Red deer; golden eagle, ptarmigan.

8. UPPER TEESDALE.

a) Of considerable geological interest, with an exceptional flora. The dominant moorland vegetation with *sphagnum* bogs and heather is of typical western type, but unusual plant communities of Arctic-alpine, continental and southern species occur, especially wherever limestone reaches the surface.

b) Upland avifauna.

9. BRIDGWATER BAY.

a) Coastal physiography and vegetation of the Parrett estuary.

b) Wildfowl and waders; only moulting ground of shelduck in Britain.

10. LOCH DRUIDIBEG.

a) The loch shore is broken into innumerable bays and islets by small penin-
sulas covered with peat or boulders : sandy beaches, dunes, short turf, fresh water
lochs and streams.

b) Most important surviving breeding-place of the grey lag goose in Britain.

11. SNOWDON (Y WYDDFA).

a) Mountain of very ancient volcanic origin, supporting a wide range of vegetation, from oak woods at 50 m, through intermediate sheep-walk grasslands and
the arctic-alpine communities of the calcareous cliffs, to sub-arctic heath in the
900 m summit area.

b) Buzzard, raven, pied flycatcher and other typical Welsh mountain species.

12. LOCH LEVEN.

a) Shallow loch in the plain of Kinross; rich aquatic flora.

b) The most important freshwater area in Britain for migratory and breeding
wildfowl : winter visitors include pink-footed and grey-lag geese in large numbers,
wild swans and thousands of ducks, of which at least five species stay to breed.

13. RANNOCH MOOR.

a) Nearly level plateau of granite and moraine, with shallow blanket bog at
the relatively high altitude of 300 m, which is not found in any other NNR.

b) Red deer; typical moorland avifauna.

14. INCHNADAMPH.

a) Karstic area of special geological interest, with underground streams and
caverns and an isolated outcrop of Torridon sandstone. Peat covered hollows
between limestone ridges support willow scrub of a type common in Scandinavia
but only recently described in Scotland. Varied flora includes whortle-leaved
willow, mountain avens, purple saxifrage, globe flower and many ferns.

b) Fauna similar to that of No. 21.

15. HERMANESS.

a) Cliffs, rocks and moorland of the north-western peninsula of Unst, most
northerly island in Shetland and northern point of Britain.

b) One of the few major breeding stations of the great skua, in the northern
hemisphere. Arctic skua, red-throated diver, gannet, kittiwake and puffin also nest.

16. ST KILDA.

a) Isolated island, rising sheer out of the ocean to a height of 425 m; luxuriant
vegetation, which includes primroses, roseroot and honeysuckle.

b) The huge concentration of sea-birds includes the world's largest colony of
gannets. Fulmars and puffins are among the most numerous nesting species and
Leach's petrel one which is otherwise rare in the eastern Atlantic. Endemic subspecies include the St. Kilda wren and two mammals, a field mouse and the
Soay sheep, a very ancient breed of domesticated sheep.

546

17. Cors Tregaron.

a) One of the best examples of a raised bog in England and Wales, with marsh-land and rush-dominated terraces; plants include marsh andromeda *A. polifolia,* crowberry and the royal fern *Osmunda regalis.*

b) Main wintering area in England and Wales for the Greenland race of white-fronted goose; blackcock, dunlin, corncrake, whinchat, grasshopper warbler, redpoll and black-headed gull breed; mammals include the polecat.

18. Scolt Head.

a) Extensive saltings with a series of dune ridges, separated from the mainland by tidal channels.

b) Fluctuating but usually large colonies of common and sandwich terns; in winter brent geese, waders, shore-larks and snow-buntings.

19. Sands of Forvie.

a) Foreshore backed by dunes, slacks and rough pasture, with an area of schistous and gneissic cliffs, overlain with boulder clay, and two small freshwater lochs.

b) Large breeding population of eider; arctic, sandwich and little terns, shelduck, shoveler, red grouse and fulmar also nest.

20. Newborough Warren (Ynys Llanddwyn).

a) Exceptionally large dune area of island of Anglesey, showing all stages of plant succession from beach zone to fixed dune grassland; includes two estuaries, a lake with water grading from salt to fresh, a salt-marsh and a peninsula of special geological interest.

b) Passage migrant and wintering birds, especially waders, are of great variety and interest.

21. Invernaver.

a) Near mouth of the river Naver, contains a wide variety of habitats, including many boreal plant associations, a mountain avens heath, an unusual development of juniper scrub on peat bordering blown sand and a small salt-marsh. Flowering plants of special interest are the primrose *Primula scotica,* purple saxifrage, narrow blysmus, purple oxytropis ans spring squill.

b) Breeding birds include greenshank, red-throated diver, ring ouzel, twite.

22. Tentsmuir Point.

a) Outstanding area for the study of coastal sand accretion and its colonisation by plants; dunes with alder, birch and willow slacks and small marshes.

b) The foreshore is a winter roost for wildfowl; exceptional concentration of eiders.

Areas excluded :

A. — Nine NNRs of over 100 ha established by March 1967, but after the List for the present edition was closed, namely : Holkham (Norfolk) (3,926 ha); Lindis-farne (Northumberland) (2,947 ha); Whiteford (Glamorgan) (782 ha); Monach Isles

(Inverness) (570 ha); Ainsdale Sand Dunes (Lancashire) (486 ha); Meall Nan Tarmachan (Perth) (457 ha); Mound Alderwoods (Sutherland) (278 ha); Hartland Moor (Dorset) (258 ha); Wye and Crundale Downs (Kent) (101 ha).

B. — Fifty-nine NNRs of less than 100 ha. Among these are certainly some, for example Old Winchester Hill referred to in the General Introduction, which could be considered as deserving of a place in the List as much or more than some areas in other countries which it has been decided to include.

C. — Eight LNR, 10 FNR and about 140 Private Reserves.

D. — Six National Wildfowl Refuges, totalling 13,237 ha in area, which are in addition to the 8 of these Refuges classified as NNR, but unlike them only enjoy partial protection and therefore do not qualify for the List. The four most important are :

Southport Sanctuary (Lancashire)	5,720 ha.
Wyre-Lune (Lancashire)	3,640 ha.
Slimbridge (Gloucestershire)	1,857 ha.
Humber (Yorkshire and Lincoln)	1,252 ha.

E. — Twelve Regional Wildfowl Refuges. There are 17 of these in all, of a total area of 4,191 ha, but some of them, such as Hickling Broad and Loch Lomond, also constitute NNR.

F. — The 'Sites of Special Scientific Interest' (SSSI), which are simply areas which the Nature Conservancy notifies to local planning authorities as having particular floral, faunal, geological or other scientific interest and which, on this basis, cannot be modified by development plans without prior consultation of the Conservancy.

G. — The ten 'National Parks' in England and Wales, which are inhabited and economically exploited areas, but are designated as areas of outstanding natural beauty, protected, on that basis, against being spoiled by industrialisation or haphazard urbanisation and also specially controlled and organised with a view to promoting and facilitating open air recreation.

The National Parks from a social point of view have a considerable importance, although the criterion of " total protection " laid down by the ICNP does not permit them to figure in the present List. In this they are closely comparable to the Naturparke of the German Federal Republic.

The ten Parks are administered by the National Parks Commission set up under the 1949 Act, referred to above. Unlike the Nature Conservancy, the Commission's remit does not extend beyond England and Wales. It plays a very active part in the matter of public education, especially by encouraging a better understanding and attitude towards wildlife (fauna and flora) and by its publication of a " Country Code for Visitors to the Countryside ".

The ten National Parks (which were briefly cited in Part Two of the previous edition of the List) cover a total area of about 1,315,000 ha, and the National Parks Commission is also responsible for some 15 " Areas of Outstanding Natural Beauty ", covering a total of 525,250 ha and nine " Long Distance Routes ", especially picturesque roads or trails of a total length of 1,890 km. The names and size of the ten National Parks are :

1. Lake District National Park	224,164 ha.
2. Snowdonia National Park	218,850 ha.
3. Yorkshire Dales National Park	176,120 ha.
4. North York Moors National Park	143,220 ha.
5. Peak District National Park	140,375 ha.

548

6. Brecon Beacons National Park ... ... 133,385 ha.
7. Northumberland National Park ... ... 103,080 ha.
8. Dartmoor National Park . ... 94,545 ha.
9. Exmoor National Park ... ... 68,645 ha.
10. Pembrokeshire Coast National Park ... ... 58,275 ha.

N.B. — It is interesting and significant that No. 5 in this list, the Peak District National Park, was the one to which the Council of Europe decided to award its first 'European Diploma', when this mark of distinction was inaugurated in 1965, although the area does not qualify for a place in the U.N. List of National Parks and Equivalent Reserves.

H. — Finally, it will have been noted that no mention has been made in the List or section V of reserved areas in Northern Ireland. The situation and prospects were described as follows in 1964 :

"Extensive areas of the Northern Ireland countryside will be designated national parks to preserve their natural beauty under the Amenity Lands Bill, which is to be considered by the Northern Ireland Parliament in October 1964. The Bill will enable the Ministry to acquire land or to enter into agreements with landowners for the purpose of creating nature reserves, and to specify other areas of scientific interest. The Bill will also give the Ministry powers to acquire areas of outstanding beauty and powers to hand over these areas to other responsible bodies, e.g. the National Trust, to be managed. Two advisory committees will be established under the Bill : an Ulster Countryside Committee, which will advise on the creation of National Parks, and a Nature Reserve Committee. "

No information has yet been received of the precise extent to which these plans have been carried out, but on 28 June 1968, a fine new wildlife reserve at Castle Caldwell Forest Park was opened : it is owned by the Forestry Division of the Ministry of Agriculture and its management has been entrusted to the RSPB.

DEPENDENT AND NEWLY INDEPENDENT TERRITORIES

Listed Areas : nil.

Areas excluded :

It has been decided to treat together, in this subsection, the overseas territories still or until recently administered by the United Kingdom, of which the size or the population is very small and does not seem to justify a separate chapter in the List. The only exception is the Falklands Islands (q.v.), which despite a population of only a few thousand, has been dealt with separately.

Most of the territories to be considered are islands of relatively small size, in which at present no national park or reserve qualifies for admission to the List. A large proportion of them are to be found in the British Antilles :

Antigua (two "public parks" : English Harbour 250 ha; Long Bay 50 ha : letter dated 10 September 1965).
Cayman, Dominica, Grenada : nil (confirmation received in the case of Grenada on 6 February 1966). One or more reserves in the virgin forest areas of Dominica have been strongly advocated, but not yet, so far as is known, established.
Montserrat (2,000 ha of forest are reported to be protected from cultivation and uncontrolled felling, but no protection is given to birds : letter of 7 September 1964).

549

St. Kitts-Nevis and Anguilla, St. Lucia : nil.

St. Vincent (4 Forest Reserves and 4 bird sanctuaries were cited in the previous edition, E/3436, of the List and were confirmed as still maintained in a letter of 25 May 1965).

Turks and Caicos Islands : nil; a marine park is however under active consideration (1969).

Windward Islands (3 Forest Reserves : Castries Water Works F.R. 1,038 ha; Dennery Water Works F.R. 146 ha; Central Forest Reserve 913 ha; but no other details in letter of 26 April 1965).

Dependent territories elsewhere in the world to which brief mention may be made :

Bahamas : " no parks or reserves " (letter of 24 July 1964).

British Solomon Islands Protectorate : a recent (1968) draft White Paper on forestry states that the Forestry Department will seek to establish Nature Reserves for scientific purposes in selected areas.

Seychelles : a letter of 3 December 1964 gave a similar negative report, but in 1968 Cousin Island was purchased through the initiative of the International Council for Bird Preservation, with World Wildlife Fund support, and has been established as a full sanctuary. Several more are planned by the Government and the British Indian Ocean Territories authorities, notably on the island of Aldabra; the necessary legislation is reported to have been enacted in 1969.

St. Helena and dependencies (Ascension and Tristan da Cunha) : nil (but active steps are now being taken in all three areas to establish reserves for a fauna and flora of the greatest scientific interest).

133. UNITED STATES OF AMERICA

I. Listed Areas : two hundred and eighty-six, comprising :

A. — 32 National Parks;

B. — 35 National Monuments, Natural Areas,
7 National Monuments, Archaeological Areas;

C. — 3 Natural Reserves with status equivalent to that of National Parks or National Monuments;

D. — 6 National Seashores;

E. — 4 National Recreation Areas;

F. — 2 National Parkways;

G. — 14 National Forests, Wilderness Areas,
30 National Forests, Wild Areas,
38 National Forests, Primitive Areas,
1 National Forest, Puerto Rico;

H. — 1 Boundary Waters Canoe Area;

I. — 20 National Wildlife Refuges;

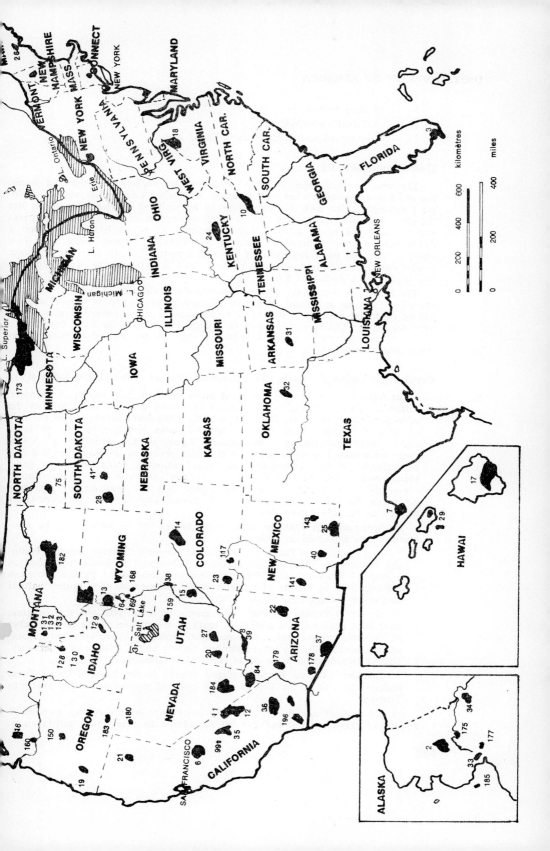

UNITED STATES OF AMERICA

J. — 89 State Parks;

K. — 3 Private Reserves;

L. — 1 Reserve-Laboratory, Panama Canal Zone.

General Introduction :

The very large number of areas qualifying for inclusion in the List would require a disproportionate amount of space, if detailed information and an ecological description for each of them were to be included in this edition. It has therefore been decided to give only a brief description of the 32 national parks and to refer the reader to the previous edition, of which E/3436 contained a description of most national monuments and national refuges, while Part Two covered the three main categories of national forests. For the rest, an abundant printed documentation is readily obtainable in the U.S.A. by anyone wishing to have full details of a particular Listed Area.

The names, in some cases dates of establishment, and size of the 286 areas are accordingly set out in Section IV below, information relevant to Sections II and III having otherwise been dealt with in a rather general and summarised way in the previous pages. The concluding part of Section IV contains the brief descriptions of the 32 national parks, which it is thus hoped can be referred to without too much inconvenience.

Details : application of criteria (II), general information (III) and description (IV) :

II.

a) Status : the wealth of protected areas in the U.S.A. has made selection difficult. Those included in the present List enjoy a status which satisfies the criteria adopted, although there are certainly some local exceptions to the rule of total protection. Thus, even in national parks, stretches of river or lakes occur where sport-fishing is authorised. Again, on the periphery of certain parks, controlled hunting is permitted at certain periods of the year, provided that it conforms to the requirements or indeed essential needs of proper game management. The same applies to the various categories of National Forest. Nevertheless, in general there is no doubt that the fundamental principles governing the effective conservation of natural environments are adequately applied in the 286 Listed Areas.

b) Area : exceeds 2,000 ha in all cases except for 24, which may be summarised and explained as follows :

(i) Two National Parks, 13 National Monuments (Natural Areas), 3 National Monuments (Archaeological Areas), 1 National Memorial (classified as a Natural Reserve) and 1 National Seashore area, stated by the American authorities to be worthy of mention in the List because they protect natural landscapes or associations of special interest.

(ii) The 3 Private Reserves : two groups of these, plus one specific area, have been included as a symbol or mark of recognition of the large number of valuable reservations, sponsored and protected by independent organisations, notably the National Audubon Society and the Nature Conservancy. One or two of these areas do in fact exceed 2,000 ha.

(iii) The 1,460 ha Barro Colorado reserve in the Panama Canal Zone, included as one of the best-known samples of protection in the American Tropics.

c) and *d*) Staff and Budget : the 286 areas have been carefully assessed in respect of these criteria and can be considered to meet them satisfactorily.

Most of the national parks certainly do so, the Yosemite and Grand Teton, for example, each heaving a permanent staff of over 50, seasonally reinforced by another 120 men, as against the 30 and 12 units, respectively, which their size (304,000 ha and 124,000 ha) would demand under the criterion. Again, the criterion would require the U.S. National Park Service (USNPS), which controls about 10 million hectares, to command an annual budget of some U.S. $ 500,000, whereas in fact even by 1964, its expenditure had reached a figure of $ 130 million, while its staff varies from a total of 6,000 in winter to 10,000 in summer (as against a criterion requirement of only 1,000).

III.
Administration : the first 89 of the Listed Areas are the responsibility of the USNPS of the Department of the Interior, established in 1916. Much could be written of the political steps whereby the Service was created and, gradually, received full recognition, in the face of innumerable external pressures which it met with tenacity, courage and skill, winning for its struggle in a steadily increasing measure the powerful support of American public opinion.

The next 104 areas on the List are administered by the U.S. Forest Service of the Department of Agriculture, while the administration of the 92 State Parks and Private Reserves is indicated by their title. Finally, the Barro Colorado reserve is administered by the Smithsonian Institution, Washington.

Tourism : the USNPS has taken great pains to put a very highly developed organisation at the service of visitors, with specialised staff and material resources of every kind, such as guides, museums, brochures, ' camp-fires ' and so on. The fundamental policy of the Service is perhaps best illustrated by the intelligent and extraordinarily extensive " interpretative services " provided for visitors, which deserve special commendation for the success with which they have given realisation to the concept of a " national park ".

Under a change in the regulations introduced in 1965, an entrance fee is charged for all Parks. Nevertheless, an estimate based on the ever increasing success achieved, gave good grounds for expecting well over 100 million visitors to the Parks in 1966. This growth of interest is not without its problems and indeed is a matter of some concern, in that it raises the whole question of how to relieve the supervisory and maintenance staff of the Parks of duties in connection with the reception of tourists, which absorb more and more of their time at the expense of their main functions. It has even been necessary to give some thought to the idea of limiting the total number of visitors allowed to visit each Park annually, although this idea is not easy to reconcile with the basic aims with which the Parks were established or with the democratic outlook of a country such as the U.S.A. It is quite possible, however, that some regulation of this sort will ultimately have to be imposed, even if it involves the difficulty of finding a compromise between the economic success which many parks derive from the plethora of visitors and the very real risks which the influx brings in its train.

' Visitor services ' are of course also promoted and organised on quite a large scale in the State Parks.

Research : most of the scientific research in the National Parks is undertaken by naturalists attached to the individual staffs and is directed mainly to applied ecology, linked with inventory descriptions of the protected biotopes and especially with the management problems which the Park staff has to resolve. In addition, a number of Universities carry out research in the national parks, sometimes in collaboration with the USNPS. At the First World Conference on National Parks (Seattle, 1962), one of the Recommendations (No. 6) laid stress on the exceptional opportunities that National Parks

553

and Equivalent Reserves offer for research into undisturbed biotopes and called for the careful planning and co-ordination of such research on an interdisciplinary basis. The U.S.A. accepted this recommendation and in 1963, the American Association for the Advancement of Science set up a special committee, which published an important report entitled " Council Study Committee on Natural Areas as Research Facilities ". Moreover, also in 1963, the National Academy of Sciences published another detailed Report entitled " A Report by the Advisory Committee to the NPS on research ". These two reports contained recommendations tending to reinforce an integrated programme of research in national parks, which is certainly the key to the rational management of these areas.

*
**

The legal basis and other legal, administrative and historical aspects :

A. — NATIONAL PARKS.

In principle protection is total and whenever it falls short of being so, the official policy is in general to make every effort to reduce the remaining easements which it has not yet been possible to extinguish.

Protection is assured for natural features, including fauna and flora, in all national parks and natural monuments, by the provisions of the Act of 25 August 1916, which included the following notable pronouncement : " The Service thus established (by the Act) shall promote and regulate the use of Federal areas known as parks, monuments and reservations hereinafter specified by such means and measures as conform to the fundamental purpose of the said parks, monuments and reservations, which purpose is to conserve the scenery and the natural and historic objects and the wildlife therein and to provide for the enjoyment of the same in such manner and by such means as will leave them unimpaired for the enjoyment of future generations ". Every exception to this fundamental principle requires specific legal provision by the Congress of the United States (for example, the Acts creating four national parks in which mineral exploitation continued to be permitted) or, alternatively, recourse to delegation of the powers of Congress in favour of the Secretary of State for the Interior (for example, the power to authorise culling of animals in Park areas where their numbers are excessive and causing degradation of the habitats). However, due to claims of title or pressures of public opinion, to pre-existing customary rights and even to the presence in national parks of areas of privately-owned land, activities have had to be permitted in Parks which some critics have considered to be quite unsuitable. They are tolerated only because they constitute inescapable obligations, but every possible step is taken to secure their progressive elimination.

Policy regarding the grazing of domestic stock in Park areas can be summed up as follows : where stock used to be grazed before the creation of the Park, this is allowed to continue during the lifetime of the original owner and his direct heir or until the grazing right is bought out by the Government. Sport-fishing is allowed by law throughout the American national parks system in recognition of a deeply-rooted tradition. But fishing has to conform to Federal and State regulations, stretches of water can be permanently closed to fishing, and the policy is to encourage the practice of " fishing for fun ", meaning that barbless hooks are used by which the fish are caught and can be returned to the water with the minimum of harm.

B. — NATIONAL MONUMENTS.

Enjoying the same degree of protection as National Parks, National Monuments differ in the fact that they are created (but cannot be done away with) by the President and not by Act of Congress. They are divided into the three categories of Natural Areas, Historical (or Archaeological) Areas and Recreation Areas (see under E below), the differences between them being indicated by their names. It should be noted that of the 17 Archaeological Areas included in the previous edition, E/3436, of the List, the seven selected for the present List are those in which the interest centres more upon their natural associations than on archaeological sites : they are in fact included because they also provide full protection for natural environments considered worthy of interest. On the other hand, all the 35 Natural Area Monuments of the previous edition are again included, though a dozen of them are less than 2,000 ha in extent.

C. — NATURAL RESERVES.

The three areas listed under this head are a rather special case. The Theodore Roosevelt National Memorial Park is only not a National Park proper, because to have made it so would necessitate giving up its name, since no National Parks can as a matter of principle bear the name of a person. In all other respects its legal status is similar. The same kind of reason places the Coronado National Memorial in this small separate category. The third area, the National Capital Parks, is anomalous in that it consists of some 780 separate pieces of land of small size, though adding up to a total of 16,379 ha, but nevertheless provides for a great city like Washington some outstanding samples of natural environments and wildlife.

D. — NATIONAL SEASHORES.

Established by Act of Congress, these are areas of which the definitive status will be assured as soon as land purchases and the buying up of user rights have been effected in sufficient number and covering the more important sectors. Meanwhile, these property and other rights continue to be exercised under control.

E. — NATIONAL RECREATIONAL AREAS.

As previously mentioned these form a category of National Monuments, but are restricted to the lakes formed by the construction of the great dams. The borders of these lakes are partly protected as a guarantee of the purposes for which these gigantic works were undertaken, but the waters are systematically developed for recreational purposes, mainly of course for aquatic sports, but also sufficiently often in the interests of conservation to justify the inclusion of four areas in the present List.

F. — NATIONAL PARKWAYS.

Although these are merely strips of natural landscape bordering highways, they can be considered also as of equal interest from the ecological and historical point of view, and as strictly protected as are the areas contained in the National Parks. Moreover the total size of the two Parkways included in the List, 26,286 and 18,119 ha, respectively, is very appreciable.

G. — NATIONAL FORESTS.

The 14 'Wilderness' and 30 'Wild' Areas (the latter until 1965 also called Wilderness Areas) qualify for the List because they constitute forest blocks which have been selected as of high quality, traversed by no roads, free from all commercial exploitation, where no hotels or camping are allowed and even aircraft are prohibited from flying over. Hunting and fishing are strictly regulated and kept to a few places only, as is the pasturing of livestock which the head of the Forest Service is empowered to authorise in specified zones as he thinks fit. The difference between Wilderness and Wild Areas is merely a matter of size and the particular administrative department authorised to set them up.

The regime applied to the 38 'Primitive Areas' is the same as that of the two categories dealt with in the previous paragraph, to which they could well be assigned were it not for the fact that they came into being first and that their status, although comparable, is of more ancient origin. Hence their re-classification as Wilderness or Wild Areas needs certain specific measures to be taken with regard to boundaries, etc., although in other respects, such as prohibition of roads and commercial exploitation, they are just as well protected.

The other National Forest area listed, namely the Caribbean National Forest or Luquillo Experimental Forest of Puerto Rico, is the only protected area on that island; it comprises tropical montane forest of special interest because of the surviving population of about 200 Puerto Rico parrots, the 'Red Book' endangered species *Amazona vittata*; the white-necked crow also occurs; the forest is supervised by a staff of 13, well above the criterion for an area of 10,525 ha.

H. — BOUNDARY WATERS CANOE AREA.

Formerly entitled the "Superior Roadless Area", this is a specially protected section of the Superior National Forest which adjoins the Canadian Quetico Provincial Park. Access to its thousands of lakes is by foot or canoe only and aircraft must keep at a height of not less than 700 m above the ground when flying over the area.

I. — NATIONAL WILDLIFE REFUGES.

The signing of the Wilderness Act in 1964 was an important event, because it enshrined a new legal concept in conferring Congressional protection on a new type of area of very great value from the conservation point of view — the 'wildlife refuge'. These areas have few if any inhabitants, little or no exploitation (except when hunting or fishing is permitted, under strict control, as in other American protected areas). Some of them are supervised, especially during the summer, by their own large staff, others by personnel drawn directly from the Bureau of Sport Fisheries and Wildlife. For the purpose of the present List a selection has been necessary and it has been decided simply to retain 20 out of the 22 Wildlife Refuges which were cited in the previous edition (E/3436).

J. — STATE PARKS.

The basis of selection has been to give preference to the areas answering most closely to the fundamental principles of status, size and effective management and to eliminate those which are too exclusively slanted towards recreation or in which natural vegetation that ought to have been protected has been eliminated.

The management of these Parks varies so much from State to State that it would be inappropriate to attempt a full description here, but the reader is referred to the published Proceedings of National Conference on State Parks of September 1963. Every State of the Union possesses one or more of these Parks, the scope ranging from large Park systems covering a vast area of natural wilderness and putting them on a par with the Federal National Parks (e.g. in California, Oregon and Maine) down to small areas chiefly designed to provide open air and sports facilities for large numbers of people. Many of them have special camping-places, shelters, jetties and other constructions. Other have no development organisation.

K. — PRIVATE RESERVES.

Very large numbers of nature reserves have been created in the U.S. by private enterprise. Among many associations too numerous to mention here, three play a particularly leading part. The National Audubon Society, founded in 1905, is " dedicated to conservation of Wildlife, Plants, Soil and Water in Relation to Human Progress " and owns various ' Sanctuaries' of which the most notable are the Corkscrew Rookery in Florida and the Rainey Wildlife Sanctuary in Louisiana, both included under a single heading in the List. The Nature Conservancy, which began in 1917 as a committee of the Ecologists' Union and had the character of a discussion group until its Statutes were modified in 1951, took up in the latter year what it called the " Race for Open Space " and, since then, has combined a policy of purchasing areas for protection with a policy of entering into agreements with owners and lessors desirous of co-operating with the Conservancy in ensuring that their land is accorded effective protection. A number of examples are included under one head of the List. The third body deserving special mention is the Hawk Mountain Sanctuary Association, which controls a reserve under that name and in doing so has paid particular attention to the protection of birds of prey, providing what is indeed model legislation for that purpose for many other States.

L. — RESERVE-LABORATORY, PANAMA CANAL ZONE.

When the cutting of the Panama Canal resulted in the flooding of the Chagres valley, several hills in the Canal Zone became islands. In 1923, one of these islands was given the status of a strict reserve and put at the disposal of the Institute for Research in Tropical America. After the death of the promoter of this ' Reserve-Laboratory ', Thomas Barbour, towards the end of the Second World War, its administration was vested in the Smithsonian Institution under the title of the ' Canal Zone Biological Area'. It enjoys total protection.

V.   The names, localities, date of establishment (where known) and size of the 286 areas selected for the List are as follows :

A. — NATIONAL PARKS.

1.	Yellowstone	Wyoming, Montana, Idaho, 1872	888,708 ha.
2.	Mount McKinley	Alaska, 1917	775,597 ha.
3.	Everglades	Florida, 1947	560,213 ha.
4.	Glacier	Montana, 1910	405,251 ha.
5.	Olympic	Washington, 1938	358,640 ha.
6.	Yosemite	California, 1890	304,380 ha.
7.	Big Bend	Texas, 1944	283,288 ha.
8.	Grand Canyon	Arizona, 1919	269,430 ha.
9.	Isle Royale	Michigan, 1940	215,740 ha.
10.	Great Smoky Mountain	North Carolina, Tennessee, 1930	205,070 ha.
11.	Kings Canyon	California, 1940	181,885 ha.
12.	Sequoia	California, 1890	154,744 ha.

13.	Grand Teton	... ...	Wyoming, 1929	124,140 ha.
14.	Rocky Mountain	... ...	Colorado, 1915	104,930 ha.
15.	Canyonlands	... ...	Utah, 1964	103,056 ha.
16.	Mount Rainier ...	... ...	Washington, 1899	96,793 ha.
17.	Hawaii Volcanoes	... ...	Hawaii, 1916	88,137 ha.
18.	Shenandoah	... ...	Virginia, 1935	84,921 ha.
19.	Crater Lake	... ...	Oregon, 1902	64,116 ha.
20.	Zion	... ...	Utah, 1919	58,813 ha.
21.	Lassen Volcanic .	... ...	California, 1916	42,773 ha.
22.	Petrified Forest ...	... ...	Arizona, 1962	37,676 ha.
23.	Mesa Verde	... ...	Colorado, 1906	20,830 ha.
24.	Mammoth Cave .	... ...	Kentucky, 1934	20,541 ha.
25.	Carlsbad Caverns	... ...	New Mexico, 1930	18,715 ha.
26.	Acadia	... ...	Maine, 1919	16,653 ha.
27.	Bryce Canyon	... ...	Utah, 1924	14,405 ha.
28.	Wind Cave ...	... ...	South Dakota, 1903	11,223 ha.
29.	Haleakala ...	... ...	Hawaii, 1961	10,560 ha.
30.	Virgin Islands	... ...	U.S. Virgin Islands, 1959	6,060 ha.
31.	Hot Springs .	... ...	Arkansas, 1921	413 ha.
32.	Platt	... ...	Oklahoma, 1906	365 ha.

B. — NATIONAL MONUMENTS, NATURAL AREAS.

33.	Katmai	... ...	Alaska, 1918	1,079,036 ha.
34.	Glacier Bay	... ...	Alaska, 1925	909,838 ha.
35.	Death Valley	... ...	California, 1933	763,104 ha.
36.	Joshua Tree	... ...	California, 1936	223,174 ha.
37.	Organ Pipe Cactus	... ...	Arizona, 1937	132,350 ha.
38.	Dinosaur ...	... ...	Colorado-Utah, 1915	83,898 ha.
39.	Grand Canyon ...	... ...	Arizona, 1932	79,312 ha.
40.	White Sands	... ...	New Mexico, 1933	58,614 ha.
41.	Badlands ...	... ...	South Dakota, 1939	44,612 ha.
42.	Saguaro	... ...	South Dakota, 1933	25,314 ha.
43.	Craters of the Moon	...	Idaho, 1924	19,274 ha.
44.	Lava Beds ...	... ...	California, 1925	18,496 ha.
45.	Copital Reef	... ...	Utah, 1937	15,669 ha.
46.	Great Sand Dunes	... ...	Colorado, 1932	14,596 ha.
47.	Arches	... ...	Utah, 1929	13,700 ha.
48.	Channel Islands .	... ...	California, 1938	7,269 ha.
49.	Colorado ...	... ...	Colorado, 1911	7,077 ha.
50.	Pinnacles ...	... ...	California, 1908	5,799 ha.
51.	Black Canyon of the Gunnison.		Colorado, 1933	5,682 ha.
52.	Chiricahua ...	... ...	Arizona, 1924	4,258 ha.

53.	Natural Bridges	Utah, 1908	3,040 ha.
54.	Cedar Breaks	Utah, 1933	2,469 ha.
55.	Chesapeake and Ohio Canal ...	Maryland-West Virgina, 1961	1,790 ha.

This area is administered separately by staff controlled by the Regional Director responsible for the National Capital Parks (No. 76 in the List); they are not officially part of the USNPS, although the Maryland and District of Columbia sections of the latter are partly involved in the supervision.

56.	Scotts Bluff	Nebraska, 1919	1,234 ha.
57.	Sunset Crater	Arizona, 1930	1,216 ha.
58.	Devils Tower	Wyoming, 1906	539 ha.
59.	Jewel Cave	South Dakota, 1908	510 ha.
60.	Buck Island Reef	U.S. Virgin Islands, 1961	350 ha.
61.	Muir Woods	California, 1908	337 ha.
62.	Devils Postpile	California, 1911	320 ha.
63.	Capulin Mountain	New Mexico, 1916	310 ha.
64.	Grand Portage	Minnesota, 1960	308 ha.
65.	Lehman Cave	Nevada, 1922	256 ha.
66.	Oregon Caves	Oregon, 1909	172 ha.
67.	Rainbow Bridge	Utah, 1910	64 ha.

NATIONAL MONUMENTS, ARCHAEOLOGICAL AREAS.

68.	Canyon de Chelly	Arizona, 1931	33,536 ha.
69.	Wupatki	Arizona, 1924	14,277 ha.
70.	Bandelier	New Mexico, 1916	10,841 ha.
71.	Chaco Canyon	New Mexico, 1907	8,604 ha.
72.	Walnut Canyon	Arizona, 1915	752 ha.
73.	Tonto	Arizona, 1907	448 ha.
74.	Montezuma Castle	Arizona, 1906	337 ha.

C. — NATURAL RESERVES, with status equivalent to that of National Parks or National Monuments.

75.	Theodore Roosevelt National Memorial Park	North Dakota, 1947	28,150 ha.
76.	National Capital Parks	D.C., Virginia, West Virginia, Maryland, 1933	16,379 ha.

Consisting of 780 separate units; the Chesapeake and Ohio Canal National Monument (No. 55 above) is under the same management.

77.	Coronado National Memorial .	Arizona, 1952	934 ha.

559

D. — NATIONAL SEASHORES.

N.B. — The Act of Congress under which these areas were established authorised the purchase of land up to a specified maximum area. It is these maxima which are quoted below.

78.	Padre Island N.S.	Texas, 1962	54,896 ha.
79.	Point Reyes N.S.	California, 1962	21,200 ha.
80.	Cape Cod N.S.	Massachusetts, 1961	17,840 ha.
81.	Assateague Island N.S.	Maryland, Virginia, 1965	14,852 ha.
82.	Cape Hatteras N.S.	North Carolina, 1937	11,400 ha.
83.	Fire Island N.S.	N.Y., 1964	1,720 ha.

E. — NATIONAL RECREATION AREAS.

84.	Lake Mead N.R.A.	Arizona-Nevada, 1936	774,791 ha.
85.	Glen Canyon N.R.A.	Arizona-Utah, 1958	495,994 ha.
86.	Coulee Dam N.R.A.	Washington, 1946	39,400 ha.
87.	Shadow Mountain N.R.A.	Colorado, 1952	7,296 ha.

F. — NATIONAL PARKWAYS.

88.	Blue Ridge Parkway	Virginia-North California, 1936	26,286 ha.
89.	Natchez Trace Parkway	Mississippi-Tennessee-Alabama, 1938	18,119 ha.

G. — NATIONAL FORESTS.

Wilderness Areas (W.A.).
Wild Areas (Wild).
Primitive Areas (P.A.).

N.B. — These areas are grouped together in the List in view of their similarity of status, but the category is indicated after each name.

ARIZONA :

90.	Mazatzal W.A.	82,000 ha.
91.	Blue Range P.A. (shared with New Mexico)	72,056 ha.
92.	Superstition W.A.	49,656 ha.
93.	Galiuro Wild	22,000 ha.
94.	Sycamore Canyon P.A.	18,380 ha.
95.	Sierra Ancha Wild	8,340 ha.
96.	Chiricahua Wild	7,200 ha.
97.	Pine Mountain P.A.	6,978 ha.
98.	Mount Baldy P.A.	2,960 ha.

CALIFORNIA :

99.	High Sierra P.A.	157,560 ha.
100.	Salmon Trinity Alps P.A.	89,320 ha.
101.	Marble Mountain W.A.	85,313 ha.
102.	Yolla Bolly-Middle Eel W.A.	43,726 ha.
103.	Emigrant Basin P.A.	38,808 ha.
104.	Mount Dana Minarets P.A.	32,872 ha.
105.	San Rafael P.A.	29,664 ha.
106.	South Warner P.A.	27,548 ha.
107.	Ventana P.A.	20,852 ha.
108.	Hoover W.A.	17,120 ha.
109.	Desolation Valley P.A.	16,537 ha.
110.	Devil Canyon-Bear Canyon P.A.	14,107 ha.
111.	San Gorgino Wild	13,559 ha.
112.	Agua Tibia P.A.	10,398 ha.
113.	San Jacinto Wild	8,226 ha.
114.	Caribou Wild	7,632 ha.
115.	Thousand Lakes Wild	6,278 ha.
116.	Cucamonga Wild	3,609 ha.

COLORADO :

117.	San Juan P.A.	95,232 ha.
118.	Flat Tops P.A.	47,120 ha.
119.	Maroon Bells-Snowmass Wild	26,440 ha.
120.	West Elk Wild	24,800 ha.
121.	Gore Range-Eagle Nest P.A.	24,482 ha.
122.	Upper Rio Grande P.A.	22,640 ha.
123.	Mount Zirkel-Dome Peak Wild	21,360 ha.
124.	Uncompahgre P.A.	21,301 ha.
125.	La Garita Wild	19,600 ha.
126.	Wilson Mountains P.A.	10,939 ha.
127.	Rawah Wild	10,232 ha.

IDAHO :

128.	Selway-Bitterroot P.A. (shared with Montana)	631,420 ha.
129.	Idaho P.A.	489,830 ha.
130.	Sawtooth P.A.	80,377 ha.

MONTANA :

131.	Bob Marshall W.A.	380,000 ha.
	(128. Selway-Bitteroot P.A. (see Idaho)	116,322 ha.)
132.	Beartooth P.A.	92,000 ha.

561

133. Anaconda-Pintlar P.A.	57,976 ha.
134. Cabinet Mountains P.A.	35,960 ha.
135. Mission Mountains P.A.	29,336 ha.
136. Absaroka P.A.	25,600 ha.
137. Spanish Peaks P.A.	19,920 ha.
138. Gates of the Mountains Wild	11,425 ha.

NEVADA :

139. Jarbridge Wild	25,867 ha.

NEW HAMPSHIRE :

140. Great Gulf Wild	2,160 ha.

NEW MEXICO :

141. Gila W.A.	175,344 ha.
142. Black Range P.A.	67,678 ha.
143. Pecos W.A.	66,000 ha.
144. Gila P.A.	51,852 ha.
145. San Pedro Parks Wild	16,453 ha.
91. Blue Range P.A. (see Arizona)	14,659 ha.
146. White Mountain Wild	11,247 ha.
147. Wheeler Peak Wild	2,420 ha.

NORTH CAROLINA :

148. Linville Gorge Wild	3,062 ha.

OREGON :

149. Eagle Cap W.A.	86,500 ha.
150. Three Sisters W.A.	78,683 ha.
151. Mount Jefferson P.A.	34,680 ha.
152. Kalmiopsis Wild	31,540 ha.
153. Mount Washington Wild	18,662 ha.
154. Diamond Peak Wild	14,176 ha.
155. Strawberry Mountain Wild	13,202 ha.
156. Mountain Lakes Wild	9,228 ha.
157. Gearhart Mountain Wild	7,484 ha.
158. Mount Hood Wild	5,664 ha.

UTAH :

159. High Uintas P.A.	96,287 ha.

WASHINGTON :

160.	North Cascades P.A., now National Park (2 Oct. 1968).	505,000 ha ([1]).
161.	Glacier Peak W.A.	183,242 ha.
162.	Goat Rocks Wild	33,072 ha.
163.	Mount Adams Wild	16,964 ha.

WYOMING :

164.	Teton W.A.	225,384 ha.
165.	South Absaroka W.A.	202,221 ha.
166.	Bridger W.A.	153,320 ha.
167.	North Absaroka W.A.	143,880 ha.
168.	Stratified P.A.	80,800 ha.
169.	Glacier P.A.	70,800 ha.
170.	Cloud Peak P.A.	37,552 ha.
171.	Popo Agie P.A.	28,000 ha.

PUERTO RICO :

172.	Caribbean National Forest : Luquillo Experimental Forest	10,525 ha.

H. — 173. BOUNDARY WATERS CANOE AREA.

(Minnesota) total		354,670 ha.
Superior Division	314,599 ha.	
Little Sioux Division	25,647 ha.	
Caribou Division	14,424 ha.	

I. — NATIONAL WILDLIFE REFUGES (N.W.R.).

174.	Arctic National Wildlife Range.	Alaska, 1960	3,460,000 ha.
175.	Kenai National Moose Range .	Alaska, 1941	822,879 ha.
176.	Kuskokwin N.W.R.	Alaska, 1960	748,000 ha.
177.	Kodiak N.W.R.	Alaska, 1941	726,000 ha.
178.	Cabeza Prieta Game Range ...	Arizona, 1939	344,000 ha.
179.	Kofa Game Refuge	Arizona, 1939	264,000 ha.
180.	Charles Seldon Antelope Range and Refuge	Nevada-Oregon, 1936	213,559 ha.
181.	Izembek N.W.R.	Alaska, 1960	166,144 ha.
182.	Fort Peck Game Range	Montana, 1936	150,095 ha.
183.	Hart Mountain National Ante- lope Refuge	Oregon, 1936	95,973 ha.
184.	Desert Game Range	Nevada, 1936	75,366 ha.
185.	Nunivak N.W.R.	Alaska, 1929	43,353 ha.

([1]) Together with two adjoining areas, established at the same time, Ross Lake and Lake Chelan National Recreation Areas, the total is 674,000 ha.

186.	Wichita Mountains W. Refuge.	Oklahoma, 1905	23,607 ha.
187.	San Andreas N.W.R.	New Mexico, 1941	22,886 ha.
188.	Pribilof Islands Reservation ...	Alaska, 1910	20,065 ha.
189.	National Elk Refuge	Wyoming, 1912	9,536 ha.
190.	National Bison Range	Montana, 1908	7,416 ha.
191.	Fort Niobrara N.W.R.	Nebraska, 1912	5,760 ha.
192.	Simeonof N.W.R.	Alaska, 1958	4,177 ha.
193.	National Key Deer Refuge ...	Florida, 1954	2,697 ha.

J. — STATE PARKS.

ALABAMA :

194.	Oak Mountain	3,976 ha.
195.	Gulf	2,675 ha.

CALIFORNIA :

196.	Anza Borrego Desert	188,000 ha.
197.	Humboldt Redwoods	9,600 ha.
198.	Cuyahaca	8,294 ha.
199.	Salton Sea	7,585 ha.
200.	Mount San Jacinto	5,186 ha.
201.	Henry W. Coe	5,000 ha.
202.	Big Basin Redwoods	4,411 ha.
203.	Prairie Creek Redwoods	4,100 ha.
204.	Jedediah Smith Redwoods	3,824 ha.
205.	Del Norte Coast Redwoods	2,341 ha.
206.	Castle Crags	2,132 ha.
207.	Calaveras Big Trees	2,126 ha.

FLORIDA :

208.	Pennekamps Coral Reef Preserve	38,000 ha.

Also named the Key Largo Coral Reef Preserve, this is one of the marine parks of which Recommendation No. 15 of the Seattle Conference (1962) called for a larger number to be created. It was set up by a Presidential Proclamation of 15 March 1960, but is administered by the State of Florida as one of its State Parks.

209.	Myakka River	11,550 ha.
210.	Seminole Necklace	2,569 ha.

GEORGIA :

211.	Hard Labor Creek	2,322 ha.

INDIANA :

212.	Brown County	6,133 ha.
213.	Versailles	2,325 ha.

KANSAS :

214. Cheyenne Bottoms W.R.	7,916 ha.
215. Cedar Bluff Reservoir	5,848 ha.
216. Morton County W.R.	5,120 ha.
217. Swan Marsh	3,147 ha.

KENTUCKY :

218. Jenny Wiley	5,200 ha.
219. Pennyrile Forest	2,422 ha.

LOUISIANA :

220. Chicot	2,592 ha.

MAINE :

221. Baxter	77,302 ha.

MICHIGAN :

222. Porcupine Mountains	23,267 ha.
223. Tahquamenon Falls	7,197 ha.
224. Hartwick Pines	2,754 ha.
224. Hartwick Pines	3,475 ha.
225. Wilderness	2,754 ha.

MINNESOTA :

226. Itasca	12,822 ha.
227. Holy Cross	12,229 ha.
228. Jay Cooke	3,616 ha.
229. The Thousand Lakes-Kathio	2,730 ha.

MISSOURI :

230. Wappapello	17,038 ha.
231. Lake of the Ozarks	6,534 ha.
232. Meramec	2,861 ha.
233. Big Spring	2,334 ha.
234. Cuivre River	2,329 ha.
235. Sam A. Baker	1,959 ha.

NEVADA :

236. Valley of Fire	2,624 ha.

NEW HAMPSHIRE :

237. Bear Brook	2,912 ha.
238. Franconia Notch	2,510 ha.

565

239.	Crawford Notch	2,380 ha.
240.	Cardigan	2,210 ha.

NEW JERSEY :

241.	High Point	4,374 ha.

NEW MEXICO :

242.	New Mexico A & M. College Area Nature Preserve.	25,195 ha.

NEW YORK :

243.	Adirondacks Forest Preserve	907,833 ha.
244.	Harriman	16,185 ha.
245.	Letchworth	5,342 ha.

NORTH CAROLINA :

246.	Pettigrew	6,731 ha.

OKLAHOMA :

247.	Lake Murray	8,400 ha.
248.	Quartz Mountain	5,748 ha.
249.	Robbers Cave	3,463 ha.
250.	Lake Wister	2,886 ha.

PENNSYLVANIA :

251.	Hickory Run	6,200 ha.
252.	Ricketts Glen	5,400 ha.
253.	Cook Forest	3,200 ha.
254.	Bucktail	3,100 ha.
255.	Raccoon Creek	3,040 ha.
256.	French Creek	2,600 ha.
257.	Blue Knob	2,239 ha.
258.	Tobyhanna	2,040 ha.

SOUTH CAROLINA :

259.	Cheraw	2,944 ha.
260.	Croft	2,854 ha.
261.	Hunting Island	2,000 ha.

SOUTH DAKOTA :

262.	Custer	27,731 ha.

TENNESSEE :

263.	Fall Creek Falls	6,400 ha.
264.	Chickasaw	5,753 ha.

265. Shelby Forest ... ... 5,020 ha.
266. Standing Stone ... ... 3,492 ha.

TEXAS :

267. Palo Duro Canyon ... ... 6,042 ha

WEST VIRGINIA :

268. Watoga . ... 6,042 ha.
269. Holly River . ... 3,037 ha.
270. Cacapon . ... 2,325 ha.
271. Tygart Lake . ... 2,248 ha.

WASHINGTON :

272. Mount Spokane . ... 9,732 ha.
273. Ginkgo State Geological Site ... ... 2,404 ha.
274. Riverside ... ... 2,200 ha.

WYOMING :

275. Boysen . ... 24,825 ha.
276. Seminoe . ... 23,198 ha.
277. Glendo . ... 9,614 ha.
278. Keyhole . ... 5,730 ha.
279. Buffalo Bill . ... 5,086 ha.
280. Guernsey ... ... 4,633 ha.
281. Big Sandy ... ... 3,072 ha.
282. Alcova . ... 2,448 ha.

K. — PRIVATE RESERVES.

283. National Audubon Society.

The examples selected are :

Corkscrew Swamp Sanctuary or Rookery, Florida ... 2,432 ha.
Rainey Wildlife Sanctury, Louisiana ... ... 10,464 ha.;

but also deserving mention are certain Reserves of State Audubon Societies, notably in Massachusetts, Michigan and Florida, and the National Audubon Society Centers, which are not only nature protection zones, but are also designed for the encouragement and training of citizens who wish to devote themselves to nature protection. This is an example which could be followed in many other countries, which would be well advised to consult the Society on how their remarkable success has been achieved.

284. Nature Conservancy.

In 26 States of the Union, there are :

a) preserves owned by the Nature Conservancy or under purchase contract, totalling 8,606 ha as at 30 June 1963 : the two largest are in California (5,647 ha) and New York State (1,327 ha);

UNITED STATES OF AMERICA

b) preserves established through financial aid, legal assistance or work of Conservancy Members, totalling 6,991 ha as at 30 June 1963 : the two largest are in Connecticut (2,304 ha) and Idaho (2,144 ha).

285. Hawk Mountain Sanctuary : about 500 ha but enlarged in 1965; owned by the Association of that name.

L. — RESERVE-LABORATORY OF THE SMITHSONIAN INSTITUTION, PANAMA CANAL ZONE.

286. Barro Colorado ... .   1,460 ha.

**

Description of the 32 National Parks (for the sate of brevity scientific names have only exceptionally been induded) :

1. YELLOWSTONE.

a) Wonderland of forested mountains, canyons, waterfalls and lakes.

b) Thousands of wapiti and other deer, antelope and bison; bighorn sheep; black and grizzly bears and countless smaller mammals; some 200 species of birds, among them the trumpeter swan.

2. MOUNT McKINLEY.

a) Peak perpetually blanketed with snow and ice. The lower slopes, supporting subarctic spruce forests, lead up permafrost tundra, dominated by willow and birch.

b) Caribou, white sheep *Ovis dalli*, moose, grizzly bear and smaller mammals; a myriad nesting shorebirds, waterfowl and other boreal species.

3. EVERGLADES.

a) The vast, level, drowned " River of grass ", supports a wealth of tropical flora : saw grass marsh interspersed with hummocks of dense jungle growth, picturesque stands of palm and cypress, and mangrove forest along the coastal margins.

b) Cougar, black bear, manatee, white tailed deer; many species of snakes and such reptiles as the American crocodile and alligator; white and wood ibises, egrets, herons and the scarce roseate spoonbill.

4. GLACIER.

a) Towering peaks, glaciers, lakes and virgin conifer forests. Wildflowers.

b) Mountain goats, bighorn sheep, moose, wapiti, mule and white-tailed deer, grizzly and black bear, pine marten, fisher *Martes pennanti*, wolverine, beaver, and other species.

5. OLYMPIC.

a) Peaks, glaciers and, in the valleys, forests of gigantic spruces and firs, carpeted with moss and ferns.

568

b) The rare " Roosevelt elk " (a race of wapiti of which about 6,000 inhabit the park), mule deer, black bear and Olympic marmot *Marmota olympus*.

6. YOSEMITE.

a) Very awe-inspiring canyon, above which the slopes are covered with dense conifer forests, leading up to alpine meadows. *Sequoia gigantea* occurs.

b) 78 species of mammals and 200 species of birds.

7. BIG BEND.

a) Vast arid basins, gouged by deep arroyos that glow with brillantly-coloured strata, support many species of cactus, yuccas and other xerophytic plants. In the centre of these flatlands soar the spectacular Chisos Mountains, where the basin flora gradually gives way to cooler pinyon *Pinus edulis* and ponderosa pine, oak and juniper forest, and bare treeless summits.

b) Characteristic desert birds and mammals in the basin and, on the mountains, a fauna with Mexican affinities; many species of birds, mammals and reptiles.

8. GRAND CANYON.

a) Tremendous pediments, mesas and buttes. In the interior of the canyon vegetation is sparse and of a desert type, but on the plateaus grow forests of pinyon and ponderosa pine, fir, aspen and spruce.

b) About 100 varieties of birds, 60 mammals, and 25 reptiles and amphibians; a half dozen kinds of fish live in the river.

9. ISLE ROYALE.

a) Covered by a thick mixed conifer-hardwood forest with dense undergrowth of smaller trees, shrubs and flowers.

b) Moose, coyote, snowshoe rabbit, beaver and other small mammals; 200 species of birds.

10. GREAT SMOKY MOUNTAIN.

a) Hardwood forest with 130 species of trees; outstanding displays of rhododendrons and azaleas and many flowering plants.

b) Deer, bear, wildcat, fox, bobcat, raccoon and other mammals; wild turkey, many colourful songbirds.

11 and 12. KINGS CANYON AND SEQUOIA.

a) The two parks are contiguous and include very fine stands of *Sequoia gigantea,* the largest tree in the world.

b) Deer, bear, bighorn sheep and many other animals in fair numbers.

13. GRAND TETON.

a) Mountain range rising above a great sagebrush basin; lodgepole pine and other conifers, aspen, willow and many flowering plants.

b) Wapiti, moose, deer, beaver and other mammals; a good variety of birds, including the rare trumpeter swan.

14. ROCKY MOUNTAIN.

a) 65 high peaks exhibiting remarkable relicts of past glaciations, broad valleys, rugged gorges, meadows full of flowers, alpine lakes and plunging streams; more than 700 species of plants.

b) Herds of wapiti, mule and other deer, bighorn sheep; many beavers, cougar; plentiful birdlife.

15. CANYONLANDS.

a) A small segment of the Greater Canyonlands typical of the Colorado River country, which is specially interesting for its geological features and strange formations caused by erosion.

b) Many mammals and birds.

16. MOUNT RAINIER.

a) Below the flower-clad mountain meadows, dense conifer forests encircle the mountain and descend into the valleys.

b) More than 50 species of mammals, including bear, mountain goat, cougar and deer; 130 species of birds.

17. HAWAII VOLCANOES.

a) Of the two active volcanoes, Kilauea supports a magnificent tropical rain forest, while Mauna Loa supports more open forests with a unique flora.

b) Habitat of many endemic species of birds; all land mammals now living in a wild state have been introduced by man (pigs, goats, etc.).

18. SHENANDOAH.

a) Beautiful gentle mountain ridge, covered with verdant deciduous and conifer forests.

b) Mammals are increasing : deer, bear, bobcat, fox; plentiful birdlife.

19. CRATER LAKE.

a) Caldera containing a lake surrounded by colourful cliffs; forest of western hemlock, whitebark pine and shasta red fir *Abies magnifica shastensis,* with at lower elevations stands of douglas fir and ponderosa and sugar (*Pinus lambertiana*) pines.

b) Small mammals, mule deer, black bear; many species of birds.

20. ZION.

a) Comprises well-forested and brilliantly-coloured canyons with sheer walls, dissecting the plateau of the Utah desert region.

b) Many kinds of animals and birds.

21. LASSEN VOLCANIC.

a) Several beautiful lakes, evergreen forests and wildflowers.

b) Mule deer, bear, small mammals and birds.

22. PETRIFIED FOREST.

a) Petrified trees and part of the colourful painted desert.

b) Jack-rabbit, cottontail, whitetail and pronghorn antelope squirrel, skunk, coyote, bobcat porcupine; songbirds.

23. MESA VERDE.

a) Large mesa gashed by canyons and covered by a heavy conifer forest.

b) Many mammals and birds; bighorn sheep and wild turkeys have been re-established.

24. MAMMOTH CAVE.

a) Five hardwood forests cover most of are surrounding the caverns.

b) Many mammals and birds; bats are abundant and cave crickets, blind craw-fish and the eyeless cave-fish occur in the cavern.

25. CARLSBAD CAVERNS.

a) The largest known caverns in the world; a variety of semi-arid plants in surrounding areas.

b) During the summer, millions of bats of eleven species.

26. ACADIA.

a) Eroded landscape of rounded mountains, great sea cliffs and headlands, and glaciated rock; mixed conifer and hardwood forest.

b) Forest wildlife and sea-birds are abundant; the beach and intertidal areas are inhabited by a myriad invertebrates.

27. BRYCE CANYON.

a) A vast amphitheatre comprising valleys carpeted with sagebrush and others dark with evergreen forests; above the rim ponderosa pines are abundant, mixed with other conifers and aspen; many flowering plants.

b) Mule deer and smaller mammals; many birds.

28. WIND CAVE.

a) Prairie grassland.

b) Herds of bison, antelope, wapiti and other deer and " prairie dog ", the marmot-like *Cynomys ludovicianus*.

29. HALEAKALA.

a) Volcano dormant for 200 years, in the crater of which the extraordinary silversword plant is found.

b) The only native mammal is a bat; many introduced rats, pigs, goats, etc.

30. VIRGIN ISLAND.

a) Green hills, beaches, tropical vegetation and secondary forest.

b) The only native land mammals are six species of bat; many kinds of birds.

31. Hot Springs.

a) A representative sample of the Ozark hills and woodlands.

b) A few common mammals such as rabbit, skunk, opossum and squirrel; plentiful birdlife.

32. Platt.

a) Wooded hills rising from the great plains toward the Arbuckle mountains.

b) A small herd of bison, raccoon, fox, skunk, opossum, armadillo, rabbit and fox squirrel *Sciurus niger*.

V. **Areas excluded :**

1. National Monuments smaller than 2,000 ha (with the exception of the 16 selected for the List);

2. The Migratory Bird Refuges controlled by the Bureau of Sport Fisheries and Wildlife;

3. The 'Natural Areas' of the U.S. Forest Service, which were cited on p. 65 of Part Two of the previous edition of the List;

4. The areas protected and managed by the National Park Service primarily because of their historical interest;

5. A new National Park established on 2 October 1968 (cf. No. 160 in the List, where the simultaneous upgrading of a Primitive Area and two N.R.A. to National Park status is recorded) :

The Redwood National Park, California : 58,000 ha.

134. UPPER VOLTA

I. **Listed Areas :** one.

1. The 'W' National Park.

General Introduction :

The administration of National Parks and reserves is the responsibility of the Water and Forest Service of the Ministry of Animal Husbandry, Waters and Forest. The land included in these areas is state-owned.

Part Two of the previous edition of the List contained a description of the 'W' National Park and also of all except one of the total and partial Faunal Reserves now relegated to section V.

Details : application of criteria (II), general information (III) and description (IV) :

1. The 'W' National Park.

II.

a) Status : total protection; forms part of a tripartite National Park, situated on the double bend of the Niger river, the two other sections of which belong to Dahomey and Niger respectively.

b) Area : 330,000 ha.

c) Staff : about 14 units, well below the minimum required under the criterion.

572

d) Budget : estimated at U.S. $ 14,000, being half the total annual expenditure on the eastern zone of the Upper Volta reserves (which includes this Park and the Arly, Pama, Kourtiagon and Singon reserves).

III.

Date established : 1954 (originally established in 1953 as a total faunal and forest reserve).

Tourism : there is a motorable track along the western boundary for about 100 km and another which does a complete circuit, 200 km long, a small section of which passes through Niger territory; about 1,000 visitors a year, accommodation in a 'camp-hotel' for 25, at Diapaga, 20 km outside the western boundary.

V.

Altitude : averages 250 m.

a) Lateritic shield or peneplain, dissected by rivers; Soudanian-type wooded savannah, with fire-climax flora (*Butyrospermum, Parkia* and *Khaya*), grading into Sahelian-type associations in the north; fine gallery-forests (in which one of the kola-nut trees *Cola laurifolia* and *Kigelia aethiopica* are dominants) —

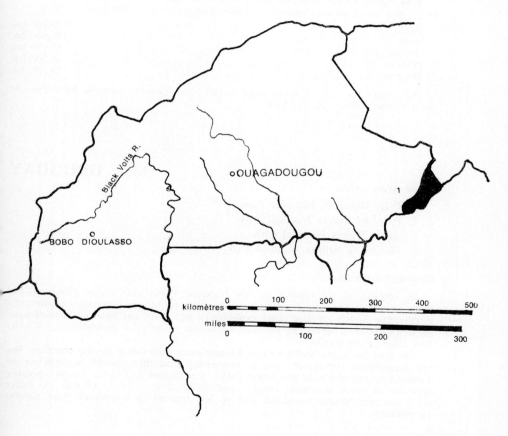

573

especially in the south along the seasonal rivers. The high ground is confined to the Dahomey sector of the park (q.v.).

b) Elephant *Loxodonta africana*, buffalo *Syncerus caffer*, warthog *Phacochoerus aethiopicus*, large savannah antelopes such as roan *Hippotragus equinus*, hartebeest *Alcelaphus buselaphus* and kob *Kobus kob*; monkeys; lion *Panthera leo*, caracal *Felis caracal*, cheetah *Acinonyx jubatus*, jackal *Canis mesomelas*; hippopotamus and crocodiles on the permanent waters.

V.   Areas excluded :

Three Total Faunal Reserves, where protection is restricted to the game animals, although in general these Reserves are well-protected and of very considerable value :

Singou	192,000 ha.
Arly	76,000 ha.
Bontioli	12,700 ha.

Five Partial Faunal Reserves (protection of certain species or seasonal protection only); two of these are annexed to Total Faunal Reserves mentioned above :

Pama	223,700 ha.
Arly	130,000 ha.
Kourtiagou	51,000 ha.
Nabéré	36,500 ha.
Bontioli	29,500 ha.

All except the last of these eight faunal reserves were cited in Part Two of the previous edition of the List.

135. URUGUAY

I.   Listed Areas : four.

> 1. F. D. Roosevelt National Park.
> 2. Paso del Puerto National Park.
> 3. Aguas Dulces National Park.
> 4. Meseta de Artigas National Park.

General Introduction :

In relation to the criteria all the National Parks are strictly protected and there are very stringent measures against hunting, no human occupancy or domestic stock. The forests are free from exploitation and there has been some reafforestation. Control is exercised by state-employed personnel. Sport-fishing is however allowed everywhere.

All four areas are smaller than the minimum laid down by the criterion, but the Uruguayan authorities have recommended that they should nevertheless be accepted in preferance to two larger Parks (San Miguel and Santa Teresa), because they are of great ecological interest and under strict control, whereas the latter are much less strictly protected and of less interest in respect of their natural associations.

574

., Grand Teton N.P.

U.S.A., Everglades N.P.

(photo : National Park S

U.S.A., Bryce Canyon N.P.

U.S.A., Big Bend N.P.

(photo : National Park Service)

U.S.A., Kings Canyon N.P.

OSLAVIA, Paklenica N.P.

YUGOSLAVIA, Plitvice N.P.

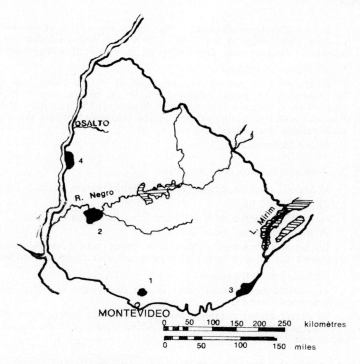

The Budgets quoted below under the individual Parks refer only to staff salaries, and account should also be taken of other expenditure on maintenance : thus the total expenditure provided for the National Parks Department by the Budget of 31 April 1964, under some ten heads in addition to salaries, was 1,550,380 Uruguayan dollars or about U.S. $ 97,000.

The National Parks Department, set up in 1953, comes under the Ministry of Public Works and is responsible for administering the Parks, all of which are public land. Entry to Parks is unrestricted and most of them have facilities for the reception of visitors. A special effort is made to attract young people and there is a great deal of educational and propaganda activity.

Scientific research is permitted and organised in the Parks under the provisions of a Decree of 1957. The establishment of laboratories is planned and scientific work is undertaken by Montevideo University.

Uruguay was not included either in E/3436 or Part Two of the previous edition of the List.

Details : application of criteria (II), general information (III) and description (IV) :

1. F. D. ROOSEVELT NATIONAL PARK.

   a) Status : total protection. See introduction.
   b) Area : 1,500 ha.
   c) Staff : 53 units.
   d) Budget : for salaries : U.S. $ 50,000.

575

III. In the Canelones Province. The proximity of an aerodrome has tended to drive away many of the birds. There is a well-developed organisation for tourists — camping sites, drinking water, sanitation, special provision for Scouts.

IV. *Altitude :* no information.

a) The Park is divided into two sections — the Duna (350 ha), occupied by plantations of pines, eucalypts, *Cupressus*, acacia, poplar *Populus*, pedunculate oak *Quercus robur*; and the Banado (1,150 ha), characterised by ash *Fraxinus* and elm *Ulmus* as well as the 'banados' or wet marshy areas, with their various native tree species.

b) No information.

2. PASO DEL PUERTO NATIONAL PARK.

II. *a*) Status : total protection (200 ha of strict nature reserve); see introduction.

b) Area : 600 ha.

c) Staff : a warden with a labour force of 7 men.

d) Budget : for salaries : U.S. $ 8,000.

III. In Soriano Province. There is a strong tourist organisation, principally developed for aquatic sports and pastimes, with camping facilities, etc.

IV. *Altitude :* no information.

a) Situated on the confluence of the Rio Negro and the Arroyo Grande, with wooded river banks.

b) Forest fauna, notably tinamous Tinamidae (often incorrectly called the " perdiz grande " — great partridge), which elsewhere in the country are nearing extinction.

3. AGUAS DULCES NATIONAL PARK.

II. *a*) Status : total protection; see introduction.

b) Area : 200 ha.

c) Staff : one warden with two labourers.

d) Budget : U.S. $ 3,000.

III. In Rocha Province. No tourist organisation as yet.

IV. *Altitude :* near sea level.

a) Part of the Atlantic coast, with white sand dunes.

b) No information.

4. MESETA DE ARTIGAS NATIONAL PARK.

II. *a*) Status : total protection; see introduction.

b) Area : 314 ha.

c) Staff : no information.

d) Budget : U.S. $ 3,000.

III. In Paysandu Province. A site of historic interest. Yachting and boating.

IV. *Altitude :* near sea level.

a) On the banks of the Uruguay river.

b) No information.

576

V. **Areas excluded :**

A. — Two Parks which were on the point of being established in 1966, but whose existence and details have not yet been confirmed :

1. Arequita : 1,000 ha; a warden with a labour force of six men and a budget of U.S. $ 6,940 to cover their salaries.
2. Arazati : 420 ha.

B. — Two National Parks under the control of the Ministry of National Defence, which are notable for the old fortresses situated in them, one of which has been restored and the other reconstructed :

1. San Miguel : 3,288 ha.
2. Santa Teresa : 1,496 ha.

Both these Parks are characterised by very secondary vegetation, much of it exotic and introduced. Hunting is forbidden and there is a well-established tourist organisation. It is still possible however that sufficiently undisturbed zones could exist in both Parks to justify their inclusion in the List.

C. — A number of areas which have been set aside for eventual designation as full National Parks but to which the necessary measures to implement this have not yet been applied :

Rio Negro National Park (200 km of the river and especially some of its islands).
The Cabo Polonia National Park : 1,000 ha.

Palmares de Rocha National Park : 500 ha.
Playa Agraciada National Park : 400 ha.
Bajada de las Penas National Park : 1,000 ha.

Recent information has been received of the establishment during 1966 of a National Park along 27 km of the coast as a refuge for seals : this could be the Cabo Polonio park mentioned above.

136. VENEZUELA

I. **Listed Areas :** seven.

1. Canaima National Park.
2. Sierra Nevada de Merida National Park.
3. Guatopo National Park.
4. Henri Pittier (Rancho Grande) National Park.
5. El Avila National Park.
6. Yacambu National Park.
7. Yurubi National Park.

General Introduction :

Legislation : the legal basis of the Parks is at present provided by Article 3 of the Ley Forestal de Suelos y Aguas of 31 August 1955, under which each Park is established by a Presidential decree. A new specific National Parks Law is under preparation.

Administration : the responsibility of the Ministry of Agriculture and Animal Husbandry, allocated to the National Parks Section of its Directorate for Renewable Natural Resources. Some responsibility also pertains to the Ministry of Public Works, especially in regard to the drawing up of the programme for the establishment of new Parks.

Land tenure : the land of the Parks is generally state-owned, but there are many enclaves of private land. A land reform policy is at present being worked out in Venezuela. The main difficulty in the way of good management of the country's National Parks very often arises from human settlement and exploitation which are difficult to prevent because of this confused land tenure situation.

Tourism : plans for development take a high place in the preoccupations of the Park authorities. Tourism is important but not of course the sole purpose of National Parks. Nevertheless there is no sector of any of the Venezuelan Parks which is closed to visitors by regulations and would therefore constitute an area of strict natural reserve.

Research : some attention has been paid to the development of scientific research in the older reserves, the typical example being the Biological Station of the Rancho Grande Park (No. 4).

Only the Parks numbered, 2, 3, 4 and 5 were included in E/3436 of the previous edition of the List.

Details : application of criteria (II), general information (III) and description (IV) :

1. Canaima National Park.

II.
    a) Status : total protection; an uninhabited region.
    b) Area : 1,000,000 ha.
    c) and *d*) Staff and Budget : no information received.

III.
    Date established : 1962.

    Tourism : access is by air only and is still to be properly organised.

IV.
    Altitude : no information.

    a) Situated in the group of mountains to the south-east of the Caroni and Carras rivers, known for their rich deposits of gold and diamonds; the Angel Falls include an unbroken drop 800 m in height, making them the highest in the world; gallery forests along the numerous streams contain a great variety of orchids and there is very extensive primary rain forest, as well as grassland savannah.

    b) Plentiful wildlife — jaguar *Panthera onca*, tapir *Tapirus* sp., peccary *Tayassu* sp., paca *Cuniculus paca,* cayman *Caiman latirostris*; parrots.

2. Sierra Nevada de Merida National Park.

II.
    a) Status : general protection, but there are two settlements (El Morro and Los Nevados), and a certain amount of cultivation has continued to be allowed in the reserve, compromising the integrity of several thousands of hectares. In view of the very extensive section which thus does not correspond with the status criterion laid down by the ICNP, it has only been possible to retain the Park in the List on the basis of the ' zoning ' principle.

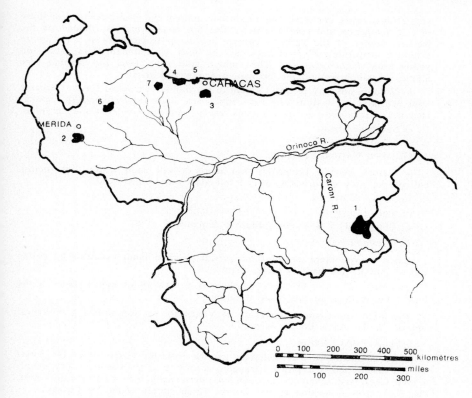

b) Area : 160,000 ha.

c) Staff : six units only, which is less than the criterion standard, but has been accepted because of the thinly populated character of the region and the fact that budgetary provision for maintenance greatly exceeds the criterion.

d) Budget : U.S. $ 18,000 (criterion demands $ 8,000).

II.

Date established : 1952.

There is some doubt whether the Park should not be referred to as the Simon Bolivar National Park, since it encircles Bolivar Mountain, the summit of which (5,007 m) is the highest point in Venezuela.

Land tenure : a small part of the Park is still privately owned.

Tourism : access is by the Transandine Highway and the Apartaderos-Barinos road. There is no motorable road through the Park itself, but one is under construction. There is a fish-farm, an experimental Forestry Station, run by the University of the Andes, and a cable-way.

V.

Altitude : 600-5,000 m.

a) Part of the western Andes comprising the Sierra Nevada de Merida with its highest peak (Bolivar, 5,007 m) and the Sierra de Santo Domingo. The

579

vegetational zones, corresponding to altitude, present the classic features of those of hot, temperate and cold climates. The hot zone, which is situated on the western border of the Park, is covered by damp tropical forest. The more extensive temperate zone is characterised by bush, an abundant flora, pines and yellow-wood *Podocarpus* sp. The highest, cold zone, level has *paramo* type alpine vegetation around the permanent snows and glaciers.

b) Wildlife not very plentiful except in the low level tropical forest. Brocket deer *Mazama* sp., various cats *Felis* spp., paca, opossum *Didelphis* sp., spectacled bear *Tremarctos ornatus*; parrots, eagles, Andean condor *Vultur gryphus*.

c) Spectacled bear.

3. GUATOPO NATIONAL PARK.

II.   *a*) Status : general protection, but there is still some cultivation (maize, coffee) not only on privately-owned but also State-owned land.

b) Area : 92,640 ha.

c) Staff : 16 units.

d) Budget : U.S. $ 18,000 (criterion demands $ 4,500).

III.   *Date established :* 1958.

Land tenure : there is still some privately-owned land, occupied by coffee estates, but its purchase is being negotiated.

Tourism : access is by road and there is a network of motor roads in the Park. Other facilities are being developed.

Research : the Central University of Venezuela has established a biological station in the Agua Blanca area.

IV.   *Altitude :* 400-2,200 m.

a) A mountainous area including, on the east, the Cerro Azul; the forest in this eastern sector is primary, ranging according to altitude from dry broadleaved forest and savannah, through an intermediate type to true rain forest; the Park gives protection to the springs which supply water for Caracas.

b) A varied wildlife; a number of mammals (jaguar, tapir, paca, peccary) enjoy good protection, and also reptiles and birds.

4. HENRI PITTIER (RANCHO GRANDE) NATIONAL PARK.

II.   *a*) Status : general protection but as in the case of the Sierra Nevada de Merida Park (No. 2), it has been necessary to allow a certain amount of settlement, with cultivation and domestic stock, along the (coastal) fringe.

b) Area : 90,000 ha.

c) Staff : 4 units, including a Chief Warden.

d) Budget : U.S. $ 60,000.

III.   *Date established :* 1937.

Land tenure : most of the Park is in public ownership, but there is still some private land.

Tourism : since 1958 there has been a big programme of tourist development — accommodation (hotels at Maracay and Bahia de Cata), picnic-sites, swimming-pool, etc. Entry is unrestricted and a road goes through the Park, running along the shores of the Caribbean to Turiamo : there are paths for visitors, of whom some 41,200 visited the Park in 1963.

580

Research : a full-time biologist is posted to Rancho Grande where there are two biological research stations, with facilities for visiting scientists, an educational museum and a scientific school.

IV.

Altitude : sea level to 2,344 m.

a) Part of the Cordillera de la Costa : varying with altitude, the main features of the vegetation are mangroves *Rhizophora,* etc. and aquatic flora; spiney bush and giant cactus; tropical broad-leaved forest and savannah; humid sub-tropical forest with an epiphytic flora. Many streams.

b) Plentiful wildlife, especially of birds such as humming-birds Trochilidae; 530 species of birds have been recorded in the various habitats, and the Park forms an important refuge for migratory species.

5. EL AVILA NATIONAL PARK.

II.

a) Status : general protection, but there is still some cultivation (" now much reduced ").

b) Area : 66,192 ha.

c) Staff : 32 units.

d) Budget : U.S. $ 48,000 (a high figure — the criterion level would be U.S. $ 3,000).

III.

Date established : 1959.

Land tenure : still some private ' haciendas ' and ranches. A re-afforestation programme is being applied in certain sectors.

Tourism : accommodation, camping facilities, road network, paths. Access is by road and is subject to a permit issued by the Ministerio de Agricultura y Cria. There is a cable-way.

IV.

Altitude : sea level to 2,700 m.

a) A mountainous area culminating in Naiguata peak, which separates the Caracas valley from the sea coast of the Caribbean; varying with altitude the features of the vegetation are — dry tropical type with giant cactus; broad-leaved forest and savannah; rain forest and Andean type scrub. Numerous streams and torrents.

b) The not very plentiful wildlife includes brocket deer, paca, agouti *Dasyprocta rubrata,* three-toed sloth *Bradypus tridactylus,* squirrels *Sciurus* sp., armadillo *Dasypus* sp. and crab-eating fox *Cerdocyon thous*; many parrots ans small birds; reptiles.

6. YACAMBU NATIONAL PARK.

I.

a) Status : general protection.

b) Area : 9,000 ha.

c) Staff : 10 units.

d) Budget : covering staff salaries.

II.

Date established : 1962.

Tourism : the Park is crossed by the Sanare-Escalera road; tourist facilities are being constructed. There is a meteorological station.

IV.   *Altitude :* no information.

a) The mountainous zone of the Sierra Portuguesa, partly covered in thick forest, where numerous river have their source.

b) No information.

7. YURUBI NATIONAL PARK.

II.   *a*) Status : general protection.

b) Area : 4,000 ha.

c) Staff : 5 units.

d) Budget : covering staff salaries.

III.   *Date established :* 1960.

Tourism : no organisation as yet but facilities are being planned.

IV.   *Altitude :* no information.

a) A wooded region with a humid and intermediate vegetation; savannahs; rugged terrain; the Park protects the upper reaches of the Rio Yaracuy and Rio Aroa.

b) A varied woodland fauna.

V.   **Areas excluded :**

A. — One National Park which is too small to satisfy the criterion :

1. Codazzi National Park : 43 ha; 1944.

B. — The following 'National Monuments' :

2. Cerro Mario Lionza (the summit area) : 40,000 ha; 1960.

3. Aristides Rojas (a rock formation) : 1,630 ha; 1949.

4. Alexandro de Humboldt (noted for its subterranean formations, including the Cueva del Guacharo 'Oil-bird Cavern'); 181 ha; 1949. The Ministry of Agriculture intends (March 1966) to upgrade this area into a " Guacharo National Park ".

There are also six Forest Reserves, totalling 1,813,000 ha and, deserving mention since they are called 'National Parks', two urban Parks in Caracas itself :

El Pinar National Park.
Gran Parque Nacional del Este.
With regard to the Forest Reserves, it should be noted that the law permits and development plans envisage the declaration of 'National Forests' and also 'Wildlife Refuges'; but so far no areas under these designations are known to have been established, and they would in any case not satisfy the criteria for admission to the List.

C. — A communication dated March 1966, has also been deemed to justify the exclusion of :

La Esmeralda National Park : 388,500 ha.

This was formerly reported to have been effectively established, but appears to have fallen into disuse or been abandoned.

582

D. — A new National Park, the declaration of which on 21 May 1969, has been reported by the Director of the National Parks Division of the Ministry of Agriculture and Animal Husbandry's Directorate of Renewable Natural Resources :

Cueva de la Quebrada El Toro : 8,500 ha.

Situated in the hydrographical catchment area of "Bull's Gorge" in Falcòn province north-west of Caracas, this comprises an area of great scenic beauty and also serves to protect one of the Oil-bird nesting caverns.

137. VIETNAM (¹)

I. **Listed Areas :** nil.

V. *a)* **Explanation :**

The first meeting of the National Commission for Nature Conservation, set up on 5 July 1961, by Decree No. 65, took place on 25 August 1964. It decided to approve a proposed Decree for the establishment of Bachma-Haivân National Park, but the decree was still awaiting the necessary official endorsement by the Minister for Rural Affairs, when the present List was closed in 1966.

b) **Areas excluded :**

1. Bachma-Haivân National Park . ... 78,000 ha.
2. Four other proposed parks or reserves :

Conson (Poulo-Conder), Nui-Cam (Chaudoc), Col de Blao and Cape Varella (Hao Son-Dai Lanh).

3. Trangbom Park : 400 ha; 55 km N.E. of Saigon, attached to a Forest Department experimental station : protection is inadequate, in the face of pressures from neighbouring villages of refugees.

4. Five Hunting Reserves, in which only game-animals are protected :

Krong-Poko	533,760 ha.
Pleiku-Plei-Ta-Uan-Xer	56,480 ha.
Kinder	53,760 ha.
Bantur	27,840 ha.
Lang Bian	4,800 ha.

5. Two Private Hunting Reserves, kept strictly for the Chief of State and his guests : total area 160,160 ha.

For the seven Hunting Reserves, covering nearly 850,000 ha, referred to above, the supervisory staff consists of a superintendent, six guards and ten auxiliaries.

(¹) No information has yet been received from North Vietnam.

I. Listed Areas : nil.

V. Explanation :

No response yet received from the authorities at San'a, but private information suggests that no areas exist with the necessary qualifications for inclusion in the List.

139. YUGOSLAVIA

I. Listed Areas : twenty-one.

A. — Bosnia and Herzegovina :

1. Sutjeska National Park.
2. Hutovo Blato Reserve.

B. — Croatia :

3. Plitvice Lakes National Park.
4. Paklenica National Park.
5. Mljet National Park.
6. Risnjak National Park.
7. Licka Pljesevica Strict Nature Reserve.

C. — Macedonia :

8. Mavrovo National Park.
9. Galicica National Park.
10. Pelister National Park.

D. — Montenegro :

11. Durmitor National Park.
12. Biogradska Gora National Park.
13. Lovcen National Park.

E. — Slovenia :

14. Triglav National Park.
15. Mala Pisnica Reserve.

F. — Serbia :

16. Fruska Gora National Park.
17. Resava Reserve.
18. Zvijezda Reserve.

19. Rajac Reserve.
20. Obedska Bara Reserve.
21. Monostrorski Riitovi Reserve.

General Introduction :

Administration of Parks and Reserves varies from region to region and is there-fore dealt with separately. Part Two of the previous edition of the List cited and briefly described the areas now numbered No. 2-4, 6, 8-13 and 16.

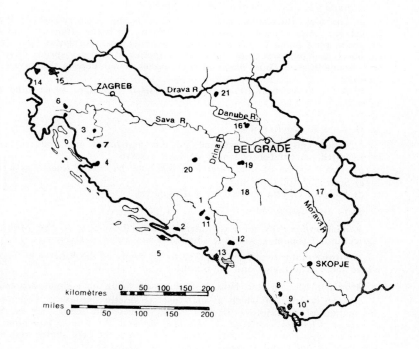

Details : application of criteria (II), general information (III) and description (IV):
A. — BOSNIA AND HERZEGOVINA.

1. Sutjeska National Park.

II.   *a*) Status : the greater part of the Park is subjected to exploitation (forest produce, hunting, fishing), but there is a section of strict nature reserve known as the Perucica Forest.
b) Area : 1,434 ha of strict reserve in the 17,250 ha of the whole Park.
c) Staff : 20 full-time units.

d) Budget : criteria should be covered by staff salaries : the Park is said to be 90 % self-supporting.

III.   *Date established :* 13 January 1962, under Law No. 5 of the Executive Committee of the Bosnia-Herzegovina Peoples' Republic; the strict reserve of the Perucica virgin forest was set up by a decision of the National Institute for the Protection of Historic Monuments and Natural Beauty on 3 June 1964.

Administration : the Park has its own authority.

Tourism : free entry; hotel, youth centre, six lodges, at Tjentiste (where the headquarters are also situated); mountain huts; camping; access by tarmac road, the main Dubrovnik-Belgrade highway passing through the Park.

IV.   *Altitude :* 532-2,386 (summit of Mt. Maglic).

a) The most interesting part of the Park is the strict reserve of Perucica Forest, the lower margin of which is at 680 m; fir/beech *Abies* sp. and *Fagus illyricum,* pure beech *F. illyricum* and *montanum,* oak/hornbeam (*Quercus* and *Carpinus*) and pine woods of the local subspecies of Norway spruce *Picea abies* and mountain pine *Pinus mugo*; a rare species found here is the spruce *Picea omorika.*

b) A few brown bear *Ursus arctos*; chamois *R. rupicapra*; capercaillie *Tetrao urogallus.*

2. Hutovo Blato Reserve.

II.   *a)* Status : no human occupancy in this marshland area, but exploitation is permitted, except for one area of total reserve.

b) Area : 300 ha of total reserve in the 3,400 ha of the reserve as a whole.

c) Staff : 27 full-time units.

d) Budget : criteria covered by staff salaries.

III.   *Date established :* 1954.

Administration : by an Experimental Farm (belonging to the Ministry of Agricultural Economy), which is situated 7 km away at Capljina.

Tourism : motor road from Capljina to the centre of the Reserve at Karaotok, where there is a Lodge and an ornithological museum.

IV.   *Altitude :* 1.5-6 m (the Hutovo Blato itself being in a slight depression).

a) Marshy area, of which a small part is strictly preserved : vegetation on the margin of the Hutovo Blato includes sedges and reeds such as *Scirpus sylvaticus, Cladium mariscus, Typha latifolia* and *Phragmites communis,* with waterlilies *Nymphaea alba* and *Nuphar lutea* along the lake shores and willows and poplars *Salix* and *Populus* between the lakes.

b) The birds include great white heron *Egretta alba,* little egret *Egretta garzetta,* golden eagle *Aquila chrysaetos,* spotted eagle *A. clanga,* white-tailed eagle *Haliaetus albicilla,* large numbers of coot *Fulica atra* and rock partridge *Alectoris graeca.*

B. — CROATIA.

3. Plitvice Lakes National Park.

II.   *a)* Status : stated to be similar to that of the American national parks : there are still 3,316 ha of private property (10 % of it under forest) and 25 small villages with a total of 2,500 inhabitants, within the park boundary.

b) Area : 19,172 ha, of which 1,700 ha could be considered as totally protected, with even forest exploitation no longer permitted; other parts of the forests are subject to felling and removal of old timber and of about half the annual increment.

c) Staff : 102 units, of which 17 are full-time (including 13 guards).

d) Budget : U.S. $ 330,000 (250 million dinars).

III.

Date established : 1949 (each Park was created under a specific Law).

Administration : by the Cultural Section of the Secretariat for National Education, Culture and Physical Education of the People's Republic, each Park having its own administrative Committee.

Tourism : free entry, access by the Zagreb-Karlovac-Plitvice-Gospic road which crosses the Park; a first-class and several smaller hotels and lodges at Plitvicki-Ljeskovac, where the staff headquarters are also situated.

IV.

Altitude : 417-1,270 m (the two Lakes are at 498 and 636 m).

a) The limestone Lika region, between the Kopela and Pljesevica massifs; beech and fir forest, with some unusual features such as the Corkova Depression; other Karstic phenomena, waterfalls on the numerous travertine instrusions.

b) A very few brown bears; wild cat *Felis silvestris,* otter *L. lutra,* pine and stone marten *Martes martes* and *foina.*

4. PAKLENICA NATIONAL PARK.

II.

a) Status : total protection, strengthened by the general inacessibility of much of the region, but there are six privately owned houses and gardens.

b) Area : 3,616 ha.

c) Staff : 5 units, including 3 guards.

d) Budget : U.S. $ 9,000.

III.

Date established : 1949.

Administration : as for No. 3 above.

Tourism : free entry, a considerable tourist attraction, but with no accommodation inside the Park except for one alpine hut; a motel and camping site not far away. Access by motor road, including a branch road into the Park along the bottom of the Velika Paklenica gorge.

IV.

Altitude : sea level to 1,563 m.

a) Southern slopes of the Velebit massif in Dalmatia; many types of beechwood (largely undisturbed), also forests of Austrian pine *Pinus nigra* (probably surviving because of the relative inaccessibility of the massif); typical Karstic phenomena, including the remarkable Velika and Mala (Great and Small) Paklenica gorges.

b) Brown bear, wild cat, pine and stone marten; griffon vulture *Gyps fulvus,* golden eagle.

5. MLJET NATIONAL PARK.

II.

a) Status : some forest exploitation on private property but solely for domestic use; hunting is permitted but under strict control; fishing permitted; some ancient agricultural holdings are still maintained.

b) Area : 3,100 ha.

c) Staff : 6 units.

d) Budget : U.S. $ 24,000.

III.

Date established : 1960, formerly since 1948 declared as a "natural rarity" under special law.

Administration : as for No. 3 above.

Land tenure : state ownership, except for 554 ha of private ownership.

Tourism : a great attraction both for its natural landscape and also for the Polace port ruins dating from the IIIrd Century and a Benedictine Monastery of the XIIth Century on an island in the Veliko Jezero (Great Lake).

IV.

Altitude : sea level to 381 m.

a) Western part of the Mljet island near Dubrovnik; typical Mediterranean vegetation, the Aleppo pines *Pinus halepensis* being regarded as the best to be found in any protected area; there are two lakes, the Veliko and Malo (Great and Small), which are connected to the sea by a narrow channel and have very peculiar ecological characteristics.

b) The lakes have a specially rich fauna and provide shelter also for the Mediterranean monk seal *Monachus m. albiventer,* which also finds a retreat in the caves along the south coast of Mljet island. The brackish water fauna includes *Chrysophrys aurata, Dicentrarchus labrax* and the crayfish *Homarus vulgaris* which finds the sandy bottom, the salinity and the abundance of mussels (*Mytilus* sp. and *Arca noae*) much to its taste.

c) Mediterranean monk seal.

6. RISNJAK NATIONAL PARK.

II.

a) Status : stated to be that of a strict scientific reserve; very little exploitation has ever occurred and much of the forest is in its original condition.

b) Area : 3,014 ha.

c) Staff : 8 units.

d) Budget : U.S. $ 36,000.

III.

Date established : 1953.

Administration : as for No. 3; staff headquarters at Crni Lug.

Land tenure : state ownership except for 80 ha of privately-owned land.

Tourism : not much developed and to be restricted to a peripheral zone outside the boundary; there is, however, one alpine hut.

IV.

Altitude : 670-1,528 m.

a) The Risnjak massif is situated in the extreme west of the Dinaric Alps; composed of calcareous and magnesian limestone, it presents numerous Karstic features. The massif divides Croatia into two regions, a continental type to the north and a Mediterranean type to the south; the vegetation is largely undisturbed, rich in endemics and relic species, including edelweiss *Leontopodium alpinum* and hairy alpenrose *Rhododendron hirsutum.*

b) Brown bear, chamois, wild cat, pine and stone marten; capercaillie.

588

7. LICKA PLJESEVICA STRICT NATURE RESERVE.

II.
    a) Status : total protection.

    b) Area : 126 ha, well below the criterion, but the area is retained because of the extreme botanical interest of the biotope, the area in which the celebrated Croat botanist I. Horvat carried out the studies in 1925 which have become classic.

    c) Staff : supervision provided by the Forest Guards of the Pljesevica range.

    d) Budget : Forest Department allocation to cover salaries.

III.
    Date established : 1961.

    Administration : as for No. 3.

    Tourism : not yet developed, but facilities to visit this primary forest area are possible and being planned.

IV.
    Altitude : 878-1,649 m.

    a) Massif on the boundary between Croatia and Bosnia-Herzegovina : the reserve protects the last remnants of the original mixed beech/fir forest *Fagetum croaticum abietetosum.*

    b) No information.

C. — MACEDONIA.

8. MAVROVO NATIONAL PARK.

II.
    a) Status : the Park is divided into three zones, of which one is exploited and could not be considered for the List, the second is a strict nature reserve and therefore a straightforward choice, while the third, though developed for tourism, enjoys a standard of protection good enough to allow it to be considered as meeting the ICNP criteria. Bear and lynx are in part protected in the first-mentioned zone, but there is an annual open hunting season for chamois.

    b) Area : 79,070 ha, of which the strictly protected zone occupies 3,950 ha and the tourist zone 59,920 ha. The seasonal hunting zone is therefore 15,200 ha.

    c) Staff : 32 full-time and 15 part-time, based at Tetovo.

    d) Budget : U.S. $ 150,000.

III.
    Date established : 1949.

    Legislation and administration : each of the Macedonian parks was created by a specific law and, while the Department of Agriculture and Sylviculture is generally responsible, has its own governing authority.

    Land tenure : public ownership, no private properties.

    Tourism : access by road or rail from Skopje; no entry fees : accommodation and other facilities available.

IV.
    Altitude : 600-2,764 m.

    a) Spruce *Picea* forest (the most southerly in Europe); horse chestnut *Aesculus hippocastanum.*

    b) Brown bear, chamois, roe deer *C. capreolus*; lynx *Felis lynx.*

9. GALICICA NATIONAL PARK.

II.
    a) Status : similar to that of No. 8 above, but the zones are less clearly demarcated. The bear is not protected in the hunting zone.

      b) Area : 23,000 ha.

      c) Staff : 9 units, based at Ohrid.

      d) Budget : U.S. $ 20,000.

III.   *Date established :* 1958.

      Tourism : numerous hotels (500 beds) at the bottom end of the Park along the shores of Ohridsko and Prespanko lakes, through which the Albanian border passes.

IV.   *Altitude :* 695-2,285 m.

      a) Noteworthy species are *Pinus heldreichii,* horse-chestnut and the junipers *Juniperus excelsa* and *foetidissima.*

      b) Brown bear, lynx.

10. PELISTER NATIONAL PARK.

II.   *a*) Status : similar to that of No. 8 above.

      b) Area : 10,400 ha, of which the strictly protected zone occupies 4,000 ha, and the tourist zone 2,400 ha.

      c) Staff : 10 full-time and 20 part-time, stationed at Bitola.

      d) Budget : U.S. $ 90,000.

III.   *Date established :* 1949.

      Tourism : well developed : a hotel and three lodges.

IV.   *Altitude :* 900-2,601 m.

      a) A 1,690 ha forest of Rumelian pine *Pinus peuce*; also beech and oak forests *Fagus sylvatica* and *Quercus* sp.

      b) Brown bear, chamois, roe deer.

D. — MONTENEGRO.

11. DURMITOR NATIONAL PARK.

II.   *a*) Status : protection is not complete in the Park as a whole, since, except for some strictly protected zones, forest produce is exploited (though on a carefully drawn up programme); domestic livestock grazes scme two or three thousand hectares, there are patches of cultivation and, on special permit, chamois and capercaillie may be hunted in certain sectors.

      b) Area : 32,000 ha, of which 1,200 ha are strictly protected.

      c) Staff : according to a letter of 6 January 1966, supervision is carried out by the regional Forest Department.

      d) Budget : incorporated in that of the Forest Department.

III.   *Date established :* 1952, this and all other Parks in Montenegro having been created by a law enacted on 6 August in that year.

      Administration : by the Nature Protection Institute of the People's Republic. Park headquarters at Zabljak.

      Tourism : free entry; access by three roads; a first-class hotel and other accommodation; winter sports.

IV.

Altitude : 538-2,522 m.

a) The Durmitor alpine massif comprises a great deal of wild country, lakes and gorges; the gorge of the Tarn river, 1,000 m deep in places, forms one boundary; coniferous forest of Norway spruce, silver fir *Abies alba,* Austrian pine and Scots pine *Pinus sylvestris* at medium altitudes and, higher up as far as the three line, mountain pine *Pinus mugo.* Alpine meadows.

b) A few brown bears; chamois; capercaillie.

12. BIOGRADSKA GORA NATIONAL PARK.

II.

a) Status : total protection in the 2,000 ha uninhabited zone, which is difficult of access, except for fishing in Biograd lake; the remainder is grazed by domestic stock.

b) Area : 3,600 ha, of which 2,000 ha are strictly protected.

c) Staff : 11 units, based at Kolasin.

d) Budget : U.S. $ 20,000.

III.

Date established : 1952; see under No. 11.

Administration : a special controlling body has been set up for this " Biograd Mountain Park ".

Tourism : free entry; tourist paths; sport-fishing.

IV.

Altitude : 832-2,116 m.

a) Part of the Bjelasica massif near the river Tara; 85 % of the Park is covered by a mixed forest (much of it primary) of spruce, juniper, beech and maple *Acer* sp.; some alpine pasture; lakes.

b) Brown bear, roe deer; capercaillie; trout.

13. LOVCEN NATIONAL PARK.

II.

a) Status : the extent of protection had not been decided in 1966, but the establishment of 800 ha of strict reserve was under consideration.

b) Area : 2,000 ha.

c) Staff : part-time supervisor by a Forest Officer and two guards stationed at Cetinje.

d) Budget : covering part-time salaries of staff.

III.

Date established : 1952; see under No. 11.

Administration : no special authority created for this Park.

Tourism : well developed; the Park contains the tomb of the national poet Bishop Njegos and is also of archaeological interest.

IV.

Altitude : 1,200-1,749 m.

a) Mountainous region between Cetinje and Kotor, offering fine views over Montenegro; beech and Austrian pine.

b) Hare *Lepus europaeus* (in exceptional numbers); stone marten; rock partridge.

E. — SLOVENIA.

14. TRIGLAV NATIONAL PARK.

a) Status : total protection; no occupancy or exploitation.

b) Area : 2,000 ha (an extension was being considered in January 1966).

591

c) Staff : 7 units, assisted by 29 volunteers to whom allowances are sometimes paid.

d) Budget : U.S. $ 800 (1964).

III.   *Date established :* 1961, by special decree made under the National Parks Law (Uradni list LRS No. 6 of 1959).

Administration : by a special Commission attached to the Assembly of Radovljica Commune.

Tourism : access by road to the Park entrance, thence by tourist paths; alpine huts.

IV.   *Altitude :* 660-2,568 m.

a) Part of the Julian Alps, in which the landscape bears the imprint of former glaciations; waterfalls; the endemic flora includes the monkshood *Aconitum angustifolium*, the poppy *Papaver julicum*, the hogweed *Heracleum siifolium*, the bellflower *Campanula zoysii*, the knapweed *Centaurea haynaldii mulica* and *Iris cengialti*.

b) Endemic species are the newt *Triturus alpestris lacusnigri* Seliskar-Pehani and the lizard *Lacerta horvathi* Meh.

15. Mala Pisnica Reserve.

II.   *a*) Status : general protection; there is scarcely any human occupancy or economic exploitation in the closed valley in which the Reserve is situated.

b) Area : 868 ha, below the criterion requirement, but the Reserve is retained for its scientific interest.

c) Staff : 2 units, a Forest Officer and guard, from the local Forest Service establishment.

d) Budget : covered by staff salaries.

III.   *Date established :* 1951.

Administration : no special authority; responsibility of Forest Service.

Tourism : very limited; there are no roads.

IV.   *Altitude :* 830-1,940 m.

a) A valley of the Julian Alps, with narrow defiles, waterfalls and mountain torrents; its main interest is the indigenous forest of the larch *Larix decidua*.

b) No information.

F. — SERBIA.

16. Fruska Gora National Park.

II.   *a*) Status : general protection, except for limited forest exploitation, permission for hunting given in certain sectors and the celebrated vineyards which occupy non-forested areas.

b) Area : 22,000 ha.

c) and *d*) Staff and Budget : no information.

III.   *Date established :* 1960.

Administration : the headquarters of Fruska Mountain Park is at Sremska Kamenica (or according to a report presented at the Seattle Conference in 1962, Sremski Karlovci) in the autonomous Province of Voivodina.

Tourism: very active; access by road from several directions and various facilities open throughout the year.

IV. *Altitude:* 150-539 m.

a) Isolated massif rising above the plain between the rivers Danube and Sava; the original forest is largely deciduous, dominated by beech and oak, but large areas are now covered by introduced conifers.

b) Wild cat, European hare, roe deer, wild pig *Sus scrofa;* white-tailed sea-eagle, imperial eagle *Aquila heliaca,* hobby *Falco subbuteo,* saker *Falco cherrug,* black kite *Milvus migrans,* white and black storks *Ciconia ciconia* and *nigra* and several woodpeckers.

17. RESAVA RESERVE.

II. *a)* Status : unknown.

b) Area : 10,000 ha.

c) and *d)* Staff and Budget : no information.

III. *Date established :* 1957.

Tourism: one particularly fine cavern, discovered in 1963, among the many in the area, is being developed as a tourist attraction.

IV. *Altitude:* no information.

a) A region of eastern Serbia of great natural beauty, with typical Karstic features including about a hundred caverns.

b) No information.

18. ZVIJEZDA RESERVE.

II. *a)* Status : total protection; uninhabited and unexploited forest.

b) Area : 1,500 ha.

c) and *d)* Staff and Budget : no information.

III. *Date established :* 1950.

Tourism: little development.

IV. *Altitude:* no information.

a) Part of Mt. Tara, near Titovo Uzice, reserved specially for the protection of the spruce forest *Picea omorica.*

b) No information.

19. RAJAC RESERVE.

II. *a)* Status : general protection; uninhabited forest.

b) Area : 1,200 ha.

c) and *d)* Staff and Budget : no information.

III. *Date established :* 1963.

Tourism: a good potential in this area of exceptional beauty not far from Ljiga (Valjevo district).

IV. No information.

20. OBEDSKA BARA RESERVE.

II.

a) Status : a ' zoological and forest ' reserve given general protection, except for one small strictly preserved sector.

b) Area : 750 ha, well below criterion.

c) and *d*) Staff and Budget : no information.

III.

Date established : 1951.

Tourism : this ' Picnic Pool ' reserve is said to have a good potential as a tourist attraction.

IV.

Altitude : no information.

a) Comprises forest, meadow and marsh near Kupinovo and Obrez villages; old forest of pedunculate oak *Quercus robur,* ash *Fraxinus* sp. and hornbeam *Carpinus betula*; good marsh flora.

b) Avifauna stated to be very varied and plentiful.

21. MONOSTORSKI RIITOVI RESERVE.

II.

a) Status : general protection, the forest is not exploited.

b) Area : 600 ha, well below criterion.

c) and *d*) Staff and Budget : no information.

III.

Date established : 1963.

Tourism : no claim to be a tourist attraction.

IV.

Altitude : no information.

a) On the left bank of the Danube, between the river and the new cause-way protecting the bank of the Danube-Tissa-Danube Canal; mixed forest of black and white poplars *Populus nigra* and *P. alba* and willow *Salix alba*; good marsh flora.

b) No information.

V.   **Areas excluded :**

A. — BOSNIA-HERZEGOVINA :

a) Two proposed National Parks :

1. Treskavica	33,000 ha.
2. Prenj	54,000 ha.

b) One park which is stated to be designed mainly for " rest and recreation " and does not appear to serve any special purpose in the conservation of natural habitats :

3. Jahorina and Trebevič	3,945 ha.

c) Several reserves of too small a size to meet the criterion requirement :

4. Lom	278 ha.
5. Janj	198 ha.
6. Suvajsko	100 ha.
7. Omar	97 ha.
8. Pljesevica	40 ha.

B. — CROATIA :

a) Four proposed reservations :

9. Kopacki Rit reserve	...	11,000 ha.
10. The Krka National Park	...	10,000 ha.
11. Hadjucki reserve	...	3,000 ha.
12. Bijele reserve	...	840 ha.

b) Two reserves of too small a size to meet the criterion :

13. Dundo	...	106 ha.
14. Lokrum	...	72 ha.

c) A ' Forest Park ' :

15. Medvednica Mountain	...	1,000 ha.

C. — MACEDONIA : nil.

D. — MONTENEGRO :

One proposed national park :

16. Orjen (size unknown).

E. — SLOVENIA :

17. Martuljek : an area set aside for " conserving the character of landscape, sites and farming practices ".
18. Robanov Kot : 1,580 ha; also for the conservation of the farmland landscape.

F. — SERBIA :

Five reserves of less than 500 ha (the minimum criterion) :

19. Ludiosalake	...	380 ha.
20. Mustafa	...	304 ha.
21. Deliblatska Pescara	...	285 ha.
22. Ostrozub	...	180 ha.
23. Koznjar	...	150 ha.

140. ZAMBIA

I.   **Listed Areas :** seven.

1. Kafue National Park.
2. Luangwa Valley Game Reserves.
3. Mweru Marsh Game Reserve.
4. Sumbu Game Reserve.
5. Lunga Game Reserve.
6. Lusenga Plain Game Reserve.
7. Kasanka Game Reserve.

General Introduction :

The legal basis for the development and organisation of Zambian national parks is provided by Chapters 106 and 241 of the Laws. The Game Reserves were originally constituted under the 'Game Ordinance' of the former Northern Rhodesian Government, but in 1957 were placed directly under the administration of the Governor in Council by Government Notice 175 made under the new Fauna Conservation Ordinance. All the areas are now the responsibility of the Ministry of Natural Resources and Tourism and are administered by the Department of Game and Fisheries. At no stage were they placed under administration of the Federation, now dissolved, like those of Southern Rhodesia. An Advisory Board assists in the management of the Kafue National Park.

The land of the Parks and reserves is in public ownership. It is worth noting, however, that with the accession of Zambia to independence the precise legal situation regarding land tenure became in doubt and a new law is in the course of preparation. Meanwhile, extensive powers have been granted to the President of the Republic, who can use them both for consolidating the status of existing parks and reserves and also for creating new ones.

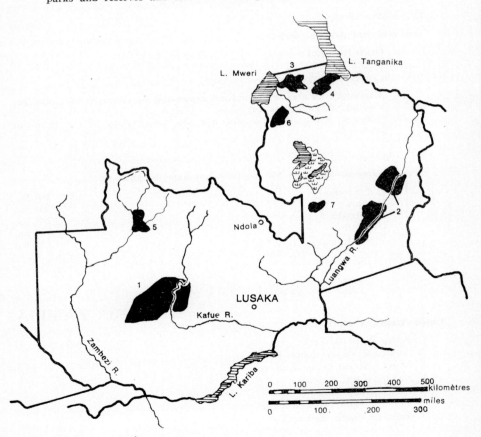

The previous edition of the List, E/3436, included all the present listed areas together with two now relegated to Section V in agreement with the Zambian authorities.

Details : application of criteria (II), general information (III) and description (IV) :

1. KAFUE NATIONAL PARK.

II.

a) Status : total protection in the Park as a whole, but there are the following exceptions which the authorities are making efforts to eliminate :

(i) Fishing rights are held by 17 villages but are being bought out. Meanwhile, it must be admitted that the exercise of these rights has in in some places reached the level of commercial exploitation, which certainly prejudices the integrity of the areas in which it is taking place.

(ii) Mineral rights, now bought out; but mention must be made of the possible construction of a dam in connection with the Kafue hydro-electric project.

(iii) Human occupancy, now terminated by the resettlement of the 2,000 people still living in the Park in 1950.

b) Area : 2,200,000 ha.

c) Staff : about 300 units, including a warden and one biologist.

d) Budget : U.S. $ 256,999 (1965).

III.

Date established : 1950.

Tourism : well organised; hotel at Ngoma; several rest-camps; access by road and air, with 800 km of road in the Park itself; the Park is open from July to the end of December; brochures, maps and aids to identification of the fauna are available; airstrip.

Research : the work carried out by the biologist and other staff is directed mainly to developing a policy for the ecological management of the Park.

IV.

Altitude : about 1,200 m.

a) A plateau, partly composed of Kalahari sands, covered by *Julbernardia* woodland; *Brachystegia* woods on the alluvial soils in the south-east; some *Colophospermum mopane* forest; vast alluvial grasslands in the north.

b) Hippopotamus *H. amphibius,* buffalo *Syncerus caffer,* zebra *Equus burchelli,* elephant *Loxodonta africana,* black rhinoceros *Diceros bicornis,* large carnivores including wild dog *Lycaon pictus*; but above all a big variety of antelopes (sable and roan *Hippotragus niger* and *equinus,* oribi *Ourebia oribi,* kudu *Tragelaphus strepsiceros,* impala *Aepyceros melampus,* lechwe *Kobus leche,* eland *Taurotragus oryx,* hartebeest *Alcelaphus lichtensteini,* wildebeest *Connochaetes taurinus,* sitatunga *Tragelaphus spekei,* blue duiker *Cephalophus monticola,* grey duiker *Silvicapra grimmii,* steinbok *Raphiceros campestris* and Sharpe's grysbok *Raphiceros sharpei*).

c) Black rhinoceros.

2. LUANGWA VALLEY GAME RESERVES.

II.

a) Status : stated by the authorities to be 'strict nature reserve' (February 1965), although this is not altogether true of the southern sector of 460,000 ha, which they admitted should probably be excluded from the List. However, this has not been done because the whole area, like the Kafue National Park (No. 1 above), is interspersed with a number of Game Management Areas, where controlled hunting is allowed and which in fact help to strengthen the integrity of the protected zones. This does, of course, affect the assessment of how far the supervisory staff meets the criteria of effective management, as in the case of Kafue.

It should also be noted that two reserves, of which the first was included in the previous edition of the List, have been incorporated in the complex : Lukusuzi and Lundazi Dam; unfortunately the former is considered to be subject to a great deal of poaching (see further under Section V).

Finally, the Reserves are noted for the ' game-cropping ' project being conducted under FAO auspices.

b) Area : 1,290,000 ha, divided into two zones, the northern of 460,000 ha and the southern of 830,000.

c) Staff : 159 units, including a warden and two biologists.

d) Budget : U.S . $ 200,000.

III.   *Date established : 1938.*

Tourism : access by road and air; 320 km of road in the actual Reserves; open June-October; many rest-camps of which some are new hotel-type camps, in the central and southern sections of the reserve. There are also ' game watching ' camps in the two annexed reserves of Nsefu and Luambe.

Research : undertaken by the two staff biologists in connection with an FAO survey project.

IV.   *Altitude :* 300-600 m.

a) The humid broad sunken trench which the Luangwa river has carved out in its meandering course; fault escarpment on the west and hilly area on the east; *Colophospermum mopane* forest on the skeletal soils and *Acacia* associations; *Combretum* bush on the alluvial soils along the rivers and ' miombo ' (*Brachystegia/Isoberlinia*) at foot of the escarpments.

b) Elephant, hippopotamus, buffalo, impala, kudu, eland, zebra, giraffe, a special race of wildebeest (Cookson's) and bushpig *Potamochoerus porcus*; lion and leopard *Panthera leo* and *pardus*, crocodile; main haunt of black rhinoceros in Zambia.

c) Black rhinoceros.

3. MWERU MARSH GAME RESERVE.

II.   *a*) Status : in general total protection, but :

(i) Fishing rights persist, though they are being bought out; there is a sizeable fishery on the lake.

(ii) The Mweru-wa-Ntipa flats are one of the main breeding-grounds of the Red Locust and constant attacks are made on the hoppers.

b) Area : 310,000 ha.

c) Staff : 14 units, well below criterion, but attempts are being made to get the number reinforced, especially in view of the pressure of poaching. The reserve has, however, been retained in the List at the express wish of the Zambian authorities.

d) Budget : U.S. $ 29,000.

III.   *Date established : 1942.*

Tourism : little development.

IV.   *Altitude :* about 1,000 m.

a) Lakes at the foot of a fault escarpment, marsh with *Phragmites* and papyrus associations; *Bussea-Combretum* bush, *Brachystegia* and *Julbernardia* woodland on the plateau soils and " dambos ".

b) Elephant, hippopotamus, buffalo, zebra, sable and roan antelope, eland, duikers, bushbuck *Tragelaphus scriptus,* sitatunga, Sharpe's grysbok; lion, leopard, some black rhinoceros, warthog *Phacochoerus aethiopicus,* bushpig.

c) Black rhinoceros.

4. SUMBU GAME RESERVE.

II.

a) Status : total protection, with the exception that although the area is uninhabited fishing rights are maintained and a hundred fishermen are annually permitted to establish their camps on the shore of Lake Tanganyika from 1 June to 31 October.

b) Area : 200,000 ha.

c) Staff : 14, somewhat below the criterion and perhaps insufficient to deal effectively with poaching.

d) Budget : U.S. $ 29,000.

III.

Date established : 1942.

Tourism : access by water (Lake Tanganyika) and by air; projects for construction of an aerodrome and of a road of access, of which the preliminary trace has been completed; limited accommodation; safe bathing; fishing in the lake.

IV.

Altitude : 800-1,000 m.

a) Southern shore of Lake Tanganyika; deltas covered by *Acacia albida*; stony hills overlooking the Lake covered by *Bussea-Combretum* bush and at higher elevations and further from the Lake by *Brachystegia-Julbernardia* woodland and some patches of open grassland.

b) Elephant, hippopotamus, warthog, buffalo, eland, zebra, sable and roan antelope, waterbuck *Kobus defassa,* puku *Kobus vardoni,* bushbuck, Sharpe's grysbok, duikers including the yellow-backed *Cephalophus silvicultor,* klipspringer *O. oreotragus.*

5. LUNGA GAME RESERVE.

II.

a) Status : total protection, uninhabited.

b) Area : 165,000 ha.

c) Staff : 17 units (exactly meeting criterion).

d) Budget : U.S. $ 20,000.

III.

Date established : 1951.

Tourism : little development; a start has been made with construction of a road of access; at present arrangements have to be made individually by prospective visitors to be allowed into the area.

IV.

Altitude : about 1,200 m.

a) Mainly Kalahari sand plains, in places wooded with *Cryptosepalum* (known as 'mavunda' country); some *Julbernardia-Brachystegia* woodland and open grassland; papyrus swamp.

b) Elephant, hippopotamus, buffalo, eland, roan, sable, impala, duikers, hartebeest, waterbuck, puku, reedbuck *Redunca arundinum,* bushbuck, klipspringer, sitatunga, oribi, zebra, warthog, bushpig; lion, leopard, cheetah *Acinonyx jubatus*; blue monkey *Cercopithecus* sp.

599

ZAMBIA

6. LUSENGA PLAIN GAME RESERVE.

II.
 a) Status : total protection; uninhabited.
 b) Area : 80,000 ha.
 c) Staff : 6 units, below criterion but the area does not suffer much from poaching.
 d) Budget : U.S. $ 5,000.

III.
 Date established : 1942.
 Tourism : no special organisation.

IV.
 Altitude : 1,000 m.
 a) The Lusenga plain itself occupies the west of the Reserve, the east consisting of *Brachystegia-Julbernardia* woodland on plateau soils.
 b) Elephant, buffalo, sable, roan, waterbuck, eland, hartebeest, klipspringer, duikers, zebra, warthog.

7. KASANKA GAME RESERVE.

II.
 a) Status : total protection; uninhabited swampy area surrounded by heavily populated country, but there is not much poaching.
 b) Area : 38,000 ha.
 c) Staff : 7 units.
 d) Budget : U.S. $ 6,200.

III.
 Date established : 1941.
 Tourism : visitors have to make individual arrangements.

IV.
 Altitude : 900 m.
 a) Extensive wetland with papyrus and reed-beds; some areas of grassland and of *Brachystegia-Julbernardia* woods.
 b) Sitatunga, elephant, hippopotamus, buffalo, sable, roan, bushbuck, puku, waterbuck, hartebeest, reedbuck, Sharpe's grysbok, various duikers, eland, zebra, lion, leopard. The whale-headed stork *Balaeniceps rex* may occur.

V. **Areas excluded :**
 A. — Two Reserves, listed in the previous edition, which in agreement with the Zambian authorities it has been decided must be omitted from the List because they suffer from heavy poaching and their staff is insufficient to bring this under control :
 1. Lavushi Manda Game Reserve ... ... 150,000 ha.
Established in 1941, this Reserve has only two game guards (criterion requires 15) and no special budgetary allocation; at the time when it was included in the previous edition, poaching was already reported to be serious and the area as subjected to frequent bush-fires.
 2. Isangano Game Reserve ... ... 84,500 ha.
Established in 1957, but has only 2 game guards (criterion : 8) and an annual budget of U.S. $ 2,100 (criterion : $ 4,200); main reason for exclusion is the fact, reported in E/3436 of the previous edition, that with a dense human population in the vicinity, illegal poaching and fishing are practised both inside and round the borders of the Reserve.

600

The information quoted above dates from 1960, but in February 1965 the Zambian authorities confirmed that the comments on these two reserves and also the Lukusuzi reserve (now incorporated in the Luangwa Valley Game Reserves, No. 2 above, q.v.) remain valid, although " it is hoped to both increase the staff in these areas and form anti-poaching units, but at present little can be done to obviate... their degradation ".

B. — Various other reserves, conservation areas (there are 38 controlled hunting areas) and forestry reserves.

C. — It is planned that by 1970, the general area of the Victoria Falls, as well as appreciable sections of the downstream gorges and of important upstream riverine habitats, all at present in the care of the Victoria Falls Trust, will be established as the Mosi-oa-Tunya (" Smoke-that-thunders ") National Park.

PRINTED IN BELGIUM

D/1970/0211/2.

IMPRIMERIE HAYEZ, S.P.R.L.

IMPRIMEUR - ÉDITEUR

RUE FIN 4, 1080 BRUXELLES

UNITED NATIONS LIST OF NATIONAL PARKS AND EQUIVALENT RESERVES

ADDENDUM 1972

HAYEZ

ADDENDUM - CORRIGENDUM

TO THE SECOND EDITION
OF THE UNITED NATIONS LIST
OF NATIONAL PARKS
AND EQUIVALENT RESERVES

including data received to 30 June 1972

Prepared by

Jean-Paul HARROY

Chairman of the
IUCN International Commission on
National Parks

1972
Publishers HAYEZ
Brussels

AN ALPHABETICAL INDEX OF COUNTRIES

3

Country	Number of areas listed in 1967-1970	Number of areas listed at mid-1972	Page
132. Union of Soviet Socialist Republics ...	51	80	93
133. United Arab Republic	—	—	97
134. United Kingdom of Great Britain and Northern Ireland, and Overseas	74	74+1	98
135. United States of America	286	290	99
136. Upper Volta	1	1	101
137. Uruguay	4	8	102
138. Venezuela	7	8	103
139. Vietnam (South)	—	—	103
140. Yemen	—	—	103
141. Yugoslavia	21	22	104
142. Zaïre	3	7	104
143. Zambia	8	17	105
144. Antarctic	—	—	107
Total	1,204	1,422	

Added : 261.

Excluded : 43.

PREFACE

The second edition of the United Nations List of National Parks and Equivalent Reserves was established under the responsibility of the International Commission of National Parks of the International Union for Conservation of Nature and Natural Resources by Dr. Jean-Paul Harroy, professor at the University of Brussels, Chairman of ICNP. The English translation of this Second Edition of the List was prepared in consultation with Professor Harroy by Sir Hugh Elliott of the IUCN Secretariat pursuant to Resolution No. 810 (XXXI) of the United Nations Economic and Social Council. It was published by Hayez ([1]) in January 1971 and included data received up to 30 June 1970.

The present Addendum-Corrigendum to the Second Edition of the List includes new data received to 30 June 1972. It covers brief descriptions of 261 new national parks and reserves not included in the Second Edition together with information on changes in titles, areas or other important corrections to entries in the Second Edition. It also covers the deletion of some parks and reserves from the List; these have been removed because it is considered that they no longer meet the criteria for inclusion set out in pages 23-33 of the Second Edition.

As a continuation of this activity, starting with 1973, IUCN will publish an annual UN List of National Parks and Equivalent Reserves. This document will list those protected areas which meet selection criteria adopted by IUCN on the recommendation of its International Commission on National Parks, and will give the title, area and location of the selected areas.

Detailed information, based on the data of the Second Edition and the present Addendum - Corrigendum, about the protected status, physical description, ecology, presence of conspicuous flora and fauna, endangered species, and the like, will appear in a loose-leaf publication "World Directory of National Parks and Other Protected Areas" which will be issued separately by IUCN and continuously up-dated by reissued sheets.

_____

([1]) Hayez, rue Fin 4, 1080 Bruxelles.

7

IUCN also plans to issue similar information in loose-leaf form on outstanding or threatened landscapes, wetlands, and other areas that should be considered for protection.

The present document is to be read in conjunction with the Second Edition of the UN List and decisions for inclusion of new areas into the List have been based on the same criteria as those used in that Edition. It has been prepared by Professor Harroy with the splendid assistance of Miss Jacqueline Henricot. It is issued on the occasion of the Second World Conference on National Parks in the centenary year of the pioneering Yellowstone National Park.

IUNC expresses its gratitude to Professor Harroy and his colleagues at the University of Bruxelles for their arduous and devoted work which has resulted in the publication of the first two editions of the UN List and this Addendum-Corrigendum. Their pioneering efforts have resulted in a valuable tool for conservation and an inestimable contribution to the cause of national parks throughout the world.

HAROLD J. COOLIDGE
President, IUCN.

8

1. AFGHANISTAN

I.   **Listed Areas :** none.

II.   **Areas added or excluded from the List since 1970 :** none.

2. ALBANIA

I.   **Listed Areas :** four.
        List 1970, p. 41.

II.   **Areas excluded or added since 1970 :** none.

3. ALGERIA

I.   **Listed Areas :** none.

II.   **Areas excluded from the List since 1970 :** two.

Chréa National Park	1,351 ha
Ouarsenis National Park	1,030 ha

Information from private sources all conclude that authorities do not have the means to enforce in the reserves the measures enacted in very old legal decrees. People enter freely with their cattle in the sanctuaries, cut trees, hunt.

III.   **Areas added to the List since 1970 :** none.

Various recommendations for the creation of new protected areas or improvement of former national parks (Babors, etc.) have been made but no steps have been taken (see " Biological Conservation ", Vol. 4, No. 2, January 1972).

4. ARAB EMIRATES

I.   **Listed Areas :** none.

II.   **Areas added or excluded :** none.

I.   **Listed Areas :** thirteen.

1.	Nahuel Huapi National Park	785,000 ha
2.	Los Glaciares National Park	600,000 ha
3.	Lanin National Park	395,000 ha
4.	Rio Pilcomayo National Park	285,000 ha
5.	Los Alerces National Park	263,000 ha
6.	Perito Francisco P. Moreno N. P.	115,000 ha
7.	Tierra del Fuego N. P.	63,000 ha
8.	Iguazu National Park	55,000 ha
9.	El Rey National Park	44,162 ha
10.	Chaco National Park	15,000 ha
11.	Laguna Blanca National Park	11,250 ha
12.	Petrified Forest National Park	10,000 ha
13.	*Palmar de Colon National Park*	8,500 ha

II.   **Areas excluded from the List since 1970 :** none.

III.   **Areas added to the List since 1970 :** one.

13. *Palmar de Colon National Park :* staff : one superintendent, three guards and auxiliary staff. Came under the N.P. Dept in April 1971 (first protective measures in 1965). Is being organized. Created especially to protect palm tree *Butia yatay = Syagrus yatay.* Fauna is scarce. Located in the province Entre Rios.

IV.   **Further Information :**

Since 1970 a few national parks were divided into "national parks" and "national reserves": Los Glaciares, F.P. Moreno, Laguna Blanca, Nahuel Huapi, Lanin, Los Alerces. (the area indicated above is the total surface). All activity and services for tourists are concentrated in the national reserves adjoining the national parks.

6. AUSTRALIA

I.   **Listed Areas :** hundred and thirteen.

A. —	New South Wales	28
B. —	Victoria	17
C. —	South Australia	10
D. —	Western Australia	14
E. —	Northern Territory	6
F. —	Queensland	35
G. —	Tasmania	3
H. —	Papua and New Guinea	0

II.   **Areas added to the List since 1970 :** fourty-two.

       A. — New South Wales   17
       B. — Victoria   3
       C. — South Australia   0
       D. — Western Australia   9
       E. — Northern Territory   2
       F. — Queensland   11

III.   **Further Information :**

A letter received from Sydney (8 Aug. 1972) said : National Parks in Australia are in transition. New legislation has been passed in several States and Territories during the last three years which has completely re-organized the old system and this trend is continuing with legislation which is now being drafted. Broad picture of the relative increase in acreage : Australian total : 1970, 6,776,399 ha; 1971, 6,827,411 ha and 1972, 12,635,628 ha.

A. — NEW SOUTH WALES.

I.   **Listed   Areas :** twenty-eight.

   1. Kosciusko National Park ... ...   611,882 ha
   2. Blue Mountains National Park (size indicated in 1967-1970 :
      68,000 ha) ... ...   100,875 ha
   3. Morton National Park (size indicated in 1970 : 18,000 ha) ...   77,819 ha
   4. *Kanangra-Boyd National Park* ... ...   56,975 ha
   5. *Kinchega National Park* ... ...   44,009 ha
   6. *Guy Fawkes River National Park* ... ...   25,434 ha
   7. New England National Park ... ...   23,369 ha
   8. Mt Kaputar National Park (1970 : 14,080 ha) ... ...   16,943 ha
   9. *Sturt National Park* ... ...   16,362 ha
  10. Warrumbungle National Park (1970 : 9,541 ha) ... ...   15,496 ha
  11. *Myall Lakes National Park* ... ...   15,441 ha
  12. The Royal National Park ... ...   14,908 ha
  13. Ku Ring Gai Chase National Park ... ...   14,614 ha
  14. Gibraltar Range National Park . ...   14,495 ha
  15. *Barrington Tops National Park* . ...   14,005 ha
  16. *Dharug National Park* . ...   13,873 ha
  17. *Willandra National Park* ... ...   13,081 ha
  18. *Ben Boyd National Park* ... ...   8,910 ha
  19. *Weddin Mountains National Park* ... ...   8,302 ha
  20. *Cocoparra National Park* ... ...   8,289 ha
  21. Brisbane Water National Park (1970 : 6,077 ha) ... ...   7,826 ha
  22. *Crowdy Bay National Park* ... ...   5,346 ha
  23. *Mt Imlay National Park* ... ...   3,766 ha
  24. *Nalbaugh State Park* ... ...   3,766 ha
  25. *Heathcote State Park* . ...   2,252 ha
  26. *Mount Warning State Park* ... ...   2,140 ha
  27. *Bald Rock National Park* ... ... about   2,106 ha
  28. Dorrigo National Park ... ...   1,642 ha

AUSTRALIA

II.   **Areas excluded from the List since 1970 :** none.

III.   **Areas added to the List since 1970 :** seventeen.

4. *Kanangra-Boyd National Park :* established in 1969; steeply dissected country, located on the eastern margin of a high plateau which is abruptly terminated to the south and east of the gorges of the Kowmung, Kanangra and Jenolan Rivers; altitude : 229-1,289 m; sclerophyll eucalypt open forest; fauna : brush-tailed rock wallaby, koala, red-necked pademelon, sugar glider, grey glider, satin bower-bird, lyre-bird; a few facilities near the Jenolan caves adjacent to northern boundary.

5. *Kinchega National Park :* established in 1967; flood plain of the Darling River; includes ephemeral lakes and swamps; riverine forest and eucalypt forest, arid scrub, and shrub steppe; faunal communities of the arid and semi-arid habitats including red kangaroo, emu and various waterfowl and other birds; altitude : 61-74 m.   Tourism is developing.

6. *Guy Fawkes River National Park :* gazetted in 1972; undeveloped wilderness and wild river; steep slopes and vertical rock walls; sclerophyll forest, woodland and isolated pockets of rainforest; altitude : about 250 to 1,400 m; fauna includes grey kangaroo, walaroo, red-necked wallaby, red-legged pademelon, bandicoot, possum, etc. and various birds.

9. *Sturt National Park :* gazetted in 1972; low undulating plain in the north-western corner of the State; altitude 150 to 230 m; has been very badly over-grazed; however with the elimination of stock it is anticipated that the ecology of the area will recover; present vegetation pattern is dominated by tough, microphyllous shrubs and annual grasses; fauna communities have been greatly reduced (kangaroos, emu...); no tourist development; accommodation at nearby Tibooburra.

11. *Myall Lakes National Park :* gazetted in 1972; largest undeveloped system of coastal lakes in the State; comprises two sand-ridge plains, or barrier systems approximately parallel to the coast, separated by a swamp; flora includes terrestrial, aquatic and lagoon communities; altitude : 0-98 m; high population of waterfowl; tourist development is rapidly expanding; tourist centres at nearby Port Stephens and Forster-Tuncurry; mineral beach sand mining will continue on limited areas until 1988.

15. *Barrington Tops National Park :* created in 1969; plateau with bogs and swamps; the great range in altitude and vegetation type provides a wide spectrum for fauna which includes wombats, grey kangaroo, dingo, short-eared possum, and various birds; flora includes grasslands, woodlands, rain forest and wet sclerophyll forest; altitude : 426-1,580 m; access is difficult and tourism not yet developed.

16. *Dharug National Park :* created in 1967; deeply dissected plateau located 50 km north of Sydney; sclerophyll forest, salt marsh and mangrove communities; fauna is typical of semi-arid sandstone belt; vehicle access by perimeter road only; limited tourist facilities; altitude : 0-245 m.

17. *Willandra National Park :* created in 1972; was intensively overgrazed prior to acquisition and reservation as a national park; rehabilitation will be the major management task facing the National Parks and Wildlife Service of N.S.W.; the saltbush and the black box are the two major associations found within this area; fauna includes red and western grey kangaroos and emu; riverine habitats (Willandra Billabong) are most valuable for birds; altitude : about 100 m; no tourist development.

18. *Ben Boyd National Park :* created 1971; this park is in two sections north and south of Eden; coastal range which rises to 320 m and coastline with cliffs, and beaches; coastal heaths and woodlands; fauna includes grey kangaroos, red-necked and swamp wallabies; migratory honeyeaters; no tourist developments at present.

19. *Weddin Moutains National Park :* established 1971; the Weddin Range runs as a sharp moutain ridge on the west of Grenfell; altitude 382-782 m the most outstanding feature is its high degree of naturalness; to date (June 1972) there exists only one major track, across the area; woodland dominated by the Ironbark-Red Gum type; valuable area for larger macropods and emu.

20. *Cocoparra National Park :* established 1969; surrounded by Murrumbidge Irrigation Area and other extensive commercial agriculture; located on Cocoparra Range; vegetation cover typical of stony ridges in the semi-arid interior with dry sclerophyll eucalypt forest woodland, and scrub; habitat of Western Grey kangaroo, and echidna; day visitors only.

22. *Crowdy Bay National Park :* gazetted 1972; heavy mineral beach sand mining will occur within this N. P. until 1988; wet heathland which seasonally becomes a swamp; altitude : 0-115 m; fauna includes grey kangaroo, emu, koala, lace monitor, death adder and various birds; tourist developments occur mainly on the headlands and in the calm river estuaries of the coast north and south of the National Park.

23. *Mt Imlay National Park :* gazetted 1972; Mt Imlay, 886 m above sea level is a dominant feature in the Far South Coast of NSW; located near Eden city and Ben Boyd N.P. (No. 18); flora is mainly sclerophyll forest; however noteable for some of the most southerly samples of sub-tropical rainforest on the east coast of Australia; animal communities typical of the rugged costal hinterland and sclerophyll forest; no tourist developments.

24. *Nalbaugh State Park :* gazetted 1972; as Mt Imlay, largely unknown to tourist because of difficult access; massif between two major drainage headwaters comprising the twin peaks of Wog Wog, 1,138 m and White Rock 1,093 m; sclerophyll forest and a southerly occurrence of rainforest; fauna includes a representative sample of animal communities of the southern New South Wales coastal and tablelands region.

25. *Heathcote State Park :* established in 1963, permanently reserved 1967; dissected northern margin of Woronora Plateau located at about 40 km from Sydney; altitude 6-242 m; dry sclerophyll eucalyptus woodland on the plateau, wet sclerophyll forest in valley; fauna typical of semi-arid sandstone belt habitat including moist valley bottoms; vehicle access is restricted to the margins of the park.

26. *Mount Warning State Park :* established in 1928, permanently reserved in 1967; eroded core of a very large shield volcano the remnant cone of which is still traceable; Mount Warning itself is a high very sharply pointed peak; altitude : 240-1,138 m; sclerophyll eucalypt forest and rainforest, with fauna typical of these habitats; no tourist developments.

27. *Bald Rock National Park :* gazetted 1969; the central feature is Bald Rock which is an excellent example of a granite exfoliation dome; it is approximately 140 m high, 686 m long and 457 m wide; located near Girraween N. P. in Queensland; great habitat diversity from high wind swept rocks through the steep timbered slopes and ridges, wet gullies and open grassy swamps with correspondent fauna diversity; particularly noticeable are the numbers and species of macropods recorded; casual day visitors only.

IV.   **Further Information :**

Most of these areas have Service Staff assigned to them and resident either on the park or stationed close by. The National Parks and Wildlife Service of NSW is the responsible authority for the overall administration of the nature conservation system.

Mention should be made as well of five State Parks which are under the size criterion : Macquarie Pass (1,064 ha, 1969), Wallaga Lake (1,053 ha, 1972), Bouddi (1,024 ha, 1937), Seven Mile Beach (664 ha, 1971), Thirlmere Lakes (628 ha, 1972) and of three national parks which are expected to be declared by the end of 1972 : Angourie (3,766 ha), Hat Heath (3,726 ha) and Red Rock (1,903 ha).

Furthermore there are at this time (May 1972) eighty five nature reserves totalling 235,135 ha. Many of these are small areas but of ecological viability and great significance — for example offshore islands for seabird breeding colonies, pockets of rainforest adequately protected by surrounding eucalypt forest and many reserves for the maintainance of communities of threatened species such as mallee fowl and koala. Some of these could very well qualify for inclusion in the U.N. List but full detail are not yet available.

B. — VICTORIA.

I.   **Listed areas :** seventeen.

1.	Wyperfeld National Park	56,000 ha
2.	Wilson's Promontory National Park	48,340 ha
3.	*Little Desert National Park*	34,000 ha
4.	Hattah Lakes National Park ... ... about	20,000 ha
5.	Mt Buffalo National Park	10,912 ha
6.	*Lower Glenelg National Park*	8,960 ha
7.	King Lake National Park	5,632 ha
8.	Mallacoota Inlet National Park	4,490 ha
9.	Fraser National Park	3,100 ha
10.	*Captain James Cook National Park*	2,680 ha
11.	Alfred National Park	2,270 ha
12.	The Lakes National Park	2,115 ha
13.	Wingan Inlet National Park	1,897 ha
14.	Lind National Park	1,153 ha
15.	Mt Richmond National Park	800 ha
16.	Port Cambell National Park	750 ha
17.	Fern Tree Gully National Park	372 ha

II.   **Areas excluded from the List since 1970 :** none.

III.   **Areas added to the List since 1970 :** three.

3. *Little Desert National Park :* created in 1968, enlarged in 69; one full time ranger; budget : about 10,000 U.S. $; flat to undulating sandy land in reasonable rainfall but very poor nutrient status; flora rich with many different associations; open heathland and heath woodland; fauna includes *Leipoa ocellata, Macropus melanops, M. rufogriseus, Pseudomys albocinereus, Amphibolorus pictus, Tiliqua occipitalis,* honeyeaters and insectivorous birds; altitude : 140-200 m; a few facilities for tourists.

6. *Lower Glenelg National Park :* created in december 69; even though there is neither staff nor budget this park was recommended for inclusion in the List because of its features and potential; dry sclerophyll eucalypt forest, limestone cliffs of Glenelg River; outstanding flora (660 recorded species); rich fauna including macropods, dasyures, phalangers and monotremes; altitude : 0-150 m; no tourist facilities.

10. *Captain James Cook National Park :* gazetted in 1969; located in the far east of Victoria on the southern coast; contains the point of land first sighted by Captain James Cook's « Endeavour » crew in 1770; giant, raw sanddunes and superb coastal features; granite hills; tall forest; fauna : reptiles marsupials, birds; among the rare mammals are the Tiger Cat and the Potoroo; despite the lack of staff and funding this park was recommended for inclusion in the U.N. List because of its great potential; tourist facilities are planned.

C. — SOUTH AUSTRALIA.

I.

Listed Areas : ten.

1. Hincks, Murlong and Nicholls Wild Life Reserve	65,326 ha
2. Flinders Chase Reserve	54,298 ha
3. Hambidge Wild Life Reserve	37,544 ha
4. Billiatt Wild Life Reserve	36,350 ha
5. Archibald Makin Wild Life Reserve	17,420 ha
6. Lincoln Wild Life Reserve	14,208 ha
7. Wilpena Pound	7,960 ha
8. Peebinga Wild Life Reserve	1,610 ha
9. Belair National Park	897 ha
10. Chauncey Line (Ferries-Mc Donald) Reserve	800 ha

II.

Areas excluded or added since 1970 : none.

III.

Further Information :

P.S. — News received in August 1972, when this booklet was already in the press, indicate that the name of "Wild Life Reserve" was changed to "National Park" (No. 2 and 6) or "Conservation Park". Archibald Makin (No. 5) is now called Mount Rescue Conservation Park and increased to 28,400 ha. Billiatt is now 37,700 ha and Wilpena Pound (No. 7, 7,960 ha) is now included in Flinders Ranges National Park (58,000 ha). Mention should now be made of thirteen further protected areas :

Unnamed Conservation Park	2,130,000 ha
Simpson Desert Conservation Park (cf. Queensland)	690,000 ha
Yumbarra Conservation Park	106,000 ha
Elliott Price Conservation Park	65,000 ha
Scorpion Springs Conservation Park	30,400 ha
Bascombe Well Conservation Park	29,000 ha
Gammon Ranges National Park	15,500 ha
Canunda National Park	8,950 ha
Mt Remarkable National Park	8,200 ha
Innes National Park	6,100 ha
Coorong National Park	5,100 ha
Para Wirra Recreation Park	1,206 ha
Cleland Conservation Park	750 ha

D. — WESTERN AUSTRALIA.

I.   **Listed Areas :** fourteen.

1.	*Hamersley Range National Park*	583,372 ha
2.	*Cape Arid National Park*	256,800 ha
3.	*Chichester Range National Park*	148,865 ha
4.	*Kalbarri National Park*	146,058 ha
5.	Stirling Ranges National Park (size indicated in 1970 : 108,000 ha)	114,350 ha
6.	*Watheroo National Park*	30,658 ha
7.	*Frank Hann National Park*	25,792 ha
8.	*Cape le Grand National Park*	21,950 ha
9.	*Nambung National Park*	16,000 ha
10.	*Cape Range National Park*	13,270 ha
11.	Nornalup National Park	13,200 ha
12.	Yanchep National Park	2,758 ha
13.	Porongorups National Park	2,212 ha
14.	John Forrest National Park	1,565 ha

II.   **Areas excluded from the List since 1970 :** none.

III.   **Areas added to the List since 1970 :** nine.

1. *Hamersley Range National Park :* created in 1969; totally protected; one full-time ranger; budget for 1970-1971 about 11,000 U.S. $; very remote area; situated in the North West of the State; contains the highest peaks in Western Australia (1,200 m). Dominant tree is Mulga (*Acacia aneura*); varied and interesting fauna including dingo, red kangaroo, several species of bats, reptiles and interesting avifauna; very limited tourism.

2. *Cape Arid National Park :* created in 1969; supervision is maintained by mobile rangers; very remote area; situated in the South-east of the State approximately 65 miles East of Esperance; rugged coastal scenery; rich in plant species; over fifteen endemic species. Altitude : 150 m; tourism is very limited.

3. *Chichester Range National Park :* created in 1969; supervision maintained by the ranger from Hamersley range N.P.; tourism is limited as the area is quite inaccessible; situated in the North West of the State, south of Roebourne; contains great scenic beauty including aboriginal rock engravings, picturesque pools and gorges; mean altitude is 300 m.

4. *Kalbarri National Park :* created in 1963; supervision : two full-time rangers; budget : about U.S. $ 11,000; situated approximately 400 miles North of Perth; includes most of the spectacular gorge of the Murchison River (150 m deep) and part of the coast; gently rolling sand-plain contry stretches on either side of the gorge; the only large trees in the area occur in the gorge (gums) which also contains endemic plants; fairly popular to tourists; fauna includes water-fowl, kangaroos, emus, etc.

6. *Watheroo National Park :* created in 1969; supervision maintained by mobile rangers; budget in 1970-1971 was about 2,500 U.S. $; limited tourism as area has been left in its natural state; situated approximately 100 miles North of Perth, set aside to protect the abundant wildflowers growing there; mean altitude is 300 m.

7. *Frank Hann National Park :* created in 1970; supervision maintained by mobile rangers; limited tourism; situated in the South West of the State consisting of a strip of land one mile wide on each side of the Lake King-Norseman road; mean altitude is 300 m.

8. *Cape le Grand National Park :* proclaimed in 1966; supervision maintained by mobile rangers and an Honorary ranger; budget : about 1,200 U.S. $; limited tourism; coastal reserve situated 20 miles east of Esperance; Archaen granite/gneiss; interesting flora including one endemic species of *Leptospermum* which has not been found elsewhere in the world; fauna includes the rock wallaby and honey possum (*Tarsipes spenserae*); mean altitude is 150 m.

9. *Nambung National Park :* proclaimed in 1968; one full-time ranger; budget about 23,000 U.S. $; situated approximately 100 miles North of Perth; most of the area consists of dense scrub with the exception of a sand plain containing " Pinnacles " and fossilised roots; mean altitude is 150 m; no facilities but popular to tourists.

10. *Cape Range National Park :* proclaimed in 1965; mobile rangers and honorary rangers; budget : about 700 U.S. $; centred around the Cape Range area near Exmouth; contains rugged spectacular canyons; great potential for tourism; accommodation in the town of Exmouth; mean altitude : 150 m.

IV.   **Further Information :**

Beside the fourteen above listed national parks the National Parks Board of Western Australia has under its control eighteen national parks under the ICNP size criterion and twenty-two other reserves. On the other hand there are some 265 wild life sanctuaries controlled by the Western Australian Wild Life Authority under the Fauna Conservation Act and Regulations (Department of Fisheries and Fauna). The largest of these is Northern Nullarbor Wildlife Sanctuary, 2,400,000 ha.

E. — NORTHERN TERRITORY.

I.   **Listed Areas :** six.

1. Cobourg Peninsula Sanctuary	192,660 ha
2. Ayers Rock-Mt Olga National Park	124,672 ha
3. *Finke Gorge National Park*	45,310 ha
4. *Simpson's Gap National Park*	30,592 ha
5. Katherine Gorge National Park	22,424 ha
6. Howard Springs National Park	280 ha

II.   **Areas excluded from the List since 1970 :** none.

III.   **Areas added to the List since 1970 :** two.

3. *Finke Gorge National Park :* declared in 1967; totally protected; uninhabited area; one full time curator; budget 1971-1972 : about U.S. $ 9,248; located 160 km south west of Alice Springs; access is difficult; no accommodation; sandstone mountains and hills; relic palm (*Livistona Mariae*), 60 species of birds. Altitude max. 900 m.

17

4. *Simpson's Gap National Park :* declared in 1970; located 22 km from Alice Springs; many visitors; area bisected by a mountain range rising to 900 m. Water gap cut through the MacDonnell Ranges by floodwaters; vegetation embraces a varied range of shrubs and trees and 65 species of trees; a few mammals, 135 bird species.

F. — QUEENSLAND.

I. **Listed Areas :** thirty-five.

1. *Simpsons Desert National Park .* ... ... 505,047 ha
2. Windsor Tableland National Park (size indicated in 1970 : 58,823 ha) (or Daintree Gorge) ... ... 56,453 ha
3. Eungella National Park ... ... 49,614 ha
4. Hinchibrook Island National Park ... ... 39,348 ha
5. Bellenden Ker National Park ... ... 32,431 ha
6. Carnarvon National Park ... ... 26,903 ha
7. Salvator Rosa National Park ... ... 26,272 ha
8. Mt Elliott National Park (1970 : 24,301 ha) ... ... 25,594 ha
9. Lamington National Park ... ... 19,776 ha
10. Conway Range National Park ... ... 19,449 ha
11. *Dipperu National Park* ... ... 11,088 ha
12. Whitsunday Island N. P. ... ... 10,926 ha
13. Bunya Mountains National Park. ... ... 9,805 ha
14. *Yamanie Falls National Park* ... ... 9,717 ha
15. Robinson Gorge National Park ... ... 8,903 ha
16. *Southwood National Park .* ... ... 7,705 ha
17. Crystal Creek National Park ... ... 7,224 ha
18. Girraween National Park (=Castle Rock+Bald Rock N. P.) .. 5,501 ha
19. *Cape Upstart National Park .* ... ... 5,463 ha
20. Mt Barney National Park ... ... 5,253 ha
21. Hook Island National Park . ... 5,180 ha
22. *Forty Mile Scrub National Park .* ... ... 4,619 ha
23. Isla Gorge National Park ... ... 4,310 ha
24. *Dawson River Gorge National Park .* ... ... 3,367 ha
25. *Cunningham's Gap National Park* ... ... 3,035 ha
26. Mt Walsh National Park ... ... 2,987 ha
27. Flinders Island Group (or McClear) N. P. ... ... 2,962 ha
28. *Porcupine Gorge National Park .* ... ... 2,938 ha
29. Barron Falls National Park . ... 2,833 ha
30. Palmerston National Park . ... 2,556 ha
31. Magnetic Island National Park . ... 2,533 ha
32. Gloucester Island National Park ... ... 2,460 ha
33. *Herbert River Falls National Park* ... ... 2,428 ha
34. Thornton Peak National Park ... ... 2,331 ha
35. *Mt Tempest National Park .* ... ... 2,104 ha

II. **Areas excluded from the List since 1970 :** none.

III. **Areas added to the List since 1970 :** eleven.

1. *Simpsons Desert National Park :* on the border with South Australia and Northern Territory, declared in 1967; inaccessible to the general public; the

desert is waterless for most of the year; abundant flowering after rain; 85 species of plant, 5 of which are new records for Queensland; fauna includes red kangaroo, marsupial mouse, hopping rat, bearded dragon, painted dragon, blind snake, and birds. Altitude : 40 m.

11. *Dipperu National Park :* declared in 1967; located close to the main Mackay-Clermont road; no facilities; flooded country with numerous lagoons and numerous wetland avi-fauna; 40 % poplar box woodland; isolated thickets of sandalwood; 60 % Brigalow (*Acacia harpophylla*); fauna includes various marsupials. Altitude : 150-185 m.

14. *Yamanie Falls National Park :* declared in 1963, modified in 1970; predominantly rain forest; main water courses : Yamanie Creek and Herbert River; altitude : 45-845 m; no facilities for tourists.

16. *Southwood National Park :* declared in 1970; adjoins main Moonie Highway and in the future when facilities are provided will be very accessible to the public; purpose : preserve a sample of the brigalow scrubs mostly dense forest of Brigalow with Belah (*Casuarina cambagei*), Wilga (*Geijera parviflora*) and sandalwood; cypress forest; fauna includes many birds and grey kangaroo. Altitude : 230 m.

19. *Cape Upstart National Park :* declared in 1969; rugged hilly country; predominantly low layered eucalyptus woodland in which ironbark species are prominent; some fairly extensive areas of Acacia thicket and broadleaved deciduous and evergreen species from littoral woodlands adjacent to some of the beaches; altitude : 0-735 m; no facilities for tourists.

22. *Forty Mile Scrub National Park :* declared in 1970; major feature of park for which it was reserved is the semi-evergreen vine thicket developed on krasnozems; surrounding the vine thicket are areas of grassy eucalypt woodland; main watercourse : Lynd River which begins in park; altitude : 705-780m; no facilities for tourists.

24. *Dawson River Gorge National Park :* declared in 1969; 50 % layered brigalow (*Acacia harpophylla*) woodland; 50 % layered open sclerophyll woodland (*Eucalyptus* species); altitude from 385 to 595 m; no facilities for tourists.

25. *Cunningham's Gap National Park :* declared in 1930, modified 1954 and 1969; notophyll vine forest and tall layered eucalyptus forest are the major communities of the park; altitude : 260-1,170 m; picnic and camping grounds with amenities; several km of track.

28. *Porcupine Gorge National Park :* declared in 1970; ironwood woodland and forest with rock outcrops; altitude : 430-610 m; no facilities.

33. *Herbert River Falls National Park :* declared in 1970; river flows along tablelands then falls into Herbert River Gorge over Herbert River Falls; altitude : 185-605 m; no facilities for tourists but good potential.

35. *Mt Tempest National Park :* declared in 1966; Mt Tempest is a sand dune 285 m high and considered one of the highest in the world; layered eucalypt woodland developed on high quartzite sand dunes; dominant tree species are *Eucalyptus intermedia, E. micrantha* and *Tristania conferta* situated on Moreton Island; altitude : 10-285 m; no facilities.

IV.   **Further Information :**

The previously listed Castle Rock National Parks and Bald Rock National Park were amalgamated in 1966 to form No. 18 : Girraween National Park.

To date there are 280 national parks in Queensland; many of these are very small and do not meet U.N. criteria; they include 170 islands off the Queenslands Coast. Expenditure for listed parks is about 400,000 U.S. $.

A new national park of some 24,500 ha has recently been declared on the northern section of Fraser Island. No detail are yet available. Other important legislation was passed in 1971 to provide for the establishment of Marine National Parks. No such areas have been reserved as yet.

G. — TASMANIA.

I. **Listed Areas :** three.

1. Cradle Mount-Lake St Clair National Park . ...   135,398 ha
2. Mount Field National Park . ...   16,023 ha
3. Freycinet National Park   ... ...   7,368 ha

II. **Areas excluded or added since 1970 :** none.

III. **Further Information :**

If recent information could have been obtained from Hobart, some of the four areas indicated in 1970 as « unstaffed and therefore not effectively protected » (Lake Pedder, Ben Lomond, Frenchman's Cap and Hartz Mountains National Parks) could possibly have been added to the List.
Lake Pedder N. P., in South West Tasmania is submitted to a development plan authorized by the Government which will flood this beautiful lake and gave rise to much protest locally.

H. — PAPUA AND NEW GUINEA.

I. **Listed Areas :** none.

II. **Areas added or excluded since 1970 :** none.

There are in Papua and New Guinea a number of national parks and reserves which still are in the formative stage and fail to qualify for inclusion on the U.N. List, the most outstanding being Wariata National Park (or Mt Astrolabe, Papua, 6,562 ha) and Mount Bosavi N. P. (Papua, about 510,000 ha).
A National Parks Board was established in 1970. Its executive Director is at present the former responsible authority of Kosciusko N. P. in New South Wales.

7. AUSTRIA

I. Listed Areas : seven.

A. — STRICT NATURE RESERVES.

1. *Marchauen-Marchegg Nature Reserve*	1,200 ha
2. Rothwald	600 ha

B. — RESERVES.

3. Tauern	34,000 ha
4. Neusiedlersee and Seewinkel	2,940 ha
(or 35,000 including 31,060 ha with less strong status)	

C. — NATURSCHUTZGEBIETE.

5. Karwendelschutzgebiet	72,000 ha
6. Grossglockner and Paterze mit Gamsgrube	3,698 ha
7. Lainzer Tiergarten im Wienerwald	2,300 ha

II. Areas excluded from the List since 1970 : none.

N.B. — Naturalists however suggested the exclusion of Lainzer Tiergarten, mainly forest area, entirely walled up, where game (red deer, wild sheep, boars, etc.) is anormally abundant, as a result from the care which is taken of them. Tourism highly developed, especially on Sundays.

III. Areas added to the List since 1970 : one.

1. *Marchauen-Marchegg Nature Reserve :* the river March (or Morava) forms a natural border between Slovakia and Austria before joining the Danube about 20 miles from Vienna; the March was formerly flanked by vast gallery forests; such a piece of forest (1,200 ha) has remained intact in an estate which was put on the market in 1969; it was feared that it might be sold off in separate lots; WWF intervened and was able, in collaboration with the Municipality of Marchegg, to acquire the land in its entirety; creation : June 1st, 1970; feeding area for migratory birds and particularly for ducks and geese.

IV. Further Information :

Efforts have been made for the last few years by several institutes and private persons to obtain the official creation and especially the equipment and organization of « Hohe Tauern National Park » (see 3. Hereabove). Matters are complicated owing to the fact that the area depends upon three authorities : Salzburg, Kärntern, Tirol. A treaty was signed by these three " Länder " on October 21st, 1971 at Heiligenblut at the foot of Grossglockner to create this national park. The Federal Government of Vienna also decided to intervene.

8. BARBADOS

I. Listed Areas : none.

II. Areas added or excluded : none.

I.   Listed Areas : none.

II.   Areas added or excluded : none.

10. **BELGIUM**

I.   Listed Areas : nine.

A. — NATIONAL NATURE RESERVES.

1. Hautes Fagnes National Nature Reserve ... ...   3,894 ha
2. Kalmthout National Nature Reserve . ...   812 ha
3. *Mechelse Heide National Nature Reserve* . ...   388 ha
4. Westhoek National Nature Reserve ... ...   340 ha
5. *Plateau des Tailles National Nature Reserve* ... ...   203 ha

B. — PRIVATE RESERVES.

6. Areas protected by the Association for « Réserves Naturelles et Ornithologiques de Belgique » of which the three most important are :
   Blankaert ... ...   400 ha
   de Ronde Put . ...   280 ha
   Genk ... ...   220 ha

7. Areas protected by the « Ardenne et Gaume » Association, of which the four most important are :
   Lesse et Lhomme . ...   980 ha
   Bois du Pays . ...   601 ha
   Viroin . ...   505 ha
   Bois du Grand Pré ... ...   303 ha

8. Areas protected by the Association « De Wielewaal », of which the most important is :
   de Terlaemen ... ...   288 ha

9. Areas protected by the Association " Vereniging voor Natuur- en Stedenschoon " of which the most important is :
   Grobbendonk . ...   221 ha

II.   Areas excluded from the List since 1970 : none.

In fact, presentation having changed, the total number for Belgium remained nine as in the previous editions.

III.   Areas added to the List since 1970 :

Presentation having changed the total number of listed areas is of no importance. Kalmthout which was a private reserve is now a national nature reserve. Two other national nature reserves have been declared : *Mechelse Heide* (1967) one of the last heathland characteristic of the Campine region, and *Plateau des Tailles* (1967 and 1968) : great peatland.

11. BHUTAN

I.   **Listed Areas :** none.

II.   **Areas excluded or added :** none.

12. BOLIVIA

I.   **Listed Areas :** one.

     1. *Reserva Nacional de Fauna Ulla Ulla .* ... ...   215,125 ha

II.   **Areas excluded from the List since 1970 :** none.

III.   **Areas added to the List since 1970 :** one.

     1. *Ulla Ulla National Reserve :* officially declared by presidential decree in January 1972; purpose : protection of the vicugna; some livestock (alpaca breeding); three fully equipped wardens; located 60 km from Titicaca Lake near the Peruvian border, accessible by jeep; pampa located at an altitude of 4,300 m; beside the vicugna is the habitat for condor and waterfowl; proposals to extend the reserve on the opposite side of the frontier in Peru and thus create an international reserve.

13. BOTSWANA

I.   **Listed Areas :** eight.

     1. *Central Kahalari Game Reserve* . ... 5,280,000 ha
     2. Gemsbok National Park (was in 1967 : 960,000 ha) . ... 2,480,000 ha
     3. *Chobe National Park* ... ... 1,036,000 ha
     4. *Makgadikgadi Game Reserve* ... ... 390,000 ha
     5. *Khutswe Game Reserve* (or Khutse) ... ... 250,000 ha
     6. *Nxai Pan National Park* ... ... 210,000 ha
     7. *Moremi Wild Life Reserve* ... ... 181,300 ha
     8. *Mabua Sehube Game Reserve* ... ... 180,000 ha

II.   **Areas excluded since 1970 :** none.

III.   **Areas added to the List since 1970 :** seven.

     1. *Central Kahalari Game Reserve :* at the limit of being included as there is no resident field staff; but administered by Game Warden, Ghanzi. Quite inaccessible. Bushmen are allowed to follow their traditional hunting and gathering way of life. No hunting is permitted by other persons. Not open to tourism. Created in 1963.

3. *Chobe National Park :* controlled by seven units : considered adequate the areas surrounding the park being only slightly settled. Was a game reserve since 1961, proclaimed national park in March 1968. Much of the park remains undeveloped. Game viewing roads concentrated in the northern and south eastern section. One hotel (Chobe River hotel); another will soon be open. Wide variety of habitats including river, flood-grass lands, thicket, woodland and forest, pans and water holes, inland delta. Contains all the major african species and over 80 varieties of birds.

4. *Makgadikgadi Pans Game Reserve :* totally protected; controlled by resident field staff and a game warden (Maun). Created in 1970.

5. *Khutswe Game Reserve :* totally protected; controlled by resident field staff and by game warden (Molopolole). Proclaimed in 1971.

6. *Nxai Pan National Park :* totally protected. Controlled by resident field staff and by game warden (Ngamiland). Proclaimed in 1971.

7. *Moremi Wild Life Reserve* (Okavango): this reserve belongs to and was created by the Batawana tribe on whose land it is situated. Final gazetting in 1965. Controlled by resident senior and field staff. The natural beauty of the reserve has been preserved by restricting tourist facilities. Bad and often very sandy roads. No accommodation in the reserve. Khwai River Lodge at 9 miles. Its waterways, lagoons, islands and reedbeds make it the home of countless birds. Buffalos, wildebeests, zebras, impala, tsessebees, sitatunga, lechwes, lions, cheetahs, etc. Infested by tsetse fly.

8. *Mabua Sehube Game Reserve :* totally protected; no resident staff but administered by game warden (Souther Kgalagadi). According to local authorities, the protection given to this reserve justifies its inclusion on the U.N. List. Proclaimed in 1971.

IV.   **Further Information :**

National parks and game reserves are administered by the Ministry of Commerce, Industry and Water Affairs through the Department of Wildlife and National Parks.

14. BRAZIL

I.   **Listed Areas :** twenty.

1. *Araguaia National Park .* ... ...   460,000 ha
2. *Chapada dos Veadeiros National Park* (Tocantins) . ...   171,924 ha
3. Iguaçu National Park (size indicated in 1970 : 180,000 ha) ...   170,000 ha
4. *Serra da Bocaina National Park .* ... ... about 140,000 ha
5. *Emas National Park* . ...   100,000 ha
6. *Cara Cara Biological Reserve* ... ... about 70,000 ha
7. *Rio Doce Forest Park .* ... ...   35,000 ha
8. Brasilia National Park (1970 : 13,000 ha) . ...   28,000 ha
9. Sooretama Biological Reserve (1970 : 12,000 ha) ... ...   24,000 ha

10. Monte Pascoal National Park (1970 : 37,000 ha)	22,500 ha
11. Itatiaia National Park	12,000 ha
12. Aparados da Serra National Park (1970 : 13,000 ha)	10,500 ha
13. Caparao National Park (1970 : 10,400 ha)	10,435 ha
14. Serra dos Orgãos National Park (1970 : 10,500 ha) . ... about	10,000 ha
15. Sete Cidades National Park (1970 : 7,770 ha)	6,221 ha
16. *Nova Lombardia Biological Reserve*	4,350 ha
17. Tijuca National Park	3,300 ha
18. *Corrego do Veado Biological Reserve*	2,400 ha
19. *Serra Negra Biological Reserve*	1,100 ha
20. *Ubajara National Park*	563 ha

II. **Excluded from the List :** one area.

Jacarepagua State Biological Reserve, 2,800 ha. According to local authorities should be excluded as this reserve has been drastically reduced and its objectives changed. No longer has significance.

III. **Areas added to the List :** ten.

1. *Araguaia National Park* (Bananal Island) : totally protected; pratically no disturbing activities. Controlled by one administrator, three guards and two assistants. Proclaimed in December 1959. It was originally proposed to include the entire island (2,000,000 ha) : the inhabited areas have been excluded. Transitional region between Amazonian area and the central planalto. Woody savanah and forest galleries. Rare species include *Myrmecophaga tridactyla, Chrysocyon brachyurus, Speothus venaticus, Pteronura brasiliensis, Blastocerus dichotomus, Ozotocerus bezoarticus, Harpia harpyja*.

2. *Chapada dos Veadeiros National Park* (Goias State) : 171,924 ha. Was originally to have 625,000 ha and to be named Tocantins N. P. Controlled by six units. Visitors are scarce as access is difficult; no accomodation. Created in 1961. Flora and fauna are typical of central Brazil and include woody savannah and forest galleries, *Chrysocyon brachyurus, Pteronura brasiliensis, Speothus venaticus, Priodontes giganteus, Myrmecophoga tridactyla, Blastocerus dichotomus, Ozotocerus bezoarticus, Taoniscus nanus*.

4. *Serra da Bocaina National Park :* located in Serra do Mar. totally protected on 90 % of the area. Controlled by three units. Created in 1971. Great tourist potential : located between Rio de Janeiro and Sao Paulo. Tropical rain forest. Altitude : 0-2,000 m. Among the threatened species are *Brachyteles arachnoides, Pteronura brasiliensis, Lutra platensis, Myrmecophaga tridactyla, Tinamus solitarius, Harpia harpyja, Spizaetus ornatus, Spizaetus tyrannus, Pipile Jacutinga, Pionopsitta pileata*.

5. *Emas National Park* (Goias State) : totally protected. Practically no disturbing activities. Controlled by four units only, but uninhabited area. Created in 1961. Visitors are scarce. Woody savannah, with forest galleries along the rivers. Among the threatened species are *Chrysocyon brachiurus, Myrmecophaga tridactyla, Blastocerus dichotomus, Ozotocerus bezoarticus*.

6. *Cara Cara Biological Reserve* (« pantoral » of Mato Grosso) : totally protected : tourism is forbidden. No staff has yet been appointed but remote and inaccessible area protected de facto. Created in 1971. Woody savannah, with forest-galleries. Threatened species include : *Chrysocyon brachyurus, Pteronura brasiliensis, Lutra platensis, Speothus venaticus, Priodontes giganteus, Myrmecophaga tridactyla, Blastocerus dichotomus, Ozotocerus bezoarticus*.

25

7. *Rio Doce Forest Park :* is totally protected on more than 80 % of its superficy. Controlled by 10 units. Was created in 1944. Is a State Park. No data available about its fauna and flora.

16. *Nova Lombardia Biological Reserve :* totally protected; tourism is not permitted. Controlled by one resident guard. First protective measures in 1948; officially proclaimed in 1970. Located in a mountain region, influenced by maritime climate. Flora includes Bromeliaceae and Orchidaceae species. Red data book species include *Oryzoborus crassirostris, Oryzoborus angolensis, Pionopsitta pileata, Discosura longicauda, Colibri delphinae greenwalti, Augastes lumachelus.* More than sixty specimens of *Brachyteles arachnoides.*

18. *Corrego do Veado Biological Reserve :* totally protected; tourism is not permitted. Controlled by one guard. First measures in 1948. Federal control since 1970. Tropical semi-deciduous forest. Forest fauna typical of low altitude. Contains unique specimens of *Ramphodondohrni* (« beija-flor »). Threatened species include *Myrmecophaga tridactyla, Bradypus torquatus, Priodontes giganteus, Pteronura brasiliensis, Tinamus solitarius, Harpia harpyja, Crax blumenbachii, Pipile jacutinga, Discosura longicauda, Cotinga maculata, Xipholaena atropurpurea, Oryzoborus crassirostris, Oryzoborus angolensis.*

19. *Serra Negra Biological Reserve :* totally protected; tourism is not permitted. Staff numbers are unknown but Brazilian authorities affirm this reserve should be included in the U.N. List. Created in 1970. Oasis of tropical flora : great pluviosity. Isolated elevation called « inselberg » of rocks.

20. *Ubajara National Park* (Ceara State): totally protected. Controlled by 25 units. Created in 1959. Main tourist attraction : Ubajara caves. Woody savannah (« cerrados »), dense forest with Amazonian species. Fauna forms a transition between « cerrados » and « caatinga ».

IV.   **Further Information :**

Mention must be made of a large national park officially created in 1968, the « Parque Indigena de Tumucumaque », 2,500,000 ha, which is completely independent from the N.P. system of Brazil and is not in any way controlled. According to Brazilian authorities, it should not be included in the U.N. List.

15. **BRITISH HONDURAS** (BELIZE)

I.   **Listed Areas :** none.

II.   **Areas excluded or added :** none.

16. **BRUNEI**

I.   **Listed Areas :** none.

II.   **Areas excluded or added :** none.

I. **Listed Areas :** thirty.
    List 1970, p. 118.

II. **Areas excluded or added since 1970 :** none.

III. **Further Information :**
    No recent information could be obtained from Bulgaria. It must be reminded that a number of very small reserves were included only at the special request of Bulgarian authorities in 1967 because of their scientific interest. Their retention gave rise to some controversy.

18. **BURUNDI**

I. **Listed Areas :** none.

II. **Areas added or excluded :** none.

19. **BURMA**

I. **Listed Areas :** three.
    1. Pidaung Game Sanctuary ... ...   70,190 ha
    2. *Shwe-U-Daung Game Sanctuary* . ...   32,735 ha
    3. *Maymyo Game Sanctuary* ... ...   12,690 ha

II. **Areas excluded from the List since 1970 :** none.

III. **Areas added to the List since 1970 :** two.
    2. *Shwe-U-Daung Game Sanctuary* (or Shur-U-Daung) : established in 1918; totally protected; staff : four units; budget : about 90 U.S. $+staff salaries; 75 % dense forest : evergreen forests; the sanctuary contains animals indigenous to Northern Burman including Sumatran rhinoceros, Indian elephant, gaur, banteng, sambar, black serow, Burmese tiger, leopard; great scenic value; altitude : 1,200-1,800 m; no tourism.

    3. *Maymyo Game Sanctuary :* established in 1918; totally protected; no separate staff : under the charge of local range officer; budget is about 450 U.S. $ for maintainance; part of Shan plateau with small hills and valleys; Dry Gak and Chestnut forest; altitude : 900-1,400 m; is at present a wild bird refuge; no tourism.

IV. **Further Information :**
    According to recent information which should still be confirmed, a dozen other totally protected sanctuaries seem to exist in Burma, effectively supervised or under development, the largest being Tamanthi Wildlife Sanctuary (226,000 ha), Yegauk (88,600 ha), Shwesettaw (53,450 ha), Lemro (27,600 ha), Kyatthin (26,100 ha). Those which are presently the better controlled are Shwesettaw and Kyatthin.

20. BYELORUSSIAN SSR

See under No. 132 Union of Soviet Socilist Republics.

21. CAMBODIA

I.   **Listed Areas :** two.

1. *Phnom Prich Faunal Reserve*   ...   .   195,120 ha
2. Angkor National Park .   ...   10,717 ha

II.   **Areas excluded from the List since 1970 :** none.

Angkor National Park was maintained on the List for obvious reasons and in spite of the very unsettled political situation in Siem Reap since 1969 and of news received concerning injuries caused by warriors from both sides to the fauna living in the protected forest around Angkor Vat and other temples.

III.   **Areas added to the List since 1970 :** one.

1. *Phnom Prich Faunal Reserve :* the possible inclusion of this reserve was already hinted in the previous English edition of the U.N. List; it still deserves inclusion although war conditions as for Angkor may have caused damages to this reserve where any kind of exploitation is totally forbidden.   Supervision : one officer and ten guards.   Created especially to protect the rare kouprey *Novibos sauveli.*

22. CAMEROON

I.   **Listed Areas :** seven.

1. *Faro Forest and Faunal Reserve .*   ...   .   330,000 ha
2. Boubandjidah National Park .   ...   220,000 ha
3. Benue National Park   ...   .   180,000 ha
4. Waza National Park   ...   .   170,000 ha
5. *Kimbi River Game Reserve .*   ...   .   5,012 ha
6. *Kala Maloue National Park .*   ...   .   4,000 ha
7. *Mbi Crater Game Reserve*   ...   .   366 ha

II.   **Areas excluded from the List since 1970 :** none.

III.   **Areas added to the List since 1970 :** four.

1. *Faro Forest and Faunal Reserve* (North Cameroon) : only 7 guards and 4,000 U.S. $ for 330,000 ha but included on the advise of local authorities as it will soon be developed.   Some poaching; abundant and varied fauna including Derby's eland, rhinoceros, buffalo, various antelopes, lion, etc.   Created in 1947.

5. *Kimbi River Game Reserve* (West Cameroon): totally protected; four guards; budget about 4,265 U.S. $; created in 1969 (first measures in 1964); located in a thickly populated area on the Bamenda Plateau; altitude about 1,500 m; gallery-forests along the rivers. Since constitution, wildlife has considerably increased; includes buffalo, various antelopes. warthog, leopard, etc. Rest house.

6. *Kala Maloue National Park* (North Cameroon): totally protected; declared in February 1972; four guards, located in Logone-Chari area, 10 km from Fort-Lamy; biotopes are varied : savannah, gallery-forests, areas inundated during rainy season; various antelopes including Buffon's kob, topi, duikers, etc.; *gazella rufifrons,* leopard, elephant, waterfowl. Altitude : 293 m.

7. *Mbi Crater Game Reserve :* totally protected; created in 1969 (first measures in 1964); included in spite of its small size on the advice of local authorities as it is established in area with heavy population density : to have acquired this reserve is creditable; staff : three units; budget : about 2,145 U.S. $; situated in the crater of an extinct volcano; great tourist attraction; montane grassland, relic montane tropical forest (buffalo) and marshes (sitatunga). Altitude : 1,800 m.

23. CANADA

I. **Listed Areas :** fourty-eight.

A. — NATIONAL PARKS.

1. Wood Buffalo National Park (size indicated in 1970 : 4,428,000 ha)	4,480,700 ha
2. Jasper National Park (1970 : 1,075,000 ha)	1,087,000 ha
3. Banff National Park (1970 : 656,000 ha)	664,076 ha
4. Prince Albert National Park (1970 : 383,000 ha)	387,464 ha
5. Riding Mountain National Park (1970 : 294,000 ha)	297,850 ha
6. *Gros Mourne National Park*	194,250 ha
7. *Pukaskwa National Park*	187,775 ha
8. Kootenay National Park (1970 : 139,000 ha)	140,637 ha
9. Glacier National Park (1970 : 133,250 ha)	134,939 ha
10. Yoho National Park (1970 : 129,750 ha)	131,313 ha
11. Cape Breton Highlands National Park (1970 : 93,950 ha) ...	95,053 ha
12. *La Mauricie National Park*	54,390 ha
13. Waterton Lakes National Park (1970 : 51,950 ha)	52,777 ha
14. *Kejimkujik National Park*	36,960 ha
15. Mt Revelstoke National Park (1970 : 25,600 ha)	25,900 ha
16. *Forillon National Park*	24,087 ha
17. *Kouchibouguac National Park*	22,533 ha
18. Fundy National Park (1970 : 20,350 ha)	20,720 ha
19. Elk Island National Park (1970 : 19,250 ha)	19,425 ha
20. *Pacific Rim National Park*	12,655 ha
21. Serpentine National Park	9,200 ha
22. Point Pelee National Park (1970 : 1,535 ha)	2,486 ha
23. Prince Edward Island National Park	1,813 ha
24. Georgian Bay Islands National Park (1970 : 1,380 ha)	1,295 ha
25. St Lawrence Islands National Park (1970 : 69 ha)	104 ha

CANADA

II.   **National Parks excluded from the List since 1970 :** none.

III.   **National Parks added to the List since 1970 :** seven.

6. *Gros Mourne National Park* (Newfoundland) : declared in 1970; staff : 12 full-time units; on Newfoundland's western coast about 50 miles north-west of Corner Brook; contains the most spectacular section of the Long Range Mountains; fjord-like lakes, dense forest, seacoast with shifting sand dunes; fauna includes moose, caribou, arctic hare, lynx and marten; birdlife includes ptarmigan, cliff nesting birds, bald eagle; the park is presently under development; campsites. Altitude : 0-806 m.

7. *Pukaskwa National Park* (Ontario) : declared in 1971; 9 full time guards; characterized by the rugged Precambrian topography and extensive (80 km) Lake Superior shoreline; numerous lakes and streams; plants and animals representative of the boreal forest; among the mammals are the woodland caribou, white-tailed deer, moose, timber wolf, black bear, mink, muskrat, beaver, marten, lynx and fisher; the park is under development and visitor facilities have not yet been installed. Altitude : 180-360 m.

12. *La Mauricie National Park* (Quebec) : created in 1970; 13 full-time guards and two part time; heavily wooded, largely unspoiled section of the Laurentian Mountains near Trois-Rivières; numerous lakes; transition zone between the deciduous forest and the boreal forest; animal population is abundant and diversified : moose, white-tailed deer and a great variety of fur-bearing mammals; about 150 species of birds; presently under development. Altitude : 100-450 m.

14. *Kejimkujik National Park* (Nova Scotia) : established in 1964-1969; 21 full time guards; 19 part-time; superb example of inland Nova Scotia, rolling landscape, numerous lakes, with countless islands and concealed coves; Indian petroglyphs; in the easter part broad-leaved trees are dominant, the western part having mainly a coniferous cover; animals include white-tailed deer, black bear, racoon, bobcat, flying squirrel, beaver, etc.; the park is interesting for its variety of reptiles and amphibians; two campgrounds; many visitors. Altitude : 85-183 m.

16. *Forillon National Park* (Quebec) : created in 1970; 12 full-time and 11 part-time guards; Scenic tip of Forillon Peninsula on Gulf of St Lawrence; the vegetation represents a portion of the Great-Lakes-Lower St Lawrence forest region and the boreal forest; the Gaspé Peninsula fauna is well represented in the park and its avifauna is abundant and diversified; the park is presently under development; all accommodation but camping is located outside the park boundary. Altitude : 0-548 m.

17. *Kouchibouguac National Park* (New Brunswick) : created in 1969; staff : 9 full-time, 2 part-time; the park occupies a 22 km crescent around the shores of Kouchibouguac Bay, a shallow indention in the New Brunswick coastline at the northern end of Northumberland Strait; most outstanding feature : 15 1/2 mile sweep of off-shore sand-bars; lagoons, bays; lies in the eastern lowlands section of the Acadian forest (coniferous); bog and dune plants; few mammals; large number of fishes; seabird and waterfowl breeding area; plans to construct many campsites. Altitude : 0-30 m.

20. *Pacific Rim National Park* (or Long Beach N. P.) (British Columbia) : created in 1970; staff : 9 full-time, 1 part-time; located on the west coast of Vancouver Island; consists of three distinct areas : long, sandy beaches, a group of rocky islands and a 72 km shoreline section of the historic Lifesaving Trail;

30

the total superficy, including water, is 38,850 ha; dense, fast-growing forest dominates the landscape; numerous migratory birds; sea lions (*Eumatopias jubata*); abundant marine life; feeding ground for gray whales (*Rhachianectes glaucus*) in the summer; the park is presently under development; no facilities. Altitude : 0-240 m.

IV.   **Further Information :**

In February 1972 three areas north of the 60th parallel have been withdrawn and protected for the purposes of National Parks. These are Kluane (2,201,500 ha), Baffin Island (2,147,110 ha) and Nahanni (476,560 ha). According to local authorities however these national parks should not yet be included in the U.N. List as they do not, at this time (June 1972) meet the criterion of effectiveness (staff and budget).

B. — PROVINCIAL PARKS and RESERVES.

a) SASKATCHEWAN.

26. *Wildcat Hill Wilderness Area*	18,200 ha
27. *Waskwei River Protected Area*	960 ha

b) ONTARIO.

28. Algonquin Provincial Park	753,599 ha
29. Quetico Provincial Park	453,258 ha
30. Lake Superior Provincial Park	136,236 ha
31. Missinaibi Provincial Park Reserve (1970 : Mississagi; 38,593 ha)	45,585 ha
32. Killarney Provincial Park	36,261 ha
33. Sibley Provincial Park	24,346 ha
34. Obatanga Provincial Park Reserve	13,500 ha
35. Bon Echo Provincial Park	6,644 ha
36. Nagagamisis Provincial Park	4,807 ha
37. Rondeau Provincial Park (1970 : 2,227 ha)	4,634 ha
38. Greenwater Provincial Park	4,439 ha
39. Neys Provincial Park	3,298 ha
40. Esker Lakes Provincial Park	3,109 ha
41. Ojibway Provincial Park Reserve	2,481 ha
42. Grundy Lake Provincial Park	2,481 ha

c) QUEBEC.

43. La Verendrye Provincial Park	1,142,000 ha
44. Les Laurentides Provincial Park	927,500 ha
45. Mont Tremblant Provincial Park	278,750 ha
46. Gaspesie Provincial Park	127,500 ha
47. Mont Orford Provincial Park	3,750 ha

d) NEWFOUNDLAND and LABRADOR.

48. Barachois Pond Provincial Park	2,800 ha

CANADA

II.   **Areas excluded from the List since 1970 :** eight.

1) The four previously listed provincial parks in *Alberta* : Cypress Hills, Dinosaur, Crimson Lake and Entrance. The Province authorities have decided that their provincial parks do not meet ICNP selective criteria.

2) Four provincial parks in *Newfoundland/Labrador* : Serpentine, Pitts Pond, Butter Pot and Sir Richard Squires Memorial Park. Similarly local authorities advised that these provincial parks should be deleted as they do not meet ICNP criteria.

III.   **Areas added to the List since 1970 :** two.

26. *Wildcat Hill Wilderness Area* (Saskatchewan) : totally protected (no hunting, no logging or lumbering, no mining, no grazing, no vehicular access...) area managed by regional administrative staff; established in 1971; tourist facilities will be limited to outside boundary; part of the Pasquia Hills area; includes two lakes, swamps and wetlands; black bear, caribou, moose, etc. and *Felis concolor*.

27. *Waskwei River Protected Area* (Saskatchewan) : as the above area totally protected against any kind of exploitation and no vehicular access; one conservation officer is looking after the area in conjunction with other areas in the district; created in 1964; campgrounds outside the boundaries of the protected area; protection of *Picea glauca*; fauna includes white-tailed deer, moose, caribou, lynx, etc.

IV.   **Further Information :**

Ontario : mention should be made of two other areas : Wakami Lake Provincial Park which is not yet supervised and expected to be established in 1972, 8,806 ha of which nearly half is water of Wakami Lake, and Polar Bear Provincial Park, 2,408,741 ha located on Hudson Bay, accessible only by airplane or boat with no full time staff, established in 1970.

Manitoba : there are ten provincial parks in Manitoba but according to local authorities timbering, fishing and hunting is allowed in some of them. When full details will be available maybe one or another could be added to the List. Here are their names : Birds Hill (3,360 ha), Grand Beach (3,258 ha), Duck Mountain (127,418 ha), Turtle Mountain (18,914 ha), Whiteshell (273,619 ha), Grass River (229,052 ha), Clearwater (59,595 ha), Asessippi (2,332 ha), Spruce Woods and Hecla.

Prince Edward Island, Nova Scotia, British Columbia and *New Brunswick* have, as Alberta, decided that heir provincial parks do not meet ICNP criteria.

24. CENTRAL AFRICAN REPUBLIC

I.   **Listed Areas :** four.

List 1970, p. 155.

II.   **Areas excluded or added since 1970 :** none.

III.   **Further Information :**

It has not been possible to obtain an answer to our enquiry from Bangui. Under these circumstances the list has been left unchanged although contradictory information was obtained from private sources. Some indicate that uncontrolled poaching occurs in the four areas and even that Saint-Floris has been seriously devastated by invasion of nomadic tribes and livestock. Other point out the interest shown by local authorities and even by the President of the Republic towards the good management of protected areas and the development of international tourism. Mention is made of credits given to Yata Nyanga reserve, near André Félix N. P., of Miamere Miadiki faunal reserve (250,000 ha, budget of about $ 10,000) including a presidential reserve of 56,000 ha, of a « piste de vision » (Ouandjia Vakaga) near which good protective measures seem to be applied, etc.

25. CEYLON

I.   **Listed Areas :** seven.

A. — NATIONAL PARKS.

1. Wilpattu National Park (1970 : 65,000 ha)	108,780 ha
2. Gal Oya National Park	25,000 ha
3. Ruhunu National Park	23,000 ha

B. — STRICT NATURAL RESERVES.

4. Wasgomuwa Strict Natural Reserve	28,000 ha
5. Yala Strict Natural Reserve	27,500 ha
6. Ritigala Strict Natural Reserve	1,450 ha
7. Hakgala Strict Natural Reserve	1,100 ha

II.   **Areas added or excluded since 1970 :** none.

26. CHAD

I.   **Listed Areas :** two.

1. Zakouma National Park   ... ...   297,200 ha
2. Manda National Park ...   .   110,000 ha

II.   **Areas excluded or added since 1970 :** none.

An enormous protected area was established in 1969, of which a portion could possibly deserve inclusion in the U.N. List : Ouadi Rime-Ouadi Achim Faunal Reserve. The total superficy of the reserve is 4,892,500 ha, to which must be added a « hunting area » of 2,902,500 ha. In the reserve, where the most interesting species are addax and oryx, supervision is progressively developing. In 1971 staff numbers increased from a few units to some fourty guards, unfortunately with no transport means. New progresses are expected for 1972. However it was considered premature to already include this area on the List (ICNP criterium would require 489 guards for 4,892,500 ha) where it would stand as the second biggest in the world, just before Wood Buffalo National Park (Canada) which has 4,428,000 ha and after Etosha National Park (South West Africa) which still has 6,500,000 but could possibly be reduced to 2,227,000 ha. Another reason for not retaining this area for the List is that French military men with their jeeps and automatic weapons are indulging in game slaughters.

27. CHILE

I.   **Listed Areas :** six.

1. *Villarica National Park .* ... ...   167,000 ha
2. Cape Horn National Park ... ...   63,093 ha
3. *Torres del Paine National Park .* ... ... between 10,000 and 20,000 ha
4. Fray Jorge National Park ... ...   6,845 ha
5. Nahuelbuta National Park ... ...   5,415 ha
6. Tolhuaca National Park . ...   3,500 ha

II.   **Areas excluded from the List since 1970 :** none.

III.   **Areas added to the List since 1970 :** two.

1. *Villarica National Park :* located in southern Chile, south of Temuco; practically inaccessible and uninhabited area; staff : five units; created in 1940; protects Villarica volcano and the forests on its flanks; opportunities for water and mountain sports.

2. *Torres del Paine National Park :* no occupation, no poaching; approximately three guards; beautiful mountain scenery; glaciers; located in the extreme south of Chile, near Puerto Natale. Some tourism.

34

IV. **Further Information :**

There are 43 national parks in Chile. Unfortunately it seems that in most of them illegal occupants destroy the forests, practicing a primitive agriculture. Boundaries are vague and adequate supervision staff is lacking. Measures have been taken to face these problems in some of these park and if they are carried into effect perhaps one or another sanctuary could be added to the List, for instance Puyehue National Park, 18,300 ha, including private properties which are being expropriated.

28. CHINA

I. **Listed Areas :** none.

II. **Areas added or excluded :** none.

III. **Further Information :**

Various attempts made to obtain official information from the Wildlife Department at the Ministry of Forests in Pekin have up to now been left unanswered. It was therefore necessary to make no mention of any national park or equivalent reserves for China although the certitude exists that nature reserves have been set aside, some of them, at least in some sectors, answering the ICNP criteria.

8,400,000 ha seem to have been set aside either as zoological sanctuaries « where hunting of all or of some animal species is forbidden during a few years » (which does not correspond to criteria), either as « animal reserves where scientific research is carried out » (which might meet ICNP criteria). The most important of these latter reserves are located in Tchangpai mountains in North east China, in the more tropical region of Sichouangpanna and in Taipai mountains in Chensi Province. Mention has been made of a reserve in Yunnan where a few *Rhinoceros sondaicus* would be protected, and of another, in Se-Tchouann, habitat of the giant panda.

29. COLOMBIA

I. **Listed Areas :** six.

1. *Sierra de la Macarena National Park* . ... 600,000 ha
2. *El Tuparro Faunistic Reserve* ... ... 380,000 ha
3. *Purace National Park* ... ... about 80,000 ha
4. *Isla de Salamanca National Park* . ... 20,912 ha
5. *Tayrona National Park* . ... 15,000 ha
6. *Cueva de los Guacharos National Park* ... ... 700 ha

COLOMBIA

II.   **Areas excluded from the List since 1970 :** none.

III.   **Areas added to the List since 1970 :** six.

1. *Sierra de la Macarena National Park :* declared in 1971 (first measures in 1948); some « colonos » are still inhabiting the area, mostly at the periphery; staff : 23 units; located south-east of Villavicencio; zone in which the flora of the Andes and Guyanas meet; tropical rain forest; very interesting fauna including three species of deer, spectacled bear, tapir and endemic species of birds. Altitude : 240-2,500 m.

2. *El Tuparro Faunistic Reserve :* established in 1970; no occupation; rather inaccessible area; staff : 22 units, flat country, partly inundated most of the year (altitude : 75-250 m); forest-galleries; rich savannah and forest fauna including puma, jaguar, paca, tapir, etc. Very few visitors.

3. *Purace National Park :* established in 1968; some occupation; staff : 13 units (+labourers); located south east of Popayan city; contains an active volcano; humid sub-tropical forest and « paramos » on the slopes; rich endemic flora and fauna; spectacled bear, mountain tapir, pudu deer, puma; some facilities for visitors (refuges, trails). Altitude : 2,500-4,700 m.

4. *Isla de Salamanca National Park :* created in 1964; still some occupation by « colonos »; staff : 14 units, not including labourers; very rich bird fauna (125 different species); access from Barranquilla-Cienaga road; facilities for visitors. Altitude : 0-8 m.

5. *Tayrona National Park :* established in 1964; still some occupation; staff : 20 units not including labourers; located in Northern Columbia east of Santa Maria city; beaches, coral reefs; 90 % is covered with virgin forest; varied fauna; breeding area for turtles *Chelonia mydas* and *Caretta caretta;* facilities in Canaveral. Altitude : 0-1,000 m.

6. *Cueva de los Guacharos National Park :* established in 1960 to ensure the protection of the « Guacharos » (*Steatornis caripensis*) but some illegal hunting; supervision staff : 6 units; located south east of Neiva city; beside various caves contains sub-tropical humid forest which shelters the *Tinamus esgoodi*, an endemic bird. Altitude : 1,700-4,000 m; many visitors.

IV.   **Further Information :**

In September 1968 the National Institute for Renewable Resources (INDERENA) was created which now administers every national park as well as Tuparro Faunistic Reserve.

Two other national parks could possibly be added to this List but present information concerning their protective status and supervision staff are insufficient. They are Farallones de Cali (15,000 ha, created in 1968) and Sierra Nevada (50,000 ha, created in 1964).

30. CONGO

I.   **Listed Areas :** one.

    1. Odzala National Park ... ...   110,000 ha

II.   **Areas added or excluded :** none.

III.   **Further Information :**

    Information received from local authorities in June 1972 indicate that Odzala N. P. is quite insufficiently controlled; at present only Military Police men are ensuring its supervision and six labourers are working on tracks to be opened in the area; however, a guard will soon be appointed.

31. COSTA RICA

I.   **Listed Areas :** four.

    1. *Tortuguero National Park* ... ...   18,000 ha
    2. *Santa Rosa National Park* ... ...   9,904 ha
    3. *Poas Volcano National Park* . ...   4,000 ha
    4. *Cabo Blanco National Reserve* ... ...   1,172 ha

II.   **Areas excluded from the List since 1970 :** none.

III.   **Areas added to the List since 1970 :** four.

    1. *Tortuguero National Park :* totally protected; controlled by two guards; budget of U.S. $ 2,117; created in September 1970 for the protection of green turtle (*Chelonia mydas*); located on Carribbean Coast, 60 miles north of Limon; includes beach estuary and rain forest; extensive portion of the park are covered by a virtually pure stand of swamp palm (*Raphia* sp.); fauna includes tapir, jaguar, mountain lion, ocelot, kinkajou, giant anteater, manatee, etc.; marine species beside *Chelonia mydas* include *Eretmochelys imbricata* and *Dermochelys coriacea*. No tourism at present.

    2. *Santa Rosa National Park :* totally protected; controlled by 10 units; created in 1970 to preserve the site of a battle against forces from Nicaragua held in 1856; located in the province of Guanaste, 30 km north of Liberia; borders the Pacific Ocean and the Panamerican highway; dry forest including woody savannah, gallery-forest, estuaries and beach. White-tail deer, peccary, Baird's tapir, monkeys and five species of cats. Forest avifauna and migratory water-fowl; nesting beaches for turtles (*Lepidochelys olivacea, Chelonia mydas agassizii, Dermochelys coriacea schlegelii*). Facilities for tourists in progress of construction.

    3. *Poas Volcano National Park :* totally protected; staff : thirteen units; budget in 1971 was about U.S. $ 13,500; created in 1970; located in the northwestern corner of the Central Valley, part of the Central Mountain Range; includes five craters, one still active; montane cloud forests; rare fauna includes Quetzal (*Pharomachrus mocino*) and Poas Mountain Squirrel (*Syntheosciurus poasensis*),

endemic to the park; altitude : 1,600-2,708 m.   Facilities for tourists (camp-ground, etc.); 60 km north-west of San Jose.

4. *Cabo Blanco National Reserve :* totally protected; staff : three units, budget for 1971 was about 2,000 U.S. $; created in 1963; located at the southern-most tip of the Nicoya Peninsula in the Province of Puntarenas; tropical dry forest; endangered species represented but rare in the reserve are *Tapirus bairdii* and *Felis onca, Atleles geoffroy frontatus, Cebus capucinus* and four cat species : *Felis wiedii, F. yagnaroundi, F. pardalis, F. concolor.* Tourism, at least at present, is considered detrimental.

IV.   **Further Information :**

A fifth sanctuary had been created in 1970, Cahuita National Monument, 1,100 ha, on the Caribbean Sea.   However current studies now in process are examining possible relocation of the park southwards where another reef occurs and where population pressure is reduced.   Therefore N. P. authorities of Costa Rica advised that this area be excluded from the U.N. List for the time being (inf. February 1972).

These protected areas are all administered by the Department of National Parks under the Forestry Service at the Ministry of Agriculture.

32. CUBA

I.   **Listed Areas :** four.

List 1970, p. 179.

II.   **Areas excluded or added since 1970 :** none.

33. CYPRUS

I.   **Listed Areas :** none.

II.   **Areas added or excluded since 1970 :** none.

34. CZECHOSLOVAKIA

I.   **Listed Areas :** three.

List 1970, p. 182.

II.   **Areas excluded or added since 1970 :** none.

<h1 style="text-align:right">35. DAHOMEY</h1>

I.   **Listed Areas :** two.

1. The « W » National Park ... ...   502,050 ha
2. Boucle de la Pendjari National Park ... ...   275,000 ha

II.   **Areas added or excluded since 1970 :** none.

<h1 style="text-align:right">36. DENMARK</h1>

I.   **Listed Areas :** three.

List 1970, p. 188.

II.   **Areas excluded or added since 1970 :** none.

III.   **Further Information :**

As explained in the introduction to U.N. List 1970, Denmark is one of those countries where strict application of ICNP criteria would leave no protected area deserving to be included in the U.N. List. When the List was established in 1967 three areas where arbitrarily chosen, with the agreement of late Prof. Spaerck, in order that some Danish reserves be represented artificially to avoid any anomaly.

A recent exchange of correspondence (1972) with the competent service in Copenhaguen showed that nothing had changed and that it was still possible to mention for 1972 the above three areas « picked out among a number of other and equally important areas ».

Moreover the Greenland Law Commission has recently completed the drafting of a bill for a Conservation of Nature Act for Greenland. Experts also have been working on the setting up of a Northeast Greenland National Park. This park which is going to be the largest in the world, will include breathing areas and migration path of a considerable number of important arctic species, e.g. the Polar Bear and the Musk Ox.

<h1 style="text-align:right">37. DOMINICAN REPUBLIC</h1>

I.   **Listed Areas :** one.

1. El Vedado Haina-Duey   ... ...   5,030 ha

II.   **Areas excluded or added since 1970 :** none.

39

38. ECUADOR

I.   **Listed Areas :** one.

1. Galapagos National Park ... ...   10,000 ha

II.   **Areas excluded or added since 1970 :** none.

III.   **Further Information :**

a) Great activity is developed by the Ecuadorian Government in order to reinforce the supervision and enlarge the size of Galapagos National Park where scientific surveys made by the Charles Darwin Foundation are developing.

b) It was decided to proceed in two steps to the creation of a national park system on the continent : first the creation of a « reserva nacional » already supervised where the definitive creation of a national park is prepared.   This was applied for the first time on August 29th 1968 when a presidential decree declared Cayapas National Reserve, strip 16 km long from the Pacific to Cotacachi, to the East.

39. EQUATORIAL GUINEA
(including Rio Muni and Fernando Po)

I.   **Listed Areas :** two.

1. Monte Raices Territorial Park (Rio Muni) . ...   26,000 ha
2. Pico de Santa Isabel Strict Faunal and Botanical Reserve (Fernando Po) ... ...
between 5,000 and 10,000 ha

II.   **Areas excluded or added since 1970 :** none.

III.   **Further Information :**

These two areas have been maintained on the U.N. List although alarming news received from private source, indicated that due to the present political situation poaching and lumbering considerably increased in these reserves and supervision is practically non-existent.

Information was requested from the local authorities but no answer was received.

The maintainance of these two reserves on the List can therefore very well be only provisory.

40. ETHIOPIA

I. **Listed Areas :** three.

1. *Awash National Park*	8,800 ha
2. *Simien Mountain National Park*	6,000 ha
3. Menagasha Forest Reserve	3,000 ha

II. **Areas excluded from the List :** none.

III. **Areas added to the List since 1970 :** two.

1. *Awash National Park :* there was pressure from the Danakil and Karayu and their livestock; however these have been resettled outside the park in 1970. One game warden, with land rover. Located 150 km south-east from Addis Ababa. Two hotels. Lies at the eastern foot of the Shoa escarpment, on the edge of the arid semi-desert country of Danakil. Species include oryx, Grevy's zebra, Soemmerring's gazelle, Chanler's reedbuck, cheetah, leopard, klipspringer, ostrich, waterbuck and hippopotamus. Somali wild ass, Swayne's hartebeest and generuk to the east of the Awash. Created in January 1969.

2. *Simien Mountain National Park :* proclaimed in october 1969. Controlled by two game wardens, with land rover. Threatened by overgrazing of domestic stock and subsequent erosion. The primary object of this park is to provide protection for the Walia ibex, a species unique to Ethiopia. Includes spectacular series of cliffs which are the main habitat of Walia ibex. Other species include the Simien fox and Gelada baboon, leopard, klipspringer, and bushbuck; also a wide variety of birds. The area is best reached by road from Gondar to Davarik and thence by horse or mule (a day's ride). Altitude : 2,400-3,600 m.

41. FALKLAND ISLANDS

I. **Listed Areas :** two.

1. Kidney Island Nature Reserve	29,5 ha
2. Cochon Island Nature Reserve	7,5 ha

II. **Areas excluded or added since 1970 :** none.

III. **Further Information :**

Two nature reserves could possibly be added to the U.N. List but sufficient information is still lacking : Flat Jason Island Reserve (about 360 ha, created in 1966, important sea lion breeding ground) and Bird Island Reserve created in 1969 (120 ha). The protective status of these two reserves is more difficult to control than that of Kidney Island as both islands are so remotely situated from Stanley. However, by virtue of this fact alone, and the difficulty of making successful landings, they are practically self-protected. (Letter of the Colonial Secretary, 1st August 1972).

I.   **Listed Areas :** two.

       1. Ravilevu Nature Reserve ... ...   3,972 ha
       2. Nadarivatu Nature Reserve (size indicated in 1970 : 1,674 ha) ..   1,280 ha

II.   **Areas excluded or added since 1970 :** none.

43. FINLAND

I.   **Listed Areas :** twenty-four.

       List 1970, p. 202 (9 National Parks and 15 Nature Parks = Strict Natural Reserves).

II.   **Areas excluded or added since 1970 :** none.

III.   **Further Information :**

       Since the previous editions of the U.N. List Lemmenjoki National Park has been considerably enlarged to the frontier of Norway, its size increasing from 38,500 ha to 172,000 ha. If the Norwegian plans of a N. P. to the other side of the frontier will become true it will mean a trans-frontier park of 284,000 ha.

44. FRANCE

I.   **Listed Areas :** seventeen.

       A. — NATIONAL PARKS.

       1. La Vanoise . ...   52,839 ha
           (not including a buffer zone of 143,637 ha)
       2. *Pyrénées Occidentales* . ...   45,707 ha
       3. Port-Cros ... ...   685 ha
           (plus marine protected zone all around the island some 600 m wide)

       B. — « RESERVES CYNEGETIQUES NATIONALES ».

       4. Burrus . ...   4,387 ha
       5. Les Bauges . ...   4,070 ha
       6. Casabianda . ...   1,760 ha
       7. La Pointe d'Arçay . ...   550 ha
       8. Les Sept Iles ... ...   82 ha

C. — « RESERVES CYNEGETIQUES D'INTERET NATIONAL ».

9. Mercantour . ...   27,843 ha

D. — SPECIAL OR PRIVATE RESERVES.

10. The Camargue Zoological and Botanical Reserve . ...   9,366 ha
11. Le Pelvoux Reserve or State Park ... ...   8,714 ha
12. Mont Vallier State Reserve . ...   8,208 ha
13. Le Combeynot ... ...   4,720 ha
14. Etangs des Imperiaux Reserve (contiguous to No. 10) ... ...   2,777 ha
15. Néouvielle Reserve ... ...   2,300 ha
16. The combined biological and artistic reserve of the Forêt de Fontainebleau   ... ...   551 ha
17. *Cap Sizun Reserve* ... ...   43 ha

II. **Areas excluded from the List since 1970 :** twelve (in fact fourteen).

When the French edition of the List was issued in 1967 many protests arose in France because the « réserves cynégétiques nationales » were included on the roll of honour : they are not sanctuaries as defined by the ICNP criteria. No criticisms were however made for two important bird sanctuaries : Sept Iles and Pointe d'Arçay, neither for Burrus, les Bauges and Casabianda. The inclusion of the « réserves cynégétiques d'intérêt national » was questioned as well. Hence the decision to exclude from the U.N. List the nine areas mentioned as B. 3, B. 5, B. 7 to 11, B. 13, B. 15 and C. 19 in the previous editions. Here are their names :« réserves cynégétiques nationales » : Chambord, Petite Pierre, Bavella Sambucco Conca, Markstein, Chizé, Canal de Dronzère Mondragon, Belval, Sainte-Opportune; « réserve cynégétique d'intérêt national » : étangs de l'Hérault. Three private reserves were also excluded on the advice of the concerned French authorities because they also do not meet ICNP criteria : Bure Aurouze (former D. 23), Le Carlitte (D. 24) and Asco (D. 26).

Finally two seeming exclusions are the « réserve cynégétique nationale » of Cauterets (B. 9) and the « réserve cynégétique d'intérêt national » of Pic du Midi d'Ossau (C. 18) which are now included in the Pyrénées Occidentales National Park described hereafter.

III. **Areas added to the List since 1970 :** two.

A. 2. *Pyrénées Occidentales National Park :* 110 km long by 1,5 to 15 km wide in uninhabited country in the high Pyrénées against the Spanish border; adjoins Ordesa National Park in Spain and Néouvielle Reserve (above 15); staff : 36 units; budget 1972 : 42,000 U.S. $; declared in 1967; access by foot and horse only; refuges; fauna includes brown bear, chamois; Egyptian and griffon vultures, eagles, etc. Altitude : 1,070-3,298 m; some summer cattle and sheep grazing.

D. 18. *Cap Sizun Reserve :* coast and cliffs in Briton; nesting place for cormorants, penguins, guillemots, fulmars, kittiwakes; private property leased and administered by the Society for Nature Protection in Briton. Small entrance fee; guided visits.

FRANCE

IV.   **Further Information :**

1. In spite of their great social interest the « Parcs Naturels Régionaux », totalling 8 in 1972 were not retained for the U.N. List because they do not meet ICNP criteria.

2. Similarly the Cevennes National Park established in 1970 was not included either because it has only of a national park the legal status allowing the financial support of central government (the parcs naturels régionaux do not have this advantage) but for the rest it has chosen the same status as the above mentioned nature parks.

3. Provisions are made in the Sixth Plan for the creation of two other national parks : Ecrins and Mercantour. The first one would absorb the reserves mentioned in D. 9 (Pelvoux) and D. 12 (Combeynot). The second would do the same with C. 6 (Mercantour).

4. A special effort has been made in 1971 for the Camargue Reserve (D. 8). One million FF was notably given by the WWF to President Pompidou to consolidate the status and enlarge this excellent nature reserve.

5. Two private reserves could possibly be included in the List when full details will be available : Massane and le Caroux (including several reserves, Hérault).

OVERSEAS TERRITORIES

A. — NEW CALEDONIA.

I.   **Listed Areas :** one.

1. *Yves Merlet Maritime Reserve* ...   .   15,760 ha

II.   **Areas excluded since 1970 :** none.

III.   **Areas added to the List since 1970 :** one.

1. *Yves Merlet Maritime Reserve :* includes two islets (1 to 2 ha) and the water between la Havannah and la Sarcelle pass. Is a strict nature reserve except for customary fishing on traditional feasts. Will be entirely marked out. All traffic (even the passage of boats) is forbidden. Two guards. Created in 1970. Situated 4 h by boat from Noumea. The two islets are covered with natural vegetation. A few birds and snakes. This reserve is consequent to the intense scientific work of the Singer Polignac Foundation.

IV.   **Further Information :**

A number of other reserves exist in New Caledonia, which do not qualify for inclusion in the U.N. List, including one National Park, Iles des Pins (20,000 ha) where every kind of exploitation is still permitted (except in Oro Peninsula).

B. — FRENCH POLYNESIA.

I.   **Listed Areas :** none.

II.   **Areas added or excluded since 1970 :** none.

III.   **Further Information :**

In 1971 regulations have been made for the preservation of two islets in the Marquesas islands : Eiao (3,000 ha) and Motane (size unknown, but similar) and of a lagoon in Scilly atoll (windward islands, Society archipielago). Steps are taken to suppress some old rights (cattle breeding in the islets, coprah exploitation and capture of turtle in Scilly) and to equip and control these various areas.

Projects exist as well for an atoll near Tahiti, even for a peninsula in Tahiti island. And other proposals concern the big Rengiroa atoll in Tuamotu islands.

C. — FRENCH GUYANA.

I.   **Listed Areas :** none.

II.   **Areas excluded or added :** none.

D. — FRENCH SOMALILAND (Afars and Issas).

I.   **Listed Areas :** none.

II.   **Areas excluded or added :** none.

E. — REUNION.

I.   **Listed Areas :** none.

II.   **Areas excluded or added :** none.

III.   **Further Information :**

There are three very small strict nature reserves on the island, the largest being only slightly over 20 ha. A project concerns a national park to be created on 3,600 ha in Behour Forest.

French authorities have gazetted four Marine National Parks on July 17th 1971 : Europa Island, Juan de Nova, the Glorious Islands, Tromelin Island. They have a great interest, especially Europa Island which has an important turtle population. Executive measures seem to have started.

45. GABON

I. **Listed Areas :** three.

1. Ofoue Strict Natural Reserve	150,000 ha
2. Okanda National Park	190,000 ha
3. *Wonga-Wongue National Park*	82,760 ha

II. **Areas excluded from the List since 1970 :** none.

III. **Areas added to the List since 1970 :** one.

3. *Wonga-Wongue National Park :* totally protected; is the best protected area in Gabon; one warden, 17 rangers; established in 1967; contiguous to three hunting reserves, the total area covering 358,000 ha; situated in western Gabon south of Estuaire du Gabon and River Ogooué, just south of the equator; lowland plain (altitude 100-200 m); rain forests cover about 70 %, grassland savannas on the remaining part; numerous ungulate species; leopard, civet, primates including the gorilla, drill and mandrill; proximity of Libreville. Great touristic opportunities.

IV. **Further Information :**

An enquiry which is presently being conducted could very well prove that supervision is so poor in Ofoue and Okanda that they will have to be excluded

46. GAMBIA

I. **Listed Areas :** none.

II. **Areas excluded or added :** none.

47. GERMAN FEDERAL REPUBLIC

I. **Listed Areas :** twenty-five.

A. — Naturschutzparke : two.

B. — Naturschutzgebiete : nineteen.

C. — Additional « Naturschutzgebiet » which although extremely marginal cases are included at the request of German authorities : four.

II.   **Areas excluded from the List since 1970 :** none.

III.   **Areas added to the List since 1970 :** none.

As for other industrialized countries (see Denmark) it was deemed advisable to leave the arbitrary list made in 1967 and 1970 as it was, being only an example of the German achievements.

Active correspondence was kept these last few years with competent authorities in the German Federal Republic and notably with the « Bundesanstalt für Vegetationskunde, Naturschutz und Landschaftspflege » in Bonn. The conclusion was that either an entirely different list, — just as arbitrary because it would concern areas which do not meet ICNP criteria — could have been made, or that the previous list could remain as it was.

IV.   **Further Information :**

a) A first German national park was set aside in October 1970 : *Bayerischer Wald,* 37,400 ha. On one hand it does not meet ICNP criteria and, on the other hand, being a creation of one of the Länder of the Republic it has not yet obtained the necessary acknowledgment of the Federal Government to be considered as a Naturschutzgebiet. It may include some more severely protected sectors which, as the « Special Protection Areas » in Japan, will allow the inclusion of this national park in the U.N. List by virtue of the zoning principle (see as well United Kingdom). ;

b) A similar important project including some ten existing reserves is developed near the Danish frontier : the *North Frisian Wadden Sea National Park* (Nordfriesisches Wattenmeer), 140,000 ha.

c) The term « Naturschutzpark » is no longer used : Lüneburger Heide and Siebengebirge have been absorbed by the Naturparke;

d) Further information and up-to-date data can be found in the book « Die Naturschutzgebiete in der Bundesrepublik Deutschland » issued by the Bundesanstalt mentioned hereabove in 1970.

48. GHANA

I.   **Listed Areas :** three.

1. Mole National Park (size indicated in 1970 : 388,500 ha) .   ...   491,191 ha
2. *Digya National Park* ...   .   312,436 ha
3. *Bui National Park* .   ...   154,368 ha

II.   **Areas excluded from the List since 1970 :** none.

III.   **Areas added to the List since 1970 :** two.

2. *Digya National Park :* established in 1971; totally protected; villages yet to be resettled; supervision staff : 55 units; budget (1971-1972) U.S. $ 50,490; located west of Volta Lake; Guinea savannah woodland with transitional and

riverine forests along the major rivers; fauna includes various monkeys, elephant, red river hog, warthog, buffalo and various antelopes; no tourism.

3. *Bui National Park :* established in 1971; totally protected but villages yet to be resettled; supervision staff : 55 units; budget for 1972 : about U.S. $ 40,000; located on each side of Black Volta River, near Ivory Coast border; savannah woodland with riverine forests along the main river banks; mammals include hippopotamus, buffalo, various antelopes, and primates; plans to open a motel.

49. GREECE

I.

Listed Areas : eight.

1. *Pindus National Park* ... ...   12,935 ha
2. Samarias Ravines National Park (1970 : 3,700 ha) ... ...   4,850 ha
3. *Mount Olympus National Park* ... ...   3,998 ha
4. *Parnassus National Park* ... ...   3,512 ha
5. *Mount Ainos National Park* . ...   2,841 ha
6. Dias Island Reserve ... ...   1,200 ha
7. Guioura Island Reserve ... ...   1,000 ha
8. Antimylos Island Reserve ... ...   800 ha

II.

Areas excluded from the List since 1970 : one.

Mount Parnes National Park (3,700 ha) : according to Greek authorities this park should be excluded from the List because of human activities : military occupation, tourist equipment, casino, etc. It no longer may be considered as a national park.

III.

Areas added to the List since 1970 : four.

1. *Pindus National Park* (Epirus) : controlled by 5 units; budget in 1969 was 270,000 U.S. $; totally protected (no cultivation, no grazing, no lumbering, no hunting). Created in 1966. No tourism. Mountainous region. Flora includes many plant species of Northern Greece. Fauna includes *Ursus arctos, Canis lupus, Capreolus capreolus, Rupicapra rupicapra, Sus scrofa,* as well as birds of prey. Altitude : from 800 to 2,200 m.

3. *Mount Olympus National Park :* totally protected, no occupation or exploitation; controlled by 4 units; budget in 1969 was 500,000 U.S. $. Accommodation in Alpine refuges. Mountainous region (altitude : from 600 to 2,917 m). Flora includes various endemic species. Fauna includes *Capreolus capreolus, Canis lupus,* and birds of prey.

4. *Parnassus National Park :* totally protected but mining operations occuring before the creation of the park still subsist; however, according to Greek authorities, this park should be included in the U.N. List. Staff : 8 units; budget in 1969 was 200,000 U.S. $. Created in 1938. Accommodation in Alpine refuges and in neighbouring villages. Mountainous region (altitude : from 1,100 to 2,000 m). Flora includes numerous endemic species. Fauna includes *Canis lupus, Sus scrofa,* etc. as well as birds of prey.

5. *Mount Ainos National Park :* (Cephalonia) totally protected; staff : 3 units; budget in 1969 was U.S. $ 400,000. Created in 1962. Controlled tourism. Mountainous region (altitude : from 800 to 1,628 m). Created for the protection of pure stands of *Abies cephalonica.*

50. GUATEMALA

I. **Listed Areas :** three.

1. *Tikal National Park* ... ... 57,600 ha
2. Atitlan National Park ... ... 19,300 ha
3. Rio Dulce National Park (size indicated in 1970 : 20,000 ha) ... 9,600 ha

II. **Areas excluded from the List since 1970 :** two.

1. *Santa Rosalia National Park .* ... ... 4,061 ha
2. *Naciones Unidas National Park .* ... ... 450 ha

Reason : statement of the Director of N. P. Department : Santa Rosalia is no longer under State Control; Naciones Unidas is a recreation area.

III. **Areas added to the List since 1970 :** one.

1. *Tikal National Park :* interest is mainly archeological, but strict protective status (hunting and any kind of exploitation forbidden, cattle grazing under strict control); staff : 9 units; budget : 12,180 U.S. $ (1971); created in 1955-1957; important Maya centre; many visitors; easy access; the forest includes a great variety of species; among the mammals are the jaguar, puma, central American tapir, whitetail deer, north American racoon, opossum, etc.

IV. **Further Information :**

In 1968 was created a Department of National Parks under the Ministry of Agriculture, in charge of Atitlan and Rio Dulce. Because of its archeological character Tikal is administered by the Direccion de Antropologia e Historia under the Ministry of Education.

51. GUINEA

I. **Listed areas :** one.

1. The Nimba Mountains Strict Nature Reserve ... ... 13,000 ha

II. **Areas excluded or added since 1970 :** none.

52. GUYANA

I. **Listed Areas :** one.

    1. The Kaieteur National Park . ...   11,655 ha

II. **Areas excluded or added since 1970 :** none.

53. HAITI

I. **Listed Areas :** none.

II. **Areas excluded or added :** none.

54. HONDURAS

I. **Listed Areas :** none.

II. **Areas excluded or added :** none.

55. HONG KONG

I. **Listed Areas :** none.

II. **Areas excluded or added :** none.

56. HUNGARY

I. **Listed Areas :** nine.

A. — NATIONAL PARKS.

1. Tihany   .. ..   1,100 ha

B. — RESERVES.

2. Little Balaton Reserve .. ..   1,403 ha
3. The Baradla Stalagmite Cave, Aggtelek-Jósvafö . ...   778 ha
4. The Cave of Peace ... ...   643 ha
5. Szalajka Valley   . ...   558 ha
6. *Heath-pasture and Primeval Juniperetum of Bugac-puszta* ...   518 ha

50

7. *Natron Lake of Kardoskut* ... ...   488 ha
8. *Natron Lake of Pusztaszer* ... ...   443 ha
9. Lake Velence . ...   420 ha

II.   **Areas excluded from the List since 1970 :** none.

III. **Areas added to the List since 1970 :** three.

6. *Heath-pasture and Primeval Juniperetum of Bugac-puszta :* totally protected; wardening is carried out by forestry and agricultural organizations which manage the protected area; established in 1969; landscape of sandy heath and primeval Juniperetum with sand-hills on the Hungarian Plain between the Danube and the Tisza rivers; altitude 129 m; tourism.

7. *Natron Lake of Kardoskut :* totally protected; entry by permit only; one warden; established in 1966; shallow natron lake on the Hungarian Plain with alkali heath-pasture and scattered ranches around it; great ornithological importance (avocet, Kentish plower, great bustard,...); altitude : 91 m.

8. *Natron Lake of Pusztaszer :* totally protected; entry by permit only; one warden; established in 1966; same location as No. 7 hereabove and also important for nesting birds; altitude 86 m; observation tower.

IV.   **Further Information :**

Since 1968 is announced the impending creation of Hortobagy National Park in the Puszta, almost endless plain in Eastern Hungary. In mid-June 1972 news was received that its preservation would presumably be pronounced at the end of the year. The wet meadows and marshes in the valley of the Hortobagy, transformed periodically into one gigantic swamp, are a paradise for various aquatic birds, but primarily for geese. Protection temporarily ensured because this area serves as a shooting field for Russian artillery, which on the other hand delays its declaration into a national park.

At the moment of printing this brochure (June 22, 1972) news was received that Tihany is not a national park but a landscape reserve. Information will be sought to determine the exact significance of this term and to see wether its protective status allows its maintainance on the U.N. List, as the inclusion of two other landscape reserves established in 1965 and 1971 : Badacsony (1,330 ha) and Mártély (2,260 ha).

57. ICELAND

I.   **Listed Areas :** three.

1. *Skaftafell National Park* ... ...   100,000 ha
2. Thingvellir National Park ... ...   4,000 ha
3. Eldey Nature Reserve . ...   1,5 ha

II.   **Areas excluded from the List since 1970 :** none.

III. **Areas added to the List since 1970 :** one.

1. *Skaftafell National Park ;* established in 1967 thanks to assistance by the WWF, in South eastern Iceland, not far from the coast; glaciers; hills covered with birches; very rich flora (210 plant species); bird species are abundant; rare insects; no road or paths; accessible by boat; camping grounds nearby.

51

I.   Listed Areas : sixteen.

1. Gir Wild Life Sanctuary (Gujarat)	126,422 ha
2. Periyar Wild Life Sanctuary (Kerala)	77,700 ha
3. Corbett National Park (Uttar Pradesh)	52,547 ha
4. Sariska Wild Life Sanctuary (Rajasthan)	49,182 ha
5. Kaziranga Wild Life Sanctuary (Assam)	42,994 ha
6. Mudumalai Wild Life Sanctuary (Madras)	32,116 ha
7. Kanha National Park (Madhya Pradesh)	31,598 ha
8. Manas Wild Life Sanctuary (Assam)	27,195 ha
9. Hazaribagh National Park (Bihar)	18,389 ha
10. Shivpuri National Park (Mandhya Pradesh)	15,799 ha
11. Taroba National Park (Maharashtra)	11,654 ha
12. Jaldapara Wild Life Sanctuary (West Bengal)	10,464 ha
13. *Borivli National Park* (Maharashtra)	about 6,930 ha
14. Bandipur Wild Life Sanctuary (Mysore)	5,695 ha
15. *Keoladeo Ghana Bird Sanctuary* (Rajasthan)	2,800 ha
16. Jaisamand Wild Life Sanctuary (Rajasthan) ... ... 2,267 ha (or 5,267 ha)

II.   **Areas excluded from the List since 1970 :** none.

III.   **Areas added to the List since 1970 :** two.

13. *Borivli National Park* (or Borivali): forest-land, protecting part of the catchment of Bombay's water supplies; effective measures have been taken for its preservation; forest exploitation is forbidden but domestic stock still to be withdrawn; staff : 22 units; located 35 km from Bombay; rest house near Tulsi Lake; hills rising fron sea level to 453 m; vegetation : southern tropical moist deciduous type; rich flora; wild life is near extinct except for occasional leopard and barking deer; langurs are common; several chital and sambar have been recently released.

15. *Keoladeo Ghana Sanctuary* (Bharatpur): former shooting preserve of the rulers of Bharatpur; now hunting is completely forbidden and even the Maharajas rights have recently been curtailed; established in 1956; might be upgraded into a national park soon; shallow depression sparsely covered with medium sized trees and shrubs; turned into a shallow lake during the monsoons; best sanctuary in India for water birds which congregate for breeding from July until October (stork, white egret, snake-bird, white ibis, spoonbill, greylag geese, 15 species of ducks, etc.); located 45 km from Agra; rest house.

IV.   **Further Information :**

Other national parks or wild life sanctuaries could possibly be added to the U.N. List, but information at present is not sufficient.

59. INDONESIA

I. **Listed Areas :** fourty-eight.

A. — NATURE RESERVES.

1. Udjung Kulon-Painaïtan (1970 : 41,150 ha) ... ... 66,620 ha
divided into three contiguous reserves :

Udjung Kulon	39,120 ha	
Panaïtan	17,500 ha	
Gunung Hondje	10,000 ha	

B. — RESERVES OVER 500 Ha.

a) JAVA.

2. *Meru Betiri*	60,000	ha
3. *Baluran*	25,000	ha
4. *Tjikepuh*	10,000	ha
5. Nusa Barung	6,000	ha
6. Lautan Pasir, Tengger	5,250	ha
7. Kawah Idjen Merapi	2,560	ha
8. Rawa Danau (ou Rantja)	2,500	ha
9. Ranu Kumbolo	1,340	ha
10. Tjibodas, Gunung Gede	1,040	ha
11. Nusa Kambangan Barat	928	ha
12. Pulau Sempu	877	ha
13. Kawah Papandajan	844	ha
14. Ardjuno Lalidjiwo	580	ha

b) SUMATRA.

15. *Mount Löser* ... ... 436,500 ha
divided into two contiguous reserves :

Mt Löser	416,500 ha	
Kluet	20,000 ha	

16. *Mount Wilhelmina*	200,000	ha
17. *Berbak*	190,000	ha
18. Gunung Indrapura (Kerintji)	12,530	ha
19. Rimbo Panti	3,500	ha
20. Krakatau Mountain	2,500	ha
21. *Bengkulu*	2,148	ha
22. Dusun Besar (in 1970 : 12 ha)	1,155	ha

c) KALIMANTAN (Borneo).

23. Padang Luwai (in 1970 : 1,080 ha)	5,000	ha
24. Mandor (in 1970 : 195 ha)	2,000	ha

d) SULAWESI (Celebes).

25. Gunung Tangkoko Batuangus	4,446	ha
26. Panua	1,500	ha

e) BALI.

27. West Bali	20,000	ha

f) LESSER SUNDA ISLANDS.

28. *Komodo Island, Padar, Rintja and Wao Wuul* (in four sections: 31,000, 15,000, 15,000 and 3,000 ha) ... ... 64,000 ha

C. — RESERVES OF LESS THAN 500 HA.

a) JAVA.

29. *Panandjung Pangandaran*	457	ha
30. Saobi	430	ha
31. Ranu Darangan	380	ha
32. *Telagabodas*	285	ha
33. Takokak	50	ha
34. Palau Dua, Palau Bokor and Palau Rambut (three contiguous reserves: 8+18+20 ha)	46	ha
35. Sigogor (in 1970: 190 ha)	20	ha
36. Tjigenteng Tjipanji (2 ha+3 ha)	5	ha

b) SUMATRA.

37. Rafflesia Serbödjadi	300	ha
38. Dolok Tinggi Radja	167	ha
39. Sibolangit	115	ha
40. Dolok Saut	39	ha
41. Batang Palupuh	3,4 ha
42. Tjawang	3,2 ha
43. Despatah	0,3 ha

c) SULAWESI (Celebes).

44. Mas Papaja Radja	160	ha
45. Tanggala	125	ha
46. Bantimurung	10	ha
47. Napabalano	9	ha

d) MALUKU (Moluccas).

48. Gunung Api	80	ha

II.   **Areas excluded from the List since 1970:** one.

Gunung Djagat (Java): invaded and devastated according to competent authorities.

Three contiguous reserves in Java: Pulau-Dua, Pulau Bokor and Pulau Rambut formerly listed as separated areas are now mentioned together. Similarly Rafflesia reserve in Java is no longer mentioned separately.

III.   **Areas added to the List since 1970:** eleven.

2. *Meru Betiri:* 60,000 ha; created in 1966; unspoiled forest, not much threatened, in eastern Java on the southern coast; two guards: a considerable increase of staff number is expected; javan tiger; sea turtle.

3. *Baluran:* 25,000 ha; at the extreme east of Java, north of Ketapang; along the ocean; created in 1937 but recent development; road; guesthouse, watchtower; 20 guards; poaching; savannah; banteng (or wild ox), wild buffalo, deer, black leopard, peacock.

4. *Tjikepuh :* 10,000 ha in West Java, on the southern coast, at Djakarta meridian approximately; especially strict protection; 30 guards; banteng, black panther, sea turtle; some tourism.

15. *Mount Löser :* with the adjoining reserve of Kluet (20,000 ha : orang-utan, Rafflesia) this reserve created in 1934 in northern Sumatra on 416,500 ha receives the carefull attention of several instances, notably WWF, but is also the object of some anxiety owing to human pressure; 15 guards; staff number expected to increase; lumbering is forbidden in this forest which is the habitat for Sumatran rhino, orang-utan, elephant, mountain goat; headquarters at Kotatjane.

16. *Mount Wilhelmina :* was only included on the List because of the insistance of authorities who promised a soon reinforcement of staff numbers; created in 1938 is eastern Sumatra; 200,000 ha of forest, habitat of tapir, mountain goat, orang-utan.

17. *Berbak :* in central Sumatra; officially declared in 1935 but staff appointed only recently; six guards, which is not much for 190,000 ha but enough owing to the uninhabited character of the area; rhinoceros, tapir, wild buffalo, etc.

21. *Bengkulu :* in southern Sumatra; created in 1937, recently developed and enlarged; one guard for 2,140 ha; *Rafflesia arnoldi.*

27. *West Bali :* also named Bali Barat; in the extreme north-west of the island, near Bali and Java strait; created in 1941 but organized recently only since provisions were made for a local section of the " Reserves " Division of Bogor Directorate of Nature Conservation and Wildlife Management, with headquarters at Singaradja; still some occupation; poaching; 20 guards for 20,000 ha; deer, banteng, white starling.

28. *Komodo Island,* etc. : group of islands where protective measures, some of them dating back to 1938, were recently reinforced; four temporary guards; consolidation is expected; the main purpose of the reserve is the preservation of habitat of Giant Monitor *Varanus komodoensis.*

29. *Panandjung Pangandaran :* on the southern coast of Java, SE of Bandoeng; created in 1934; careful attention has recently been given to this reserve; 15 guards to control 457 ha; habitat of Banteng; tourism; " flora, scenery, aesthetics and biology very interesting ".

32. *Telagabodas :* not far from Bandoeng; good supervision; created in 1934-1935; no threat; vegetation characteristic of sulfur rich soil; geological monument; lake with sulfuric mud; 285 ha.

IV.   **Further Information :**

a) Recent development of the competent Service resulted in the achievement of various projects, notably in Sumatra where several areas which were either called nature parks or nature reserves are now being organized : Kerumutan (120,000 ha), Taluk (120,000 ha), Bankinang (150,000 ha), Sungai Rangan (80,000 ha), the four of them protecting rhinoceros, elephant, tapir. Similarly in Kalimantan : important projects at Kotawaringin (205,000 ha) and Kutai (306,000 ha) to protect orang utan, *Nasalis larvatus,* banteng, etc.

b) Authorities are also concerned with the important Mt Lorentz Reserve in West Irian (New Guinea) whose supervision will be reorganized; steps will be taken first in 40,000 ha from the 320,000 ha of the " Natuurmonument " formerly created by the Dutch.

60. IRAN

I. **Listed Areas :** five.

1. *Mohammad Reza Shah Wildlife Park* . ... 91,890 ha
2. *Tandoureh Wildlife Park* ... ... 73,435 ha
3. *Kolah Ghazi Wildlife Park* ... ... 41,000 ha
4. *Dez Wildlife Park* . ... 3,837 ha
5. *Karkheh Wildlife Park* . ... 1,538 ha

II. **Areas excluded from the List since 1970 :** none.

III. **Areas added to the List since 1970 :** five.

1. *Mohammad Reza Shah Wildlife Park :* first measures in 1962; under present status since 1964; staff : 18 units; budget : 33,300 U.S. $; some pig cropping; mountainous reserve located in north-east Iran; bunchgrass-*Artemisia* steppe and eastern edge of contiguous Caspian forest; forest wildlife is abundant; Urial sheep (*Ovis ammon*); Persian Ibex, Goitered Gazelle. Altitude : 380-2,410 m.

2. *Tandoureh Wildlife Park :* established in 1970; staff : 8 units; budget : 9,800 U.S. $; located in north-east Iran near the Turkmen SSR border.

3. *Kolah Ghazi Wildlife Park :* established in 1970; staff : 6 units; budget : 17,300 U.S. $; located in central Iran next to Shah-kuh Protected region.

4. *Dez Wildlife Park :* established in 1970; staff : four units; budget : 17,300 U.S. $; *Tamarix* spp. *Populus euphraticus* forest along the Dez river; set aside to protect the shrinking habitat of the Mesopotamian Fallow Deer (*Dama mesopotamica*); located in western Iran.

5. *Karkheh Wildlife Park :* established in 1970; located in western Iran, just west of the above mentioned Dez WLP; same kind of forest along Karkheh River; same purpose : protection of Mesopotamian Fallow Deer; also shelters jungle cats, jackals, wolves, honey badgers; staff : 2 units; budget : 20,000 U.S. $.

IV. **Further Information :**

There are two kinds of protected areas in Iran : 1° the *Protected regions* (including 4 wetland protected regions) where hunting is forbidden unless by special license, with some occupation and restricted exploitation, and 2° the *Wildlife Parks* totalling at present seven [two small WLP. Dash-i-Naz, (55 ha) and Khoshkedaran (227 ha) have not been included in the present List, being under ICNP size criterium].

A Wildlife Park enjoys much the same status as national parks elsewhere but there are provisions for culling of surplus wildlife for management purposes through authorized Department personnel or licensed hunter, under the strict supervision of the Game and Fish Department. According to local authorities such harvest is extremely limited and wildlife parks deserve to be included in the U.N. List.

I.   **Listed Areas :** none.

II.   **Areas excluded or added :** none.

I.   **Listed areas :** one.
      1. Bourn Vincent Memorial Park ... ...   4,250 ha

II.   **Areas excluded or added since 1970 :** none.

I.   **Listed Areas :** fifteen.

       1. Mount Meron Nature Reserves . ...   10,500 ha
       2. Mount Carmel National Park and Nature Reserves ... ... (*) 7,000 ha
       3. *Hai Bar* (*Wild Animals*) *Reserve* ... ...   3,000 ha
       4. Wadi Shorek Nature Reserves ... ...   990 ha
       5. Ein Gedi Nature Reserve ... ...   850 ha
       6. The Wadi Tabor Nature Reserve ... ...   800 ha
       7. The Wadi Bezet Nature Reserve ... ...   765 ha
       8. The Wadi Amud Nature Reserve ... ...   720 ha
       9. The Wadi K'ziv Nature Reserve . ...   650 ha
      10. Mount Gilboa Nature Reserve ... ...   610 ha
      11. The Wadi Dishon Nature Reserve ... ...   600 ha
      12. Huleh Swamp Nature Reserve ... ...   308 ha
      13. The Solelim Forest Nature Reserve . ...   300 ha
      14. The Eilat Gulf Nature Reserve . ...   100 ha
      15. *Nahal Hermon, Nahal l'yon and Tel Dan Nature Reserves* ..   100 ha
      16. (**).

II.   **Areas excluded from the List since 1970 :** none.

(*) Information received at the beginning of July 1972, when this text was already printed, indicates that Mt Carmel National Park totals 17,000 ha, including 5 nature reserves totalling 3,100 ha.

(**) The same information indicates that a sixteenth protected area could be added to this list : Wadi Harbasor Nature Reserve, 640 ha, established in 1967, supervised by one part-time ranger; arid country in Western Negev with several springs in the wadi beds; desert reptiles, lynx, caracal.

III. **Areas added to the List since 1970 :** two.

3. *Hai Bar (Wild Animals) Reserve :* located 40 km North of Eilat Gulf Nature Reserve (No. 14); one guard; part of the desert; one half includes salt pans and the other is covered with acacia trees; adjoining the road leading to Eilat, in the Southern Rift Valley (Azava). In the reserve animals are kept that were in the past indigenous to the Negev or still live there under the threat of extinction; gazelles, ibexes, wild asses; carnivorous animals and birds of prey will be added.

15. *Nahal Hermon, Nahal l'yon and Tel Dan :* these three small reserves totalling some hundred hectares only have been included together on the List because of their ecological interest and because they protect the three sources. separated by a few km from each other, of the Jordan River : Snir, Dan and Hermon; each of these three tributaries of the Jordan has been set aside as a nature reserve; plane and willow trees and myrtles; giant therebinth; laurel; rock doves.

IV. **Further Information :**

Big or small, there are now in Israel some 60 reserves declared and 40 in the process of being declared, including 8 large reserve in the Negev, which will total 200,000 ha.

Moreover, in areas occupied since the six day war, numerous reserves have been established and are strictly protected under military supervision. Among them : Yahudiya, 7,600 ha, uniform developed forest of the park forest type of the Mt Tabor oak, which in the past constituted the climax vegetation of the Lower Golan (Syria) : jujube, white poplar, hawthorn. Other reserves under military status in the Sinaï or in the former Jordan territory : Ein Fashkha, strip of land of great ecological interest along the Dead Sea.

64. ITALY

I. **Listed Areas :** fifteen.

A. — NATIONAL PARKS.

1. Gran Paradiso	62,000 ha
2. Stelvio	57,772 ha
3. Abruzzo	29,160 ha
4. *Calabria*	18,000 ha
5. Circeo	7,445 ha

B. — STRICT NATURE RESERVES (State Land, Ministry of Agriculture).

6. Cossogno or Val Grande	1,000 ha
7. *Lastoni-Selva Pezzi*	977 ha
8. *Tre Cime del Monte Bondone*	185 ha
9. *Piaie Longhe-Millifret*	129 ha
10. *Bosco Nordio*	115 ha

11. Sasso Fratino ... ...   100 ha
12. Poggie Tre Cancelli ... ...   100 ha

C. — MANAGED SCIENTIFIC RESERVES (State Land, Ministry of Agriculture).

13. *Pian di Landro-Baldassarre* ... ...   266 ha
14. *Guadino-Pradaccio* .. ..   240 ha

D. — NATURE RESERVES (Consiglio delle Ricerche).

15. *Montecristo* . ...   1,031 ha

II.   **Areas excluded from the List since 1970 :** none.

The ICNP would have preferred to exclude Circeo National Park for reasons already explained in 1967 and 1970, but the Italian government maintained its former position (see 1970 edition, p. 294).

III.   **Areas added to the List since 1970 :** eight.

4. *Calabria National Park :* established by Decree No. 503 of April 2, 1968; split into ten different zones which are separated by an average distance of 50 km, moreover each zone is itself subdivided into four parts : *a)* a strict nature reserve; *b)* an area in which wildlife species are raised under semi-captive conditions; *c)* a woodland and grassland zone and *d)* a treeless zone; demarcation in progress; organization slowed down by budgetary problems born from constitutional changes and transfer of some power to Regions; inclusion in the U.N. List might be premature.

7. *Lastoni-Selva Pezzi Strict Nature Reserve :* State forest on Mount Baldo, Verona. Established 1970; rocky country with deciduous and coniferous forests in the north. Altitude : 1,200-2,000 m.

8. *Tre Cime del Monte Bondone Strict Nature Reserve :* peatland located some 1,550 m above sealevel (torbiere alte, Hochmoor); the three Mount Bondone peaks culminate at 2,098 to 2,155 m; various *cyperaceae* and *araminaceae*; drosera, carnivorous plant; roe deer; interesting insect species; located near Trent city. Established 1969.

9. *Piaie Longhe-Millifret Strict Nature Reserve :* State Forest in Cansiglio (Belluno and Treviso). Established 1970; rocky country; remnants of beach, red fir and larch forests. Altitude : 1,360-1,577 m.

10. *Bosco Nordio Strict Nature Reserve :* located in Venezia Province; coastal reserve presenting mediterranean and continental aspects. Established 1970. Altitude : sea level.

13. *Pian di Landro-Baldassarre Managed Reserve :* State Forest in Cansiglio, Belluno and Treviso; established 1970; deciduous and coniferous forests; interesting clearing called Lambio plain which serves as a refuge for wild ducks; roe deer, red deer, hare, francolin, marten. Altitude : 900-1,150 m.

14. *Guadino-Pradaccio Managed Reserve :* located in Val Parma; includes an interesting lacustrian zone; fir trees and beaches, reintroduction of chamois and shoveler. Established 1970. Altitude : 1,450 m.

15. *Montecristo :* island located between the continent and Corsica, 45 km south of Elba Island; access permitted only for research or pratrolling purposes; staff headquarters at Cala Maestra (former Royal villa); brushwood-covered heath, pines, *Quercus ilex,* eucalyptus; a characteristic animal species is the *Capra aegagrus;* presence also of some seals (*Monachus monachus*) on the coast; established in 1971 through the combined action of the Ministeries of Merchant Marine, Agriculture and Finance and the National Research Council. Altitude : 0-645 m.

IV.   **Further Information :**

a) In 1971 Gran Paradiso National Park suffered from a guard strike; poachers availed of this opportunity to kill a number of ibexes and chamois.

b) Problems were raised also in Stelvio National Park due to the Regional administrative changes.

c) The total number of strict nature reserves now exceeds twenty.

d) One of these, which is not mentioned hereabove because under 100 ha, is located within Abruzzo N. P. : Colle di Licco, 95 ha.

65. IVORY COAST

I.   **Listed Areas :** three.

1. Komoe National Park (formerly Bouna-Komoe Faunal Reserve and Protected Forest) ... ... 1,140,000 ha

2. *Tai Forest Reserve* (or Sassandra)   ... ...   425,000 ha

3. Nimba Mountains Strict Nature Reserve ... ...   5,000 ha

II.   **Areas excluded from the List since 1970 :** none.

III.   **Areas added to the List since 1970 :** one.

2. *Tai Forest Reserve :* is presently receiving IUCN attention at the Government's request with the objective to up-grade this reserve into a national park; part of the last intact lowland tropical rain forest on the west side of the Dahomey Gap; habitat for many large mammals including a number of endangered species; is currently under pressure by forest exploiters; established in 1956 as a reserve; staff : about 12 units (other information indicate only three).

IV.   **Further Information :**

Four other national parks have been created during the last few years which do not yet qualify for inclusion on the U.N. List : Marahoue (101,000 ha), Mount Peko (34,000 ha), Asagny (30,000 ha) and Banco (3,000 ha, 17 units, experimental centre for sylviculture).

I.   **Listed Areas :** none.

II.   **Areas excluded or added :** none.

67. JAPAN

I.   **Listed Areas :** twenty-three.
         List 1970, p. 300.

II.   **Areas excluded or added since 1970 :** none.

III.   **Further Information :**

         a) The sizes indicated for the Special Protection Areas — whose importance for ICNP criteria is great — were carefully up-dated for the English version of the U.N. List which was printed in 1971. Since, only a few changes occurred as far as SPA are concerned : Daisetsuzan increased by 1,319 ha and Seto Naikai passed from 370 to 996 ha.

         b) A marine parks system is now developing in Japan. The main recently created Marine Parks are Toyooka, Takeno, Hamasaka, Uradomikaigan, Kushimoto, Kesennuma, Tomioka, Amakusa, Ushibuka, Sakurajima and Satamisaki.

68. JORDAN

I.   **Listed Areas :** none.

II.   **Areas excluded or added :** none.

69. KENYA

I.   **Listed Areas :** fourteen.

         A. — NATIONAL PARKS.
         Seven : List 1970, p. 313.

         B. — COUNTY COUNCIL GAME RESERVES.
         Two : ibid.

C. — OTHER RESERVES.

Three : ibid.

D. — MARINE PARKS.

13. *Watamu*	1,165 ha
14. *Malindi*	583 ha

II.   **Areas excluded from the List :** none.

III.   **Areas added to the List :** two.

13. *Watamu Marine Park :* created in 1968; fishing and removal of coral or shells forbidden; controlled by a Marine Park Ranger with patrol boat; coral garden which is the habitat of many thousands of different species of colourful fish; touristic development along Watamu Beach; every hotel provides boats for visitors; entry free.

14. *Malindi Marine Park :* created in 1968; as for Watamu fishing and shell collecting are forbidden; coral and spectacular fish.

70. KOREA

I.   **Listed Areas :** one.

1. *Chiri-San National Park* . ...   43,890 ha

II.   **Areas excluded from the List since 1970 :** none.

III.   **Areas added to the List since 1970 :** one.

1. *Chiri-San National Park* (or Chiri Mountain N. P.) : established in December 1967; two resident officers, one janitor; Chiri Mountain rises on the south-western ranges of Sobaek Mountains; max. altitude is 1,915 m; densely forested with conifers, mostly *Pinus densiflora* and broad leaves; bushes of rhododendron, 300 year old Early Flowering Cherry Tree (natural monument); wildlife includes musk deer, black bear, large flying squirrel, Korean mink, etc. and 168 species of birds; the park includes seven large old temples and many significant relics; many visitors; lodges.

IV.   **Further Information :**

Seven other national parks have been established after Chiri-san, but are not yet supervised : Hanry Sea (34,660 ha : five islands), Kiongju (10,205 ha). Halla Mountain (or Han Ra) (8,200 ha), Kyeryong Mountain (6,010 ha), Sokni Mountain (6,000 ha), Sorak Mountain (46,879 ha) and Naejangsan (established in November 1971, 81,800 ha).

71. KUWAIT

I.   **Listed Areas :** none.

II.   **Areas excluded or added :** none.

72. LAOS

I.   **Listed Areas :** none.

II.   **Areas excluded or added :** none.

73. LEBANON

I.   **Listed Areas :** none.

II.   **Areas excluded or added :** none.

74. LESOTHO

I.   **Listed Areas :** one.
1. *Sehlabathebe National Park* . ...   6,500 ha

II.   **Areas excluded from the List since 1970 :** none.

III. **Areas added to the List since 1970 :** one.
1. *Sehlabathebe National Park :* established in February 1970; still under process
of development; located in the area adjoining the central western border of
Natal Cape; situated on the roof of a mountain complex (altitude : 2,400 m),
offers admirable panoramic views; geomorphologically very attractive; unique
mountain flora of grass flowering plants, geophytes shrubs and stunted trees;
includes rare birds as the Lammergeier and the Bald Ibis, alpine fauna;
various antelopes will be reintroduced when the area will be fenced.

75. LIBERIA

I.   **Listed Areas :** none.

II.   **Areas excluded or added :** none.

III.   **Further Information :**
A very small reserve was established on the South Western coast : Cape Mount. Its protection is still subject to contestations from neighbouring people.

76. LYBIA

I.   **Listed Areas :** none.

II.   **Areas excluded or added :** none.

77. LUXEMBOURG

I.   **Listed Areas :** none.

II.   **Areas excluded or added :** none.

78. MALAGASY REPUBLIC
(Madagascar)

I.   **Listed Areas :** thirty-one.

A. — STRICT NATURE RESERVES.
Eleven : List 1970, p. 324.

B. — NATIONAL PARKS.
Two : ibid.

C. — SPECIAL RESERVES.
Eighteen : ibid. (one excluded and one added).

II.   **Areas excluded from the List since 1970 :** one.
Ambohitantely Special Reserve : 3,453 ha; reason : according to local authorities this area is no longer a special reserve and should be excluded from the U.N. List.

64

III.　　**Areas added to the List since 1970 :** one.

31. *Nosy Mangabe Special Reserve :* island in north-eastern Madagascar; great
scientific and conservation interest despite its small size; established in 1967;
laboratory; access by boat from Maroantsetsa; purpose : provide a refuge for
some of the last surviving aye-aye *Daubentonia madagascariensis*; shelters other
interesting lemurs.　Controlled by a technical agent; two labourers are staying
permanently on the island.　Size : 520 ha.

IV.　　**Further Information :**

According to news received at the end of May 1972 from the competent
authority in Tananarive proposals are presently made to regrade Masoala Nature
Reserve (76,000 ha) which had been cancelled as a reserve in 1964 (cf. Resolution No. 12 of Madagascar Conference, 1970).

On the other hand the same authority advised the exclusion from the next edition
of the List of the Special Reserves quoted hereabove.

79.　MALAWI

I.　　**Listed Areas :** three.

1. *Kasungu National Park .* ... ...　204,800 ha
2. Nyika National Park (formerly Malawi National Park,
103,600 ha) .. ..　93,300 ha
3. *Lengwe National Park .* ... ...　12,800 ha

II.　　**Areas excluded from the List since 1970 :** none.

III.　　**Areas added to the List since 1970 :** two.

1. *Kasungu National Park :* located in the northwest corner of the Central
Region, some 30 miles west of Kasungu township; game reserve in 1922,
national park in August 1970; totally protected; staff : 33 units; undulating
Brachystegia woodland with numerous wide open grass covered seasonal riverain
swamps; rocky outcrops; wide variety of animals including antelopes, rhinoceros,
lion, cheetah, leopard, etc. and many water birds; mean altitude 1,200 m;
accommodation in rondavels; airstrip; open from June to December.

3. *Lengwe National Park :* lies in the Chikwawa district of Southern Malawi,
in a densily populated region; one game ranger, 10 game guards.　Game
reserve in 1928, declared national park in 1970; flood plain adjacent to the
Shire River; one third of the area is covered with dense dry thorny thicket with
most of the remainder with savannah; fauna includes various antelopes, notably
nyala and Livingstone's suni; lion, leopard, etc.; proximity of Blantyre (45 miles)
8 bed camp; open from June to December; altitude : about 100 m.

IV. **Further Information :**

In 1969 a Chief Game Warden was appointed to take charge of the Game Division of the Department of Forestry and Game and a Special National Park Act became law on August 1, 1970.

Mention should be made of three reserves which according to competent authorities do not qualify for inclusion : Nkhota-Kota Game Reserve (170,000 ha), Majete Game Reserve (64,000 ha) and Mwabi Game Reserve (15,000 ha).

A new national park will soon be gazetted south of Lake Malombe : Liwonde National Park.

80. MALAYSIA
(includes the States of Malaya, Sabah and Sarawak)

I. **Listed Areas :** five.

a) MALAYA :
1. Taman Negara National Park ... ... 434,340 ha
2. *Sungei Dusun Game Reserve* (Malaya) ... ... 4,280 ha
3. Templer Park ... ... 1,200 ha

b) SABAH :
4. Kinabalu National Park ... ... 68,635 ha

c) SARAWAK :
5. Bako National Park ... ... 2,550 ha

II. **Areas excluded since 1970 :** none.

III. **Areas added to the List since 1970 :** one.

2. *Sungei Dusun Game Reserve* (Malaya) : set aside to conserve a small family of Sumatran Rhinceros (*Didermoceros sumatrensis*). Three game rangers, two labourers and staff quarters are maintained at the expense of the Selangor State Game Department. Yearly expenditure U.S. $ 13,653 (1971). Created in 1964. Situated south west of Tanjong Malim, Perak. Not opened to tourists.

IV. **Further Information :**

In 1971, at the request of Government, slightly under ten square miles of Kinabalu N. P. has been de-reserved for copper mining developments.

81. MALDIVE ISLANDS

I. **Listed Areas :** none.

II. **Areas excluded or added :** none.

82. MALI

I.   **Listed Areas :** one.

     1. La Boucle du Baoulé National Park ... ...   350,000 ha

II.   **Areas excluded or added since 1970 :** none.

83. MALTA

I.   **Listed Areas :** none.

II.   **Areas excluded or added :** none.

84. MAURITANIA

I.   **Listed Areas :** one.

     1. Mauritanian Islands Strict Nature Reserve . ...   about 10,000 ha

II.   **Areas excluded or added since 1970 :** none.

85. MAURITIUS

I.   **Listed Areas :** two.

     1. Bel Ombre Reserve   ... ...   919 ha

     2. Macabe-Mare Longue Reserve ... ...   507 ha

II.   **Areas excluded or added since 1970 :** none.

III.   A letter of 7th August 1972 said : " The enumeration must be left unchanged except that Natural Reserve Ile aux Aigrettes (23 ha) should be added under item V. B. ".

86. MEXICO

I.   **Listed Areas :** fifteen.

1. La Malinche National Park	41,711 ha
2. Iztaccihuatl-Popocatepetl National Park	25,679 ha
3. Zoquiapan National Park	20,454 ha
4. Pico de Orizaba National Park	19,750 ha
5. Bosencheve National Park	15,000 ha
6. Cofre de Perote National Park	11,700 ha
7. Lagunas de Chacahua National Park	10,000 ha
8. *Lagunas de Montebello National Park*	6,022 ha
9. Lagunas de Zempoala National Park	4,669 ha
10. Desierto de Los Leones National Park	1,900 ha
11. Insurgente Miguel Hidalgo y Costilla National Park	1,836 ha
12. El Chico National Park	1,835 ha
13. *Insurgente Jose Maria Morelos y Pavon National Park*	1,813 ha
14. El Tepeyac National Park	1,420 ha
15. Desierto del Carmen National Park	529 ha

II.   **Areas excluded from the List since 1970 :** none.

III.   **Areas added to the List since 1970 :** two.

8. *Lagunas de Montebello National Park* : located in Independencia and La Trinitaria Municipalities (Municipios), in Chiapas State, 70 km east of Comitan; totally protected; staff : 3 units; budget (1972) : U.S. $ 2,000; created in November 1959; includes 59 lakes and forests of temperate and semi-tropical zones; numerous orchids; access by road; a few paths within the park; Motel at 5 km.

13. *Insurgente Jose Maria Morelos y Pavon National Park :* located in Michoacan state, roughly half-way between Mexico City and the Pacific Coast; totally protected; as the above park was recommended for inclusion in May 1972; staff : 2 units; budget (1972) : 1,500 U.S. $; extremely mountainous and hilly terrain including many springs; some facilities; proximity of Morelia. Created in 1939.

87. MONGOLIAN REPUBLIC

I.   **Listed Areas :** none.

II.   **Areas excluded or added :** none.

III.   **Further Information :**

This country certainly has established national parks and equivalent reserves deserving to be included in the U.N. List but no information is available.

I.   **Listed Areas :** one.

    1. Tazekka National Park . ...   580 ha

II.   **Areas excluded or added :** none.

III.   **Further Information :**

    As for Algeria and Tunisia, the justification of maintaining this small reserve on the U.N. Roll of Honour could be questioned.

I.   **Listed Areas :** three.

    1. Chitawan Rhinoceros Sanctuary ... ... about 80,000 ha
    2. Sukla Phanta Sanctuary   ... ...   12,500 ha
    3. *Tappu Sanctuary* . ...   5,698 ha

II.   **Areas excluded from the List :** none.

III.   **Areas added to the List :** one.

    3. *Tappu Sanctuary* (or Biratnagar) : established in 1962; 11 forest officers; located in Eastern Nepal; created for the protection of the last breeding population of wild buffalo in Nepal; includes tiger, leopard, wild boar, barking deer and chital.

IV.   **Further Information :**

    Two further national parks have been proposed but are not yet officially gazetted : Lantang (about 77,700 ha) and Khumbu (in the Himalayas).

I.   **Listed Areas :** eighteen.

    A. — RESERVES.
    Fourteen : List 1970, p. 357.

    B. — NATIONAL PARKS.
    Four : ibid.

II.   **Areas excluded from the List since 1970 :** none.

III.   **Areas added to the List since 1970 :** none.

The same principle as for some other industrialized countries was adopted for Netherlands : maintainance of the List as decided in 1967-1970.

However it must not be concluded that the efforts made to increase the size of protected areas by successive purchases was interrupted in this country which has one of the highest population density in the world.
These purchases are made by parcels rarely very large, through official or private initiatives.

In 1970 almost 7,000 ha could thus be acquired and included in natural reserves. In 1972 state budget for such purchases was unfortunately slightly under that of previous years.

91. NEW ZEALAND

I.   **Listed Areas :** twenty-one.

A. — NATIONAL PARKS.

Ten : List 1970, p. 364.

B. — ISLAND RESERVES.

11. *Auckland*	... ...	62,551 ha
12. *Campbell*	... ...	11,329 ha
13. *Kermadec*	.. ..	3,197 ha
14. *Kapiti*	. ...	2,000 ha
15. *Antipodes*	.. ..	611 ha
16. *Snares*	. ...	243 ha
17. *Bounty*	. ...	135 ha

C. — MARITIME PARK.

18. Hauraki Gulf . ...   8,000 ha
(including Little Barrier Island, 2,800 ha)

D. — FOREST SANCTUARIES.

19. *Waipoua Forest Sanctuary*	. ...	10,122 ha
20. *Rocky Hills Forest Sanctuary*	... ...	404 ha
21. *Whirinaki Forest Sanctuary*	... ...	162 ha

II.   **Areas excluded from the List since 1970 :** none.

III.   **Areas added to the List since 1970 :** eleven.

B. — ISLAND RESERVES.

The following islands, with the exception of Kapiti and Kermadec, are sub-antarctic islands situated to the south of New Zealand. They possess interesting flora and fauna and are the home of large numbers of sea birds. They all have been preserved for some time, access to them being restricted to authorized visits from representative of scientific organizations. They are now administered for the Preservation of Flora and Fauna and qualify for inclusion in spite of the fact that staffing of them is generally not practicable but they are all periodically inspected. Here are some further data :

11. *Auckland :* uninhabited; entry by permit only; project to exterminate feral domestic animals introduced a long time ago; the south especially is unspoiled; comprises several islands, the main one being 50,980 ha of volcanic origin; mountains, cliffs, peat; forest and sea birds. Altitude 0-610 m. Established 1934.

12. *Campbell :* entry by permit only; meteorological station : the officer in charge acts as honorary ranger; the area was sheep grazed; part of the island has been fenced; several islands, the main one being 11,268 ha (volcanic origin); birds, sea elephant, sea lion. Established 1954.

13. *Kermadec :* comprises Raoul (2,938 ha), Macauley (306 ha), Curtis (52 ha) and Cheeseman (8 ha) islands, l'Esperance Rock (5 ha) and the Herald Islets; all situated north west of New Zealand; each of the main islands is the summit of a volcanic cone, some of which show sign of activity; great abundance of birdlife including parakeets, petrels, gannets, sooty terns, kingfishers and tuis; eradication program is planned for feral domestic animals; uninhabited; meteorological station on Raoul Island : the officer in charge of the station acts as honorary ranger; entry by permit only; periodic inspections and scientific expeditions. Established in 1934. Altitude : 0-525 m.

14. *Kapiti :* situated about 4 miles of Paraparaumu Beach on the West Coast of Wellington Province; entry by permit only; one resident ranger; important bird sanctuary. Established in 1925.

15. *Antipodes :* strictly protected; entry by permit only, comprises the main island (587 ha) and small adjacent islands; birds, sea elephant. Established 1961.

16. *Snares :* entry by permit only; small scientific station depending from Canterbury (Christchurch University) : the officer in charge acts as honorary ranger; several rocky islands, the main one being 214 ha; forests; breeding ground for migratory birds. Established 1961.

17. *Bounty :* as for the above islands entry by permit for scientific purpose only, issued by the Department of Lands and Survey (Wellington); some 13 granite islets and rocks entirely devoid of vegetation and soil; sea birds, penguins, seals, Bounty islands shags. Established 1961.

C. — 18. *Hauraki Gulf Maritime Park :* made up of a dozens of islands which have been established as a Marine Park by Act of Parliament; three categories : 1) strict nature reserves, including Little Barrier Island (2,800 ha, one resident ranger, bird sanctuary since 1895), Poor Knights, Hen and Chicken, Mokohinau, Mercury, The Aldermen islands, where entry is by permit only; 2) scenic reserves, where access is permited but strictly protected (Bream, Cuvier islands) and 3) recreation reserves already spoiled by farming (Kawau, Rangitoto, Motuihe, Browns); in the latter tourist facilities are available (hotels on Kawau).

D. — FOREST SANCTUARIES.

19. *Waipoua Forest Sanctuary :* totally protected; supervised in conjunction with adjoining exotic forest which has four officers on permanent staff plus casual workmen; set aside in July 1952 for the purpose of preserving the kauri forest (*Agathis australis*) of Waipoua; a scenic highway traverses the sanctuary and a number of walking tracks lead off the highway.

20. *Rocky Hills Forest Sanctuary :* totally protected; supervised in conjunction with nearby exotic and indigenous forests; set aside to preserve a remnant of the once typical but now scarce podocarp-hardwood forest type of the Wairapa hill country with examples of related regenerating hardwood stands.

21. *Whirinaki Forest Sanctuary :* totally protected; this area was set aside as a forest sanctuary to preserve virgin stands of high quality podocarp forest; there are five stands of predominantly rimu (*Dacrydium cupressinum*) and matai (*Podocarpus spicatus*) as well as a variety of other minor species; a rich understorey contains the commoner lowland native scrubs and an abundance of tree ferns.

IV.   **Further Information :**

Beside the above three forest sanctuaries six forest parks were recently established where great emphasis is given to conservation and recreation but where commercial exploitation for timber production and mining are still recognized as quite legitimate uses. Here are their names : North-West Nelson (358,089 ha), Tararua (95,216 ha), Kaimanawa (76,074 ha), Coromandel (64,736 ha), Pirongia (10,931 ha) and Craigieburn (4,980 ha).

92. NICARAGUA

I.   **Listed Areas :** none.

II.   **Areas excluded or added :** none.

93. NIGER

I.   **Listed Areas :** one.
   1. The " W " National Park .   ...   300,000 ha

II.   **Areas excluded or added since 1970 :** none.

94. NIGERIA

I.   **Listed Areas :** two.

1. *Borgu Game reserve* ... ...   397,047 ha
2. Yankari Game reserve (size indicated in 1970 : 182,160 ha) ...   207,800 ha

II.   **Areas excluded from the List since 1970 :** none.

III.   **Areas added to the List since 1970 :** one.

1. *Borgu Game Reserve :* is a good reserve although there are still some poaching problems amid the edges; virtually no management; 2 senior staff and 22 game scouts; gazetted in 1966; located between Niger river and Dahomey border near to Kainji Lake, Kwara State; no facilities (accommodation at Kainji Motel, 25 miles from reserve entrance); Northern Guinea savanna with patches of dense *Diosporus* forest; fringing forest along Oli river, seasonal swamps; animals include various kinds of antelopes, elephant, lion, leopard, side striped jackal, serval, caracal, monkeys, manatee, etc.

95. NORWAY

I.   **Listed Areas :** twelve.

1.	Börgefjell National Park	109,500 ha
2.	*Øvre Dividal National Park*	95,500 ha
3.	Rondane National Park	57,200 ha
4.	*Femundsmarka National Park*	38,500 ha
5.	*Gressämoen National Park*	18,000 ha
6.	*Rago National Park*	16,700 ha
7.	*Stabbursdalen National Park*	9,600 ha
8.	*Øvre Pasvik National Park*	6,300 ha
9.	*Anderdalen National Park*	5,300 ha
10.	*Gutulia National Park*	1,900 ha
11.	*Ormtjernkampen National Park*	900 ha
12.	Fokstumyra Nature Reserve.	900 ha

II.   **Areas excluded since 1970 :** none.

III.   **Areas added to the List since 1970 :** nine.

2. *Øvre Dividal National Park :* one warden, budget : about 1,340 U.S. $ (1972); created in 1971; five lodges and some old dug-outs in the park, road park; some marked footpaths. Located in the eastern part of the Troms country bordering the Swedish frontier. Pine and birch forests, valleys, and plateaus, high and low mountains, lakes and bogs. Rich flora and fauna including wolf, lynx, wolverine and bear.

4. *Femundsmarka National Park :* two wardens, budget of about 700 U.S. $ (1972) created in 1971; one lodge and some old dug outs in the park, some footpaths, road just outside the park. The area between lake Femunden and the Swedish border is one of the most marked wilderness area of Southern

Norway. Forests, lakes, creeks and rough rugged ground. Large areas are covered by a dead-ice moraine partly consisting of immense blocks. Poor conditions for plant life. Fauna includes bears. On the adjacent side of the border the Swedish authorities are planning a national park.

5. *Gressämoen National Park :* one warden, budget about 550 U.S. $ (1972); created in 1970; no lodges in the park, only one just outside; road to the park, not into; some footpaths. Most of the park consists of mountanous areas. In Gressämoen (North Trondelag) a large part is covered by coniferous — mainly spruce — forests. No special floristic or faunistic peculiarities. The moose is very common in these forests.

6. *Rago National Park :* one warden, budget about 550 U.S. $ (1972); created in 1971; one lodge and two hotels, no road and no marked footpaths. This park is situated one the border to Sweden and is bounded by the Swedish Padjelanta N. P. Peaks, deep valleys and water-courses with a lot of swift parts and waterfalls. The forest contains pine, birch and some spruce. Fauna is very rich and includes lynx and wolverine.

7. *Stabbursdalen National Park :* one warden, budget of about 500 U.S. $ (1972); created in 1970; one lodge in the park, no roads, no marked footpaths. The park is situated on the western side of the Porsanger Fjord. Is of great scientific interest because includes the northermost pine forest in the world. The pines are in some places of considerable dimensions and some are approximately 500 years old. Some cutting has been undertaken but large areas are covered with primeval forests.

8. *Øvre Pasvik National Park :* one warden, budget of about 640 U.S. $ (1972); created in 1970; three open huts in the park; no roads and no marked footpaths. Is the north-easternmost park, situated in the county of Finnmark. One half is forest, the other bogs and lakes. The forest is mainly predominated by spruce and pine and connected with boreal coniferous forest of Finland. Part is of primeval character. Upper Pasvik has very characteristic fauna and flora. It has been described as the last intact borderland between two biologcial worlds : Europe and Asia.

9. *Anderdalen National Park :* one warden, budget of about 300 U.S. $ (1972); created in 1970; no lodges but an old dug-out; no road, some footpaths. Located on the large island of Senja. Comprises primeval coastal forests, birch forest and bogs. The latter one displays a rich variety of birds, and the steep mountains offer nesting places for the golden eagle (*Aquila chrysaetos*).

10. *Gutulia National Park :* one warden, budget of about U.S. $ 185 (1972); created in 1970; no lodges in the park; two just outside, 4 at a distance no road, some footpaths. Includes interesting primeval coniferous forest characterized by trees of big dimensions.

11. *Ormtjernkampen National Park :* one warden, budget of about 160 U.S. $ (1972); no lodges in the park, three just outside; no road, some footpaths. Similar to Gutulia this is a small area of forests, of importance because it represents the spruce forest of the lowland of Eastern Norway in an original state. Only a few small areas of primeval spruce forests are still left.

IV.   **Further Information :**

These parks are all strictly protected except for hunting of certain species (ptarmigan, hare, red fox...) which is allowed for a short season and under strict official control (except in Øvre Pasvik, Anderdalen, Gutulia, and Ormtjernkampen where hunting is generally forbidden.)

96. OMAN

I.   **Listed Areas :** none.

II.   **Areas added or excluded :** none.

97. PAKISTAN

I.   **Listed Areas :** one.

1. *Kalabagh Reserve* . ...   about 4,000 ha

II.   **Areas excluded from the List since 1970 :** none (the two areas listed in 1967-1970 were located in East Pakistan, now Bengla Desh).

III.   **Areas added to the List since 1970 :** one.

Kalabagh Reserve : created in 1966 in West Pakistan; private reserve resulting from an agreement between the World Wildlife Fund and the Nawab of Kalabagh; is one of the very few effective wildlife conservation areas in West Pakistan; hunting is forbidden; closely protected by armed guards; created for the protection of urial (*Ovis orientalis punjabiensis*); excellent accommodation available; however, being a private reserve, is at the limit of inclusion in the U.N. List.

IV.   **Further Information :**

An area of some 25,000 ha (22,015 according to some sources, 33,200 according to others) could possibly be included one day on the U.N. List if the destocking process inititated with the help of the WWF could regenerate the vegetation cover now badly degraded. It is Lal Sunhara Wild Life Sanctuary where a few sectors are already effectively supervised by rangers and where proposals are made for the reintroduction of some species (notably blackbucks).

BENGLA DESH

I.   **Listed Areas :** none.

II.   **Areas excluded from the List since 1970 :** two.

Chittagong Hill Tracts (25,900 ha) and *Madhurpur National Park* (10,360 ha) : it seems that the term " national park " is a name of convenience, having no basis on any existing Act or Ordinance; both national parks are overgrazed and overcultivated and are inhabited; according to local authorities they do not deserve inclusion in the U.N. List.

III.   **Areas added to the List since 1970 :** none.

IV.   **Further Information :**

Mention should be made of Sunderbans project in Bengal Bay which has a good chance of becoming a conservation area worthy of inclusion in the U.N. List; project is two national parks of 31,000 and 18,000 ha and two strict nature reserves 13,000 ha each; purpose is the conservation of tiger and its main prey species; owing to recent troubles plans were postponed.

98. PANAMA

I.   **Listed Areas :** one.

1. *Altos de Campana National Park*   ...   .   2,600 ha

II.   **Areas excluded from the List since 1970 :** none.

III.   **Areas added to the List since 1970 :** one.

1. *Altos de Campana National Park and Biological Reserve :* officially declared in 1966; totally protected : hunting, cultivation, lumbering are forbidden; supervised by the administrative authorities of the district and regular patrols from the Forest Service; boundaries are marked; rugged terrain, cool wet climate, volcanic activity; the meeting place of several different ecological zones with a very varied vegetation; altitude : 250-1,034 m; located about 75 km from Panama city; no road within the park and no facilities.

99. PARAGUAY

I.   **Listed Areas :** none.

II.   **Areas excluded or added :** none.

76

I.   **Listed Areas :** four.

1. *Manu National Park* ... ... 1,400,000 ha
2. *Pacaya National Reserve* ... ...
                                          about 400,000 ha
3. *Pampa de Galeras National Reserve* ... ...   65,000 ha
4. *San Andres de Cutervo National Park* ... ...   2,500 ha

II.   **Areas excluded from the List since 1970 :** none.

III.   **Areas added to the List since 1970 :** four.

1. *Manu National Park :* totally protected; Indian tribes are still living in the park; staff includes a forest engineer and 8 fully equipped guards; budget in 1971-1972 was about 34,000 U.S. $; created in March 1968. Lies at the proximity of tourist centres such as Cuzco and Machu Pichu. Tourism is not yet organized, only small specialized groups are admitted; access by the rivers; small airstrip. Located in an area of unspoilt Amazon forest; represents the last important stronghold for Amazonian fauna and flora in Peru.

2. *Pacaya National Reserve :* totally protected : no occupation, no exploitation, no hunting and no fishing; supervised by one administrator and twelve guards; created in 1968. Access is difficult (by river). Created for the protection of a fish, the " paiche " (*Arapaima gigas*) living in the Pacaya River; the reserve includes the area surrounding the river and lakes and marshes. Rare animals species.

3. *Pampa de Galeras National Reserve :* totally protected except for cattle grazing still occuring in the reserve. Not a threat to the vicugna, for the protection of which the reserve was created. Staff : 11 fully equipped units. Budget : about 33,320 U.S. $. Created in 1966. Situated in the Ayacucho region, rising to 4,000 m. Access : two hours by road from the coastal town of Nazca (90 km).

4. *San Andres de Cutervo National Park :* totally protected : no occupation, no exploitation; lumbering is now forbidden almost everywhere. Staff head-quarters at the town of San Andres de Cutervo, 3 km from the park.
Created in 1961. A section of the Peruvian Andes, containing the San Andres caverns and forests. Fauna includes rare species. Altitude is from 2,200 to 3,000 m.

101. **PHILIPPINES**

I.   **Listed Areas :** twenty-three.

List 1970, p. 384.

II.   **Areas excluded or added since 1970 :** none.

102. POLAND

I.   **Listed Areas :** thirty-five.

A. — NATIONAL PARKS.
Eleven : List 1970, p. 396.

B. — RESERVES.
Twenty-four : ibid.

II.   **Areas excluded or added :** none.

III.   **Further Information :**

It must be reminded that the twenty last mentioned reserves have been included in spite of their small size at the special request of Polish authorities because they have the highest scientific interest.

A twelfth national Park exists but has not yet been officially created :
Bieszczady National Park, 6,000 ha.

103. PORTUGAL

A. — METROPOLITAN.

I.   **Listed Areas :** one.

1. *Geres National Park* ...   .   50,115 ha

II.   **Areas excluded since 1970 :** none.

III.   **Areas added to the List since 1970 :** one.

1. *Geres National Park* (or Peneda Geres) : includes nature reserves (where all exploitation except grazing are forbidden, opened to tourists, 12,800 ha), strict nature reserves (for scientific purposes only 2,315 ha) tourist reserves (including facilities, 26,500 ha) and " landscape " reserves (providing sport facilities, 8,500 ha). Proclaimed in May 1971, still in process of organization. One director 12 forest officers, 42 guards. U.S. $ 880,000 for 1972. Located in North-Eastern Portugal, close to the Spanish frontier. Serras with altitudes varying from 350 to 1,355 m. Fauna includes *Capreolus capreolus canus* Miller. wild boar, King eagle, partridge, etc.

78

B. — ANGOLA.

I.   **Listed Areas :** four.

1. Iôna National Park (size indicated in 1970 : 270,750 ha) ... ...   1,604,875 ha
2. Quiçama National Park . ...   996,000 ha
3. Luando Strict Nature Reserve   ...   .   828,000 ha
4. Cangandala Strict Nature Reserve   ...   .   60,000 ha

II.   **Areas excluded or added since 1970 :** none.

Since 1971 a Wildlife Ecologist post was created at the Veterinary Services in Luando which are responsible for national parks and reserves in Angola.

Rather alarming news was gathered which indicate that the situation degraded seriously in the above mentioned four areas.   Sectors where big wild life is still abundant are adjoining others where fields, inhabitants and cattle alternate with oil exploration tracks, oil wells, military camps.   This situation is especially serious in Quiçama where illegal farms have already resulted in drastic habitat degradation.   Proposals were recently made to reduce the park area by about 75,000 ha to be given up to farming.   As for poaching, it is a problem in the whole country.   International assistance would be welcome to improve this situation.

P.S. — News received at mid July 1972, when this booklet was already in the press, indicate that the above mentioned problems are being studied and could possibly be soon resolved.   It is however suggested to exclude from the List Luando where problems are very serious (18,000 people, 14 trading stores) and which " can certainly not be regarded as a Strict Nature Reserve ", and to include instead *Bicuari National Park,* 790,000 ha, uninhabited, controlled by 6 units, budget 24,000 U.S. $.

C. — MOZAMBIQUE.

I.   **Listed Areas :** two.

1. Gorongosa National Park   ...   .   567,000 ha
2. *Bazaruto Marine Park* . ...   about   8,000 ha

II.   **Areas excluded from the List since 1970 :** none.

III.   **Areas added to the List since 1970 :** one.

2. *Bazaruto Marine Park :* includes three islands : one, Bangué, completely uninhabited, and two, Sto Antonio and Sta Isabel, inhabited by some ten people each, and five km zone around; located North of S. Sebastiao Peninsula; created in May 1971; depends from the Maritime Department; vegetation is scarce; *Ipomea pescarse brasiliensis* and *Scaevla plumieri*; waterfowl; giant turtle, dugong.

IV.   **Further Information :**

A project exists to extend Gorongosa up to 870,000 ha but nothing has yet been finalized.

104. QATAR

I. **Listed Areas :** none.

II. **Areas added or excluded :** none.

105. RHODESIA

I. **Listed Areas :** twenty.

A. — NATIONAL PARKS.

1.	Wankie National Park (1970 : 1,439,080 ha)	1,443,200 ha
2.	Victoria Falls National Park (1970 : 58,440 ha)	56,640 ha
3.	Rhodes Matopos National Park	43,320 ha
4.	Rhodes Inyanga National Park	34,609 ha
5.	Kyle Dam National Park (*was a Game Reserve on 4,040 ha; is N. P. since 1967*)	18,000 ha
6.	Chimanimani National Park	13,680 ha
7.	Mushandike National Park	12,888 ha
8.	Ngesi National Park	5,818 ha
9.	Robert McIlwaine National Park	5,736 ha
10.	Sebakwe National Park (1970 : 2,654 ha)	2,227 ha
11.	Zimbabwe National Park	729 ha

B. — GAME RESERVES.

12.	Chewore Game Reserve	282,800 ha
13.	Matusadona Game Reserve	210,080 ha
14.	*Chirisa Game Reserve*	171,140 ha
15.	*Gona-re-zhou Game Reserve*	149,600 ha
16.	Chizarira Game Reserve	145,440 ha
17.	Mana Pools Game Reserve	121,000 ha
18.	Chete Game Reserve	64,640 ha
19.	*Dande Game Reserve*	54,390 ha
20.	*Malipati Game Reserve*	18,130 ha

II. **Areas excluded from the List since 1970 :** none.

III. **Areas added to the List since 1970 :** four.

14. *Chirisa Game Reserve :* fully protected; staff : 50 units; established in 1969; borders Chizarira (No. 16) in the east; *Brachystegia* woodland, *Colophospermum mopane* and *combretum* riverine, acacia, and jesse; fauna includes warthog, elephant, buffalo and various antelopes except wildebeest; altitude : 720-930 m; no tourist development.

15. *Gona-re-zou Game Reserve :* fully protected; staff : 30 units; budget : U.S. $ 65,000 (1972); established in 1968; contiguous to Mozambique border;

wide variety of vegetation types including a piece of relict riverine forest with several giant *Chlorophora excelsa,* a very rare tree in Rhodesia; fauna includes elephant, impala, buffalo, black rhino, kudu, nyala, oribi and many other bucks and hippo; accomodation at Mabalauta and Chipinda Pools; the area is closed during the rainy season.

19. *Dande Game Reserve :* this area and the following one, Malipati, have been included in spite of the lack of supervision staff on the advice of Rhodesian competent authorities; both are said to be fully protected and have a budget which covers a larger area; established in 1969; bounded on the east by Portuguese Territory and on the west by Chewore Game Reserve; flora includes mopane, Mahobahoba and Mukwa; fauna : elephant, duiker, sable, buffalo, rhino and elephant; altitude : 600 m; tourism is still minimal.

20. *Malipati Game Reserve :* fully protected (cf. No. 19); established in 1969; the entire area is demarcated by the Nuanetsi River from the Gona-re-zou, except for the western side which borders Tribul Trust Land; mopane trees, scrub, riverine forest; fauna : elephant, buffalo, nyala, impala, kudu, bushbuck, etc.; altitude : 270-360 m; no tourist facilities at present; Safari lodge under construction (June 1972).

106. ROMANIA

I.   **Listed Areas :** sixteen.

List 1970, p. 423.

II.   **Areas added or excluded since 1970 :** none.

107. RWANDA

I.   **Listed Areas :** two.

1. Akagera National Park	251,000 ha
2. Volcanoes National Park	23,000 ha

II.   **Areas excluded from the List since 1970 :** none.

Situation in Volcanoes National Park gives way to more and more anxiety. A pyrethrum cultivation project, unfortunately with EEC financial assistance, resulted in the clearing up of hundreds of hectares of montane forest within the park, habitat of the gorilla, and poaching, illicit cultivator occupation and cattle grazing increased considerably on thousands of ha. Local authorities are unable to improve this situation which endangers the very existence of this park which was in 1925 set aside as the " gorilla sanctuary ", from which was born Albert National Park.

III.   **Areas added to the List since 1970 :** none.

108. SALVADOR

I.   **Listed Areas :** none.

II.   **Areas added or excluded :** none.

109. SAUDI ARABIA

I.   **Listed Areas :** none.

II.   **Areas added or excluded :** none.

110. SENEGAL

I.   **Listed Areas :** three.

1. Niokolo Koba National Park	813,000 ha
2. *Djoudj National Park*	11,000 ha
3. *Basse Casamance National Park*	3,500 ha

II.   **Areas excluded from the List since 1970 :** one.

Djovol strict nature reserve : 3 ha; no management or supervision; invaded by cultivators and cattle; according to local authorities should be excluded from the List.

III.   **Areas added to the List since 1970 :** two.

2. *Djoudj National Park :* declared in April 1971; strict protection; one warden and 8 rangers, fully equipped; located about 80 km from St Louis; marshy region containing a very rich bird fauna. As well a few mammals including cheetah; guides compulsory; camping ground.

3. *Basse Casamance National Park :* proclaimed in 1970; strictly protected; 8 rangers, fully equipped; located on Oussouye-Cape Skiring road, near the Portuguese Guinea frontier; guinean type forest including high trees; leopard, serval cat, mangoose, buffalo, hippopotamus, and various antelopes; interesting forest birds; guides available; tracks; lodge for twenty persons.

111. SIERRA LEONE

I.   **Listed Areas :** none.

II.   **Areas added or excluded :** none.

112. SINGAPORE

I.   **Listed Areas :** three.

1. Water Catchment Area (size indicated in 1970 : 1,620 ha) . ...   2,717 ha
2. Bukit Timah Reserve (1970 : 74 ha) ... ...   66 ha
3. Kranji Reserve (1970 : 21 ha) ... ...   14 ha

II.   **Areas excluded from the List since 1970 :** one.

Pandan Reserve, 549 ha; reason : according to local authorities has been deleted as a reserve.

III.   **Areas added to the List since 1970 :** none.

113. SOLOMON ISLANDS

I.   **Listed Areas :** one.

1. Queen Elizabeth Park . ...   6,080 ha

II.   **Areas added or excluded since 1970 :** none.

114. SOMALI REPUBLIC

I.   **Listed Areas :** one.

1. Bubasci Strict Reserve . ...   625,000 ha

II.   **Areas excluded or added since 1970 :** none.

115. SOUTH AFRICA AND SOUTH WEST AFRICA

I.   **Listed Areas :** thirty-three.

A. — NATIONAL PARKS.

1. Kruger National Park (size indicated in 1970 : 1,817,146 ha) .. 1,948,528 ha
2. Kahalari Gemsbok National Park (1970 : 895,316 ha) ... ...   959,103 ha
3. Addo Elephant National Park (1970 : 6,397 ha) ... ...   6,852 ha
4. Mountain Zebra National Park (1970 : 5,020 ha) ... ...   6,536 ha
5. *Aughrabies Falls National Park* . ...   5,403 ha
6. Golden Gate Highlands National Park (1970 : 4,010 ha) .. ...   4,792 ha

83

7. *Tsitsikama Forest and Coastal National Park* . ...   3,318 ha
8. Bontebok National Park (1970 : 1,330 ha) . ...   2,786 ha

B. — PROTECTED AREAS IN THE CAPE PROVINCE.

Four : List 1970, p. 443.

C. — RESERVES.

a) NATAL.

Fourteen : ibid.

b) TRANSVAAL.

Five : ibid.

c) ORANGE FREE STATE.

One : ibid.

II.   **Areas excluded from the List since 1970 :** none.

III.   **Areas added to the List since 1970 :** two.

5. *Aughrabies Falls National Park :* created in 1966; controlled by 23 units; budget for 1971-1972 : U.S. $ 58,498; lies astride the Orange River; spectacular falls, gorges with steep cliffs, scattered trees and bushes away from the river; rich bird fauna; *Papio ursinus* is the most abundant species; altitude : about 700 m; one camp, with facilities.

7. *Tsitsikama Forest and Coastal National Park :* created in 1964; staff : 71 units, budget 254,263 U.S. $ consists of two portions : an indigenous forest situated on the northern side of the Garden Route, 63 miles east of Knysna (478 ha), and a narrow strip of coast roughly 47 miles long (2,840 ha); the forest is famous for its yellow-woods (*Podocarpus falcatus*) and at least 30 other species; typical coastal rain forest; the coast is a popular angling resort; spearfishing is forbidden; camping grounds with all facilities.

SOUTH WEST AFRICA.

I.   **Listed Areas :** one.

33. Etosha National Park . ... 6,500,000 ha

II.   **Comment :**

There is a project to cut off about half of the park to make a homeland for Bantu. A letter of 7th August 1972 of the Director of Nature Conservation and Tourism, Windhoek, said : Size : 2,270,000 ha. Staff : 219 units. Budget : U.S. $ 1,014,000.

III.   **Further Information :**

The same letter also enumerated four equivalent reserves and three game reserves which definitely merit mention in the List : Namib Desert Park (1,409,500 ha, 15 units, U.S. $ 53,000); Naukluft Mountain Zebra Park (21,985 ha, 13 units, U.S. $ 16,000); Daan Viljoen Game Reserve (3,953 ha, 31 units, U.S. $ 25,500); Skeleton Coast Park (800,000 ha, 8 units, U.S. $ 8,000); Fish River Canyon Park (46,117 ha); Waterberg Plateau Park (40,000 ha) and Hardap Game Reserve (15,845 ha).

116. SOUTH YEMEN

I.   **Listed Areas :** none.

II.   **Areas added or excluded :** none.

117. SPAIN

I.   **Listed Areas :** three.

1. Coto Doñana National Park (1967 : 6,500 ha)	35,000 ha
2. Covadonga National Park	16,925 ha
3. Valle de Ordesa National Park	2,046 ha

II.   **Areas excluded or added since 1970 :** none.

III.   **Further Information :**

In the French edition of the U.N. List issued in 1967 Coto Doñana was mentioned as Marismas Nature Reserve. In the English edition issued in 1970 the name Coto Doñana appeared but it was not yet a national park (declared in August 1969). The considerable extension obtained since 1967 is mostly due to the efforts of the World Wildlife Fund.

118. SUDAN

I.   **Listed Areas :** nine.

List 1970, p. 467.

II.   **Areas excluded or added since 1970 :** none.

III.   **Further Information :**

Consequent to the political situation these last few years contact was lost with several protected areas located in Southern Sudan. According to some rumours groups of rebels would have occupied some sectors and hunt openly. Other sources indicate that lack of ammunition contributed to the increase of wildlife in other sanctuaries.

Since April 1972 an agreement was reached between authorities in Karthoum and rebel leaders, and normalisation of the political situation can be foreseen. Awaiting further information it was decided to leave the enumeration given in the previous edition of the U.N. List, with the above reservations.

119. SURINAM

I.   **Listed Areas :** eight.

1. Eilerts de Haan Gebergte Nature Reserve (Kaysergebergte)
   (size indicated in 1970 : 160,000 ha) ... ...   220,000 ha
2. Tafelberg Nature Reserve (1970 : 40,000 ha) ... ...   140,000 ha
3. Voltzberg-Raleighvallen Nature Reserve (Coppename River) ...   56,000 ha
4. Wia Wia Nature Reserve ... ...   36,000 ha
5. Coppename-mouth Nature Reserve (1970 : 10,000 ha) ... ...   12,000 ha
6. *Brownberg Nature Park .* ... ...   11,200 ha
7. Brinckheuvel Nature Reserve (Saban-pasi Savannah) . ...   6,000 ha
8. *Galibi Nature Reserve* .. ..   4,000 ha

II.   **Areas excluded from the List since 1970 :** none.

III.   **Areas added to the List since 1970 :** two.

6. *Brownberg Nature Park :* established in January 1970 as a Long Term Lease from the Governent to the Foundation for Nature Preservation in Surinam (Stinatsu); totally protected; uninhabited area; three guards; lowly forested plateau at 500 m, surrounded by heavy forested slopes; peculiar flora with species from the far interior; smaller forest animals. 5 guesthouses on the plateau.

8. *Galibi Nature Reserve :* totally protected; located at the north-eastern tip of Guyana, just east of Wia-Wia, on the coast; established in 1969; one guard, plus 5 additional staff during the breeding season of sea-turtles (*Lepidochelys olivacea, Chelonia mydas, Dermochelys coriacea*); guesthouse on the beach; access by boat from Albina.

IV.   **Further Information :**

A project, Sipaliwini Nature Reserve, 100,000 ha, next to Tumucumaque Indigenous National Park in Brazil, still awaits legislation.

120. SWAZILAND

I.   **Listed Areas :** one.

1. Mlilwane Game Sanctuary (was 480 ha in 1970)   ... ...   2,800 ha

II.   **Areas added or excluded since 1970 :** none.

III.   **Further Information :**

From Mbabane, letter of Aug. 10, 1972 :

Mlilwane Wildlife Sanctuary, 4,200 ha. Staff approximately 30. Budget : U.S. $ 35,000.

Hlane Game Sanctuary, same status as Mlilwane, 14,000 ha. 12 guards. Budget : U.S. $ 10,000.

86

I.   **Listed Areas :** twenty-three.

1. Sjaunja Zoological and Forest Reserve	290,000 ha
2. Padjelanta National Park	204,000 ha
3. Sarek National Park	195,000 ha
4. Stora Sjöfallet National Park	150,000 ha
5. Svaipa Zoological and Forest Reserve	49,400 ha
6. Muddus National Park	49,200 ha
7. Peljekaise National Park	14,600 ha
8. Reivo State Reserve	8,700 ha
9. *Store Mosse-Kävsjön Nature Reserve*	7,750 ha
10. Abisko National Park	7,500 ha
11. Gotska Sandön National Park	3,640 ha
12. Sonfjället National Park	2,700 ha
13. Vadvetjåkko National Park	2,450 ha
14. Komosse Private Reserve	2,300 ha
15. Buberget State Reserve	2,270 ha
16. *Klingvälsån Nature Reserve*	2,175 ha
17. *Licknevarpefjärden Nature Reserve*	1,650 ha
18. Tjuoltavuobme State Reserve	1,500 ha
19. Töfsindalen National Park	1,365 ha
20. *Ottenby Nature Reserve*	995 ha
21. *Stora Karlsö Nature Reserve*	240 ha
22. Haparanda Sandskär Nature Reserve	200 ha
23. Lilla Karlsö Nature Reserve	150 ha

II.   **Areas excluded from the List since 1970 :** two.

Mittådalen (100,000 ha) and Luletjarve (600 ha) nature reserves have been excluded at the request of Swedish authorities as they do not have an appropriate protection.

III.   **Areas added to the List since 1970 :** five.

9. *Store Mosse-Kävsjön Nature Reserve :* general protection in a large uninhabited area. Included 6,700 ha of land and 850 of water. One district officer and one part-time forester; budget : U.S. $ 12,000 (1971). Created in 1971. Is the most expansive peatland in southern Sweden including rare fauna and flora. Birds round lake Kävsjön include whooper swan (*Cygnus cygnus*). Altitude is 170 m.

16. *Klingvälsån Nature Reserve :* general protection; some parts of the area are forbidden to enter; a superintendent looks after the reserve; budget for 1970 was U.S. $ 3,000. Created in 1968. No real tourism, only ornithologists. Altitude is 50 m. Situated in the southern part of Sweden. Wetlands round a small winding river (meander process). Rich bird life.

17. *Licknevarpefjärden Nature Reserve :* general protection; some parts are forbidden to visit during the breeding season. One part time forester; budget for 1971 was U.S. $ 800. Created in 1970. Tourism is not yet developed; roads are bad. Situated in southern Sweden on the eastern coast; is partly mainland and partly archipelago with unexploited nature rich in birds and other animals (roe deers). Altitude : 0-50 m.

87

20. *Ottenby Nature Reserve :* total protection except an area around the lighthouse; some parts are forbidden to visit during spring and summerseasons; one district forester, one forester and one special warden; budget is U.S. $ 5,500 (1971). Created in 1970. 40,000 visitors yearly. Altitude is sea level.
Situated on the south tongue of land of the island of Öland in the Baltic Sea. Internationally known as a resting place for migrating birds.

21. *Stora Karlsö Nature Reserve :* total protection under AB Karlsö och Djursdkyddsförening which owns unhabited island. 240 ha, well below the criterion even for an area situated in a well-populated region (off Gotland) but admitted on the List as one of the most important bird sanctuaries in the Baltic. Two wardens, plus four guides in summer. Budget is 15,000 U.S. $ (1971).

IV.   **Further Information :**

Hydro-electric power exploitation has been planned in the Kaitum and the Saunja Bird Sanctuary regions in the North of Sweden. This project gave rise to much protest.

122. SWITZERLAND

I.   **Listed Areas :** three.

List 1970, p. 489.

II.   **Areas excluded or added since 1970 :** none.

III.   **Further Information :**

As for other industrialized countries selection was relatively arbitrary for Switzerland. Of course the famous National Park in Engadine can be included in the first place and without discussion, but other small interesting reserves could possibly be added to this List or take the place of Aletch and Derborence included in 1967, for instance the La Pierreuse Reserve, 880 ha, which recently received the attention of the World Wildlife Fund.

An important game control operation in the Swiss National Park has been recently decided. It refers to the elimination of a thousand deers (september 1972)

123. SYRIA

I.   **Listed Areas :** none.

II.   **Areas added or excluded since 1970 :** none.

124. TANZANIA

I. **Listed Areas :** eight.

A. — NATIONAL PARKS.

Seven : List 1970, p. 492.

B. — CONSERVATION AREA.

One : ibid.

II. **Areas excluded or added since 1970 :** none.

III. **Further Information :**

Conservationists were deeply moved at the beginning of 1972 to learn that the Tanzanian government decided to give a special concession to the Wakuria people to use the Lamai Wedge of the Serengeti National Park for grazing their domestic animals. President Nyerere wrote a reassuring letter to the President of the World Wildlife Fund in this concern but did not deny that this concession had been granted.

125. THAILAND

I. **Listed Areas :** four.

1. Khao Yai National Park	208,500 ha
2. Tung Slang Luang National Park	128,000 ha
3. Phu Kradueng National Park	34,813 ha
4. Khao Sam-roi-yod National Park	6,128 ha

II. **Areas excluded from the List since 1970 :** five.

1. Khao Salob Wildlife and Forest Reserve, 400,000 ha.
2. Khao Luang Forest Reserve, 205,600 ha.
3. Kha Phu Phan Forest Reserve, 131,500 ha.
4. Doi Pui Forest Reserve, 16,000 ha.
5. Larn Sang Forest Reserve, 14,200 ha.

Reason : these reserves have never been designated as national park as proposed in 1959; Doi Pui has been 90 % cleared by opium cultivators; Khao Luang has been opened to mining operations and no longer meets ICNP criteria; according to local authorities there are now only four national parks under administration and open to the public.

III. **Areas added to the List :** none.

I.   **Listed Areas :** three.

       List 1970, p. 505.

II.   **Areas excluded or added since 1970 :** none.

127. TRINIDAD AND TOBAGO

I.   **Listed Areas :** none.

II.   **Areas added or excluded since 1970 :** none.

128. TUNISIA

I.   **Listed Areas :** one.

       1. Bou-Hedma State Park (size indicated in 1970 : 10,300 ha) ...   16,488 ha

II.   **Areas excluded or added :** none.

In June 1971 the competent Tunisian State Secretariat confirmed to the ICNP that Bou-Hedma State Park, enlarged since 1969, deserved to stay on the U.N. List and that proposals were made in the Four Years Plan to create another park : Djebel Ich Keul (1,305 ha, near Bizerte).

On the contrary a british ecologist after his visit to Bou-Hedma wrote : " you were misled over Bou-Hedma. It is the absence of effective supervision and of a plan management which nullifies the steps which have been taken on paper, even though some guards have been appointed. The Tunisians, however, are anxious to rectify this... ".

129. TURKEY

I.   **Listed Areas :** twelve.

       1. *Olympus Beydaglari Seashore National Park* ... ...   69,620 ha
       2. *Munzur Valley National Park* ... ...   42,800 ha
       3. Uludag National Park (size indicated in 1970 : 27,300 ha) ...   11,338 ha
       4. Dilek Yarimadasi (Kusadasi) N. P. (1970 : 16,000 ha) ... ...   10,700 ha

5. Karatepe National Park (Aslantas)	7,715 ha
6. *Termessus National Park*	6,702 ha
7. *Kovada Lake National Park*	6,534 ha
8. *Spil Dagi National Park*	5,505 ha
9. Yedigöller National Park (1970 : 2,019 ha)	2,030 ha
10. Soguksu National Park (Kizilçahaman)	1,025 ha
11. Çamlik National Park (Yozgat) (1970 : 294 ha)	264 ha
12. Lake Manyas National Park (Bird Lake)	52 ha

II. **Areas excluded from the List since 1970 :** none.

III. **Areas added to the List since 1970 :** five.

1. *Olympus Beydaglari National Park :* created in 1970; totally protected; one superintendent, 4 guards; budget : U.S. $ 12,000 (1972); bordered by the sea to the east and south, the first of a series of mountain ranges to the west and the western edge of the Antalya plain to the north; well forested mountains dipping steeply to precipitous sea cliffs or long narrow beaches (pines, firs, cedars); fauna includes bear, wolf, wild boar, jackal, mountain goat, lynx and birds; no touristic developments.

2. *Munzur Valley National Park :* created in 1972; only partly protected; 60 % is forested, 25 % is grassland and 10 % is farmland; no staff yet; budget : U.S. $ 1,000; mountain lakes, canyon valleys; mammals include bear, wolf, lynx, boar, mountain goat, ibex; no facilities for visitors. Vegetation : oaks, maple, poplar, oriental plane, ash.

6. *Termessus National Park :* created in 1970; totally protected; one superintendent and 4 guards; budget : U.S. $ 8,000; located north of Antalya (30 km), at the steep slopes of Güllük Mountain; includes remnants of the Greco-Roman Solim city; rich maquis species of Mediterranean; fauna includes bear, mountain goat, jackal, lynx, fallow dear and birds; easy access from Antalya where all facilities are located.

7. *Kovada Lake National Park :* created in 1970; main resources are protected but includes a village and two small settlements; the lake is under a 5-year commercial fishing lease; one superintendent, 4 guards; budget : 12,000 U.S. $; located in the heart of western Tauros Mountains; high elevation, forests, deep canyons, lakes; wild boar, wolf, roe deer, fallow deer, wild goat, leopard, syrian bear and waterfowl; no touristic developments.

8. *Spil Dagi National Park :* created in 1972; totally protected; no staff yet; small budget : U.S. $ 1,000; mountain complex; geological and geomorphological value; canyon valley, lakes, caves; special plant cover; mammals include bear, wolf, wild boar, mountain goat; no touristic activities and facilities.

IV. **Further Information :**

Master Plans exist for five other national parks including historical sites : Pamukkale, Pergamus, Troy, Ephesus, Göreme.
In 1970 was created a National Park Department, administering all national parks, under the Ministry of Forests.

I.   Listed Areas : seven.

1. Murchison Falls National Park ... ...   384,000 ha
2. Queen Elizabeth National Park ... ...   220,000 ha
3. Kidepo Valley National Park (size indicated in 1970 : 125,000
   ha) . ...   84,000 ha
4. *Karuma Game Reserve* . ...   82,000 ha
5. *Bugungu Game Reserve*   ... ...   52,000 ha
6. *Ajai Game Reserve*   ... ...   15,800 ha
7. *Gorilla Game Reserve* . ...   4,800 ha

II.   **Areas excluded from the List since 1970 :** four.

Lumunga Game Reserve has been degazetted. As for *Toro Game Reserve*
(55,488 ha), *Kigezi Game Reserve* (33,000 ha), and *Aswa-Lolim Game Reserve*
(27,800 ha) they have been excluded from the U.N. List because trophy hunting
is allowed on a quota basis within these areas.

III.   **Areas added to the List since 1970 :** four.

4. *Karuma Game Reserve :* established in 1964; totally protected; 10 guards;
U.S. $ 7,000; is in fact a buffer zone for Murchison Falls, as the following
Bugungu G.R. and has a similar fauna (elephant, buffalo, giraffe, rhinoceros,
various antelopes, etc.); elephant grass and *Hyparrhenia rufa* dominant with
isolated forest and savannah trees; flow of tourists passing into or out of
Murchison National Park. Altitude : 900-1,300 m.

5. *Bugungu Game Reserve :* established in 1968; 4 guards; U.S. $ 5,000;
together with Karuma borders the whole of the southern boundary of Murchison
Falls N. P. (see above); no threat to wildlife in any way; fauna : elephant,
various antelopes, lion, etc.; flora : bush land and dry thickets; tourism is not
yet developed. Altitude : 600-1,300 m.

6. *Ajai Game Reserve :* established in 1965 primarily for the protection of
white rhino; hunting in any form is strictly prohibited; staff : 4 units; budget :
U.S. $ 6,000; apart from the white rhino fauna includes Uganda Kob,
elephant, hartebeest, hippo in the Albert Nile, etc. grassland and woodland
communities; tourism not yet developed. Altitude : 700-1,000 m.

7. *Gorilla Game Reserve :* established in 1964 strictly for the protection of
Mountain Gorilla and Chimpanzee; no settlement is allowed in this area and
a constant lookout is maintained for any likelihood of disturbing the Gorilla
habitat; the survival of the species will depend on how much de-forestation is
carried out on the mountains by residents on the slopes; the reserve is administered by a Game Warden who also looks after Kigezi G.R.; covers the three
volcanic mountains of Muhavura, Mgahinga and Sabinio on the border with
the Republic of Rwanda; altitude 2,700-4,000 m; high montane forest and
bamboo on mountain and montane savannah on the lower slopes; high tourist
potential.

131. **UKRAINIAN S.S.R.**

See under No. 132 : Union of Soviet Socialist Republics.

132. UNION OF SOVIET SOCIALIST REPUBLICS

I.

Listed Areas : eighty.

A. — RUSSIAN SOCIALIST FEDERATED SOVIET REPUBLICS.

1.	*Kronotsky*	964,000 ha
2.	*Altai*	864,200 ha
3.	Pechora Ilych	721,322 ha
4.	Sikhote-Alin	310,000 ha
5.	Kavkaz	262,500 ha
6.	Barguzin (size indicated in 1970 : 248,200 ha) .	247,100 ha
7.	*Baikal*	167,200 ha
8.	*Lapland*	158,400 ha
9.	*Lazovsky*	116,520 ha
10.	Darvin	112,600 ha
11.	Teberda	83,400 ha
12.	Zeya	82,300 ha
13.	Astrakhan	72,500 ha
14.	Bashkiri	72,049 ha
15.	Khingan	58,300 ha
16.	Bolshe-Khekhtsiri (1970 : 46,000 ha) .	47,900 ha
17.	Stolby or " Pillars "	47,200 ha
18.	Kandalaksha (was mentioned with Lapland in 1970)	35,030 ha
19.	Komsomol	32,200 ha
20.	Ilmen	32,100 ha
21.	*Mordovsky*	31,100 ha
22.	Voronesh	30,800 ha
23.	Oka	22,900 ha
24.	*Tsentralno-Lesnoi*	21,400 ha
25.	*Zhiguli*	19,400 ha
26.	Kedrovaya Pad	17,900 ha
27.	Suputinsk	16,500 ha
28.	*Khopersky*	16,200 ha
29.	*Mari*	14,452 ha
30.	Kivach	10,460 ha
31.	*Visim*	9,300 ha
32.	Volga-Kama (1970 : 4,538 ha)	7,540 ha
33.	Prioksko-Terrasny	4,900 ha
34.	Tsentralno-Chernozyomi	4,200 ha

B. — AZERBAIJAN SSR.

35.	Kyzyl-Agach	88,000 ha
36.	Zakataly	25,300 ha
37.	*Shirvan*	17,700 ha
38.	Turianchai	12,700 ha
39.	Gek-Gel	7,500 ha
40.	*Pirkulin*	1,506 ha

C. — KAZAKH SSR.

41.	*Naurzum*	185,000 ha
42.	*Kurgaldzhino*	177,200 ha
43.	*Alma-Atinsky*	89,530 ha

93

44. Aksu-Dzhabagly	74,320 ha
45. Barsa-Kelmes (1970 : 19,800 ha)	18,500 ha

D. — LATVIAN SSR.

46. Slitere (1970 : 7,848 ha)	9,330 ha
47. Engure	1,340 ha
48. Moritsala	890 ha
49. Grini	790 ha

E. — LITHUANIAN SSR.

50. Zhuvintas	5,421 ha

F. — BYELORUSSIAN SSR.

51. Berezina	76,200 ha
52. Belovezha Pushcha	74,200 ha
53. *Pripyat*	60,325 ha

G. — GEORGIAN SSR.

54. Lagodekhi (1970 : 13,283 ha)	18,100 ha
55. Borzhom	18,082 ha
56. Ritsa-Avadkhar	16,120 ha
57. Kintrish	6,943 ha
58. Saguram	5,083 ha
59. Adzhamet	4,848 ha
60. Vashlovan (1970 : 5,952 ha)	4,700 ha
61. Babanauri-Batsari (ex Batsara) (1970 : 3,052 ha)	3,780 ha
62. Satapli (1970 : 300 ha)	340 ha

H. — TURKMEN SSR.

63. *Krasnovodsky, with Hassan-Kuli section*	262,000 ha
64. Badkhyz	133,000 ha
65. Repetek	34,600 ha

I. — UKRAINIAN SSR.

66. Chernomora (1970 : 49,695 ha)	35,000 ha
67. *Polessky*	20,097 ha
68. *Carpathian*	12,672 ha
69. Askania Nova (1970 : 10,500 ha)	11,000 ha
70. Ukrainski Stepni (1970 : 2,211 ha)	1,636 ha
71. *Kanev*	1,035 ha
72. *Lugansky*	998 ha

J. — UZBEK SSR.

73. *Chatkalsky*	34,800 ha
74. Zaaminski Gorno-Lesnoe	10,500 ha

K. — MOLDAVIAN SSR.

75. *Kodry state forest reserve*	2,740 ha

L. -— ARMENIAN SSR.

76. *Dilizhan* ... ...   29,000 ha
77. *Khosrov* ... ...   23,140 ha

M. — KIRKHIZ SSR.

78. *Issyk Kul* ... ...   781,600 ha
79. *Sary-Chelek* . ...   20,700 ha

N. — TADZHIK SSR.

80. *Ramit* .. ..   16,180 ha

II.   **Areas excluded from the List since 1970 :** none.

III.   **Areas added to the List since 1970 :** twenty-nine.

1. *Kronotsky* (RSFSR), 964,000 ha; eastern coast of the Kamchatka Peninsula; is the single geyser basin in the country.

2. *Altai* (RSFSR), 864,200 ha; located in Gorno-Altaiskaya autonomous province, near Teletzkoye lake; *Pinus sibirica* forest; sable, *Cervus elaphus sibirica*.

7. *Baikal* (RSFSR) : 1969; the nature reserve (zapovedniki) is 167,200 ha and located on the southern bank of lake Baikal; in 1969 was also created a national park (or natural park ?) on 1,250,000 ha on the western bank, with much less strict protective status which it was not deemed yet necessary to include in the List for lack of sufficient information, although this large territory must include some zones answering at least de facto ICNP criteria. Lake Baikal is the deepest in the world. The river mouthes are spawning grounds for fishes : including several endemic species. Forests include birch, spruce, pine, fir and larch. Fauna is typical of Siberia.

8. *Lapland* (RSFSR), 158,400 ha; located in Murmansk Province; northern taiga; dedicated to the restoration of reindeer.

9. *Lazovsky* (RSFSR), 116,520 ha; located in Primorsky territory; includes the southern part of the Sikhote-Alin Range. Manchurian flora and fauna : aralia, shizandra, ginseng, cork tree; tiger, goral, *Cervus elaphus xanthopygnus, Cervus nippon.*

21. *Mordovsky* (RSFSR), 31,100 ha; located in Mordovian SSR. European zone of broadleaved forest. Beaver, desman, acclimitization of *Cervus elaphus sibiricus, Bison bonasus, Cervus nippon* (see Part IV).

24. *Tsentralno-Lesnoi* (RSFSR) (Central Forest), 21,400 ha; located in Kalinin Province; includes the north-western part of the Middle Russian Upland; spruce and mixed spruce and broad-leaf forests; elk, bear, lynx, marten, capercaillie.

25. *Zhiguli* (RSFSR), 19,400 ha; located in Kuibyshev Province; natural complex and historical monunents of the Zhiguli Hills.

28. *Khopersky* (RSFSR), 16,200 ha; located in Voronezh Province; flood plain of the Khoper River. Fauna : desman; breeding of *Bison bonasus* and *Cervus nippon;* white poplar (*Populus hybride*).

95

7

29. *Mari* (RSFSR), 14,452 ha; created in 1968; located south of Starozhilsk, between the Bolshoi Kokshag and Bolshoi rivers; subzone of southern taiga and mixed conifer/broad leaved forests; fauna includes *Felis lynx, Vulpes vulpes,* etc.

31. *Visim* (RSFSR), 9,300 ha; created in 1971; located in Sverdlovsk Province. " Gate " connecting Europe and Asia; typical landscapes of lowered belt of middle Urals; relics of glacial and preglacial floras; fauna : *Alces alces, Capreolus capreolus, Martes martes, Tetrao urogallus, Tetrastes bonasia.*

37. *Shirvan* (Azerbaijan SSR), 17,700 ha; created in 1969; located in Salyany district; purpose : protection of desertic vegetation (*Artemisia salsoloides* and others) and restoration of stock of *Gazella subgutturosa.*

40. *Pirkulin* (Azerbaijan SSR), 1,506 ha; located in Shemakha district; floristic reserve; purpose : reconstitution of stock of Persian gazelle (*Gazella subgutturosa*) and regeneration of yew.

41. *Naurzum* (Kazakh SSR), 185,000 ha; located in Kustanay Province; Naurzum pine forest and lakes in the steppe; wildfowl breeding ground and resort on the flyway.

42. *Kurgaldzhino* (Kazakh SSR), 177,200 ha; created in 1958 was formerly a game reserve of 15,000 ha; located in Tselinograd Province; wildfowl breeding, moulting and resort grounds on Lake Kurgaldzhino; tract of desertic steppes with *Artemisia,* fescue and feather grass. *Scirpus lacustris* around the lakes; wildfowl.

43. *Alma-Atinsky* (Kazakh SSR), 89,530 ha; located in Alma Ata Province; natural complex of the Western Tien Shan.

53. *Pripyat* (Byelorussian SSR), 60,325 ha; created in 1969; located in Polesskaya Province; purpose : research of the influence of marshland drainage in the Central part of the Byelorussian Polessye (forest country) upon hydrology and productivity of forest formations; forests of lime, maple, oak, hornbeam; 105 species of birds.

63. *Krasnovodsky,* (192,300 ha) with Hassan-Kuli section (69,700 ha); located in Turkmenian SSR on the Caspian coast; wildfowl wintering grounds; *Francolinus francolinus.*

67. *Polessky* (Ukrainian SSR), 20,097 ha; created in 1968; located in Zhitomir Province; pine forests, " subor " (forest on transitional, relatively poor soils), sphagnum bogs, with cranberry; fauna : *Alces alces, Capreolus capreolus, Felis lynx, Sus scrofa,* etc.

68. *Carpathian* (Ukrainian SSR), 12,672 ha; Ivano-Francovsk and Zakarpatskaya provinces; created in 1968; purpose : rehabilitation of natural complexes of the high altitude landscape of the Carpathian Mountains and restoration of stock of rare and vanishing species of plant and animals; over 2,000 species of flowering plants; animals : *Cervus elaphus montani, Capreolus capreolus, Sus scrofa, Felis lynx, Felis silvestris,* etc.

71. *Kanev* (Ukrainian SSR), 1,035 ha; created in 1968; located in Cherkassy Province; relic hornbeam forests; fauna : *Alces alces, Capreolus capreolus, Sus scrofa,* etc.

72. *Lugansky* (Ukrainian SSR), 998 ha; created in 1968; includes sections of Streltsovskaya Steppe and Kondrashev Forest; flood-plain forests, meadows,

vegetation of virgin steppe rich in various species with fescue and feather grass; restoration of stock of *Desmana moschata* and *Marmota bobak* (cf. Part IV).

73. *Chatkalsky* (Uzbek SSR), 34,800 ha; Western part of the Tien Shan; Juniperus forests; mountain fauna : bear, *Capra ibex, Panthera uncia.*

75. *Kodry State Forest Reserve* (Moldavian SSR), 2,740 ha; created in 1971; central Moldavia; vegetation includes *Tilia tomentosa, Ulmus foliacea, Acer platanoides, Cornus mas, Pyrus communis.* 70 species of mammals; birds : *Asio otus, Gyps fulvus, Aegypius monachus,* etc.

76. *Dilizhan* (Armenian SSR), 29,000 ha; natural complex of the northern part of the Little Caucasus.

77. *Khosrov* (Armenian SSR), 23,140 ha; located in Vedi district; *Ovis ammon, Capra aegagrus.*

78. *Issyk Kul* (Kirkhiz SSR), 781,600 ha; natural complex of lake Issyk Kul; wildfowl wintering grounds.

79. *Sary-Chelek* (Kirkhiz SSR), 20,700 ha; south-western part of the Tien Shan mountains; natural forest of nut and fruit trees; mountain ungulates; breeding of European bisons.

80. *Ramit* (Tadzhik SSR), 16,180 ha; located in Ordzhonikidzeabad district; nut and fruit forests; *Cervus elaphus bactrianus.*

IV.   **Further Comments :**

As for other large countries selection was somewhat arbitrary. Moreover, in order to include some zapovedniki in the U.N. List it was necessary to apply the notion that an area can be considered as an " equivalent reserve " when responsible authorities have taken management steps under strict control (first condition) in order to orientate the local ecosystem towards another, as well non-domesticated (second condition), even if the latter is not locally spontaneous. For instance some zapovedniki whose primary purpose is acclimatization of exotic species, mainly animal species, have in spite of this characteristic been considered as deserving to be included in the U.N. List, because of the strict scientific supervision given to these ecological manupulations.

133. UNITED ARAB REPUBLIC

I.   **Listed Areas :** none.

II.   **Areas added or excluded since 1970 :** none.

I.   **Listed Areas :** seventy-four, comprising.

A. — National Nature Reserves :
   a) 22 of over 500 ha;
   b) 34 between 100 and 500 ha.
B. — Local Nature Reserve : 7.
C. — Forest Nature Reserves : 3.
D. — Private Reserves : 8.

II.   **Areas excluded or added since 1970 :** none.

Conforming to the general ideas expressed already for Germany, it is admitted that the enumeration made in the editions of 1967 and 1970 was somewhat arbitrary, examplative and not justifying a change for the present booklet.

The description of the above mentioned areas can be found pp. 539 to 550 of the 1970 edition.

Of course if this list had been made today some recently created national nature reserves would have been included such as : Dyfi (Cardiganshire, 1,422 ha) and Glen Roy (Invernesshire, 1,168 ha) or even Quoile Podaga (Down, 182 ha), which is the largest Governmental Nature Reserve in Northern Ireland.

Similarly a few private reserves could have been added :

a) three reserves which should have been on the List in 1970 :
   Torridon, Rosshire, N.T.S. (National Trust of Scotland), 5,706 ha,
   Ben Lawers, Perthshire, N.T.S., 3,238 ha,
   Grey Mare's Tail, Dumfriesshire, N.T.S., 923 ha;

b) the recent R.S.P.B. reserve :
   Ouse Washes, Cambridge-shire, 380 ha;

c) the recent Scottish Wildlife Trust Reserve :
   Loch Fleet, Sutherland, 514 ha.

III.   **Further Comments :**

Readers remember that at New Delhi, in December 1969 a definition of the term " national park " was voted by I.U.C.N., which added : " governments are requested not to designate as national parks an inhabited and exploited area where landscape planning and measures taken for the development of tourism have led to the setting up of recreation areas, where industrialization and urbanization are controlled and where public outdoor recreation takes priority over the conservation of ecosystems (parc naturel régional, nature park, Naturpark, etc.). Areas of this description which may have been established as " National Parks " should be redesignated in due course ".

This recommendation was considered as concerning most particularly the national parks in the United Kingdom which indeed, in spite of their name, do not satisfy on their whole superficy the criteria of protective status established at New Delhi and defined by the I.C.N.P.

It may be hoped that English national parks would one day, by virtue of the zoning principle, provide for the inclusion within their area of more severely protected sectors such as the " Special Protection Area " in Japan, which would thus allow the progressive inclusion of such territories in the United Nations List of National Parks and Equivalent Reserves.

DEPENDENT AND NEWLY INDEPENDENT TERRITORIES.

SEYCHELLES.

I. **Listed Areas :** one.

1. *Cousin Island Nature Reserve* ... ...   1,800 ha

II. **Areas excluded from the List :** none.

III. **Areas added to the List :** one.

1. *Cousin Island :* was bought in 1968 by the International Council for Bird Preservation and the World Wildlife Fund to be a permanent reserve; supervised by the manager of the island, his wife and three labourers, plus a resident scientific administrator; home of up to 20,000 fairy tern, and of the Seychelles fody (red list); only home of the colony's finest songster, the Seychelles brush warbler (red list).

135. UNITED STATES OF AMERICA

I. **Listed Areas :** two hundred ninety.

A. — LISTED NATIONAL PARKS : thirty-six.

1.	Yellowstone National Park (Wyoming, Montana, Idaho)	888,708 ha
2.	Mount McKinley National Park (Alaska)	775,797 ha
3.	Everglades National Park (Florida)	560,213 ha
4.	Glacier National Park (Montana)	405,251 ha
5.	Olympic National Park (Washington)	358,840 ha
6.	Yosemite National Park (California)	300,528 ha
7.	Big Bend National Park (Texas)	283,288 ha
8.	Grand Canyon National Park (Arizona)	269,430 ha
9.	Isle Royale National Park (Michigan)	216,236 ha
10.	Great Smoky Mountain National Park (North Carolina, Tennessee)	206,650 ha
11.	*North Cascades National Park* (Washington)	202,000 ha

12.	Kings Canyon National Park (California)	184,132 ha
13.	Sequoia National Park (California)	154,744 ha
14.	Grand Teton National Park (Wyoming)	124,140 ha
15.	Rocky Mountain National Park (Colorado)	104,930 ha
16.	Canyonlands National Park (Utah)	103,056 ha
17.	Mount Rainier National Park (Washington)	96,712 ha
18.	Hawaii Volcanoes National Park (Hawaii)	88,137 ha
19.	*Voyageurs National Park* (Minnesota)	87,772 ha
20.	Shenandoah National Park (Virginia)	77,415 ha
21.	Crater Lake National Park (Oregon)	64,116 ha
22.	Zion National Park (Utah)	58,813 ha
23.	Lassen Volcanic National Park (California)	42,773 ha
24.	Petrified Forest National Park (Arizona)	37,676 ha
25.	*Guadalupe Mountains National Park* (Texas)	32,911 ha
26.	*Redwood National Park* (California)	22,837 ha
27.	Mesa Verde National Park (Colorado)	20,830 ha
28.	Mammoth Cave National Park (Kentucky)	20,541 ha
29.	Carlsbad Caverns National Park (New Mexico)	18,701 ha
30.	Acadia National Park (Maine)	16,657 ha
31.	Bryce Canyon National Park (Utah)	14,405 ha
32.	Wind Cave National Park (South Dakota)	11,223 ha
33.	Haleakala National Park (Hawaii)	10,913 ha
34.	Virgin Islands/(US Virgin Islands)/National Park	6,060 ha
35.	Hot Springs National Park (Arkansas)	413 ha
36.	Platt National Park (Oklahoma)	365 ha

B. — OTHER PROTECTED AREAS : two hundred fifty four.

To avoid a too long list it has been decided to enumerate in this booklet only the U.S. National Parks and not to repeat the 254 other protected areas included in 1967 and 1970 somewhat arbitrarily (see Germany) as equivalent reserves deserving to be mentioned in the U.N. List whose repartition was :

B. 35 National Monuments, Natural Areas
    7 National Monuments, Archeological Areas
C. 3 Naturel Reserves with status equivalent to N.P. or National Monuments
D. 6 National Seashores
E. 4 National Recreation Areas
F. 2 National Parkways
G. 14 National Forests, Wilderness Areas
   30 National Forest, Wild Areas
   38 National Forests, Primitive Areas
    1 National Forest, Puerto Rico
H. 1 Boundary Waters Canoe Area
I. 20 National Wildlife Refuges
J. 89 State Parks.
K. 3 Private Reserves.
L. 1 Reserve Laboratory, Panama Canal Zone.

Of course if this arbitrary list had been established today it would have been somewhat different, owing to recent creations. Mention would for instance been made of 2 further national seashores and 4 national lakeshores established since 1967.

II.   **Areas excluded from the List since 1970 :** none.

III.   **Areas added to the List since 1970 :** four.

11. *North Cascades National Park* (Washington) : established in October 1968; wild alpine region of jagged peaks, mountain lakes, glaciers, and wildlife; presents America's finest example of classical alpine scenery; includes one third of all the glaciers to be found in USA; altitude : 600-2,700 m.

19. *Voyageurs National Park* (Minnesota) : established in January 1971; encompass segments of the " voyageurs highway ", the canoe route used by fur traders until mid-19 cy; superb system of interconnecting lakes, bogs and streams; green forests, interesting geology; wildlife is typical of the northern coniferous forest; limited facilities.

25. *Guadalupe Mountains National Park* (Texas) : established in October 1966; mountain mass rising from desert; contains portions of the world's most extensive and significant Permian limestone fossil reef; also features a tremendous earth fault, lofty peaks, unusual flora and fauna and a colorful record of the past; not yet open to the public.

26. *Redwood National Park* (California) : established in October 1968; Coastal redwood forest (*Sequoia sempervirens*); contains virgin groves of ancient trees, including the world's tallest tree (110 m); the park includes 40 miles of scenic Pacific coastline.

136. UPPER VOLTA

I.   **Listed Areas :** two.

1. The " W " National Park ... ...   330,000 ha
2. *Arly Faunal Reserve* ... ...   206,000 ha

II.   **Areas excluded from the List since 1970 :** none.

III.   **Areas added to the List since 1970 :** one.

2. *Arly Faunal Reserve :* formed by two reserves : Arly Total Faunal Reserve (76,000 ha) and Arly Partial Reserve (130,000 ha); the protection in the second one is less strict and limited to some species; located on the north and northwestern bank of the Pendjari River, adjoining Pendjari Reserve in Dahomey, and Singou and Pama reserves in Upper Volta; established in 1954; Soudanian-type wooded savannah; altitude : about 300 m; large numbers of animals can easily be seen from the park's road.

I.   **Listed Areas :** eight.

1. *Cabo Polonio National Park* (or Faunal Refuge ?) ... ... 14,250 ha
2. *Santa Teresa National Park*   ... ... 3,290 ha
3. F. D. Roosevelt National Park ... ... 1,500 ha
4. *San Miguel National Park* ... ... 1,238 ha
5. *Arequita National Park* . ... 1,000 ha
6. Paso del Puerto National Park ... ... 600 ha
7. *Andresito National Park*   ... ... 239 ha
8. Meseta de Artigas National Park (indicated as 314 ha in 1970) . 164 ha

II.   **Areas excluded from the List :** none.

A seeming exclusion is Aguas Dulces which now forms part of No. 1 Cabo Polonio National Park.

III.   **Areas added to the List since 1970 :** five.

1. *Cabo Polonio National Park* (or Faunal Refuge ?) : includes the former Aguas Dulces N. P., (200 ha), the former Laguna del Castillo game refuge (8,000 ha), a former coastal dunes natural monument (1,000 ha) and a former forest reserve (5,050 ha); total staff, including labourers is 23; budget : U.S. $ 30,400; totally protected; fishing only is permitted; located on the Atlantic, in Rocha Province; declared in 1966 (first measures in 1942); abundant marine fauna; the highest dunes are 60 m high.

2. *Santa Teresa National Park :* located in Rocha Province on the Atlantic coast; totally protected; staff including military staff and labourers is about 60 units; budget 76,400 U.S. $; includes a fortress built during the Spanish colonisation; depends from the Ministerio de la Defensa Nacional; coastal dunes and beaches; marine fauna; altitude : 0-50 m; fishing is permitted. Created in 1927.

4. *San Miguel National Park :* located in Rocha Province near the Brazilian border; as Santa Teresa contains an ancient fortress completely restaurated and depends from the Ministerio de la Defensa Nacional; totally protected; staff, including military staff and labourers, totalling 81 units; budget : 22,000 U.S. $; created in 1927; indigenous flora. Altitude : 20-60 m.

5. *Arequita National Park :* located in Lavalleja Province; one guard, 6 labourers; 12,000 U.S. $; mountain scenery (sierras); interesting bird fauna; reptiles, small mammals; *Lutra platensis* in the river, some camping facilities; fishing is permitted. Altitude : 40-150 m. Created in 1964.

7. *Andresito National Park :* located in Rocha Province along the coast; one forest officer and 5 " peones "; 7,300 U.S. $; created in 1967; dunes, beaches, pines, eucalyptus; abundant marine fauna; a few birds; camping facilities; fishing is permitted; proximity of Paloma.

IV.   **Further Information :**

In 1967 was created a Forest, Parks and Fauna Service at the Ministry of Agriculture. Under its juridiction come all national parks except Santa Teresa and San Miguel which, as stated hereabove, depend from the Ministry of National Defense.

Three other protected areas should be mentioned : Rio Negro National Park (1,800 ha, 80 km of rivers with 18 islands more or less protected), Anchorena National Park (500 ha) and San Pedro de Timote Refuge which is a private reserve of 20,000 ha supervised by the owner's staff.

I.   **Listed Areas :** eight.

1. Canaima National Park ... ...   1,000,000 ha
2. Sierra Nevada National Park (size indicated in 1970 : 160,000 ha) . ...   190,000 ha
3. Guatopo National Park . ...   92,640 ha
4. Henri Pittier National Park . ...   90,000 ha
5. El Avila National Park . ...   66,192 ha
6. Yacambu National Park ... ...   9,000 ha
7. *Cueva de la Quebrada del Toro National Park* .. ..   8,500 ha
8. Yurubi National Park . ...   4,000 ha

II.   **Areas excluded from the List since 1970 :** none.

III.   **Areas added to the List since 1970 :** one.

7. *Cueva de la Quebrada del Toro National Park :* totally protected; some cultivation and cattle grazing which will be eliminated soon; four guards; declared in 1969; situated in the hydrographical catchment area of " Bulls's Gorge " in Falcon province north west of Caracas; comprises an area of great scenic beauty and also serves to protect one of the Oilbird nesting caverns (*Steatornis caripensis*).

I.   **Listed Areas :** none.

II.   **Areas added or excluded since 1970 :** none.

I.   **Listed Areas :** none.

II.   **Areas added or excluded since 1970 :** none.

141. YUGOSLAVIA

I. **Listed Areas :** twenty-two.

A. — BOSNIA AND HERZEGOVINA.

1. Sutjeska National Park	17,250 ha
2. Hutovo Blato Reserve	3,400 ha
3. *Kozara National Park*	3,375 ha

B. — CROATIA.

Five : List 1970, p. 584.

C. — MACEDONIA.

Three : ibid.

D. — MONTENEGRO.

Three : ibid.

E. — SLOVENIA.

Two : ibid.

F. — SERBIA.

Six : Ibid.

II. **Areas excluded from the List since 1970 :** none.

III. **Areas added to the List since 1970 :** one.

3. *Kozara National Park :* created in 1967; general protection but hunting and fishing are allowed under strict control; staff : 18 full time units; mountain range between rivers; pines, spruces, and deciduous forest; fauna includes deer, roe deer, wild boar, wild cat, otter, marten, and various birds; altitude from 400 to 978 m; camping grounds, mountain huts; hotel at Mracovica; the park contains a memorial built during World War II.

142. ZAIRE

I. **Listed Areas :** seven.

1. *Salonga National Park*	2,240,000 ha
2. Upemba National Park	950,000 ha
3. Virunga National Park (formerly Albert National Park)	800,000 ha
4. *Maïko National Park*	600,000 ha
5. Garamba National Park	492,000 ha
6. *Kundelungu National Park*	120,000 ha
7. *Kahuzi-Biega National Park*	60,000 ha

II.   **Areas excluded from the List since 1970 :** none.

III.   **Areas added to the List since 1970 :** four.

1. *Salonga National Park :* two equally sized portions of great equatorial forest, east of Mbandaka (formerly Coquilhatville); declared at the end of 1970; under development; biotope not yet much threatened but it was wise to preserve it; not yet definitively limited; forest fauna; elephant are still numerous; pygmy chimpanzee.

4. *Maïko National Park :* lowland and transition forest, quite different from the above mentioned, on the eastern flank of Zaïre basin, near Lubero; also created in December 1970; already some developments; habitat is not either much threatened; gorilla, okapi, bongo antelope; *Afropavo congensis.*

6. *Kundelungu National Park :* on Kundelungu plateau, north east of Lubumbashi; includes 60,000 of short grass steppe and same area of forests; remarkable Lofoï Falls, the highest in the African continent; splendid scenery; tourism is starting; was a game reserve since 1939, national park since December 70; old organization being now reinforced; one warden, one assitant, 15 rangers; ungulates predominate (sable antelope, eland, hartebeest, oribi, etc.).

7. *Kahuzi-Biega National Park :* west of Bukavu; was a zoological and forest reserve since 1950, national park since December 1970; the preexisting organisation is being developed, having to face heavy poaching; includes Kahuzi Volcano (3,500 m); montane forest, habitat of gorilla; tourism is being developed.

IV.   **Further Information :**

National Parks in Zaïre are administered by the National Institute for Nature Conservation depending directly from the Republic President.

143. ZAMBIA

I.   **Listed Areas :** seventeen.

1. Kafue National Park (size indicated in 1970 : 2,200,000 ha) ...	2,240,000 ha
2. South Luangwa National Park (1970 : 830,000 ha)	905,000 ha
3. North Luangwa National Park (1970 : 460,000 ha)	463,000 ha
4. *Sioma Ngwezi National Park*	527,600 ha
5. *Liuwa Plain National Park*	366,000 ha
6. Mweru Marsh National Park (1970 : 310,000 ha)	313,400 ha
7. *Lukusuzi National Park*	272,000 ha
8. Sumbu National Park (1970 : 200,000 ha)	202,000 ha
9. West Lunga National Park (1970 : 165,000 ha)	168,400 ha
10. *Lavushi Manda National Park*	150,000 ha
11. Lusenga Plain National Park (1970 : 80,000 ha)	88,000 ha
12. *Isangano National Park*	84,000 ha
13. *Lochinvar National Park*	41,000 ha
14. Kasanka National Park (1970 : 38,000 ha)	39,000 ha

15. *Luambe National Park*	25,400 ha
16. *Nyika National Park*	8,000 ha
17. *Mosi-Oa-Tunya National Park*	6,600 ha

II.   **Areas excluded from the List since 1970 :** none.

III.   **Areas added to the List since 1970 :** nine.

4. *Sioma Ngwezi National Park :* gazetted in February 1972; some land use conflict; still contains several villages which will eventually be moved out; 12 wildlife officers; budget in 1972 : U.S. $ 45,000; teak and mopane woodland with watershed plain grassland; carries one of the largest Zambian giraffe populations; not yet developed for tourism.

5. *Liuwa Plain National Park :* gazetted in February 1972; several villages will eventually be moved out; 10 wildlife officers; flood plain surrounded by woodlands on Kalahari sands carries the largest population of wildebeest occurring in Zambia; not yet developed for tourism. Budget 1972 : U.S. $ 45,000.

7. *Lukusuzi National Park :* was established as a game reserve in 1938, up-graded into national park in February 1972; totally protected; 30 wildlife officers; budget 1972 : U.S. $ 135,000; escarpment woodland, plateau woodland, scrubland and woodland on Karoo rocks; some alluvial vegetation; not yet developed for tourism; problems are uncontrolled fires.

10. *Lavushi Manda National Park :* game reserve in 1941, national park in February 1972; problems are uncontrolled fires and illegal hunting; 2 wildlife officers; budget 1972 : U.S. $ 105,000; escarpment and *Brachystegia* woodland; not yet developed for tourism.

12. *Isangano National Park :* established as a game reserve in 1957; up-graded into national Park in February 1972; some illegal hunting; 2 wildlife officers; budget 1972 : U.S. $ 105,000; *Erythrophleum-Pterocarpus* woodland with tall grassland and watershed plain grass land; not yet developed for tourism.

13. *Lochinvar National Park :* gazetted in February 1972; problems are overstocking and habitat changes induced by the Kafue gorge dam; proposals to mine gypsum (press campaign in this concern); 14 wildlife officers; budget 1972 : U.S. $ 75,000; flood plain grassland and woodland savannah sanctuary for the Kafue lechwe; 400 bird species; opened to visitors during 1971; one non-catering lodge.

15. *Luambe National Park :* established as a game reserve in 1966, up-graded into national park in February 1972; problems are uncontrolled fires and local overstocking; 10 wildlife officers; budget 1972 : U.S. $ 135,000; alluvial area along the Luangwa river with a small area of *Brachystegia* woodland; already opened to visitors, one non catering lodge.

16. *Nyika National Park :* gazetted in February 1972; no staff yet; budget 1972 : U.S. $ 75,000; montane grassland with patches of gallery-forest and escarpment woodland; open to visitors; one non-catering camp.

17. *Mosi-Oa-Tunya National Park :* gazetted in February 1972; formerly was the Victoria Falls Trust; 14 wildlife officers; budget 1972 : U.S. $ 37,000; Victoria Falls, gallery-forest mopane woodland; established to conserve the

habitat fringing the Victoria Falls; the most visited national park in Zambia; one large hotel and one non catering camp.

IV.   **Further Information :**

A National parks and Wildlife Act was issued in 1968, followed in 1972 by National Parks Regulations and National Parks Declaration Order. By virtue of this order were gazetted the seventeen above mentioned national parks. Some of these were already mentioned in the U.N. List as game reserves in 1970, for instance Luangwa Valley which was then listed as a whole. Budget 1972 : 135,000 U.S. $.

An eighteenth national park is planned : Blue Lagoon, 28,500 ha, but legal formalities connected with its purchase have not yet been completed.

144. ANTARCTIC

The IVth consulting conference (Santiago de Chile) of delegates of countries having signed the Antarctic Treaty firmly recommended to concerned governments to take urgent measures towards the preservation of fauna and flora in the antarctic and notably to create fifteen " specially protected zones " named hereafter :

1. Rookery Taylor.
2. Iles Rookery, Holme Bay.
3. Ardery and Odbert Islands.
4, Ile Sabrina, Iles Balleny.
5. Ile Baufort (Ross Sea).
6. Cap Crozier.
7. Cap Hallet, Terre Victoria.
8. Iles Dion.
9. Green Island.
10. Byers Peninsula.
11. Cap Shirreff.
12. Fildes Peninsula.
13. Ile Noe.
14. Ile Lynch.
15. Powell Island and others.

23

Printed in Belgium.

D/1972/0211/2.

Printed by HAYEZ.
Rue Fin 4 — B - 1080 Brussels
(Belgium).